CURIOSITIES

OF THE

BIBLE

PERTAINING TO SCRIPTURE

PERSONS, PLACES AND THINGS

COMPRISING

PRIZE QUESTIONS AND ANSWERS, BIBLE STUDIES AND TEST EXERCISES

FOUNDED UPON AND ANSWERED IN THE BIBLE

INCLUDING

BLACKBOARD OUTLINES, SEED THOUGHTS ILLUSTRATED, SCRIPTURE EMBLEMS AND ALLEGORIES, BIBLE READINGS, CONCERT EXERCISES, PRAYER MEETING SUBJECTS AND DAILY READINGS

WITH MANY READY REFERENCE TABLES AND MAPS.

BY

A NEW YORK SUNDAY SCHOOL SUPERINTENDENT

WITH AN INTRODUCTION BY

REV. J. H. VINCENT, D.D.

REVISED AND ENLARGED

ILLUSTRATED WITH DESIGNS BY FRANK BEARD

NEW YORK

E. B. TREAT, 5 COOPER UNION

CHICAGO: R. C. TREAT

1896

Price, $2.00 postpaid.

CANVASSERS WANTED.

NOTE.—*The most difficult and prize questions are indicated by bold-face figures in numbering.*

In addition to the illustrations from new and original designs by Frank Beard in this enlarged edition, we are indebted in part to S. W. Clark, publisher of the "The Blackboard," and to J. Fairbanks & Co. for suggestions and outlines from "HAND-BOOK OF BIBLE READINGS."

We are also under obligations to Rev. H. H. BIRKINS, and to J. SANDERSON D. D., editor of *Pulpit Treasury*, for valuable services in editorial work.

INTRODUCTION.

There is no saving power in the mere letter of the word, even though it be the word of God. It is the Spirit that giveth life.

We should not, however, despise the letter. It is the body; and the body is of some worth as a medium for the soul.

He who knows most of the word of God, though it be with an intellectual knowledge, will be that much richer when the Holy Spirit of God touches the dry bones and bids them live. The dry bones in the "Valley of Vision" were better than so many stones, when the time came for the miracle of resurrection.

We cannot give to our children too much Bible knowledge. They cannot know too much Bible history, nor too much Bible geography, nor be too well able to explain the obscure passages, nor too familiar with the true solution of the common difficulties which all Bible students sooner or later encounter, and which they should be able to explain.

In view of this need, I do most sincerely thank the industrious and ingenious "New York Sunday-School Superintendent," who has compiled the valuable little manual of biblical curiosities now presented to the public.

Let it be used wisely. Let the circle of friends, old and young, who may gather about the table or fireside to spend an hour or an evening in the profitable recreation which it may furnish—let them all remember that cheerfulness and generous rivalry are allowable here, but that irreverence and impatience, out of place always and everywhere, are especially inappropriate, while we hold in our hands the most holy word of God, or busy ourselves with the truths which are to be found in it.

May the students of the "Curiosities of the Bible" become skilled in the interpretation of the Divine Book, and, enjoying its spiritual illumination, may they prove its divinity by pure and unselfish lives.

J. H. Vincent.

PREFACE.

This collection of treasures, new and old, is the outgrowth of many years experience in devising methods and incentives to interest children and those of older growth in Bible study; and thus aid them in fulfilling the injunction—"Search the scriptures."

It has been a part of every Sunday's programme in our school, for the past eighteen years, to propose a Bible question or exercise to be answered the following Sunday upon cards distributed by the secretary and collected at the call of the bell; the correct and incorrect answers being announced from the desk, with appropriate comments and explanations.

By this method, if an incorrect answer was given, the unsuccessful seeker after truth was not exposed to ridicule in consequence of failure, but was ready for the next proposition with as much zeal as at the outset.

Such questions only were given as were founded upon the Bible and answered in it, and such as would excite in the mind of Bible readers and seekers after truth a curiosity to know how, when, where, and under what circumstances they occurred.

To secure these, a vast range of Bible literature has been searched. Among the prominent aids might be mentioned many very excellent American and British periodicals and Bible helps. My associates—officers, teachers, and scholars—have jointly interested themselves with me in solving many of the intricate problems herein contained.

PREFACE.

A large number of these are *prize questions* and puzzles, which have elicited a wide correspondence, and the deep interest manifested in them gives the assurance that the benefit derived from these exercises can never be estimated.

In verification of this statement, selections are given from the testimony of a large number who, in their researches, have not only been stimulated by the hope of winning an earthly reward, but have been led to deeper thought and richer experience, which of itself is a matchless prize.

Extracts from letters.—"I cannot tell you how pleasant and happy have been the hours spent in studying the Bible for this purpose. Time and trouble have been repaid with interest in the enlargement of biblical knowledge, and the increase of love for the Bible."

"I have derived life long benefit from the close communion with the Book of books and the Author of it, finding new beauties in the Scriptures, and obtaining a priceless treasure which neither the world nor time can take away."

"I can thankfully say, reading the Bible for these answers has shown me the truth in a way I never saw before."

"I read the entire book of psalms through five times for one answer."

This volume has a two-fold mission: to increase our knowledge of all biblical facts, and beget and intensify in all hearts a greater love for the Book of Life. That the number of those who may be thus benefitted may become *legion* is the hope of the compiler.

E. B. T.

Washington Heights, New York City.

CONTENTS.

THE BIBLE.

A nation would be truly happy if it were governed by no other laws than those of this blessed book.

It contains everything needful to be known or done.

It gives instruction to a senate, authority and directions to a magistrate.

It cautions a witness, requires an impartial verdict of a jury, and furnishes the judge with his sentence.

It sets the husband as the lord of his household, and wife as mistress of the table tells him how to rule, and her how to manage.

It entails honor to parents, and enjoins obedience on children.

It preserves and limits the sway of the sovereign, the rule of the ruler, and the authòrity of the master; commands the subjects to honor and the servant to obey, and the blessings and the protection of the Almighty to all that walk by this rule

It gives directions for weddings and burials.

It promises food and raiment, and limits the use of both.

It points out a faithful and eternal Guardian to the departing husband and father; tells him with whom to leave his fatherless children, and whom his widow is to trust and promises a father to the former, and a husband to the latter.

It teaches a man to set his house in order and how to make his will; it appoints a dowry for his wife, and entails the rights of the first born, and shows how the young branches shall be left.

It defends the rights of all, and reveals vengeance to every defaulter, over-reacher, and trespasser.

It is the first book, the best book.

It contains the choicest matter, gives the best instruction, affords the greatest degree of pleasure and satisfaction that we have ever enjoyed.

It contains the best laws and most profound mysteries that were ever penned ; and it brings the very best comforts to the inquiring and disconsolate.

It is a brief recital of all that is to come.

It settles all matters in debate, resolves all doubts, and eases the mind and conscience of all their scruples.

It reveals the only living and true God, and shows the way to Him, and sets aside all other gods, and describes the vanity of them and all that trust in such in short, it is a book of laws, to show right and wrong, of wisdom that condemns a folly and makes the foolish wise, a book of truth that detects all lies and confronts all errors, and it is a book of life that shows the way from everlasting death,

It contains the most ancient antiquities and strange events, wonderful occurrences, heroic deeds, unparalleled wars.

It describes the celestial, terrestrial, and infernal worlds, and the origin of the angelic myriads, the human tribes, and the devilish legions.

It will instruct the accomplished mechanic and the most profound critic.

It teaches the best rhetorician, and exercises every power of the most skilful arithmetician, puzzles the wisest anatomist, and exercises the wisest critic.

It is the best covenant that ever was agreed on, the best deed that ever was sealed, the best that ever will be signed.

STUDY THE BIBLE.

BY REV. HORATIUS BONAR, D.D.

Do not skim it or read it, but *study* it, every word of it; study the whole Bible, Old Testament and New; not your favorite chapters merely, but the complete Word of God from beginning to end. Don't trouble yourself with commentators; they may be of use if kept in their place, but they are not your guide. Your guide is "the Interpreter," the one among a thousand (Job xxxiii, 23) who will lead you into all truth (John xvi, 13), and keep you from all error. Not that you are to read no book but the Bible. All that is true and good is worth the reading, *if you have time for it;* and all, if properly used, will help you in the study of the Scriptures. Let the Bible be to us the one book in all the world, whose every word is truth, and whose every verse is wisdom. In studying it, be sure to take it for what it really is, the revelation of the *thoughts* of God given us in the *words* of God. Were it only the book of *divine* thoughts and *human* words, it would profit little, for we never could be sure whether the words really represented the thoughts; nay, we might be sure that man would fail in his *words* when attempting to embody divine *thoughts;* and that, therefore, if we have only man's words, that is man's translation of the divine thoughts. But, knowing that we have *divine thoughts* embodied in *divine words* through the inspiration of an unerring translator, we sit down to the study of the heavenly volume, assured that we shall find in all its teachings the perfection of wisdom, and in its language the *most accurate expression of that wisdom* that the finite speech of man could utter. Every word of God is as perfect as it is pure (Psa. xix, 7; xii, 6). Let us read and re-read the Scriptures, meditating on them day and night.

LAW
GENESIS
EXODUS
LEVITICUS
NUMBERS
DEUTERONOMY
5 BOOKS

THE BIBLE TELLS OF SALVATION

THE OLD TESTAMENT OF PREPARATION

5	LAW	OF	TYPES
12	HISTORY	OF	ORGANIZATION
5	POETRY	OF	EXPERIENCE
5	MAJOR PROPHETS	OF	ANTICIPATION
12	MINOR PROPHETS	OF	ANTICIPATION.
39			

HANDY DIAGRAM OF THE BOOKS OF THE BIBLE

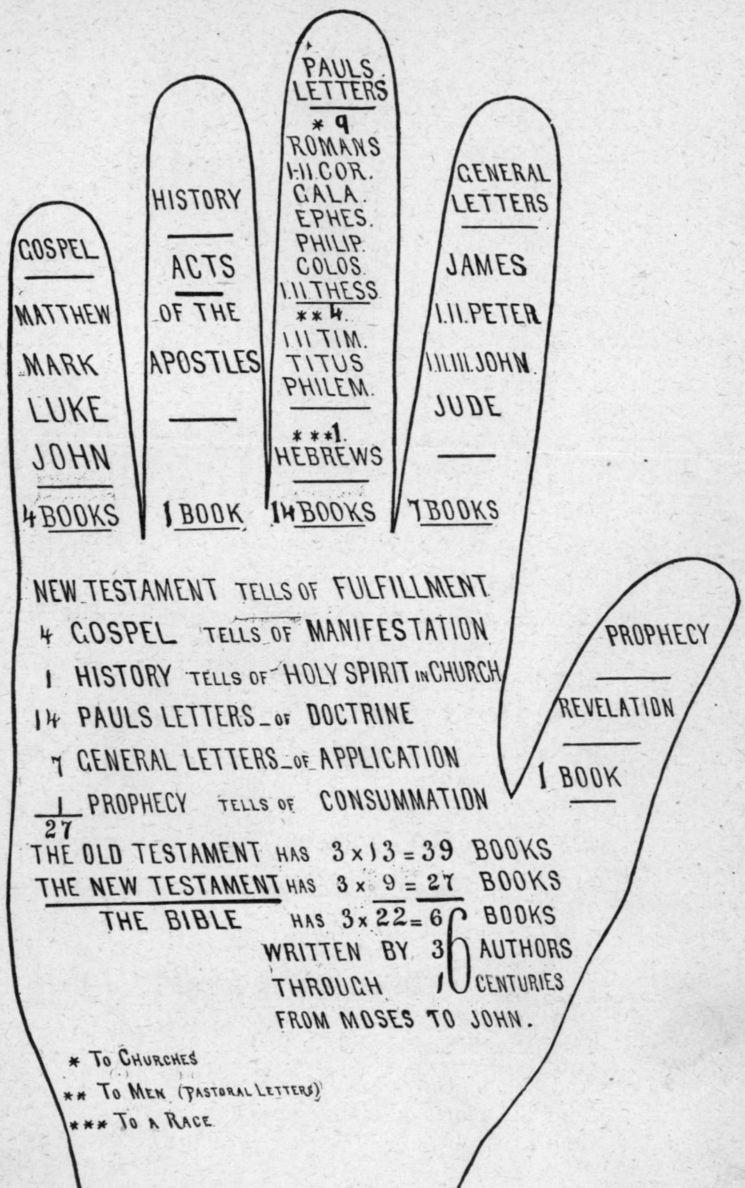

GOSPEL
MATTHEW
MARK
LUKE
JOHN
4 BOOKS
HISTORY
ACTS
OF THE
APOSTLES
1 BOOK
PAULS
LETTERS
* 9
ROMANS
I. II. COR.
GALA.
EPHES.
PHILIP.
COLOS.
I. II. THESS.
** 4.
I. II TIM.
TITUS
PHILEM.
*** 1.
HEBREWS
14 BOOKS
GENERAL
LETTERS
JAMES
I. II. PETER
I. II. III. JOHN
JUDE
7 BOOKS
PROPHECY
REVELATION
1 BOOK
NEW TESTAMENT TELLS OF FULFILLMENT
4 GOSPEL TELLS OF MANIFESTATION
1 HISTORY TELLS OF HOLY SPIRIT IN CHURCH
14 PAULS LETTERS – OF DOCTRINE
7 GENERAL LETTERS – OF APPLICATION
1 PROPHECY TELLS OF CONSUMMATION
27
THE OLD TESTAMENT HAS 3 x 13 = 39 BOOKS
THE NEW TESTAMENT HAS 3 x 9 = 27 BOOKS
THE BIBLE HAS 3 x 22 = 66 BOOKS
WRITTEN BY 36 AUTHORS
THROUGH 16 CENTURIES
FROM MOSES TO JOHN.
* To Churches
** To Men (Pastoral Letters)
*** To a Race

THE BOOKS OF THE OLD TESTAMENT.

In *Genesis* the world began ;
'Twas then that God created man.

In *Exodus* the law was given,
As Israel's guide from earth to heaven.

Leviticus, from Levi's name,
The tribe from which the priesthood came.

Then *Numbers* tells about the way
What God would have us do and say.

Deuteronomy, which means "twice told,"
The truth, once heard, must ne'er grow old

Then *Joshua* came, in Moses' place,
When Law had failed, God brought in Grace.

He next by *Judges* Israel ruled ;
His love toward them never cooled.

And then, the story sweet of *Ruth*,
Foreshadows very precious truth.

In *Samuel First* we read of Saul
The people's king his rise and fall.

In *Second Samuel* then we hear
Of David man to God so dear.

In *First of Kings* the glory filled
The Temple Solomon did build.

And *Second Kings* records the lives
Of prophets, kings, their sons and wives.

In *First of Chronicles* we're shown
The house of David and his throne.

And *Second Chronicles* records
King Solomon's *good* deeds and words.

Then *Ezra* builds God's house again,
Which had for long in ruins lain.

And *Nehemiah* builds the wall
Round Judah's city, great and tall.

Then *Esther*, Jewish maid and wife,
Raised up to save her people's life.

And *Job* his patience sorely tried
At last God's dealings justified.

Then come the *Psalms*, whose sacred page
Is full of truth for every age.

The *Proverbs*, which the wise man spake,
For all who will their teaching take.

Ecclesiastes shows how vain
The very best of earthly gain.

The *Song*, how much we need to prize
The treasures set above the skies.

Isaiah, first of prophets, who
Foretells the future of the Jew.

Then *Jeremiah* scorned by foes,
Yet weeps for faithless Israel's woes.

The *Lamentations* tell in part
The sadness of this prophet's heart.

Ezekiel tells us, in mystic story,
Departing and returning glory.

Then *Daniel*, from the lion's den,
By power Divine is raised again.

Hosea shows the Father's heart
So grieved for sin on Ephraim's part.

And *Joel* tells of judgment near;
The wicked nations quake and fear.

Then *Amos* from the herdmen sent,
Calls hardened sinners to repent.

In *Obadiah*, Edom's fall
Contains a warning word to all.

Jonah, though prophet of the Lord,
Yet fled to Tarshish from his word.

Then *Micah* sings in sweetest lays
The glory of millennial days.

And *Nahum* tells the fear and gloom
Of Nineveh and of her doom.

Habakkuk—though the fig-tree fail,
His faith and trust in God prevail.

Then *Zephaniah* tells of grace,
And love that comes in judgment's place.

And *Haggai* in the latter days,
Repeats : Consider well your ways.

In *Zachariah's* wondrous book,
We find eight visions if we look.

Then *Malachi*, the last of all,
Speaks sadly still of Israel's fall.

E.J. Carr, *London.*

CURIOSITIES OF THE BIBLE

PERTAINING TO

FIRST THINGS.

The Answers to these questions commence on pa e 380.

1. What was the first command of God ?
2. What were the first words spoken to man ? [served ?
3. When was the first Sabbath instituted and by whom ob-
4. What is the name of the first place mentioned ?
5. Who was the first gardener ? [speech ?
6. On what occasion did man first exercise his power of
7. Who was the first human transgressor ?
8. What was the first recorded prophecy ?
9. Who made the first clothing for man ?
10. Who was the first exile in Bible times ?
11. Who was the first shepherd mentioned in the Scriptures ?
12. Who was the first person who died after the Creation ?
13. Who told the first recorded human lie ?
14. Who was the first outcast and vagabond ?
15. Who built the first city ?
16. Who was the first bigamist on record ? [Eve ?
17. What is the first name of the woman mentioned after
18. Who was the first dweller in tents ?
19. Who made the first confession of murder ?
20. Who was the first machinist in brass and iron ?
21. Where is it first said that men began to call upon the name of the Lord ?
22. Who was the first person who died a natural death ?

23. What is the name of the first wood mentioned in the Bible?
24. Who built the first ship?
25. What is the first mountain mentioned?
26. When was the use of flesh as food first allowed to man?
27. Who was the first-mentioned hunter?
28. Where have we the first account of building materials?
29. Who was the first pilgrim?
30. Where are the wicked first spoken of as sinners?
31. Who was the first prisoner of war?
32. Who was the first who was called "the Hebrew"?
33. Who was the first man named by the Lord before his birth?
34. Where did an angel appear first to a woman?
35. Who offered the first recorded prayer?
36. What was the first mentioned meat for food?
37. Who was the first to weep?
38. Who first took an oath or affidavit?
39. Who first used a saddle as recorded in the Bible?
40. Who is the first woman whose age is mentioned?
41. Where is mention first madeof the purchase of land?
42. From whom was the first land purchased?
43. By whom was the first land purchased?
44. What is the first recorded use of current money?
45. For what use was a piece of ground first purchased?
46. How was the oath administered as first recorded?
47. Of what did the first wedding present consist?
48. Who wore the first bridal veil?
49. What was the first recorded dream that Jacob had?
50. Where is the first mention of giving a tenth to God?
51. Who was the first shepherdess?
52. Who was the first guilty of theft aside from Eve?
53. Who made the first confession of unworthiness to the Lord?
54. Who erected the first monument to the memory of the [dead?
55. Where were mules [*hot springs*] first found and by whom?
56. Who was first sold into slavery for money? [widow?
57. Where have we the first mention of the garments of a

58. Where have we the first account of a man shaving himself?
59. Who is first mentioned as having worn a ring on his finger and a gold chain on his neck?
60. Where are horses first mentioned?
61. With what operation are physicians first mentioned?
62. Where did an angel first appear to Moses?
63. What was the first of the ten plagues of Egypt?
64. What was the first scriptural song?
65. Give the first scriptural reference to God as a king.
66. Who was the first prophetess?
67. Who was the first judge according to the Scriptures?
68. Where is the first mention of "liquors"?
69. Who first held the office of scribe?
70. Who was the first Jewish High Priest?
71. What was the first thing engraved?
72. What was the first offering to the Lord of woman?
73. Who first broke all the Commandments?
74. Who was the first sacred historian?
75. Which of the tribes marched first in the wilderness journey?
76. Where did the Israelites first loathe the manna?
77. Who was the first woman to have the leprosy?
78. Who were the first women who demanded their rights?.
79. Who was the first by lot in the inheritance of the ten tribes of Israel?
80. What are the circumstances under which hell [*sheol*] is first mentioned?
81. What was the first city taken in Canaan?
82. Who was the first man stoned to death?
83. Where is recorded the first act of surveying?
84. Where is the first account of female government recorded?
85. To whose wife did an angel first appear?
86. Where was the first lion killed as recorded in the Bible?
87. What tribe first set up idolatry in Israel?
88. What was the occasion of the first voluntary fast?
89. What was the first prayer for a king?
90. By whom was the first draft for war made?
91. Who was the first to commit suicide, and how?

92. Who was second to commit suicide, and how?
93. By whom was the first letter written of which we have any record?
94. Where was the first ferryboat used and by whom?
95. What is the first navy mentioned?
96. Who were the first kings of the divided kingdom of Israel?
97. Who first introduced the worship of idolatry among the Jews?
98. Who was the first raised from death?
99. Where is the first mention of a library?
100. Who was the first Jew to marry a Gentile?
101. Where is the first mention of printing in the Bible?
102. Where is the first recorded song of the angels found?
103. Where is the first mention of beggars?
104. Which is the first of the prophetical books?
105. Where is the first prophecy of the millenium recorded?
106. When and by whom were temperance societies first formed?
107. Who was the first president, and by whom appointed?
108. What was the text of our Saviour's first sermon?
109. What place first rejected Christ?
110. To whom did Jesus first appear after his resurrection?
111. What was the first miracle performed by Christ?
112. Where did Jesus perform his first miracle?
113. Who delivered the first gospel sermon and wherein did it resemble modern discourses?
114. What was the first instance of the execution of divine justice in the Christian church?
115. Who was the first man struck dead for lying?
116. Who first suffered martyrdom?
117. Who was the first negro convert to Christianity?
118. Where did Paul preach his first sermon?
119. Who was the first recorded Gentile convert?
120. Where have we an account of the first missionary meeting?
121. Where do we read of the first Christian letter of recommendation?
122. When did Paul first style himself an apostle?
123. Give the name of the first woman who got a written recommendation to the churches from Paul.
124. Whom did Paul first give directions about a "holy kiss?"

125. Give the place where "Charity" (*love*) is first mentioned in the New Testament.
126. Of whom is Christ said to be the first fruits ?
127. Of whom is it promised that they shall rise first ?
128. Who are said to have given themselves first unto theLord ?
129. Where is it said in the New Testament that Adam was first formed ?
130. Who was to be rejected after first and second admonition ?
131. Give the name of the priest who did not need to offer sacrifice first for his own sins ?
132. What three things were in the first tabernacles ? [above ?
133. What is the first characteristic of the wisdom that is from
134. Where is it said that Jesus first loved us ?
135. What are we told about the angels who kept not their first estate ?
136. What is the name of the first place mentioned in the Book Revelation ?
137. What churches in Revelation were told they had left their first love ?
138. Where did the first beast rise from, in the Book of Revelation, that had seven heads and ten horns ?
139. Where have we in the Bible a description of the first resurrection ?
140. What does the Bible say happened to the first heaven and the first earth ?

CURIOSITIES OF THE BIBLE

PERTAINING TO

OLD TESTAMENT PERSONS.

Answers Page 9 in Key.

1. Who gave the name to all living creatures?
2. Who said "dust thou art and unto dust shalt thou return?
3. Who told a lie in order to cover his crime?
4. Give the name of the first farmer and builder?
5. What are the names of the only three women besides Eve living before the flood, mentioned in the Bible?
6. Who was the inventor of string and wind instruments?
7. Who was the first person who died a natural death?
8. Give the name of the men who attained to the greatest age?
9. Who built Nineveh? [greatest age?
10. Among the men born after the flood who attained the
11. Who was the founder of the Hebrew nation?
12. Who said "Let there be no strife between me and thee"?
13. Who was the King of Sodom at the time of its destruction? [tion?
14. Who was the King of Gomorrah at the time of its destruc-
15. Who was King of Salem when Sodom was destroyed?
16. Unto whom did God say "I am thy shield"?
17. To whom did God promise that his children should be as the stars of heaven?
18. Who was the founder of a race? [princes?
19. To whom did God promise that he should beget twelve
20. Of whom did God say "I will make him a mighty nation"?
21. Who said in his prayer "I am but dust"?

22. Who entertained angels unawares ?
23. Who preferred to abide in the street than to partake of hospitality ? [angel ?
24. Whose life was saved by giving heed to the warning of an
25. Who was reproved in a dream by God ? [die ?
26. What banished mother threw her child under a bush to
27. Name a child whom God heard and answered when crying ? [in Genesis ?
28. What is the name of the captain of Abimelech's host given
29. What lad carried the wood to the altar to burn himself ?
30. Who is the only woman mentioned in the Old Testament whose age is given ?
31. Mention the name of one who wept at Sarah's death ?
32. From whom did Abraham buy a burying-ground ?
33. Who were the bride and groom of the first bridal procession that entered the land of Canaan ?
34. Of whom was it said "Thou art our sister, be thou the mother of thousands of millions !
35. Who sought retirement in a field for meditation ?
36. What was the name of Abraham's second wife ?
37. Who filled up the wells that Abraham had dug ?
38. What woman said "I am weary of my life" ?
39. To what three persons was the second prophecy of the Messiah made ?
40. Who said "This is none other but the house of God" ?
41. Who was the servant of Rachel, Jacob's wife ?
42. Who was the first or oldest of the twelve sons of Jacob ?
43. What two ungodly persons recorded in Genesis were gainers by having God-fearing servants ?
44. By whom and on what occasion was a monument used as a table in eating ?
45. Who made the first recorded confession to the Lord ?
46. Who prayed all night till break of day ?
47. What was the name of Jacob's only daughter ?
48. What was the name of Rebekah's nurse who died at Bethel ?
49. Who was the youngest son of the patriarch Jacob ?

50. Who found mules [*Hot Springs Revised version*] in the wilderness ?
51. Who delivered Joseph from the hands of his brethren ?
52. Who suggested selling Joseph to the Ishmaelites ?
53. To whom did the Midianites sell Joseph ? [had ?
54. What captive was appointed ruler over all his master
55. What was the name of Joseph's wife in Egypt ?
56. What heathen priest's grandsons are often mentioned ?
57. What name did Pharaoh give to Joseph ? [old art thou "?
58. By whom and to whom was the question asked "How
[judge in Israel ?
59. By whom was it prophesied that Samson should be a
60. In whose funeral procession do we find the first mention of horsemen ? [his forgiveness ?
61. What man wept when those who had injured him asked
62. Who were commanded to kill the Hebrew male children ?
63. From whom did Moses receive his name ?
64. Who was the great reformer disregarded by those he wished to help ?
65. What was the name of the wife of Moses ?
66. Of what nation and occupation was Jethro ?
67. Who put his hand in his bosom and it became leprous ?
68. Who said "I am of slow speech and of a slow tongue ?"
69. Whom did the Lord seek to kill in an inn as he was journeying with his wife and child ?
70. What was the name of the mother of Moses and Aaron ?
71. What was the name of the wife of Aaron the High-priest ?
72. By whose act was the water turned into blood ?
73. With whom was the first battle by the Israelites ?
74. What prophetess played on a musical instrument ?
75. What aged prophet's hands were upheld in prayer ?
76. Who was Moses' father-in-law ?
77. Who saw the God of Israel ? [forty days ?
78. What two persons mentioned in the Old Testament fasted
79. Give the name of a celebrated artificer.
80. What High-priest made an idol ?
81. What prophet put a vail temporarily on his face ?

82. Who made the ark of the covenant? [burnt offerings?
83. What two persons lost their lives in using strange fire in
84. Who held his peace when his two sons were destroyed?
85. For whom were Aaron and his sons forbidden to mourn?
86. What man of Israel was stoned for blaspheming God?
87. Who were forbidden to eat anything made from the vine?
88. By whom and to whom was it said "Come thou with us and we will do thee good"?
89. What are the names of the two elders, whose names are only given of the seventy elected to help Moses?
90. Who was the young man jealous of his master's honor?
91. What was Joshua's original name?
92. What was Joshua's name up to the time he was chosen one of the twelve to search the land of Canaan?
93. Give the names of the men who were sent to search the land of Canaan?
94. Who had giant sons in Canaan?
95. Who was the father of Joshua and of Caleb?
96. What were the names of the two spies who did not bring an evil report from Canaan?
97. What leader of a rebellion among the children of Israel was swallowed by an earthquake"?
98. What High-priest stood between the living and the dead and averted a plague? [death?
99. To whom did Aaron transfer his robes of office at his
100. What two persons witnessed the death of Aaron and performed the funeral services?
101. Who was reproved by a dumb brute speaking?
102. Who said "Let me die the death of the righteous?
103. What king sent Balaam to curse Israel? [in a pit?
104. What three persons and their host were swallowed alive
105. Whose daughter was Noah? [Egypt entered Canaan?
106. Who, and how many of the 6,001,730 Israelites that left
107. What was the name of the mother of Aaron?
108. Whose daughters made an appeal for an inheritance?
109. Who was appointed the successor to Moses?
110. Who slew Balaam, the false prophet?
111. Who said, "Be sure your sin will find you out?"

112. Who rehearsed the story of God's promises for forty years ?
113. What king had an iron bedstead ? [very same terms ?
114. What two prophets spoke of the bondage of Israel in the
115. Whom did the Lord choose to be a peculiar people ? [why ?
116. What tribe had no inheritance in the land of Caanan, and
117. Who said these words, and to whom, "Be strong and of good courage ?" [in Deut. ?
118. Which of the tribes is missing from the enumerated list ?
119. What two Hebrew leaders retained their strength in old age ?
120. Who led the Israelites into Canaan ?
121. Who built a monument in the middle of a river, and why ?
122. Unto whom did an angel appear with a drawn sword ?
123. What two persons were ordered to take off their shoes ?
124. Who built Jerico and what prophecy was then fulfilled ?
125. What criminal in his confession said, "I saw, I coveted, I took"?
126. Who was stoned to death for theft ? [burnt it ?
127. What General lay in ambush against a city, took and
128. Who built an altar to the Lord at Mount Ebal ?
129. What people were condemned to bondage by the Israelites ?
130. What are the names of the five kings who made war against Gibeon and were hanged ?
131. Whom did the Lord help in battle with hailstones ? [ance.
132. The sons of what giant did Caleb drive from his inherit-
133. What noted leader had the city of Timnath-Serah for an inheritance ?
134. What two kings were driven from their dominions by hornets ?
135. Who said, "As for me and my house we will serve the Lord ?"
136. Who said "Ye are witnesses against yourselves"?
137. What captured king had his thumbs and great toes cut off, a punishment he had inflicted on others ?
138. Who was the left-handed judge that delivered Israel ?
139. Who blew a trumpet in Mount Ephraim, and said "Follow me"? [goad ?
140. Who delivered Israel by killing 600 Philistines with an ox
141. What prophetess dwelt under a palm tree ?

142. What Commander refused to lead his army to battle unless a prophetess accompanied him ?

143. Whose song is recorded in the book of Judges ?

144. What mother looked out of the window and cried for the return of her son from battle ?

145. Who said, "My family is poor in Manasseh ?"

146. Whom did the Lord send to the Midianitish camp as spies by night ?

147. Whose army was compared to "grasshoppers in multitude" and whose camels were without number ?

148. By whom was a mode of drinking once used to prove soldiers ? [men ?

149. Who used the thorns and briers of the wilderness to teach

150. Who was asked to slay Zebah and Zalmunnah ?

151. What people put golden chains on their camels' necks ?

152. What leader of Israel demanded of a conquered people their golden earings as a trophy of victory ?

153. Who slew seventy of his brothers on one stone ?

154. Who are described as highway robbers ?

155. What king beat down a city and sowed it with salt ?

156. What king in beseiging a city made his own conduct an example for his soldiers ? [woman ?

157. What king's life was endangered by a stone thrown by a

158. What king ordered his armor bearer to dispatch him that he might not be disgraced by death from a woman's hand ?

159. Who had thirty sons who had thirty cities ?

160. Who had thirty sons who took wives from abroad and thirty daughters who had husbands from abroad ?

161. What celebrated deliverer of Israel had his birth announced by an angel ? [not be shaven ?

162. Of whom was it foretold by an angel that his beard should

163. Who offered a burnt offering and had an angel ascend in the flames ?

164. Who was Samson's father ?

165. Who slew a lion at Timnath ?

166. Who said, "out of the eater came forth meat, and out of the strong came forth sweetness"?

167. Who told his life's secret to a woman with disastrous results ?

168. Who stole money from his mother and upon its return was melted into idols ? [a salary with board and clothes ?
169. Who employed a wandering Levite for his priest, paying
170. Who was it said, "Let all thy wants lie on me ?"
171. Of what people is it said that "they could fling a stone at hairbreadth and not miss"?
172. Who left Bethlehem for Moab because of a famine ?
173. What two Jews married wives in Moab and died there ten years after ? [my God ?"
174. Who said, "Thy people shall be my people and thy God
175. Who said to her mother-in-law, "where thou goest I will go ?"
176. What widow said, "Call me Mara ?"
177. What farmer said to his reapers, "The Lord be with you ?"
178. What was the name of the widow who became the wife of Boaz ?
179. What was the name of the son of Boaz and Ruth ?
180. What was the name of King David's grandfather ?
181. What husband said to his wife, "Am I not better to thee than ten sons ? [head ?
182. Who vowed that a razor should not come upon her son's
183. Who was it that watched a woman's mouth to see if she was praying ?
184. Who carried a little coat to her son every year ? [good ?"
185. Who said, "It is the Lord, let him do what seemeth him
186. What child's mother, father, grandfather and uncle died about the same time ?
187. What prophet erected a monument commemorative of a great victory, and what was the name given to the monument ?
188. Whom does the bible describe as a circuit judge ?
189. How many and what were the names of the sons of Samuel ?
190. What notable man among the Jews was higher than all the people ? [sacrifice before they would eat ?
191. What people waited for the prophet's blessing upon their
192. Who was the prophet in Israel in the time of Saul ?
193. What king offered a covenant with a people provided he might thrust out their right eyes ?

194. What prophet declared himself to be "old and grey headed?"

195. Who was very near being killed for eating a little honey?

196. What king forced into his service every strong and valiant man he saw.

197. Who said, "To obey is better than sacrifice?" [each.

198. What king was slain by a prophet? Give the name of

199. Who was ordered to go to Bethlehem and anoint David as king?"

200. To whom did God say, "Man looketh on the outward appearance, but the Lord looketh on the heart?"

201. What King of Israel was a shepherd in his youth?"

202. What boy was sent with some loaves to his brothers in the army when they gained a great victory?

203. What is the most noted instance of devoted friendship?

204. Who aided David to escape from Saul?

205. Who said, "There is but one step between me and death"?

206. What king feigned insanity in an enemy's country?

207. Who was a prophet, a seer, and a writer? [ger?

208. Who warned David while in the land of Moab of his dan-

209. Who slew eighty-five priests, and by whose command?

210. Who caused the destruction of the city of Nob?

211. Who alone escaped the massacre of the priests of Nob?

212. Six women once took a journey which resulted in a wedding. Who was the bride and groom?

213. By whom was Saul, King of Israel, slain?

214. What king's body was fastened to the wall of Bethshan?

215. Who buried the body of Saul, the suicide?

216. What king of Israel committed suicide, and how?

217. Who was guilty of worldly cunning in announcing a death in the hope of a reward? [and Jonathan?

218. Who sang a song of lamentation over the death of Saul

219. Of what defeated king does the bible say, "How are the mighty fallen"?

220. Who still persisted in following a vanquished foe after being twice entreated to turn back and suffered death in consequence?

221. How was Asahel killed and by whom?

222. What woman was won by the bravery of a warrior and became his wife, after the husband had fled from his country, she married another man, but when he became great he sent to the king of the country he had left and demanded his wife, the king took her from her husband and sent her under a soldier's escort, her husband followed weeping until sent back by the captain ?

223. Who was slain in a city of refuge and by whom ?

224. Of whom is it said "he died as a fool dieth"?

225. What king had a grandson lamed by falling from his nurse's arms ?

226. Who was slain on his bed at noon by Rechab and Baanah ?

227. What woman ridiculed a king for rejoicing and suffered for it ? [tured them ?

228. What king lost a thousand chariots in battle and who cap-

229. Who in speaking of himself said, "Such a dead dog as I am"?

230. Who did David send to fight against the Syrians ?

231. What king sent one of his soldiers to the front of the army that he might have his widow for a wife ?

232. What were Solomon's other names and by whom were they given ? [it on his own head ?

233. From what king's head did David take a crown and place

234. What people suffered torture only equalled by the inquisition of the dark ages ?

235. By whom was Ammon, one of David's sons, killed ?

236. Of whom was it said, "There was no blemish in him"?

237. Who consented to be interviewed after his barley field was set on fire ?

238. Who was David's counsellor ?

239. What king was cursed and grossly insulted, and by whom ?

240. What two persons saved themselves by hiding in a well ?

241. Who secreted Jonathan and Ahimaaz at Bahurim, and how ? [taken ?

242. Who hanged himself when he saw his advice was not

243. What king was declared by his people to be worth ten thousands of them ?

244. What Jewish prince was found suspended by his hair in the branches of an oak? [had no son?

245. Who built a pillar to make himself remembered because he [mother?

246. Who made a request to be buried beside his father and

247. What four persons were smitten under the fifth rib?

248. Whose head was cut off and thrown over a wall at the suggestion of a woman? [perfidy?

249. Whose seven sons were hanged on account of their father's [six toes on each foot?

250. Who does the Bible say had six fingers on each hand, and

251. Who slew the giant that had twelve fingers and toes?

252. Who slew eight hundred men with a spear?

253. What warrior fought so long and desperately that his hand clave to the hilt of his sword?

254. Who slew three hundred Philistines with a spear?

255. Who slew a lion in a pit in a time of snow?

256. What king in his vain glory took a census of the people?

257. What king did God punish for his haughtiness by sending three day's pestilence on his people?

258. Who preferred in the time of trouble to fall into God's hands than into man's? [manner?

259. Who, though not a king, was said to have acted in a kingly

260. Who was David's last wife?

261. Who, because of his fear of Solomon, caught hold of the horns of the altar? [a man?

262. Who, when about to die, charged his son to show himself

263. Who passed sentence of death on his own brother?

264. What man was forbidden by the king to leave Jerusalem?

265. Whose daughter was Solomon's first wife?

266. Whose judicial decision made him renowned?

267. Who was successor to David, king of Israel?

268. What people were famed for hewing timber?

269. Who built Tadmor (Palmyra) in the desert?

270. What king bought apes and peacocks? [Jerusalem?

271. Under whose reign was silver as plentiful as the stones in

272. What mighty man had his robe torn in twelve pieces by a prophet?

273. What prophet tore the robe of a mighty man in twelve pieces ?
274. What prophet foretold the division of the twelve tribes of Israel ? [father's counsellors ?
275. What young king listened to other advice than that of his
276. What king made two golden calves, and commanded the people to worship them ?
277. Who burnt incense on an altar before idols of gold ?
278. What king was punished for attempting to seize a prophet ?
279. What son of a wicked king was an exemplary youth ?
280. What blind prophet received a disguised queen ?
281. Who said " why feignest thyself to be another ?" [words ?
282. What three kings were denounced in exactly the same
283. To whom did God promise an early death as a special favor ?
284. Who plundered the temple and took away the shield of gold ?
285. Who removed his mother from being queen, and why ?
286. What queen was deprived of her throne by her son for idolatry ?
287. What king drank himself drunk and was killed ?
288. What king set fire to his palace and perished in the flames ?
289. Who was the founder of Jericho ?
290. Whose prophecy was fulfilled in the rebuilding of Jericho ?
291. What two young men fell victims to a curse pronounced five centuries before ?
292. Whose life was miraculously restored by Elijah ? [sent ?
293. In answer to whose prayers was rain both prevented and
294. Who hid one hundred prophets in a cave ?
295. Who said " How long halt ye between two opinions ?"
296. What prophet journeying hungry and alone said " O Lord take away my life !"
297. What two Old Testament persons fasted forty days ?
298. Who partook of a meal prepared by an angel and then travelled forty days and nights ?
299. Who ploughed with twelve yoke of oxen ?
300. What was the name of Elijah's father ?
301. Which of the prophets was called from the plough ?

302. What king by the advice of his wife appropriated the fruits of a poor man's vineyard ?

303. What queen sent a message with a forged signature ?

304. Who prophesied that the dogs should lick Ahab's blood ?

305. What king of Israel sold himself to work wickedness ?

306. What wicked king delayed punishment due him by humbling himself ?

307. What king of Israel disguised himself before entering battle ?

308. What king of Israel was slain in battle and the dogs [licked his blood ?

309. Who was the mother of Jehoshaphat, king of Israel ?

310. Who threw off the yoke of the Israelites on the death of Ahab ?

311. What king fell through a lattice and was killed ?

312. To whom did an angel speak on a hill-top at whose base one hundred and two men lay scorched to death ?

313. To whom did Elisha apply the words "My father, my father, the chariots of Israel and the horsemen thereof" ?

314. Who threw salt in the water and made it wholesome ?

315. What king of Moab fought against the king of Israel ?

316. What prophet called for music before delivering his prophecy ?

317. What king offered his son for a burnt-offering ?

318. What four persons does the Bible mention as being engaged in a legitimate, remarkable and profitable oil speculation ?

319. Give an instance of death by sunstroke, the person restored to life by a miracle ? Who was the person, and and who performed the miracle ?

320. Who raised the Shunamite's son to life ?

321. What Commander-in-chief did Elisha cure of leprosy ?

322. What servant of a prophet was smitten with leprosy for having obtained money and goods under false pretences ?

323. What prophet called Ahab a murderer ?

324. Who in the midst of starvation prophesied plenty on the [morrow ?

325. Whom did the Lord punish for doubting Elisha's prophecy ?

326. What woman sojourned seven years in a foreign land [during a famine in her own country ?

327. Who was smothered to death by Hazael? [whom ?
328. To whom was applied the epithet "mad fellow," and by
329. What great driver of a chariot is spoken of in the bible?
330. What woman is recorded as having painted her face?
331. What rebel general gave the blood of a queen to the dogs?
332. What woman was eaten by dogs? [stroying idolaters?
333. What Jewish king displayed his zeal for the Lord in de-
334. By whose orders was Ahab's seventy sons beheaded?
335. Who rent her clothes and cried "Treason, treason"?
336. Who were the chief actors in the reformation after the division of the children of Israel? [him?
337. What king visited a dying prophet's bed and wept over
338. What king of Israel was told by a dying prophet to take a bow and arrow and shoot out of the window and smite the ground?
339. Who delivered a prophecy on his dying bed?
340. What dead man was restored to life by touching the bones of a dead prophet? [horses to his grave?
341. What king was slain by conspirators and carried on
342. What king carried the children of Israel captive to Babylon?
343. Who was the last king of the ten tribes of Israel?
344. Who destroyed the brazen serpent which Moses made?
345. What was the name of Hezekiah's scribe?
346. To whom was it said: "I will put my hook in thy nose?"
347. Unto whom was it said: "Set thine house in order for thou shalt die and not live."? [prayer?
348. Whose life was lengthened fifteen years in answer to
349. What prophet acted the part of physician by giving a medical prescription?
350. What Jewish king was interred in his own garden?
351. What laboring men were so honest that no accounts were kept? [reformation?
352. Who was reigning as king in the time of the great Jewish
353. What king of Judah was overtaken by an invading army and had his eyes put out?
354. By whom was Solomon's temple first destroyed?
355. Who put out Zedekiah's eyes?

356. What king of Judah was overtaken by an invading army and bound with fetters ?
357. What was the name and rank of the officers under Nebuchadnezzar, that set fire to the temple at the first destruction of Jerusalem ? [Jews in Babylon ?
358. Whom did Nebuchadnezzar make governor over the
359. What nephew of David was a great military captain ?
360. Who had for a possession twenty-three cities of Gilead ?
361. To which son of Jacob was the birth-right given when taken from Reuben ? [carried into captivity ?
362. Who was king of Assyria when the Israelites were first
363. What tribes of Israel were first carried into captivity ?
364. Who are the only three persons mentioned in the Bible whose names commence with the letter V ?
365. What people were employed day and night, and how ?
366. Who was chief among the captains of David ?
367. Who slew a lion in a pit on a snowy day ? [self-defence ?
368. Who wrested a spear from a giant's hand and slew him in
369. What persons are mentioned as able to use equally both hands in hurling stones and shooting arrows ?
370. Whose faces were like the faces of lions ?
371. What tribe furnished the counsellors of Israel ? [ity ?
372. What tribe of Israel was specially characterized by sincer-
373. Who was punished with death for touching the ark of God ? [salem, and how long did it remain there ?
374. To whose house was the ark taken before it came to Jeru-
375. Who played on cymbals of brass in the temple-service ?
376. Who were doorkeepers of the ark ?
377. What two prophets reproved King David ? [themselves ?
378. Who saw the angel sent to destroy Jerusalem and hid
379. What king's name meant peaceable ?
380. Which of David's relatives acted as a scribe for him ?
381. Who were David's companions and counsellors at an early part of his reign ?
382. To whom was applied the military title of General ?
383. Who died full of days, riches and honors ?
384. Who dedicated the temple ? [night ?
385. To what king of Israel did God appear in a dream by

386. What king had eighty-eight children ?
387. What two men were stricken by the Lord ?
388. Who was in command of one million of soldiers ?
389. What king of Israel before going into battle sought help of God ? [the Lord for recovery ?
390. What king in sickness trusted more in physicians than in
391. What king of Israel established an itinerant ministry ?
392. To whom did God commit two fearful commissions against two kings of Israel ?
393. What king on the eve of a battle was encouraged by the words, "Be not afraid, for the battle is not yours but God's" ? [and died according to prophecy ?
394. What king was sick two years of an incurable disease
395. What wicked king died an ignominious death and was not permitted to be buried in the sepulchre of kings ?
396. What woman murdered her grandchildren and usurped the throne ? [in the house ?
397. Who had the legal heir to the throne hid for six months
398. Who was made king of Judah at seven years of age ?
399. What queen in bible times is described as that "wicked woman"? [why ?
400. What prophet was slain in the house of the Lord, and
401. What prophet was stoned to death, and where ?
402. What very old man had his son killed by a boy to whom he had shown kindness ?
403. Who paid one hundred talents of silver for the hire of one hundred thousand Israelites to kill them ?
404. Who cast 10,000 people down from a precipice to kill them ?
405. What king indulged in farming ?
406. What king was smitten with leprosy, and why ?
407. What King of Israel burned his children in the fire ?
408. Under the advice of what prophet was a captive host returned to their own country by the victors ?
409. What king shut up the temple of God ?
410. Who, of the Kings of Israel, was carried captive to Babylon, and brought back to Jerusalem ?
411. What King of Judah had not seen a copy of the law till he was twenty-six years old ?

412. Who is mentioned as having dwelt in the college of the prophets ?

413. Of what deceased king did all the singing men and singing women speak in their lamentations ?

414. What king was on the throne of Judah when he was only eight years old ?

415. Of whom are we told that he did that which was evil in the sight of the Lord when he was only a little over eight years old ? [to prophecy ?

416. By whom were the Jews delivered from Babylon according

417. Who restored the vessels taken from the first temple ?

418. To whom was money given at the rebuilding of the temple ?

419. By whom was the foundation of the second temple laid ?

420. What Persian General demanded from the Jews their authority for rebuilding the temple ?

421. Who was pronounced a ready scribe in the law ?

422. What captive prophet journeyed from Babylon to Jerusalem without a guard of soldiers for protection ?

423. Who rent his mantle and plucked off his hair because God's people made forbidden marriages ?

424. While the people sat in the street of Jerusalem who was expounding the law to them ? [the captivity ?

425. Give the name of the first Jew who married a Gentile after

426. What captive Jew grieved so bitterly that he was permitted to return and rebuild Jerusalem ?

427. Who was a cup-bearer to the King of Babylon ?

428. What exile returned and rebuilt the walls of Jerusalem ?

429. What women helped to rebuild the walls of Jerusalem ?

430. Who mortgaged the farms in time of dearth to buy corn ?

431. What Governor of Judea refused a salary and treated his people with princely liberality ? [whom sent ?

432. What prophet was the recipient of an open letter, and by

433. Who refused to seek refuge in the temple in a time of danger ?

434. What prophetess, with others, tried to terrify Nehemiah ?

435. Who preached from a pulpit in Jerusalem ?

436. Who were the two principal porters in Jerusalem after the captivity ?

437. Whose furniture did Nehemiah cast out of the chamber of the temple at Jerusalem ?
438. Whom did Nehemiah chase from him and why ?
439. What Queen lost her crown for disobeying her husband ?
440. Who adopted Esther as his daughter ?
441. Give the name of a beautiful Persian Queen ?
442. What were the names of Ahasuerus' two chamberlains ?
443. What King, during a sleepless night, recalled an act of faithful service ?
444. What ancient King employed dromedaries as mail carriers?
445. What Jew became a great prime minister in Shushan ?
446. Whose ten sons were hanged in Shushan ?
447. What perfect man lived in the land of Uz ?
448. Who said, "The Lord gave and the Lord taketh away ?"
449. Who said, "All that a man hath will he give for his life ?"
450. Who said, "Curse God and die ?"
451. Name three of Job's friends who came to comfort him ?
452. Who expressed a desire to be where the wicked cease from troubling, and the weary are at rest ?
453. Whose hair when frightened stood on end ?
454. Who said, "I would not live alway" ?
455. Who asked the question, "Can'st thou by searching find out God" ?
456. Who said, "Though he slay me yet will I trust him" ?
457. Of whom and by whom was it said, "They had written bitter things against him" ?
458. Who said, "If a man die shall he live again" ?
459. Who accused Job of restraining prayer before God ?
460. Who were told they were "miserable comforters" ?
461. Who accused God of delivering him over to the ungodly ?
462. Who said, "I know that my Redeemer liveth" ?
463. Who calls the grave, "the house appointed for all living" ? [visited during prosperity ?
464. Who during affliction was forsaken by all his friends but
465. Name the three handsomest women in all the land of Uz ?
466. Who likens the ungodly to chaff ?
467. Who says, "In his heart there is no God" ?

468. Who acknowledges that the lines had fallen unto him in pleasant places ?

469. Who said, "I shall be satisfied with thy likeness" ?

470. Who said, "Weeping may endure for the night but joy cometh in the morning" ?

471. Who compared a wicked judge to a deaf adder ?

472. Who acknowledged himself to be "old and grey-headed" ?

473. Who exclaimed, "Who is so great a god as our God" ?

474. Who prayed, "Take me not away in the midst of my days" ?

475. Who said, "All men are liars" ?

476. Who said, "Thy word is a lamp unto my feet and a light unto my path" ? [taketh a city" ?

477. Who said, "He who ruleth his spirit is better than he who

478. Who said, 'A man that hath friends must show himself friendly" ?

479. Who, does the Scriptures say, cannot prosper" ?

480. Who prayed, "Give me neither poverty nor riches" ?

481. What author is mentioned in Proverbs ?

482. Who said, "There is no discharge in that war" ?

483. Whose confession of sin was followed by forgiveness attested by a seraph ?

484. To whom was it revealed several hundred years before that the Redeemer should be born of a virgin ? [ment ?

485. How many prophetesses are recorded in the Old Testa-

486. Of whom was it said that baldness was produced artificially as indicative of mourning ?

487. What treasurer built for himself a sepulchre in which he was never laid ?

488. What prophet foretold the resurrection of the dead ?

489. Who were forbidden to procure horses from Egypt ?

490. Who said the "heavens shall be dissolved" ?

491. Who was commanded to put his house in order ?

492. Who turned his face to the wall in prayer ?

493. What prophet acted the part of a physician by giving a medical prescription ?

494. What king showed to another king's messenger all his silver, gold and treasures ?

495. Who lamented the "harvest is past and the summer is ended?" [elites in Egypt in the very same terms?
496. What king and prophet both refer to slavery of the Isra-
497. Who hid a linen girdle in a rock by the river Euphrates?
498. Who asked, "Can the Ethiopian change his skin"? [dren?
499. Who prophesied that the Jews should eat their own chil-
500. What prophet shared the fate of a criminal by being placed in the stocks?
501. Whose name was changed because of cruelty to a prophet?
502. What was the name of the father of Pashur?
503. Of whom did Jeremiah prophesy that he should be buried with the "burial of an ass'?
504. Who used the type of good and bad figs?
505. What prophet put bands and yokes on his neck, and why?
506. What prophet took the yoke off Jeremiah's neck and broke it? [and Judea were burned by Nebuchadnezzar?
507. What two false prophets the same as the kings of Israel
508. By whom was the first temperance society organized?
509. By whom was the prophet Jeremiah arrested and put into prison? [and what prophet was secured in it?
510. Whose house was taken by the authorities for a prison,
511. Give the name of the Ethiopian who released Jeremiah?
512. Under whose arm-holes were cloths and rags used when drawn up from prison by cords?
513. Who was captain of the guard, appointed to look after Jeremiah and remove him from prison?
514. Who was the Ethiopian who trusted in the Lord, and his life was given him for a prey?
515. What man although warned, invited his murderers to a feast?
516. Who was hypocrite enough to weep with some mourning worshippers, thus decoying them into the city, and then slew them?
517. Who set his throne upon great stones, hid in clay in a brick kiln?
518. Who predicted that an invading king should pitch his tent over the spot indicated? [self?
519. Whom did the Lord tell not to see great things for him-

520. What other nation besides Israel is to be scattered to all people?
521. Who was the last king of Judah?
522. By whom were the princes of Judah slain in Riblah?
523. What king of Babylon put out the eyes of a captured king of Judah, and then imprisoned him for life?
524. What two men had their eyes put out?
525. What king released Jehoachim, king of Judah, and treated him kindly?
526. What prophet, who was also a priest, was carried captive to Babylon?
527. Who saw a vision by the river Chelar?
528. Of whom is it recorded that he ate a book?
529. What prophet was suspended between earth and heaven by a lock of his hair?
530. Who was told to fill his hands with coals of fire?
531. What prophet mentions by name three men eminent for piety and prayer? Who are they?
532. Who, when bereft of his best earthly friend, did not weep in compliance with a command from God?
533. Who beheld the vision in the valley of dry bones?
534. Which of the prophets first mentioned the "tree of life" spoken of in Revelation?
535. Who proved themselves servants of God by partaking only of vegetables and water?
536. What prophet had understanding in all visions and dreams?
537. Who dedicated the golden image on the plain of Dura?
538. What are the names of the three Hebrew children saved from the fiery furnace?
539. Who was stricken with insanity as a punishment from the Lord for his pride?
540. Who boastfully said "Is not this the great Babylon that I have built?"
541. What king ate grass like an ox?
542. What wicked king was punished by the Lord, till his hair grew like eagle's wings and his nails like bird's claws?
543. Who could say of the Lord from sad experience "Those that walk in pride he is able to abase?"

544. Who commanded that the interpreter of the writing on the wall should be clothed in scarlet, and a chain of gold hung on his neck ?
545. Who interpreted the writing on the wall at Babylon ?
546. Who was Belshazzar's successor as king of the Chaldeans ?
547. Who was the first president mentioned in sacred history ?
548. Who opened his window toward Jerusalem when he prayed ?
549. Who wrote of being a witness to the swift flight of an angel ?
550. Who became dumb on one occasion when an angel spoke to him ?
551. Who will shine as the brightness of the firmament at the resurrection ?
552. Who said "My people are destroyed for lack of knowledge ?"
553. Who said "Ephraim is joined to his idols, let him alone ?"
554. Which of the prophets asserts that thirsty cattle call unto God ?
555. What prophet was a herdsman ?
556. What prophet attests Moses' statement as to the duration of the march of the Israelites through the wilderness ?
557. To whom did Amos say he was no prophet ?
558. Which of the prophets was a gatherer of Sycamore **fruit?**
559. What prophet first refused and afterward obeyed God's command ?
560. What prophet was sent as a missionary to the Gentiles ?
561. What prophet travelling by sea was questioned as to his nativity ?
562. By whom was prayer offered from the depths of the sea ?
563. Who prophesied the destruction of a city which was averted by the repentance of its people ?
564. Who said : "It is better for me to die than to live ?"
565. The destruction of Nineveh was the fulfilment of whose prophesy ? [knowledge of the Lord ?
566. Who prophesied that the earth shall be filled with the
567. What prophet said : "In wrath remember mercy ?"

568. What prophet said: "They save wages to put it into a bag with holes?"

569. Who prophesied that the glory of the second temple should be greater than the glory of the first?"

570. What prophet speaks of children playing in the streets of Jerusalem during prosperity?

571. What two prophets declared: "I am no prophet?"

572. Who said: "At evening time it shall be light?"

573. What prophet foretells the coming of John the Baptist?

574. Who asked the question: "Will a man rob God?"

575. Who is reported as speaking often one to another?

CURIOSITIES OF THE BIBLE

PERTAINING TO

NEW TESTAMENT PERSONS.

Answers Page 27 of Key.

1. Who was reigning in Judah when Joseph returned from Egypt with the child Jesus?
2. What prophet preached by the side of a river?
3. Who called the Sadducees "a generation of vipers?"
4. Who ministered unto Jesus after the temptation in the wilderness?
5. Who were the first called of the disciples?
6. To whom was the command given "follow me and I will make you fishers of men"?
7. What four disciples were fishermen?
8 Whose birthday was celebrated by dancing?
9. Whom did our Saviour meet on the other side of Galilee?
10. Who requested that her sons might sit the one on the right hand, and the other on the left of Jesus in the kingdom of heaven? [ing"?
11. Who said, "God is not the God of the dead but of the liv-
12. Who are said "to strain at a gnat and swallow a camel"?
13. The martyrdom of what prophet did Jesus relate when censuring the Scribes and Pharisees? [New Testament?
14. What national soldiery is symbolized by Eagles in the
15. Whose words shall not pass away?
16 With whom did Jesus spend his last Sabbath?
17. Who was governor at the time of the crucifixion?
18. Give the name of a noted robber mentioned in the gospel?
19 Who was the only person according to the sacred Scriptures who raised a voice in behalf of Jesus, during the trial?

20. Who rose from the dead without the interposition of the Prophets, Jesus, or the Apostles ?
21. Who gave the command "Go and teach all nations, baptizing them," etc.? [and lived on locusts and honey ?
22. What prophet clothed himself with the skins of animals,
23. Which of the apostles was a tax collector ? [bath ?
24. What sects sought to destroy Jesus for healing on the Sab-
25. Who said : "My name is legion"?
26. Who was the ruler of a synagogue ?
27. Who is mentioned as the carpenter's son ?
28 Upon whom did our Saviour perform a miracle by the utterance of one word ?
29. Who said, and to whom : "Get thee behind Me, Satan"?
30 What prophet was seen 1500 years after his death ?
31. Who said and to whom : "It is good for us to be here"?
32. With whom was Jesus displeased for rebuking mothers bringing their children to Him ?
33. Who said "With God all things are possible"?
34. Of whom was it said : "She hath done what she could"?
35. Which of the disciples fell asleep during the agonies of our Savior in the garden ? [of crucifixion ?
36 Who was compelled to bear the cross of Christ to the place
37. To whom was Christ's resurrection first declared ?
38. To whom did Christ first appear ?
39. To whom was the command given : "Go ye into all the world, and preach the gospel to every creature"?
40. Who said and to whom : "I am Gabriel"? [angel told him ?
41. Who did the Lord strike dumb for not believing what an
42 Whose births in the New Testament were announced by an angel ? [an angel ?
43. To what persons were messages brought from heaven by
44. Who are the only two persons spoken of in the Bible as cousins ? [herself a sinner ?
45. What highly-exalted woman by two words acknowledged
46. Who issued a decree that all the world should be taxed ?
47 What aged man waited in Jerusalem for the coming of the Messiah ?
48. Who was told he should not die until he had seen Christ ?

49 Give the name of the only woman in the New Testament
whose age is given ? [temple ?
50. Who is recorded as having prayed day and night in the
51. Whose first recorded words are, "How is it that ye sought
me" ? [give sin's ?
52. What sects among the Jews held that God only could for-
53. Who said, and to whom, "They that are whole need not
a physician" ? [men shall speak well of you ?
54. Who and to whom was it said, "Woe unto you when all
55. Whom did Christ raise to life as he was being carried to
his grave ? [upon to calm a storm ?
56. Who were sailing with our Saviour when he was called
57 Which of the disciples wished to command fire from heaven
and consume the unfriendly Samaritans ?
58. Who passed by the wounded man on the road to Jericho ?
59 Who paid the hotel bill of a man who had been robbed ?
60. What character in the New Testament believed in the
world and lived for it ? [tell that fox ?"
61. To what king did Christ refer when he said, "go ye and
62. What beggar was laid at a rich man's gate ?
63. What New Testament character wept over Jerusalem ?
64. Who was strengthened by an angel during great distress ?
65. What apostle said, "I know him not" referring to Christ ?
66. Who asked Christ "art thou the King of the Jews ?"
67. Who were told by our Saviour not to mourn for him ?
68. Who asked Jesus, "art thou only a stranger in Jerusalem?"
69. Who said that the three great divisions of the Old Testament contained predictions concerning himself ?
70. Who testified of Jesus that he was both his successor and
predecessor ? [areth ?
71. Who said, "can there any good thing come out of Naz-
72. Who told Nathaniel "to come and see?"
73. What stranger never having seen Jesus before was called by name and introduced to three apostles ?
74. Who commanded the servants "To do whatsoever he saith unto them"?
75. Who is reported as coming to Jesus by night ?
76. Who said: "Arise, take up thy bed, and walk"?

77. Of whom was it said: "He was a burning and a shining light"?
78. By whom are we told to "Search the Scriptures"?
79. Who said: "I receive not honor from men"?
80. Who is called "the light of the world"?
81 What three persons did Christ raise from the dead?
82. Who though dead four days was raised to life by the utterance of three words?
83. Who entertained Christ as recompense for the good deed once performed on him?
84. Who wiped the feet of Jesus with her hair? [another"?
85. Who gave as a test of discipleship, "If ye have love one to
86. Who said he would lay down his life for the Saviour's?
87. Whom did the Saviour say would deny him three times?
88. Whose ear did the apostle Peter cut off?
89. Who had a coat without a seam woven from the top throughout?
90 Who came to Jesus by night, defended him in his ministry, and finally helped to bury him?
91. Who intimated the manner Peter should die? [of John?
92. Which of the apostles wished to know what would become
93 Whose curiosity was checked by Christ telling him in effect to mind his own business?
94. Who said that if all the things Christ ever did were recorded the world itself would not contain the books that would be written? [the resurrection?
95. Upon whom did Christ forcibly impress his identity after
96. What Old Testament prophets' inspiration is attested to in the Acts?
97. Whose bowels fell out?
98. Who was appointed in place of Judas?
99. What young preacher on the occasion of his first sermon witnessed a large number of conversions?
100. What Levite sold his land and laid its price at the apostle's feet?
101. Who on one occasion kept back part of what they had devoted to the cause of God?

102. The violent death of what three persons may be regarded as a consequence of their convictions?
103. Sick persons were once placed where the shadow of a good man might pass over them? Who was the man? Why was it done?
104 Who is pronounced a Doctor of the Law?
105. What seven deacons were appointed at one time by the apostles?
106. Whose face while preaching shone like an angel's?
107. Whose name is associated with the stoning of Stephen?
108. Who was the first Christian martyr?
109. Who, while being cruelly put to death, prayed like his Lord for his murderers?
110. Give the name of a sorcerer mentioned in the Acts?
111. What wicked man asked for the prayers of a righteous person?
112. Who is mentioned as the Queen of Ethiopia?
113. Name the queen's treasurer converted to christianity by the evangelist Philip?
114. Who was reading the writings of a prophet while riding in a chariot?
115. Who was converted on his way to Damascus?
116. Whose first words were after conversion, "Lord, what wilt thou have me to do"?
117. Who was struck blind when converted?
118. Whom did the Lord send to restore sight to St. Paul?
119. Who was let down over the walls of a city in a basket in order to escape arrest?
120. What charitable woman's name is given?
121 Who was the first apostle to raise a dead person to life?
122. Which of the disciples was a tanner?
123. Give the name of a devout centurion?
124. What devout man prayed on the house-top?
125. Who said, "God is no respecter of persons"? [good"?
126. Who in speaking of Christ said, "He went about doing
127. What prophet in the New Testament foretells a famine which occurred in the days of Claudius Caesar?
128. By whose order was the apostle James martyred?

129. Who was commanded by an angel to bind on his sandals ?
130. Whose voice was taken for the voice of God ?
131. Whom did the Angel of the Lord strike dead because he gave not God the glory ?
132. Whom did Saul call "child of the devil" ?
133. What sorcerer was struck blind for a season ? [for gods ?
134 What two disciples, after working a miracle, were taken
135. The name of what heathen god was once applied to St. Paul ?
[nabas ?
136. The name of what heathen god was once applied to Bar-
137. What two persons disagreed about taking John as a companion ?
138. What two missionaries had a quarrel and parted ?
139. Who was the first Christian convert in Europe ?
140. What four men were put in prison for preaching Christ, two together ?
[daily "?
141. Of whom was it said: "They searched the Scriptures
142. Whose sermon was adorned with poetical quotations ?
143 What Athenian judge was converted under Paul's preaching ?
144. What Athenian woman is mentioned as being converted under Paul's preaching ?
145. What emperor banished all Jews from Rome ?
146. What apostle earned his living by tent-making ?
147. What friend of Paul was a tent-maker ?
148. Who, when the Jews would not hear him, shook his raiment and said, "Your blood be on your own heads"?
149. Of whom was it said, "He was mighty in the Scriptures" ?
150. Who expounded the gospel to Apollos ?
151. To whom did the brethren at Ephesus give a letter of introduction when on his way to Greece ?
152 Who were the men who perceived the power of God and tried to exercise it without his grace and suffered thereby ?
153. What silversmith's name is given ?
154. Who in preaching prolonged his sermon till midnight ?
155. Who fell asleep during Paul's preaching and fell out of the third story window and was killed ?
156. Who restored Eutychus to life ?

157. How many prophetesses are recorded in the New Testament? Who are they?
158 What prophet bound his own hands and feet together?
159. Who foretold Paul of the persecution awaiting him at Jerusalem? [from Cesarea to Jerusalem?
160. What was the name of Paul's host who accompanied him
161. Who in order to pacify the Jews performed their ceremonial law upon himself?
162. Who was the Ephesian Paul took with him to Jerusalem?
163. What prisoner in chains stood on the steps of a castle and addressed a multitude?
164. Who was St. Panl's teacher?
165. Who held the clothes of Stephen's murderers?
166. Who said "I was born free"?
167. Who commanded that Paul be smitten on the mouth?
168. What sect among the Jews say there is "no resurrection, neither angel nor spirit"?
169. Whose life was endangered by a conspiracy of forty men?
170. For whom did a band of men lie in wait, bound by an oath that they would not eat nor drink till they had killed him?
171. Who preferred charges against St. Paul?
172. Who was called a "ring-leader"?
173. Who was the wife of Felix? [chains?
174. What unrighteous judge trembled before a prisoner in
175 Give an example of religious convictions being stifled?
176. The christian zeal of what two persons was attributed to madness?
177. Who was captain of the guard that took Paul to Rome?
178. Who was shipwrecked on the island of Malta?
179. Who had power divine to use serpents unharmed?
180. Who was the chief man on the island of Malta where Paul was shipwrecked? stances and before daybreak?
181. Who partook of a joyful meal under adverse circum-
182. What captive preached for two whole years in Rome?
183. Of whom was it said, "Their zeal was without knowledge"?
184. Who charged the Gentiles with being a "foolish nation"?

185. What apostle expressed a desire to travel into Spain?
186. What two women whose names have each three syllables
commencing with "Try"?
187. Mention the name of a Roman Christian lady?
188. Who are mentioned by St. Paul as his kinsmen?
189 Give the name of the only person in the Bible whose
name commences with the letter Q? [pitality?
190. What Christian was recommended to the apostles for hos-
191. What woman carried St. Paul's epistle to the Romans?
192. What converts were baptized at Corinth by St. Paul?
193 To whom did St. Paul say the preaching of Christ was a
stumbling-block? [likened unto "foolishness"?
194 To what learned people was the simplicity of the gospel
195. To what converts did St. Paul refer to as the "seal of his
apostleship"? [which I give thanks"?
196. Who when speaking of food referred to it as "that for
197. Who called himself "the least of the apostles"?
198 Who were the first converts in Achaia?
199 Who are the only three persons mentioned in the Bible
whose names commence with the letter F?
200. Of whom was it said, "He knew no sin"? [prisoner?
201. What governor of Damascus attempted to make Paul a
202. What three apostles were regarded by St. Paul as pillars
of the church?
203 Who in the New Testament are said to be children of
Abraham?
204 What letter-carrier's name is recorded? "bow"?
205 Who said, "At the name of Jesus every knee should
206. Which of St. Paul's fellow-workmen does he say "was
sick nigh unto death"? [lived for it?
207. What New Testament character believed in eternity and
208. Who went up to Rome to carry contributions to Paul a
prisoner, and carried back with him the epistle to the
Philippians?
209. Who does Paul call "a faithful and beloved brother"?
210 What three persons (not including Christ) are called
Jesus?
211. Who was an evangelist, physician and writer?

212. Who said, "I would have come unto you but Satan hindered me"?
213. Who said, "Hold fast to that which is good"?
214. Who entreats his fellow-men to "be not weary in well-doing?"
215. Who oft refreshed Paul when a prisoner and was not ashamed of him?
216 What heretics' names are given in the New Testament?
217. What example have we of early piety in the New Testament?
218. What New Testament character forsook Paul and the cause of Christ for the world?
219. Who is spoken of as being a coppersmith?
220. Name three heathen writers whom St. Paul quotes?
221. Who said, "To the pure all things are pure"?
222. Which of the sacred writers debars a heretic from the house and home of a believer?
223. Give the name of a lawyer in the New Testament?
224. Who does St. Paul style "a fellow soldier"?
225. To whom did Paul write, "Prepare me also a lodging"?
226. Who are said to minister to the heirs of salvation?
227. Who did Paul say was greater than Moses?
228. To what Old Testament priest does Paul liken Christ?
229. What Old Testament woman is honored among New Testament worthies for her good treatment of suspicious emissaries?
230 Who quotes words from Moses that are not found in the Old Testament? [above"?
231. Who said, "Every good gift and every perfect gift is from
232. Who said, "The devils also believe that there is one God"?
233. Who likened life unto "a vapor that appeareth for a little time and then vanisheth away"?
234. Who called Jesus "the Shepherd and Bishop of our souls"?
235. Name three persons whose afflictions were a source of enjoyment?
seeking whom he may devour"?
236. Who said, "Your adversary, the devil, is as a roaring lion
237. Who likened the world to "a dark place"?

238. By whom is Noah mentioned as a preacher of righteousness ?
239. What member of the primitive church tried the patience of the loving disciple John ?
240. Who beheld a vision on the Isle of Patmos ?
241. Who was declared to have his seat in Pergamos ?
242. Of whom and by whom was it said they were neither hot nor cold spiritually ?
243. God will wipe away all tears from the eyes of whom ?
244. Give the name of two angels mentioned in the Bible ?
245. Over whose defeat are the inhabitants of heaven told to rejoice ?

CURIOSITIES OF THE BIBLE

PERTAINING TO

OLD TESTAMENT PLACES.

Answers Page 37 of Key.

1. Where and under what circumstance is the first mention of Heaven in the Bible ?
2. Where was the voice of God first heard by human ear ?
3. Where did Cain go after killing Abel ?
4. Where in Scripture language is the land of Canaan located ?
5. At what place and to what woman did an angel appear ?
6. What two cities were destroyed by fire and brimstone ?
7. To what mountain did Lot flee from Sodom ?
8. At what place and by whom was a grove planted, and the blessing of God invoked ?
9. At what place was the last revelation of God to Abraham ?
10. What was the city Jacob changed to Bethel ?
11. At what place did Jacob wrestle with an angel ?
12. Where was Rachel buried ?
13. At what place was the first monument erected to the memory of the dead ?
14. Where was Joseph's mother buried ?
15. Where were Abraham, Isaac and Jacob buried ?
16. On what mountain did an angel appear, and to whom ?
17. At what place did the Israelites first camp after crossing the Red Sea ?
18. On what mountain did Moses speak with God ?

19. Where were the golden earrings of the women melted to make an idolatrous image?
20. From whence was fire originally obtained which was kept perpetually burning on the golden altar?
21. At what place did the Israelites gather a surplus of quails and were punished for it?
22. Where were the children of Israel encamped when the spies were despatched to "search the land of Canaan"?
23. Where was the census of Israel taken before entering Canaan?
24. What was given to the children of Caleb as an inheritance?
25. Where did Aaron die?
26. Upon what specially designated places were the Israelites to write God's words?
27. On what mountain was a blessing for obedience promised upon the children of Israel?
28. On what mountain was curses pronounced upon a part of the children of Israel?
29. From where did Moses view the promised land?
30. Where was Moses buried?
31. At what place did the Israelites first eat strange food after living on manna for forty years?
32. At what place did the manna cease?
33. What firmly fortified place was taken by ceremonial processions?
34. At what place did Achan's sin first find him out?
35. What city was taken by stratagem and burned with 12,000 men and women?
36. The king of what city was taken alive and hung?
37. What city was saved from massacre by the strategy of its people?
38. The inhabitants of what four cities were reduced to perpetual bondage by the conqueror?
39. What cave was the hiding-place of five kings?
40. In what cities was protection afforded to murderers until trial?
41. Where was Joseph's bones, which were brought out of Egypt, buried?

42. What town was the scene of unparalleled kingly tortures?
43. At what place had seventy kings their great toes and thumbs cut off?
44. Where was the battle between Sisera and Barak fought?
45. Where at touch of a staff, did fire rise out of a rock and consume a feast?
46. At what place were the Midianites put to flight, and by whom?
47. What city was sown with salt by Abimelech?
48. The tower of a besieged city was destroyed. From whence came the wood that burned it?
49. Where was Abimelech killed by a woman?
50. What thirty neighboring cities were governed by thirty brothers?
51. What is the name of Samson's birth-place?
52. Of what city did Samson carry away the gates?
53. At what place did the idolatrous god Dagon of the Philistines fall down before the Ark of God?
54. Where was a monument erected to commemorate the destruction of the Philistines?
55. At what place did Samuel number the forces of Israel and Judah, and give the number of each?
56. Where did Samuel hew Agag in pieces before the Lord?
57. Where was the home of Goliath?
58. At what place did David eat the shew-bread?
59. Where did Saul go to seek a witch?
60. On what mountain was a king of Israel slain at his own request?
61. Where was David anointed king of Israel?
62. What city's name was changed to the name of the conqueror by the conqueror?
63. Where did David torture the people he had taken captive?
64. Up what mountain described in Old Testament did a party ascend weeping, and afterward Christ and His disciples singing. Name the mountain?
65. At what place did the Lord appear to Solomon by night and say, "What shall I give thee"?

66. At what place did a woman try to steal the child of another?
67. At what seaport town was assembled a large navy during Solomon's time?
68. At what place was a king's hand withered for an attempted assault on a prophet?
69. At what place did a king of Israel erect altars and offer sacrifice to golden calves?
70. What mountain was purchased by a king of Israel, upon which to build a city?
71. On what mountain was a king commanded to gather a whole nation?
72. On what mountain did a prophet fast forty days and forty nights, and why?
73. At what place did fire come down from heaven and consume 102 men?
74. What was the only city left standing when the Israelites subdued Moab?
75. Where was a king of Syria smothered by his servant. Give his name?
76. Where was a collection taken to repair the temple?
77. What city did God liken to a dish wiped, and turned upside down?
78. Where was King Josiah slain in battle?
79. Where were the bones of Jonathan and Saul buried?
80. In what city and during whose reign was gold and silver as plentiful as stones?
81. On what mountain was Solomon's temple built?
82. When was a celebrated edifice erected on a spot which was the scene of the greatest instance of human obedience?
83. At what place did the largest armies known in Bible times face each other?
84. Where, and how long was an heir to a throne once hid?
85. What famous city did Uzziah strengthen and fortify, and how?
86. What city was known as the city of palm-trees?
87. Where was a great revival of religion that lasted fourteen days and under whose charge?

88. The inhabitants of what city sat in the streets to hear the warnings of a prophet?

89. Where was a battle fought between the Jews and the Persians in which 75,000 were slain, and the victors plundered not?

90. What city, on account of its beauty, was once known as the "Glory of Kingdoms?"

91. What city was destroyed and never again inhabited?

92. Where was Jeremiah put in prison and why?

93. At what place were Jedekiah's eyes put out and by whom?

94. Where did Jeremiah take stones and hide them in a brick kiln when he wanted to show where Nebuchadnezzar would set up his throne?

95. What Bible city suffered the horrors of famine because of a beseiging army?

96. What city was in such a deplorable condition that the virgins hung down their heads for shame?

97. At what place were the three Jews thrown into the fiery furnace?

98. What city's destruction was in the words, "That it should come to nought?"

99. What is the oldest place from which prayer was offered?

100. What city did God say he would "set as a gazing stock?"

101. At the destruction of what city were all her great men put in chains.

CURIOSITIES OF THE BIBLE

PERTAINING TO

NEW TESTAMENT PLACES.

Answers Page 43 *of Key.*

1. What city though exalted to heaven was brought down to destruction ?
2. Where was the home of Mary and Martha so frequently visited by our Savior ?
3. Where was the withered fig tree mentioned by our Saviour situated ?
4. Where was Jesus proclaimed King of the Jews ?
5. Where did Christ ordain or commission the twelve disciples ?
6. Where was the seat of the ruling power of the world at the time of Christ ?
7. Where did Jesus perform the miracle of the draught of fishes ?
8. What place was referred to, and to whom did Peter say, " It is good for us to be here ? "
9. What place is only mentioned once in the Bible ?
10. What city was supposed to produce nothing good ?
11. Where did Christ perform His first miracle ?
12. Where did John baptize a great many ?
13. On what mountain did Christ pass many nights ?
14. Where was Lazarus buried ?
15. Where did our Lord spend his last Sabbath ?

16. Where was the home of the apostle our Lord referred to "as an Israelite indeed, in whom there is no guile?"
17. What place is said to be a Sabbath day's journey from Jerusalem?
18. Where was the Virgin Mary, the last mention of her in in the Bible?
19. At what city did St. Paul first preach Christ?
20. Where was the home of Dorcas and Simon, the tanner?
21. Where was the home of Cornelius the centurion?
22. Where were the disciples first called Christians?
23. At what city was Elymas struck blind?
24. Our Saviour bade his disciples shake the dust of those cities from off their feet, which refused to receive them? At what city did they do this?
25. At what city was Paul stoned nearly to death?
26 Where did the disciples first hold a missionary meeting?
27. Where, and of whom was it said, "These have turned the world upside down?"
28. The inhabitants of what city did St. Paul say, "They searched the Scriptures daily?"
29. Where was an altar erected to the unknown God?
30. At what city in Asia Minor did Paul preach three years?
31. What city claims the birth place of Paul?
32. On what island was a ship run aground for safety?
33. At what place was Paul attacked by a snake?
34. The church at what place does St. Paul tell us he never visited?
35. Where did John write the book of Revelation?
36. Where were the seven churches of Asia located?
37. The destruction of what city was told by an angel, who throwing a millstone into the sea, said "Thus shall that great city be thrown down?"
38. On the gates and foundations of what city are the names of the twelve apostles written?

CURIOSITIES OF THE BIBLE

PERTAINING TO

OLD TESTAMENT THINGS.

Answers Page 47 *of Key*

1. What did God create the first day?
2. What did God do on the second day?
3. What was done by God on the third day?
4. What did God make on the fourth day?
5. What was made by God on the fifth day?
6. What was God's work on the sixth day?
7. Upon what day in the week were the two greatest acts of Divine Power that affected man accomplished?
8. What did God do on the seventh day?
9. How many times has it been noticed that the Sabbath has been impressed on the observance of man?
10. Where does the Bible say that man became a living soul?
11. On what occasion did man first exercise the power of speech?
12. What three mournful events took place in a garden?
13. What was the most ancient art of sinful mankind?
14. Upon what did God pronounce the first curse?
15. What curse was pronounced on the serpent?
16. With what was the Garden of Eden guarded to prevent the return of our first parents?
17. Where is sin personified as a serpent lurking at the door of the human heart? [killing Abel?
18. What punishment did God say would come upon Cain for
19. Of what wood was Noah's Ark made?

20. What was the length of Noah's Ark?
21. What news did the first carrier-pigeon bring?
22. What bird was employed to convey a token of peace to a servant of God?
23. What miracle led to the dispersion of all mankind over the world?
24. Where do "Northward," "Southward," "Eastward," and "Westward," occur in one verse?
25. What is the most ancient war on record?
26. When was it plainly shown that the faith of one man was stronger than the united strength of many ungodly nations?
27. Where is the promise found that the children of Israel should possess the land of Canaan?
28. What are the three principal promises God made to Abraham?
29. Why were the Sodomites smitten with blindness?
30. How did God punish Sodom and Gomorrah?
31. Why was Lot's wife made a pillar of salt?
32. What witness did Abraham give that he digged a well?
33. Of what did the first wedding present consist?
34. Where has mention been made of land producing a hundred-fold in one year?
35. What is the origin and meaning of the word Mizpah?
36. What is the recorded occasion upon which the terror of God was exercised on behalf of his chosen people?
37. Mention a tree that was named from the circumstances connected with it?
38. What distinguished title was given to the descendants of Esau?
39. Why did Jacob love Joseph more than all his other children?
40. What article of clothing was the token of a father's partiality?
41. How many instances can be found in the Bible where a blessing was granted to a number of persons on account of the presence among them of one man of God?
42. What presents did Jacob send into Egypt?

43. What was the total number of the children of Israel that went down to Egypt?
44. What country was that in which the king bought all the land from his people and then treated them as slaves? Quote passage?
45. Why were the Levites scattered in Israel?
46. How many days were required for embalming in Egypt?
47. How many instances are recorded in the Bible of embalming the dead?
48. The Almighty condescended so far as to take the names of certain men that he might be known among their posterity. Who were they, and give Christ's comment upon it?
49. When Moses put his hand in his bosom at God's command what happened?
50. What change was made in the water when Moses cast it on dry land?
51. What did God give Moses when sending him to Pharaoh.
52. What did Aaron's rod become when cast before Pharaoh?
53. What did Aaron's rod do to the sorcerer's rods?
54. What was the first Egyptian plague and how long did it last?
55. Name the ten plagues in their order?
56. What Old Testament example have we of miraculous darkness?
57. What was the last of the ten plagues of Egypt?
58. What two animals may be eaten for the Passover?
59. How was the blood applied to the houses of the Hebrews in Goshen?
60. What departing nation borrowed garments of their enemies?
61. How many were the children of Israel that Moses led out of Egypt?
62. How were the children of Israel guided in their forty years' wanderings in the wilderness?
63. One and the same way was a way of deliverance and a way of death; prove this from a fact described in the Old Testament?

64. How many Egyptian chariots of war in their pursuit of the Israelites were lost in the Red Sea?
65. What act of Moses signalled the destruction of Pharaoh and his army in the Red Sea?
66. Give an instance of bitter water becoming sweet?
67. What was the appearance and the taste of manna?
68. What did the Israelites have for a morning and evening meal in the wilderness?
69. How long did the Israelites eat honey?
70. What does the Old Testament mention as being sanctified?
71. How long did a Hebrew slave have to serve to secure his freedom?
72. What rite signified perpetual voluntary service?
73. How often had males to appear annually before the Lord at Jerusalem?
74. Who are mentioned as having seen the God of Israel?
75. How long did the cloud cover the mountain before God spoke to Moses?
76. How long did Moses remain on Horeb with God?
77. Of what wood was the Ark of the Covenant made?
78. What were the dimensions of the Ark of the Covenant?
79. Of what material was the Tabernacle made?
80. How many and what were the coverings of the tabernacle?
81. Moses is made on two occasions an offer which would raise him to honors and destroy the Israelites—name them?
82. On which side of the tables of stone were the commandments written?
83. Why did Moses throw the tables down and break them?
84. What did Moses do with the golden calf made by Aaron?
85. State the occasion and who said "Who is on the Lord's side"?
86. How many perished for the sin of making the golden calf by order of Moses?
87. Why did Moses strip the children of Israel of their ornaments at Horeb?
88. When did Moses put a veil upon his face and when did he take it off?
89. What was the Ark of the Covenant and its contents?

90. What were the dimensions of the Mercy-seat?

91. Of what were the looking-glasses made that are mentioned in the Scriptures?

92. What did the "Holy of holies" in the temple contain?

93. What birds were prized in sacrifice?

94. Mention a dinner in which the shoulder was given as a mark of highest respect and to whom?

95. What peculiar ceremony did Moses perform in the consecration of Aaron and his son to the office of Priesthood?

96. What was the origin of the fire with which the Jews offered their burnt offerings?

97. Name two individuals who lost their lives from using strange fires?

98. How does the Bible say a leprous house shall be disinfected?

99. What was forbidden regarding the beard?

100. How were the Israelites commanded to treat strangers?

101. According to the Jewish policy, who could not marry widows?

102. "Whatsoever animal hath blemish that shall ye not offer," said Moses; what exception was there to this rule?

103. What was the Divinely appointed punishment for blasphemy?

104. What is the year of Jubilee mentioned in the Bible?

105. Why were not the Jews permitted to sell their land for more than a certain number of years?

106. What two diseases did God especially threaten to bring upon his people for their neglect of his commandments?

107. Where in the Bible is it recorded that fever and ague were inflicted as punishments?

108. Upon what people was consumption threatened as a punishment for sin?

109. Who were included in the count when Moses numbered the children of Israel?

110. Which of the tribes of Israel was the greatest?

111. Why was the tribe of Levi not numbered?

112. Why was the first-born freed by the Levites?

113. Which of the tribes of Israel was the smallest?

114. Where is the fact recorded of a ransom being paid for 373 persons?
115. What restitution was to be made in trespass?
116. Where do we find the mode of trial for jealousy recorded?
117. What was the Nazarite vow and where do we find it?
118. At what age were the Levites no longer allowed to work in the tabernacle?
119. Quote the words of Moses at the commencement and termination of the journeyings of the Israelites?
120. Upon what did the manna fall?
121. When Moses complained of his charge, how did God relieve him?
122. What fact shows the great quantity of quails sent to Israel?
123. In what did Moses excel other men?
124. Why was Moses' sister made leprous, and how was she healed?
125. How many men were sent to search the land of Canaan?
126. What did the spies bring back from Canaan?
127. How long did the spies search the land of Canaan?
128. What did the spies report they saw in Canaan?
129. Why did the children of Israel wander forty years in the wilderness?
130. What punishment was inflicted upon those who murmured on hearing the report?
131. How were the spies punished who brought the evil report?
132. What was the punishment inflicted by God's command upon a man who had broken the Sabbath?
133. What command was given by God to the children of Israel as to the make of their garments, and why?
134. How did Aaron stay the plague that was to destroy the children of Israel for rebellion?
135. How many perished in the plague that was to punish the Children of Israel for rebellion?
136. What fruit is recorded in the Bible as growing on a tree without root or branch?
137. For what purpose was Aaron's rod kept in the tabernacle?
138. Prove from the Scriptures that it was contrary to the Mosaic law for a Levite to possess land?

139. Of what was the water of separation made?
140. How long did the people mourn for Aaron?
141. How were the people punished for murmuring because of discouragements?
142. How were the people healed when bitten by the fiery serpents?
143. What is the shortest song in the Bible?
144. What did Balaam's ass do and say?
145. What words were once spoken to a man by a beast of burden?
146. Where have we Balaam's parable recorded?
147. Did Balaam curse Israel as Balak wanted him to do?
148. For how much did Balaam tell Balak he could not curse Israel?
149. How many children of Israel fell victims to a plague in consequence of having joined themselves in idolatry to Baal-peor?
150. What was the number of the children of Israel in the plains of Moab?
151. How many were left of those numbered at Sinai?
152. What language used by the daughters of Zelophehad show that they understood how death entered the world?
153. Where have we the law of inheritance recorded?
154. Where have we the exception to a maid's vow recorded?
155. How many out of each tribe did Moses send to war against the Midianites?
156. What six metals are mentioned in one verse in Numbers?
157. How many journeys did the children of Israel make in the wilderness?
158. How many and what were the cities appointed for refuge?
159. What especial law was given to Moses in reference to cases where property was left to the daughters of a family?
160. Where have we an instance of water being sold for money?
161. What other inhabitants of Canaan were giants besides the Anakims?
162. What king is mentioned as having an iron bedstead?
163. What did Moses pray for before his death?

164. Where do we read of gods who are less than the man who fashions them?

165. In what two different books and chapters are the ten commandments?

166. Give two reasons according to Deut. why God delivered the Jews from Egyptian bondage?

167. It may truly be said that during forty years journeying through the wilderness the children of Israel were each one a perpetual miracle. How so?

168. Why were the Israelites to remember all the ways which God led them in the wilderness for forty years?

169. What were the Israelites forbidden to do in times of mourning?

170. Where are we told that every man should give as he was able?

171. Why did God forbid the Israelites from obtaining horses from Egypt?

172. In what language did Moses foretell the terrible consequences of rejecting the Messiah?

173. How many witnesses were required among the Jews to establish a charge?

174. What kind of trees were the Israelites forbidden to cut down for use in a seige, and why?

175. What three privileges were attached to the first-born of a family?

176. What punishment was to be inflicted on a stubborn son?

177. Where and in what language is a woman not to wear a man's garments, and *vice versa*?

178. We read, according to the Mosaic law, a Jew when he came to his neighbor's vineyard might eat his fill. What restriction was imposed on one so doing?

179. For how long did marriage exempt a man from going to war?

180. What was the law among the Jews as to the pledging of raiment?

181. From whom were the Jews forbidden to take garments in pawn?

182. What privilege must an ox have when treading out the corn?
183. What kind of weights were forbidden?
184. From what two mountains were the blessings and cursings pronounced upon the children of Israel, and what tribes took part in each?
185. Where have we blessings for obedience recorded?
186. How is the blessing upon the wholesale and retail departments of business recorded?
187. What prophecy refers to the taking of Jerusalem by the Romans?
188. Where have we curses for disobedience recorded?
189. What prophecy was uttered more than 3000 years ago and is now being fulfilled?
190. What language did God say the Israelites would use when in an enemy's land and in great fear?
191. What two cities are mentioned as having been destroyed with Sodom and Gomorrah?
192. With whom was the Urim and Thummin to be?
193. Where are recorded the blessings of the twelve tribes?
194. How long did the children of Israel weep for Moses?
195. By what means did Rahab aid the escape of the spies sent to Jericho?
196. What was the sign of the covenant between Rahab and the spies?
197. The Jordan was miraculously crossed on three occasions—name them?
198. How many examples does the Old Testament give of weak things being employed to confound the Mighty?
199. What was the punishment threatened the man who should rebuild Jericho?
200. What punishment was inflicted upon Achan for stealing?
201. By what stratagem was Ai taken?
202. What was the special avocation of the Gibeonites?
203. How did God help Joshua to defeat his enemies at Gibeon?
204. What did Joshua order to stand still over Gibeon?
205. What two miracles were wrought upon the sun?

206. How long did the sun and moon stand still at the command of Joshua?
207. How many kings were hanged by Joshua and on what?
208. How many cities were given to the Levites for their use?
209. What stone, according to the Scriptures, heard all the words which the Lord spoke unto his people?
210. How many kings had their thumbs and great toes cut off by Adonibezek?
211. What reward did Othniel get for taking Kirjath-sepher?
212. Why was a man's life and family spared at the taking of Luz?
213. What was the length of the dagger with which Ehud killed the king of Eglon?
214. Where in prophetic Scriptures do we read of parlors?
215. What did Shamgar do with an ox goad?
216. How many chariots were kept by Jabin, King of Canaan?
217. In what passage of Scripture do we read of wise ladies?
218. Why did the Lord deliver Israel into the hands of the Midianites for seven years?
219. How was Gideon's army reduced from thirty-two thousands to three hundred?
220. Which of the tribes of Israel quarrelled with Gideon, when not being asked to partake in a battle?
221. What men refused to give bread to fainting soldiers?
222. How many sons had Gideon?
223. How was Abimelech killed?
224. Why did Abimelech wish his armor-bearers to despatch him?
225. Why did the daughters of Israel lament the death of the daughter of Jephthah four days in a year?
226. How many Ephraimites were slain in battle with the Gileadites?
227. How were the Ephraimites on one occasion known from the people of the other tribes?
228. How long were the children of Israel under the Philistines?
229. How many Old Testament characters had their births announced by angels?
230. From whose altar did the Angel of the Lord ascend in a flame?

231. What was Samson's riddle and what were its conditions?
232. How many of the Philistines did Samson kill to obtain the gifts for the expounders of his riddle?
233. How did Samson burn the Philistines' corn?
234. How many Philistines did Samson slay with a jaw-bone?
235. When did a weapon of destruction become a fountain of refreshment?
236. How did Samson lose his strength?
237. What did the Philistines do to punish Samson?
238. How did Samson take revenge upon the Philistines?
239. How many men and women were killed in the fall of the building that was pulled down by Samson?
240. Did Samson slay more at his death than in his life?
241. How many men of Benjamin were left-handed and could sling a stone at a hair-breadth and not miss?
242. When did every man do that which was right in his own eyes?
243. How many times did the Lord call the infant Samuel?
244. How many Israelites were slain in the battle of Ebenezer, when the Ark of the Lord was won by the Philistines?
245. What is the meaning of the word Ichabod; by whom, and to whom was it applied?
246. How was the Ark of the Lord brought from the Philistines when it was returned to Israel?
247. How did the Lord discomfort the Philistines in answer to Samuel's prayer?
248. Why did the Israelites ask for a king?
249. Whose daughters did God say should become confectioners, cooks, and bakers?
250. What was the early Bible name for prophet?
251. What were the three signs by the prediction of which Samuel confirmed his anointing of Saul?
252. What was the condition upon which Nahash would make peace with the people of Jabesh-Gilead?
253. How many instances are there on Bible record of rain being sent in answer to prayer?
254. How did God signify His displeasure when the Jews asked for a king?

255. In what instance did God send rain as a sign of his displeasure against Israel ?
256. Why had the Philistines no smith in Israel ?
257. How did the Israelites sharpen their agricultural implements ?
258. Where do we find the rending of a garment was the prophecy of the downfall of a king ?
259. What was the present sent to Saul, King of Israel, by Jesse, the Bethlehemite ?
260. What was the height of the giant Goliath ?
261. What four instances have we of caves being used as places of refuge ?
262. Give an instance of the avowed foreknowledge of God of events which would come to pass under certain circumstances, but which never did come to pass, because these circumstances did not come to pass ?
263. How did David show Saul that he had him at his mercy ?
264. How many instances have we of God sending sleep on individuals ?
265. How long did David dwell in the country of the Philistines ?
266. How long did David reign over Judah ?
267. What verse in the Bible gives us David's age ?
268. By what peculiar signal were the Israelites to know when to commence the attack on the Philistines at the valley of Rephaim ?
269. How long was the Ark in the house of Obededom ?
270. Where is it recorded that the Jews were to be God's chosen people for ever ?
271. How many Syrian horsemen fell in battle with David ?
272. Quote the exact words of the oldest letter recorded in the Scriptures ?
273. By whom and to whom was the first letter written ?
274. On what occasion did Absalom have his brother slain ?
275. What was the weight of Absalom's annual growth of hair ?
276. Where in the Bible is the only reference to a ferry-boat found ? [minated ?
277. How was the three years famine of the Gibeonites ter-

278. What songs are mentioned in the Bible besides Solomon's?
279. Where are recorded the last words of the Psalmist David?
280. Where have we a list of David's thirty-seven mighty men?
281. How did Satan tempt David?
282. How long did the pestilence sent to punish David last?
283. David in vain glory numbered the people, and for a punishment what did he choose, and what was the consequence?
284. How did David save Jerusalem from being destroyed by a pestilence?
285. When was it said that every man dwelt under his vine and under his fig-tree?
286. How many horsemen did Solomon have?
287. What people are stated to have been most clever in ancient times in cutting down timber?
288. How was the timber used in Solomon's temple conveyed to Jerusalem?
289. How did it come to pass that there was the sound of no hammer or tool of iron heard in the building of Solomon's Temple?
290. How long was the temple building, and in what year was it commenced?
291. How long was Solomon building his own house?
292. What names did Solomon give to the two pillars in the porch of the temple?
293. How did God manifest His presence at the dedication of the temple?
294. How many times did God appear to Solomon?
295. In God's covenant with Solomon what prophecy was uttered?
296. In the construction of Solomon's works what relation did Gentiles and Israelites bear to him?
297. What report was circulated which led a traveller to visit Jerusalem to see if it was true?
298. What was the value of gold presented to Solomon in one year?
299. How were the vast number of presents conveyed to Solomon?

300. What was the cost of a chariot and of a horse in the days of Solomon?
301. When was the rending of a new garment typical of the division of a kingdom?
302. What led to the division of the kingdom of Israel?
303. What wild beast was employed by God to punish a disobedient prophet?
304. What biscuit of modern use is mentioned in the Bible?
305. Where is it recorded that rain was prevented in answer to prayer?
306. On what occasion did God employ birds as messengers of mercy?
307. How many prophets of Baal met on Carmel to contest who was the true God?
308. How many instances have we in the Bible of persons fasting forty days and forty nights?
309. What became of the Syrians whom the king sent to occupy Samaria?
310. When did God prove himself God of the plain as well as God of the mountain?
311. What battle lasted seven days and with what result?
312. On what four occasions were savage beasts employed as instruments of God's anger?
313. What prophet disguised himself and how while waiting for the King of Israel?
314. Who was falsely accused of blasphemy and stoned to death?
315. What was Elijah's parting gift to Elisha?
316. Where do we read that fifty men set out in all directions to seek a corpse?
317. What was the sum of money paid yearly to the King of Israel by Mesha, King of Moab?
318. On what occasion did water look like blood?
319. What miracle did God work to enable a widow to pay her debts?
320. Where in the Bible is death by sunstroke recorded?
321. When and where was meal used as an antidote for poison?
322. What present was given to Gehazi by Naaman, the Syrian?

323. How was a miracle once wrought to recover a borrowed axe?
324. Where do we find an account of an army being sent to take one man?
325. Where it is recorded that a whole army was smitten with blindness?
326. During the seige and famine of Samaria what price was paid for the head of an ass?
327. State the circumstances under which women ate their own children?
328. How many lepers are mentioned as being outside the gates of Samaria, and who gave warning of the flight of the Syrians?
329. What army fled in confusion when none pursued?
330. What king was guilty of cruelty to animals and how?
331. How many resurrections are recorded in the Old Testament?
332. What funeral was suddenly interrupted by an armed band and with what result?
333. What name was given by King Hezekiah to the brazen serpent which Moses had made for the children of Israel in the wilderness?
334. What sacred relic divinely appointed, and by which miracles were worked, was destroyed by a good king years subsequently?
335. What instrument of healing became an occasion of sin?
336. What king was killed by his own sons?
337. By what name is the Mount of Olives called in the Book of Kings?
338. What is the shortest verse in the Old Testament?
339. Where is the only instance recorded in Scripture of the marriage of a foreign slave to his master's daughter?
340. For what were the Gadites distinguished?
341. When did David first deliver the 105th Psalm?
342. What was the weight of David's crown, and of what was it made?
343. On how many occasions were angels sent to destroy men?
344. How was David instructed in the pattern of the temple?

345. What price was paid for horses by the King of Israel?
346. How was the wood that built the temple brought from Lebanon to Jerusalem?
347. How many strangers in the land of Israel were sent to assist the servants of the King of Tyre in cutting down the cedar wood of Lebanon?
348. What parts of the temple were made of pure gold?
349. What was found in the Ark of the Covenant when first brought into the temple t
350. At what part of the dedication service was it that the clouds filled the temple?
351. What was the attitude of Solomon when offering the consecration prayer at the dedicat.on of the temple?
352. On what occasion did Solomon petition God to be favorable to his people in case they were ever captured by their enemies?
353. How did God show his acceptance of Solomon's petition?
354. What did God say he would make of the temple if the people forsook him?
355. What did Solomon's ships bring from Tarshish?
356. How many stalls were required for the accommodation of Solomon's horses?
357. What was the Israelites watch-word at the division of the kingdom of Israel?
358. What was Asa's prayer?
359. What moving word did Amaziah speak to Asa and his people?
360. What did Zedekiah make as a symbol of coming victory over the Syrians?
361. What two things are said to have happened by chance—one an act of destruction and the other resulting from neglect?
362. After what great battle was it that the men of Judah were three days in carrying the spoils of their enemies?
363. How was it that Ahaziah, the youngest son of Jehoram, came to the throne on the death of his father?
364. For what purpose was a great collection taken up in Judah and Jerusalem by order of the king?

365. Where do we read of a collection being taken and for what purpose ?
366. How many instances are recorded of persons being stoned to death ?
367. What did Zedekiah do in the first month of his reign ?
368. Where do we read of certain postmen being mocked and jeered at when they delivered the news ?
369. What great work was undertaken by King Hezekiah in order to provide a more abundant supply of water for the city of Jerusalem ?
370. What wicked king while attempting to escape, became entangled among thorns and was captured ?
371. How was Manasseh's prayer answered ?
372. Give Bible proof that God observes the acts of children ?
373. Where can be found copies of letters written to kings, who wrote them ?
374. What verse in the Bible contains all the letters of the alphabet, except "J ?"
375. The word "confiscation" is found in the Bible where and how is it used ?
376. What words of Shechaniah may be used by every sinner this side of the grave ?
377. On what occasion were laborers armed and why ?
378. When was the feast of the tabernacle celebrated for the first time after the death of Joshua ?
379. During what long journey did the clothes of travellers not get old ?
380. The temple tax according to Ex. xxx. 13 was half a shekel, what was the amount after the captivity ?
381. How were citizens chosen by dwellers in Jerusalem after the rebuilding of the temple ?
382. What was to have been the sum of money paid by Haman for the destruction of the Jews ?
383. What is the longest verse in the Bible ?
384. How were letters sent in the time of Esther ?
385. What was the origin of the two days of Purim, kept as days of feasting and joy by the Jews ?
386. Why did Job's friends sit with him seven days and nights without speaking ?

387. Give in one verse from the book of Job a most significant description of the weakness and vanity of man?
388. What are man's troubles likened unto by Job?
389. What is ripe old age likened unto by Job?
390. What common article of food is mentioned by an inspired writer as having no taste?
391. To what manufacturing implements are man's days compared?
392. How did Job characterize man that is born of woman?
393. Where is the way to heaven revealed to us in four words?
394. Prove that the custom of marking the boundaries of lands by stones and monuments is of ancient origin?
395. What chapter in the Bible is remarkable for its description of natural history.
396. Where are we told that there was joy in the firmament at God's creation?
397. When and why did the morning stars sing together?
398. Where in the Bible is it stated that the ostrich lays her eggs in the sand to be hatched by the heat?
399. Did Job ever regain his riches before his death?
400. What is the longest book in the Bible?
401. In what Psalm have we the godly and the ungodly contrasted?
402. Where do we read that the wicked shall be turned into [*Sheol?*]
403. Where are pleasures declared to be for evermore?
404. What is the most appropriate Psalm to be read during a thunder shower?
405. The first nine words of what Psalm did our Saviour repeat while on the cross?
406. What comfort did David derive from the Lord being his shepherd?
407. How did David comfort himself at the thought of his father and mother forsaking him?
408. How did David say the Lord should be worshipped?
409. Where in the Scriptures do we find the grandeur of a thunder storm depicted?
410. What did David say he had not seen during his long life?

411. What two words does the Psalmist use to describe the transient nature of his stay on earth ?
412. To what kind of a tree does David liken himself in the house of God ?
413. Where do David ask God to put his tears ?
414. What food is declared to have been eaten by travellers ?
415. What holy place did David prefer to the tents of wickedness ?
416. Name two Psalms nearly alike ?
417. What is the middle chapter in the Bible ?
418. What is the longest chapter in the Bible ?
419. What petition occurs seven times in one Psalm ?
420. To what kind of a sheep did David liken himself ?
421. How will they reap who have sown in tears ?
422. What is promised to him who goes forth weeping and bearing precious seed ?
423. How long did David say he would sing unto the Lord ?
424. Quote two verses that give the Bible description of the philosopher ?
425. What warnings do the Scriptures give to avoid bad company ?
426. Prove from the Bible that afflictions sent to the people of God are marked with the Heavenly Father's love ?
427. Whose ways are represented as "pleasantness" and her paths as "peace."
428. What is said to lead us when we go, to keep us when we sleep, and to talk with us when we wake ?
429. What may a man expect, according to Proverbs, who takes fire in his bosom ?
430. What is it that makes its possessor truly rich ?
431. Upon what does the success of a nation chiefly depend ?
432. What is a greater conquest than taking a city ?
433. What do the Scriptures say surpasses in greatness the hero who conquers his enemies ?
434. What is harder to be won than a strong city ?
435. In what way does Solomon say a child should be trained ?
436. What reward does the Bible promise a man diligent in business ?

437. Where is an unfaithful friend said to be like a broken tooth and a foot out of joint ?
438. What is good news from a far country like ?
439. What two places are said to be never full ?
440. What contrast in courage is there between the righteons and the wicked ?
441. Prove from the Scriptures that confession of sin to God is [a duty ?
442. What four things are mentioned as small but very wise ?
443. Where is the only mention of churning butter in the Scriptures ?
444. What sentence composed of three words appears no less than 25 times in one book of the Bible, and forms the chief thought of it ?
445. What one verse refers to the source, flow, and return of [rivers ?
446. What does the Bible say is better than precious ointment ?
447. To what does the Bible liken the laughter of a fool ?
448. In what war are we told all must serve ?
449. What is the summary of man's duty as given in Ecclesiastes ?
450. In what books are neither the words "God" or "Lord" found ?
451. Describe in three words the power of love ?
452. What cannot be quenched with water or drowned with floods ?
453. For what three things was Bashan renowned ?
454. What is the Bible's list of a ladies' wardrobe ?
455. Where is it foretold that the Lord would take away as plunder the whole toilet of the women of Jerusalem ?
456. What is the longest word in the Bible ?
457. The water tinkles into the pool of Shiloah so softly that it cannot be heard, travellers have remarked this. What Scripture does this confirm ?
458. Give a text from the Old Testament which contains a reason why "we should fear those who kill the body ?
459. Which of the Prophets represents the deliverance by the Messiah and the final victory of God's people over the world, as a repetition of Israel's passage through the Red Sea ?

460. What sin does the Prophet Isaiah say was the cause of the destruction of Moab ?

461. On what occasion were messengers despatched in vessels made of bulrushes ?

462. What are the words of the glutton as given in Isaiah ?

463. Quote a passage from which it would appear that in olden time beacons were used on the tops of hills as signals or land marks ?

464. Quote a verse from Isaiah in which a three-fold office of Christ is enumerated ?

465. Where is the growth of nettles mentioned as a mark of desolation ?

466. What two chapters in the Bible are nearly alike ?

467. What is the Bible remedy for boils, and what king made use of it ?

468. To what small things are nations before God compared ?

469. What is promised to those who wait on the Lord ?

470. Of whom does God speak as " my friend ?"

471. Where in the Bible do we find God's promise to supply the temporal wants of his people ?

472. Prove from the Bible that God alone (and not priests) can forgive sin ?

473. To whom does God say there is no peace ?

474. In what do we all resemble sheep according to the Bible ?

475. Can there be found in God's word a promise to the wicked ?

476. In what respectdo we all resemble a leaf ?

477. Where is the promise that human life shall be prolonged at the millenium as before the flood ?

478. What birds are referred to in the Scriptures as birds of passage ?

479. What garment was hid in a rock on the bank of a river ?

480. With what was the sin of Judah written ?

481. What was written with a pen of iron and with the point of a diamond ?

482. Prove from the Scriptures the sin and folly of leaning on human help in time of trouble ?

483. What description is given of the character of the heart in Jeremiah ?

484. Give instances of a single person being called by different names?

485. For what purpose did Jeremiah use the type of good and bad figs?

486. How many instances have we in the Old Testament of ungodly persons desiring the prayers of the righteous?

487. Where in the Old Testament are we told that God gave instructions for the concealment of certain things?

488. For what purpose did Jeremiah hide stones in the clay near the house of Pharaoh, king of Egypt?

489. Where can the prophetical accounts be found of the mode by which Babylon was taken by the Medes and Persians?

490. Where in the Bible does it say "it is good for a man that he bear the yoke in his youth."

491. What four chapters in the Bible are written in the acrostic form, each verse beginning with a letter of the Hebrew alphabet in rotation?

492. Where is it distinctively predicted that no one shall obtain strength by or in sin?

493. From the book of Ezekiel give a promise clearly showing that that which is a misfortune to individuals is a benefit to the church?

494. On what occasion did God forbid all funeral pomp and grief?

495. What sin is mentioned as having caused the destruction of Tyre?

496. Give the names of nine different stones mentioned in one verse?

497. By whom were two sticks miraculously united and became [one?

498. What is the meaning of Jehovah Shammah?

499. How many and what are the greater prophets?

500. What Scriptural examples have we of early piety?

501. When were sheriffs or officers of the law first mentioned in the Bible and how employed?

502. How many lords of the land were entertained at the feast of Belshazzar?

503. What was the interpretation of the writing on the wall at Belshazzar's feast?

504. How many Old Testament prophecies are there of the time Christ should appear?
505. In what book, chapter and verse is mention made of the archangel Michael?
506. Quote a passage from which it appears that the prophets did not always understand the meaning of the visions they saw?
507. What language is ascribed in Hosea to be uttered by those who have rejected God?
508. On what occasion are we told that the sun shall be turned into darkness and the moon into blood?
509. Where in the Bible is the constellation of Orion mentioned besides the book of Job?
510. How many instances are recorded that sailors called upon God to avert a storm?
511. How many instances of casting lots are recorded?
512. What was the message Jonah took and preached at Nineveh?
513. Give instances of God repenting or witholding the execution of a decree?
514. What plant was miraculously created and destroyed in one night?
515. Where is it recorded that "nations shall learn war no more?"
516. Where do we find that people will some day "beat their swords into plowshares?"
517. What beautiful description of a peaceful condition of a country is given by one of the prophets?
518. Where is it recorded that "the just shall live by faith?"
519. Where do we find that the earth will be filled with the knowledge of the Lord?
520. Give the works in which the removal of unclean cloths is spoken of as a sign of the forgiveness of sin?
521. Where do we find these words "not by might, not by power, but by my spirit, saith the Lord of hosts?"
522. Where in the Bible do we find the mention of "Boy" and "Girl" in the same verse?

523. Where is the prophecy recorded that the Jews will one day repent the death of the Messiah?

524. Show that to die childless was regarded by the Jews as a very bitter calamity?

525. Name in their order the minor prophets?

526. What is the first and last of the prophetical books?

527. When and where will there not be room enough to receive the blessing?

528. What three remarkable predictions are recorded in the last chapter of the Old Testament?

CURIOSITIES OF THE BIBLE

PERTAINING TO

NEW TESTAMENT THINGS.

Answers Page 71 *of Key.*

1. What title did our Saviour bear that indicated He was both God and man ?
2. For what is the village of Bethlehem noted ?
3. On what occasion did an angel notify a traveler that the king of a neighboring country was dead ?
4. What does the Bible say will be the Christian's reward after death ?
5. Where is the earth mentioned as God's footstool ?
6. What passage in the New Testament plainly states that God takes care of our temporal wants ?
7. Where do we find the statement that the "hairs of our head are all numbered" ?
8. What words found in Matthew are also found in the twelfth chapter of Isaiah ?
9. What is the only unpardonable sin ?
10. What office will the angels perform at the Judgment day ?
11. In one word name a precious pearl with which no possession on earth can bear a comparison ?
12. Prove from the Old and New Testament that the the custom of celebrating birthdays is ancient ?
13. Which of Christ's miracles are miracles of creation ?
14. What is the greatest standard of value in the Bible ?
15. How many times did Christ close the temple ?

16. On what occasion did Christ answer a question by asking another?
17. What is declared to be the first and great commandment?
18. What is declared to be the second great commandment?
19. What hangs on the two great commandments as announced by our Saviour?
20. In what chapter of Matthew have we a description of the last Judgment?
21. For how long was there darkness over the whole land when our Saviour was crucified?
22. What was the parting promise of our Saviour?
23. What power was imparted to the twelve disciples?
24. What miracle was performed by the utterance of two words?
25. What miracle was performed by the utterance of one word?
26. On what two occasions did Jesus manifest displeasure?
27. What great honor did Christ confer upon Mary Magdalene after His resurrection?
28. What great command did Christ give his disciples after His resurrection?
29. When Paul handled the snake (Acts xxviii. 3), what assertion of Christ's was proven?
30. What is the longest chapter in the New Testament?
31. On what occasions were messages brought to this world by the Archangel Gabriel?
32. By what expression did the virgin Mary acknowledge herself a sinner?
33. Where are the words "writing-table" used?
34. What remarkable event was first made known by shepherds?
35. What did the Jews endeavor to do to Christ after hearing his first sermon?
36. In what language did the devil preach a short sermon to Christ?
37. Prove St. James' assertion "The devils also believe," James ii. 9, in Christ's divinity?

38. What three things does the Lord cite as requisite for the bringing forth of good fruit?
39. In what respect does the Lord's prayer differ as given by St. Matthew and St. Luke?
40. Prove from the Scriptures that God hears and answers the cry of his children?
41. Where did curiosity of the eye through the mercy of God lead to the belief of the heart?
42. What prominent historical facts centre about Jericho?
43. On what two occasions did Christ receive the assistance of angels?
44. An unexampled sorrow was betokened by a word used only once in the New Testament. Name the passage?
45. On what occasion did Christ command those who loved Him to mourn?
46. What memorable event took place at Calvary?
47. What was the superscription written over the cross, and in what languages?
48. What three portions of the Old Testament does the Saviour say contained predictions concerning himself?
49. What does the "divine" apostle style those who would not be illuminated?
50. In what verse is Christ spoken of as a successor and also as a predecessor?
51. At what place did Christ perform His first miracle?
52. Quote the most precious statement in the Bible?
53. Locate Enon and for what is it celebrated?
54. Where and by whom is the word of God called a well of water?
55. Give an instance in the New Testament where a man was dependent for his recovery upon human help and sympathy?
56. Give the text in which our Lord himself distinguishes between His divine and human sonship?
57. Describe in five words the journey every Christian has accomplished?
58. What test does the apostle John give by which we may know the children of God?

59. What one word was employed by Christ to designate the separation from God?
60. Where have we the guide to heaven in three words?
61. Prove that even in the presence of the Lord Jesus salvation was voluntary?
62. In what way does Christ say we may know the truth of His doctrines?
63. On what two occasions were men not able to answer Christ?
64. By what act does a man lose his personal freedom?
65. Where have we the issue of performing duty given in two words?
66. Quote the Saviour's language in reference to the resurrection?
67. What is the shortest verse in the New Testament?
68. How many resurrections are recorded in the New Testament?
69. What are the only two recorded acts of the apostle Philip?
70. What test of discipleship did Jesus give?
71. The words "Jesus Christ" are placed together only once in the Gospels. Where?
72. Where is our Lord's first recorded act of intercession?
73. Where have we an instance of certain officers and gods falling backward when they were confronted by their victim?
74. Before how many tribunals was our Saviour brought, before His apprehension?
75. Quote the precise words of our Saviour the first time he was smitten on the face?
76. For the garments of what two persons were lots cast?
77. How many and what are the recorded sayings of our Saviour while on the cross?
78. On what three occasions is mention made of Nicodemus?
79. What was the first and last miracle wrought by the Saviour?
80. On what occasion did our Lord check the undue curiosity of one of his disciples?

81. Why did Christ so forcibly press his identity on his disciples after His resurrection ?
82. Give instances to prove that our Lord's body, after the resurrection was endowed with other powers than it had before ?
83. On what occasion did the voice of the Holy Ghost sound like a "rushing mighty wind"
84. On what occasion was there such spiritual happiness among the people that wicked men mocked and said, "They are full of new wine" ?
85. What was the first instance of the execution of Divine justice under the new dispensation ?
86. What was the charge brought against Stephen, the first Christian martyr ?
87. What evidence have we to prove that Jesus was seen after His ascension ?
88. How many times is it recorded of our Saviour as "seated" on the right hand of God and how many as "standing" ?
89. Where in the Bible is St. Paul first mentioned ?
90. Only one instance is found in the Bible where the name of the street is mentioned. Where ?
91. Locate Joppa, and for what is it noted ?
92. Easter is mentioned but once in the Bible. Where and under what circumstances ?
93. What New Testament instances have we of miraculous light !
94. Mention a quotation in the New Testament where the exact place in the Old Testament from which it is taken is given ?
95. Where is the first instance of church letters being used ?
96. What was the cause of the quarrel between Paul and Barnabas ?
97. Where have we conditions of salvation expressed in six words ?
98. Where have we the result of performing our duty given in four words ?

99. What missionary in a foreign country found an altar erected to his God, and what inscription was thereon?

100. How was it that two Roman Jews were found by an apostle in Greece?

101. For what is Ephesus noted?

102. Where have we the means of obtaining salvation expressed in three words?

103. Where do we find in St. Paul's own words an account of his conversion?

104. A Roman captain on releasing a prisoner endeavored to impress him with the fact that he owed his release to him. What reply did the captive give?

105. Define the individual creeds of the Pharisees and Sadducees, as they are given in the words of St. Paul?

106. What was the oath by which forty Jews bound themselves to kill an apostle?

107. Give a Scriptural example of religious convictions being stifled?

108. To what religious sect did St. Paul belong?

109. In what one verse do the words of Jesus Christ give a complete plan and draught of the New Testament ministry?

110. Where do we find glorious representation of a truly Divine ordination to the Christian ministry?

111. When did 276 men partake of a joyful meal under extreme peril?

112. What island in the Mediterranean was the scene of many miracles by St. Paul?

113. How long did St. Paul dwell in his own hired house at Rome?

114. In three words give the character of the Christian hope?

115. Where have we the essence of Gospel doctrine expressed in six words?

116. Where in the New Testament is found a passage in which Divine justice is called the highest power in the affairs of men?

117. What is the only revenge permitted by the Christian faith?

118. What one word in Scripture is said to contain the whole law?
119. Where is the Bible inventory of the christian's treasure?
120. What are we told in the Scripture to covet?
121. Where have we the spirit of the Gospel doctrine expressed in three words?
122. How is it expressed that there were more than 20 believers at the time of our Lord's ascension?
123. How many times and to whom did Jesus appear after the resurrection?
124. By what four names are Christians called in the Bible?
125. What is the specified time required to raise the dead?
126. Prove that the Church of Corinth had not adopted the practice of the Church at Jerusalem with regard to a community of goods and one common purse?
127. Where is the word of God called a mirror and why?
128. In what one point does Christ as man differ from mankind in general?
129. Prove from the Scripture that it is the duty of a church to support its ministers?
130. Give one word used by the apostle Paul to designate those who are living by faith?
131. Which of the early Christian churches set the brightest example of liberality?
132. What church did St. Paul declare he never visited?
133. What three things do the Scriptures say God cannot do?
134. Why is the Bible called the word of God when it was written by men?
135. Prove from the Bible the necessity of the new birth?
136. What are angels, and how are they employed?
137. Where is the word of God called a sword, and why?
138. On what three occasions are we expressly told "Jesus wept"?
139. What were the contents of the Ark of the covenant?
140. What texts prove that our Lord when on earth had body soul and spirit?
141. Where is the word of God compared to a looking-glass?
142. What is mentioned in the Bible as the "royal law"?

143. In what chapter are we told that faith without works is of no avail?
144. Mention a passage in the New Testament where it states that every kind of beast and serpent is capable of being tamed?
145. Where is the word of God called milk, and why?
146. What is the Bible ornament of a Christian woman?
147. Quote three words that denote the whole of the doctrine of Christ as a commandment to be believed and preached?
148. Where is it stated that a thousand years in God's sight is as one day?
149. What is the shortest book in the Bible?
150. How many books in the Bible have only one chapter?
151. What does the Bible tell us to contend earnestly for?
152. What is the longest name applied to the Almighty?
153. Our Saviour in three words gives a most awful description of what city?
154. How many and what things are we told to hold fast?
155. Give a solemn declaration made by our Saviour to one who led a wicked life under a false representation of piety?
156. On what occasions are the inhabitants of heaven called upon to rejoice?
157. Whose songs are mentioned in the New Testament?
158. Where will the great feast of the marriage supper of the Lamb be spread?
159. What is the longest verse in the New Testament?
160. Where is the passage found in which the angels are said to be fellow-workers with mankind?
161. What was the last invitation of our Saviour, and the circumstances connected with it?
162. What is the last prayer recorded in the Bible? By whom and for what?
163. Why do you (or Christians) believe the Bible to be the word of God?

CURIOSITIES OF THE BIBLE

PERTAINING TO

OLD TESTAMENT;

TIME, QUANTITY AND NUMBER.

Answers Page 81 *of Key.*

1. Which day of the creation was appointed as a day of rest?
2. How many year's warning did God give the people of the old world before sending the flood?
3. What was the length in feet of Noah's Ark?
4. How many days were given to Noah, his family, the beasts and fowls to repair to and enter the ark?
5. How long was Noah in building the ark?
6. How were the animals and fowls to repair to the ark?
7. How long was Noah and his family in the ark?
8. How many times did Abraham plead for Sodom?
9. How many years did Jacob serve for both Leah and Rachel?
10. How old was Joseph when his brethren sold him to slavery?
11. What was the interpretation of the seven fat cows and the seven good ears of corn concerning Pharaoh's dream?
12. How many years of plenty preceded the years of famine in Egypt?
13. How many years did Jacob live in Egypt?
14. How long a time was required by the Egyptians for embalming the dead?
15. How long was the infant Moses hidden to escape the death edict of Pharoah?

16. How many sisters had the wife of Moses ?
17. How old was Moses when he stood before Pharaoh ?
18. How long did the first Egyptian plague last ?
19. On what day of the month was the Passover appointed to be kept ?
20. For how many days were the Hebrews to eat unleavened bread in preparing for the feast of the Passover ?
21. How many feasts were observed each year by the Jews ?
22. How long did the children of Israel sojourn in Egypt ?
23. How many Egyptian chariots of war, in their pursuit of the Israelites, were lost in the Red Sea ?
24. How long did the Israelites journey in the wilderness before they found water ?
25. What is the estimate of the amount of manna the Israelites gathered every day while in the wilderness ?
26. How long did the Israelites feed upon honey (manna) ?
27. How long was a Hebrew slave required to serve in order to regain his freedom ?
28. How long were young animals required to be kept with the mother ?
29. How long did the cloud cover the mount before God spake to Moses ?
30. How long was Moses on the mount before God called him ?
31. How long did Moses remain in the mountain with God ?
32. For how many days were Aaron's sons to put on holy garments ?
33. How many idolatrous worshippers of the golden calf were put to death by the order of Moses ?
34. How often and how long was Moses on Mount Sinai conversing with God ?
35. How many times was the man who was to be cleansed from his leprosy, sprinkled ?
36. How long a time was required to elapse, according to the law of Moses, before the Israelites might gather the fruit of a young tree ?
37. On what occasion was there to be a blowing of trumpets among the Israelites ?
38. How long did the Feast of the tabernacle last ?

39. For how many days were the Jews to continue the offering made by fire?
40. How often did the year of Jubilee occur?
41. What did the Israelites eat in the seventh year during which they neither sowed nor reaped?
42. At what age were the Levites no longer allowed to work in the tabernacle?
43. How many elders did the Lord command Moses to select to assist him to govern the Israelites?
44. How many feet deep did the quails fall around the tents of Israel?
45. How long was Hebron in Canaan built before Zoan in Egypt?
46. How long were the spies searching the promised land?
47. How many were destroyed by fire for offering strange incense?
48. How long did a person remain unclean who touched a dead body?
49. How many altars were built, and bullocks and rams sacrificed on the top of Peor?
50. How many children of Israel fell victims to a plague in consequence of having joined themselves in idolatry to Baal-peor?
51. How many out of each tribe did Moses send to war against the Midianites?
52. How many nations greater than the Israelites did God cast out of Canaan before them?
53. How many times did Moses fast forty days and forty nights?
54. When were the Israelites to begin to number the feast of seven weeks?
55. When was the feast of the tabernacle to be observed?
56. How many witnesses among the Jews were required to establish a charge?
57. For how long did marriage exempt a man from going to war?
58. If the Israelites obeyed God's law in how many ways were their enemies to flee?

59. How long did the children of Israel mourn at Moses' death?
60. How many years did God provide manna for the children of Israel in the wilderness?
61. How many priests with trumpets marched around Jericho?
62. How many times were the walls of Jericho compassed about before they fell down?
63. How long did the sun and moon stand still at the command of Joshua!
64. How many kings hiding themselves in a cave were captured and hung to different trees?
65. How many Canaanite kings did the children of Israel destroy on taking possession of the promised land?
66. How many men from each of the seven tribes were sent throughout Canaan to describe and locate the undivided portion?
67. How many cities were appointed as "cities of refuge" in in which murderers were safe until trial?
68. How many cities were given to the Levites for their use as they had no inheritance?
69. How long was Israel oppressed by the Moabites?
70. How many chariots were kept by Jabin, king of the Canaanites?
71. How long were the Israelites in the hands of the Midianites?
72. How long was Israel oppressed by the Ammonites?
73. How many Ephraimites were slain in battle with the Gileadites?
74. How many years did Ibzan judge Israel?
75. How long were the Israelites in subjection to the Philistines?
76. How many days did Samson give his thirty companions to expound his riddle?
77. How many Philistines did Samson slay with a jaw-bone?
78. With how many green withs was Samson bound?
79. How many men and women were killed in the fall of the building that was pulled down by Samson?
80. How many chosen men were left-handed among the tribes of Benjamin?

81. How many Israelites were slain in the battle of Ebenezer when the Ark of the Lord was taken by the Philistines ?
82. How old was Eli when he fell from his seat and died ?
83. How long did the Ark of the Lord remain with the Philistines after its capture from Israel ?
84. How many oxen were employed to draw the ark when it was captured from the Philistines ?
85. How long did David dwell in the country of the Philistines ?
86. How long did David reign over Judah ?
87. How old was David when he died ?
88. How long was the Ark in the house of Obededom ?
89. How many horsemen did David capture from Hadadazer ?
90. How many Syrian horsemen fell in battle with David ?
91. How long was David's child sick before he died ?
92 What was the weight of Absalom's annual growth of hair ?
93. How long did the pestilence sent to punish David last ?
94. How many horsemen did Solomon have ?
95. How long was Solomon in building the temple ?
96. How long was Solomon in building his own house ?
97. How many days did Solomon feast at the dedication of the temple ?
98 What was the value of the gold presented to Solomon in one year ?
99. What did Gehazi see the seventh time he looked towards the sea ?
100. How many of the Syrians did the Israelites slay in a day ?
101. How many soldiers fleeing from a conqueror were killed by the falling of the wall of a city ?
102. What was the annual tribute the king of Moab paid to the king of Israel ?
103. How many days journey did the kings of Israel, Judah, and Edom travel without finding water ?
104. How many times did the Shunammite woman's son sneeze when he was coming to life ?
105. How many times was a certain leprous man commanded to wash in the river Jordan in order to be cleansed ?

106. What was the present given by Naaman, the Syrian to Gehazi, his servant?
107. During the siege of Samaria how much was paid for the head of an ass?
108. How many lepers are mentioned as being outside of the gate of Samaria and gave warning of the flight of the Syrians?
109. How old was Jehoash when he began to reign?
110. How many fables are recorded in the Bible?
111. How many years were added to Hezekiah's life in answer to prayer?
112. How many degrees did the shadow go back on the sun-dial of Ahaz in answer to Hezekiah's prayer?
113. David in his vain glory numbered the people and for a punishment what did he chose and what was the result?
114. How much did David pay for Ornan's threshing floor?
115. What quantity of gold and silver did David prepare for the building of the temple?
116. How many singers were in the grand jubilee of the temple?
117. How many overseers had the hewers of wood in Lebanon?
118. How many of the strangers in the land of Israel were sent to assist the servant of the king of Tyre in cutting the cedars of Lebanon?
119. How long did the services at the dedication of Solomon's temple last?
120. How many stalls were required for the accommodation of Solomon's horses?
121. How many Israelites fell in the battle between Israel and Judah under Jereboam and Abijah?
122. How many oxen and sheep were offered at one time during the revival under Asa?
123. What presents did the Arabians make Jehoshaphat, king of Judah?
124. How long was a young king of Judah hid in the house of God in order to save his life?

125. How many bullocks, rams, lambs and he-goats did the rulers of Israel bring for a sin offering in the time of Hezekiah ?
126. How many sheep did Hezekiah give to the congregation to keep the feast of unleavened bread ?
127. How long did the Israelites keep a feast after the dedication of the second temple ?
128. In how many days were the walls of Jerusalem rebuilt ?
129. For how long did the Israelites feast at Jerusalem after their return from captivity ?
130. What was the amount of the temple-tax before and after the captivity ?
131. On what occasion and for how long was a feast held in the grounds of a king's palace ?
132. How many maidens were given to Esther by the king, as attendants ?
133. What was to have been the sum of money paid by Haman for the destruction of the Jews ?
134. How many sons of Haman were hanged ?
135. How many camels had Job ?
136. How many of Job's children were killed by the fall of a building, caused by a whirlwind ?
137. How long did Job's three friends sit with him without speaking a word ?
138. How long did Job live after his great troubles ?
139. How pure are the words of the Lord according to David ?
140. How often did David praise the Lord ?
141. How many things does Solomon say the Lord hates ?
142. How much must a thief restore if caught with his plunder ?
143. How many pillars supported the house that wisdom built ?
144. How wise is the sluggard in his own conceit ?
145. To how many does Solomon advise men to give a portion ?
146. How light shall be the sun and moon in the day when God binds the breath of his people ?
147. How long were the Jews in Babylonish captivity ?
148. What did God say he would do to the king of Babylon after he had kept the Jews in captivity for seventy years ?
149. For how many days did the prophet Ezekiel sit astonished at the river Chebar ?

150. How was access obtained to the gate of Jerusalem which Ezekiel saw in his vision at Babylon?
151. What was the breadth of the temple door which Ezekiel saw in his vision?
152. How many years did Nebuchadnezzar eat grass like an ox?
153. How many lords of the land were entertained at the feast of Belshazzar?
154. How long was the decree that no man should ask a petition of God, under penalty of being cast into the lion's den?
155. How many weeks were allotted in Daniel's dream for the finishing of transgression?
156. How many Old Testament prophecies are there of the time when Christ should appear?
157. How long were the Ninevites given to repent?
158. How many persons were there in Nineveh who could not discern between their right and left hand?
159. How many times is it promised in the Bible that swords shall be beaten into ploughshares?
160. How many lamps and pipes had the golden candlestick in Zechariah's vision?
161. How many and what are the sacred books mentioned in the Bible but not included in it?
162. How many verses of the Bible contain all of the letters of the Alphabet except one?

CURIOSITIES OF THE BIBLE

PERTAINING TO

NEW TESTAMENT.

TIME, QUANTITY AND NUMBER.

Answers Page 89 of Key.

1. How many petitions are there recorded in the "Lord's prayer?"
2. How many baskets of fragments were gathered after Christ had fed the four thousand?
3. How often did the Mosaic Law require a man to forgive an offending brother?
4. How often did our Saviour say an offending brother should be forgiven?
5. When shall all the human race see Jesus on his throne surrounded by his attendant angels?
6. For how long was there darkness over the whole land when our Saviour was crucified?
7. How many swine, on account of a miracle of Christ were driven into the sea?
8. How long was Christ hanging on the cross?
9. How long did Anna, the prophetess, live with her husband?
10. What is the longest drought recorded in the Bible?
11. What two things are mentioned in the Bible as having happened by chance?
12. How many parables are recorded in the New Testament?
13. Before how many tribunals was our Saviour brought after his apprehension?

14. How long was Herod building his Temple?
15. After feeding five thousand with five loaves and two fishes, how many baskets of fragments were gathered?
16. According to the law of Moses, how many were required as witnesses to establish a fact?
17. How many resurrections are recorded in the Bible?
18. How many wounds did Christ receive while on the cross?
19. How many wonderful events occuring in gardens are recorded in the Bible?
20. How many were in the great draught of fishes taken after Christ's resurrection?
21. How long was Christ on the earth after his resurrection?
22. At the first gathering of the disciples after the ascension how many were there?
23. How many were converted at the first sermon of Peter?
24. What is the largest number converted at any one time?
25. How old was the person upon whom the first miracle was wrought after the ascension?
26. How many deacons were appointed by the apostles?
27. How old was Moses when he visited his brethren in Egypt?
28. How long did Moses sojourn in the land of Midian?
29. How many times is it recorded of our Saviour as standing, on the right hand of God, and how many times as sitting?
30. How many instances have we in the Bible of persons being stoned to death?
31. How long was Saul of Tarsus blind when converted?
32. How many times was an apostle entreated by an angel to "Arise, slay and eat?"
33. How many years was Israel governed by judges?
34. How many instances have we in the Bible of persons being put in prison?
35. What was the value of the books burned by the inhabitants of Ephesus after hearing one sermon of Paul?
36. How long did St. Paul remain at Troas?
37. How many murderers was St. Paul accused of leading into the wilderness?
38. How many men once banded themselves in order to inflict injury on an apostle?

39. How many men were sent with Paul to protect him when on his way to Felix?
40. What instance have we in the New Testament where the lives of over two hundred persons were saved on account of one righteous man in their midst?
41. How long did St. Paul stay at Puteoli, when on his way to Rome?
42. How long did St. Paul dwell in his own hired house at Rome?
43. How often did Christ appear after his resurrection?
44. What length of time will God require to raise the dead?
45. How often was Paul flogged by the Jews, and how many stripes did he receive?
46. To what country did St. Paul first go after his conversion, and how long did he remain there?
47. How many times in Bible history has the Sabbath been impressed upon the observance of man?
48. How many seals had the book which John saw in his vision at Patmos?
49. On what occasion and for what length of time was there silence in heaven?
50. How many men were slain by the earthquake mentioned in Revelation?
51. How many singers were singing in praise of the Lamb in John's vision?
52. What was the weight of the heaviest hailstones mentioned in Scripture?
53. How long a time, according to Scripture, was occupied in the destruction of Babylon?
54. For how long was the devil chained and thrown into a bottomless pit?
55. How many gates has the New Jerusalem, and what is written thereon?
56. What is the length and breadth (in furlongs) of the New Jerusalem?
57. How many years subsequent to the event did Christ say "Remember Lot's wife?"

CURIOSITIES OF THE BIBLE.

PERTAINING TO

OCCUPATIONS.

Answers Page 93 of Key.

Give the names of one or more mentioned in the Bible as being an—

1. Artificer?
2. Author?
3. Beggar?
4. Bishop?
5. Boat-builder?
6. Builder of city?
7. Captain?
8. Carpenter?
9. Centurion?
10. Chamberlain?
11. Chief ruler?
12. Chronicler?
13. Commander?
14. Coppersmith?
15. Counsellor?
16. Cup-bearer?
17. Deacon?
18. Deliverer?
19. Director of Music?
20. Doctor of the Law?
21. Diviner?
22. Emperor?
23. Evangelist?
24. False Prophet?
25. Fisherman?
26. Founder of a Race?
27. General?
28. Goldsmith?
29. Governor?
30. Herdsman?
31. Heretic?
32. Hunter?
33. Inventor?
34. Judge?
35. Lawyer?
36. Leader?
37. Liberator?
38. Musician?
39. Master of Music?
40. Magician?
41. Minister?
42. Mighty?

43. Officer ?
44. Orator ?
45. Physician ?
46. President ?
47. Prince ?
48. Prophetess ?
49. Proconsul ?
50. Recorder ?
51. Robber ?
52. Ruler ?
53. Saleswoman ?
54. Secretary ?
55. Seer ?
56. Servant ?
57. Scribe ?
58. Shepherd ?
59. Singer ?
60. Slave ?
61. Soldier ?
62. Sorcerer ?
63. Steward ?
64. Tanner ?
65. Tax Collector ?
66. Teacher ?
67. Tent-maker ?
68. Tetrach ?
69. Tiller ?
70. Usurper ?
71. Writer ?
72. Wizard ?

CURIOSITIES OF THE BIBLE.

INVOLVING THE FUNDAMENTAL PRINCIPLES OF MATHEMATICS

Answers Page 95 of Key.

Quote a Passage, with Reference, Illustrating :—

1. Addition ?
2. Subtraction ?
3. Multiplication ?
4. Division ?

CURIOSITIES OF THE BIBLE.

INVOLVING ARITHMETICAL CALCULATIONS IN THEIR SOLUTION.

Answers Page 97 *of Key.*

1. A TEACHER being asked how many scholars were in his Sunday-school, replied: "If you MULTIPLY the number of Jacob's sons by the number of times which the Israelites compassed Jericho on the seventh day, and ADD to the product the number of measures of barley which Boaz gave Ruth; DIVIDE this by the number of Haman's sons. SUBTRACT the number of each kind of unclean beasts that went into the ark; MULTIPLY by the number of men that went to seek Elijah after he was taken to heaven; SUBTRACT from this Joseph's age at the time he stood before Pharaoh; DIVIDE by the number of stones David selected to kill Goliath; SUBTRACT the number of furlongs that Bethany was distant from Jerusalem; MULTIPLY by the number of anchors cast out at the time of Paul's shipwreck; SUBTRACT the number of people saved in the ark, and the REMAINDER will be the number of scholars in the school." How many were there? 188.

2. A SHEPHERD being asked the number of sheep in his flock, replied: "If you DIVIDE the number of camels which Job had before their capture by the Chaldeans, by the number of men sent to take Jeremiah from the dungeon; ADD to the quotient the number of lords entertained at the feast of Belshazzar; from this amount SUBTRACT the number of righteous persons who could have saved Sodom; MULTIPLY by the age when David began to reign; DIVIDE by the number in Gideon's band; ADD the number of Philistines whom Samson slew with a jaw-bone; SUBTRACT the number of Solomon's songs; MULTIPLY by the number of days Job's friends tarried without saying a word; SUBTRACT the number of fish caught in the draft of the miracle of fishes, and the REMAINDER will be the number of sheep in my flock." How many had he? 575.

3. A CLERGYMAN being asked the cost of his church and the

height of its spire, replied: "If you DIVIDE the talents of gold presented to Solomon in one year, by nine times the temple tax (shekels) after the captivity; MULTIPLY this by the pieces of silver for which our Lord was betrayed; SUBTRACT from this the number of singers in the grand jubilee of the temple; ADD to the remainder the number of prophets hid in the cave; MULTIPLY this by half the years the children of Israel were in Babylonish captivity, and the product will be the cost of the church in dollars. DIVIDE the cost of by the length in cubits of Noah's Ark; from the quotient SUBTRACT the number of Rehoboam's children; to the remainder ADD the number of persons who suffered shipwreck with St. Paul; DIVIDE this by one-fourth of the number of fingers and toes which the man of Gath had; from the quotient SUBTRACT the number of years it took Solomon to build the temple; ADD to this twice the height in cubits of Solomon's temple, and the sum TOTAL will be the height of the spire." The cost, $96,600, and height 138 feet.

4. A PASTOR being asked his age, replied: "The years of my life have been twice that of my ministry, and those could be ascertained by DIVIDING the number of years generally allotted to man in the Bible by the number of green withs with which Samson was bound, MULTIPLYING this by the number of cubits the giant Goliath of Gath was in height. ADDING the number of yoke of oxen Job had in his latter days, and ADDING to this the number of men of Judah that came to bind Samson; also ADDING the number of years the children of Israel sojourned in Egypt, SUBTRACTING the number of letters in the longest word in the Bible, and SUBTRACTING the number of years it was prophesied Tyre should be forgotten; ADDING the number of murderers that an Egyptian led into the wilderness in the time of Paul, SUBTRACTING the number of talents of silver David prepared to overlay the walls of the temple; DIVIDING by the number of disciples which Jesus sent together to preach the gospel, SUBTRACTING the number of times our Saviour said an offending brother should be forgiven; ADDING the number of wounds Christ received on the cross, DIVIDING by the number of lepers at the gate of Samaria during the siege." Age 54.

CURIOSITIES OF THE BIBLE.

PERTAINING TO

QUOTATIONS.

WHO SAID IT? AND WHERE FOUND?

Answers Page 99 *of Key.*

The common use of many passages of Scripture make it desirable that all should know from whence they came, and under what circumstances they were originally written or uttered. A few of the more familiar quotations are given as an exercise in "Searching the Scriptures."

1. "Every imagination of the thoughts of man's heart was only evil continually," showing the need of Divine grace and discipline.
2. "Whoso sheddeth man's blood, by man shall his blood be shed."
3. "Shall not the Judge of all earth do right?"
4. Where is Jehovah described as, "Glorious in holiness, fearful in praises, doing wonders?"
5. "Eye for eye, tooth for tooth."
6. "Thou shalt not follow a multitude to do evil," Alas! how many do "custom and example" lead "to swerve from the truth."
7. "Where to "love thy neighbor as thyself!"
8. "Thou shalt honor the face of the old man."
9. "Let me die the death of the righteous."
10. "Be sure your sin will find you out."

11. Where is there first found the command to "love and serve the Lord with all the heart and with all the soul?"
12. "The apple of his eye."
13. "As thy days so shall thy strength be."
14. Where is it said, "Them that honor Me I will honor; and they that despise me shall be lightly esteemed?"
15. "A man after my own heart."
16. "Man looketh on the outward appearance, but the Lord looketh on the heart."
17. "Lovely and pleasant in their lives, and in their death they were not divided."
18. "Thou art the man."
19. "The half was not told me."
20. "There is death in the pot."
21. "Shall we receive good at the hand of God, and shall we not receive evil?"
22. "Man is born unto trouble, as the sparks fly upward."
23. "We are but of yesterday, and know nothing."
24. Who said: "No doubt but ye are the people, and wisdom shall die with you?"
25. "Though he slay me, yet will I trust in him."
26. "The righteous shall hold on his way, and he that hath clean hands shall be stronger and stronger."
27. "The Lord is my shepherd, I shall not want."
28. "Escaped with the skin of my teeth."
29. "A horse is a vain thing for safety."
30. "Spreading himself like a green bay tree."
31. "Oh, that I had wings like a dove! for then I would fly away and be at rest."
32. "As far as the east is from the west."
33. "Let all the people say, Amen."
34. "We hanged our harps upon the willows."
35. Where is the humane injunction: "A righteous man regardeth the life of his beast?"
36. "The way of transgressors is hard."
37. "The heart knoweth his own bitterness."
38. "A soft answer turneth away wrath."
39. "A merry heart maketh a cheerful countenance."

40. "A hoary head is a crown of glory."
41. "He that ruleth his spirit is greater than he that taketh a city."
42. "The eyes of the fool are on the ends of the earth."
43. "Even a fool when he holdeth his peace is counted wise."
44. "A prudent wife is from the Lord."
45. "A gift in secret pacifieth anger."
46. "A good name is rather to be chosen than great riches."
47. "The borrower is servant to the lender."
48. "Seest thou a man diligent in his business? He shall stand before kings."
49. "Put a knife to thy throat."
50. "Riches certainly make themselves wings."
51. "Heap coals of fire upon his head."
52. "Answer not a fool according to his folly."
53. "Let another man praise thee, and not thine own mouth."
54. "Faithful are the wounds of a friend."
55. "The kisses of an enemy are deceitful."
56. "He that covereth his sin shall not prosper."
57. Showing the danger of trifling with conviction and warning: "He that being often reproved hardeneth his neck, shall suddenly be destroyed, and that without remedy."
58. Where is the wise reminder, "The fear of man bringeth a snare?"
59. "Give me neither poverty nor riches."
60. "There is no new thing under the sun."
61. "To everything there is a season, and a time to every purpose under heaven."
62. "Better is it that thou shouldest not vow, than that thou shouldest vow and not pay."
63. "Of making books there is no end."
64. Showing the debasing effects of a worldly spirit, "Let us eat and drink for to-morrow we shall die?"
65. Where will you find the common phrase: "To make a man an offender for a word?"
66. "Their strength is to sit still. In quietness and in confidence shall be your strength."

67. Who first employed the powerful simile, "Like a wild bull in a net?"
68. "Peace, peace, when there is no peace."
69. Showing the hardening tendency of a long course of sin. "Can the Ethiopian change his skin etc.?"
70. Where the solemn warning, "Cursed be the man that trusteth in man."
71. "The heart is deceitful above all things."
72. "Because of swearing the land mourneth."
73. "Ephraim is joined to idols."
74. "Can two walk together, except they be agreed?"
75. "Nor by might nor by power, but by My Spirit, saith the Lord," showing use of means but dependence only on God.
76. "Even Solomon, in all his glory, was not arrayed like one of these."
77. "Neither cast ye your pearls before swine."
78. "Get thee behind me, Satan."
79. "It is more blessed to give than to receive."
80. "The world by wisdom knew not God."
81. "Evil communications corrupt good manners."
82. Let not the sun go down upon your wrath."
83. "Prove all things; hold fast to that which is good."
84. "Godliness with contentment is great gain."
85. I will show thee my faith by my works."
86. "Behold how great a matter a little fire kindleth?"
87. "Charity shall cover the multitude of sins."
88. "The day of the Lord will come as a thief in the night."
89. "Perfect love casteth out fear."
90. "Behold, the Lord cometh with ten thousand of His saints."
91. "Be thou faithful unto death and I will give thee a crown of life."
92. "God shall wipe all tears from their eyes."
93. "Whosoever will, let him take the water of life freely."

BIBLE SCENES.

FROM THE BOOK OF RUTH.

Answers Page 102 *of Key.*

1. A hostile LAND a Gentile name describes,
   Apart from Israel's tribes.
2. FOUR strangers there, by famine forced to roam,
   Found refuge and a home.
3. Of Judah's lineage, and of good renown,
   They left their native TOWN.
4. One of the four was to his BURIAL borne,
   And one was left to MOURN.
5. Two Gentile DAMSELS gave their heart and hand,
   To join that little band.
6. THREE widowed mourners now our tears engage,
   Alike—but not in age.
7. TWO WENT their husband's heritage to find,
   But ONE was LEFT behind.
8. And ONE, though urged to stay, with fixed intent,
   To that far country went.
9. When earth again th' abundant harvest yields,
   SHE goes to glean the FIELDS.
10. Led by God's providence, she turns her hand
    To glean a kinsman's LAND.
11. The lowly stranger there her kinsman spied,
    And she became his BRIDE.
12. The once lone widow, with maternal joy,
    Embraced a darling BOY.
13. And from her darling, crowned with manly grace,
    Sprang a right royal RACE.

What is the leading point in each of the ten commandments?

What is the new commandment as given by Christ?

CURIOSITIES OF THE BIBLE

PERTAINING TO

METAPHORS OF GOD'S WORD.

Answers page 103 *of Key.*

A METAPHOR is a form of illustrating a truth by a figurative expression showing the similarity which one object bears to another.

The following questions are to be answered by the mention of words, all of which commence with the letter at the head of each section:—

A.

1. What creature may be regarded as metaphorical of sin in four particulars?
2. What professional office does an apostle make metaphorical of the work of Christ?
3. What instrument is made emblematical of a moral affection, and why?
4. What is made metaphorical of industry, forethought and individual responsibility?
5. Name something which is made emblematical of frailty, humiliation and sin? Why?
6. What metaphor is used alike for repentance and resurrection?

B.

7. To whom are young believers metaphorically compared? Give three illustrations with references?
8. Name a disease which is used metaphorically for sin?
9. What five creatures are tyrants and wicked men compared to?
10. What is treated as metaphorical of great faults in contrast with smaller faults?

11. Name three words which are used as metaphorical of Christ in relation to His church?
12. What is made metaphorical of wisdom, prosperity and consolation?
13. What is used metaphorically in connection with Divine judgment?

C.

14. Find a word which is used metaphorically of immortal life, eternal glory and heavenly purity?
15. One word represents man's soul, God's favor and spiritual life? Name it?
16. What word is used metaphorically of protecting and forgiving?
17. Name a word which is used metaphorically to express death, ruin, strength, enlargement, love, affliction and sin?
18. What word is used metaphorically for a king, an empire, and the faithful people of God?
19. What word is there that equally represents in metaphor false doctrine and the destruction of the wicked?

D.

20. Name a species of animals to which wicked men are compared? Justify the metaphor in five particulars from Scripture?
21. Name nine words taken from water, which are all used metaphorically?
22. Name a word which is used metaphorically in connection with sorrow, death, secrecy, sin and hell?
23. Name seven ways in which the word door is used metaphorically, and give Scripture reference?
24. What word is applied metaphorically to Jerusalem and its temple?

E.

25. Give two texts where a word is used metaphorically for reward?
26. What external application is used to indicate spiritual enlightenment?

F

27. What words are used metaphorically of Christ?
28. What is put metaphorically for the life of man?
29. What occupation is that of Satan compared to?
30. Name a metaphor for dispersing and scattering?
31. Name a word used mataphorically of false prophets and a wicked ruler.

G

22, Name some things metaphorical of national decay.
33. How are multitudes expressed metaphorically?
34. Name two things which the wicked are compared to.
35. What is metaphorical of truth? And why?

H.

36. What is used metaphorically for the grave, the body, the church, and heaven?
37. Name two things with which God's Word is compared.
38. Name something used metaphorically illustrative of the love of Christ.

I.

39. What word is used metaphorically to express the Gentiles?
40. What word expresses prayer and the merits of Christ?

J.

41. What is metaphorical of glorified saints?

K.

42. What is thus used for love, reverence, submission, and deceit?
43. What are the saints now compared to which will be a truer comparison hereafter?

L.

44. What word is used metaphorically in connection with prosperity, eternal life. mortality, and timidity?
45. Name two things to which both Christ and believers are compared.
46. Name something to which Christ, believers, Satan, and wicked men, are all compared.

47. Name a word used metaphorically both of sin and of grace.
48. What is made metaphorical of the word of God, happiness, a good king, and true believers.
49. Name some ways in which leprosy is metaphorical of sin.
50. Name a word used for temporal calamity and spiritual weakness.

M.

51. Name four things metaphorical of spiritual blessings.
52. What is put for swiftness, Divine truth, and the resurrection?
53. What words are used metaphorically to describe the saints of God!
54. Name something used to express sin and contempt.

N.

55. What is put for death, a time of ignorance, and affliction.
56. What is put for a time of prosperity?
57. What is made metaphorical of safety and security?
58. What word expresses metaphorically the duty of Christian kings and ministers?

O.

59. What is metaphorical of Christ's name, and of brotherly unity?
60. Who are put metaphorically for the church without a comforter?
61. Name something which is made a symbol of vitality.

P.

62 Name something metaphorical of great teachers in the church.
63. What is made metaphorical both of the temple of Jerusalem and the church of God?
64. Name a word which equally describes sin and the grave.
65. What word is used to express the royal dignity of Christ?

66. What is put for a snare, sorrow and the grave?
67. What is the conversation of the wicked compared to?

Q.

68. Name a word which is used metaphorically in connection with love, life, temptation, the Holy Spirit, and Divine wrath.

R.

69. What is put metaphorically for deceitful speech, and for desolating judgment?
70. Name a word used metaphorically for instability, despondency, and disappointing hope.
71. What work is applied metaphorically to ministers and angels?
72. What metaphor denotes the Christian life?

S.

73. Name several metaphorical titles of the Lord's people.
74. Name a metaphor used to describe death, Divine care and the law?

T.

75. Give several metaphorical expressions for wicked men.
76. Name a word used metaphorically of God.
77. What are made metaphorical both of the heavens and of the church?

V.

78. What two words are used metaphorically of the church, including both formalists and true believers?
79. What are wicked men compared to?
80. What is put for human life?

W.

81. What two things is the Holy Ghost compared to?
82. Name three words to denote false teachers in religion.

Y.

83. What word metaphorically describes the service of Christ, cruel oppression and spiritual bondage?

To appreciate and understand the Bible it should be studied.

ENTERTAINMENTS

At HOME,
In the CLASS,
or SCHOOL.

The AGED and INFIRM,
The YOUNG and MIDDLE-AGED,
May find pleasure and profit

MORNING,
NOON,
and NIGHT,

SUNDAYS & WEEK DAYS.

HOW? *As a helpful means to a successful end,*

Take up any one, or a series of the following

BIBLE

STUDIES.

With your Bible in hand, take the questions in their order, turn to the Key for the reference, and read not only the answer but all the facts connected therewith, that you may see how much there is new to you on these topics.

WHAT YOU STUDY
You are likely to remember.
WHAT YOU READ
You are liable to forget.

BIBLE STUDIES.

PERTAINING TO

SCRIPTURE CHARACTERS.

Answers Page 111 *of Key.*

BIBLE CHARACTERS, No. 1.

An eastern king, whose lying awake at night had important consequences.

The initials of the following prove the name.

1. A woman whose discretion and courteous behavior led to great exaltation.
2. The place where an eminent high priest died.
3. The cousin of Saul, who was captain of his host.
4. A violent opposer of the rebuilding of the temple.
5. One whose ill-timed zeal provoked the anger of the Lord.
6. A servant, the first named in Scripture.
7. A city of refuge.
8. A monosyllabic name, the early home of an old Testament character.
9. An Old Testament name of Christ.

BIBLE CHARACTERS, No. 2.

A noted Patriarch and son.

The initials form the name of the son whose life was in danger, but who was saved in answer to prayer. The finals form the name of his father.

1. One of David's chief rulers
2. The youngest son of the builder of a noted city.
3. One whose sons sold part of their land.
4. The assumed name of a child of sorrow.
5. A farmer who offered some of his property to the service of God.
6. The country of an anxious inquirer after truth.
7. The character of one of the early churches.

BIBLE CHARACTERS, NO. 3.

The meeting-place of four hundred discontented Israelites.

The imtials of the following prove the name :—

1. One "who through faith quenched the violence of fire."
2. The feeding-place of Israel's flock, ana in later times the scene of a miracle.
3. The name of a king of Judah who was punished for his presumption.
4. The uncle of Esau.
5. The old name of Bethel.
6. The name of one who, through covetousness. "troubled Israel."
7. A Danite, the father of a famous judge in Israel.

BIBLE CHARACTERS, NO. 4.

A flourishing church of Asia Minor.

The initials of the following prove the name :—

1. A Christian householder.
2. A kinsman of St. Paul.
3. One of the divisions of the Holy Land mentioned in the New Testament.
4. A place where St. Paul was in peril from his own countrymen.
5. An eloquent man, and one mighty in the Scriptures.
6. A city from which St. Paul narrowly escaped with his life.
7. The first fruits of Achaia.
8. One of the apostles.
9. A succorer of St. Paul.
10. A political sect among the Jews.
11. A division of the Roman army.
12. A New Testament prophet.

BIBLE CHARACTERS, NO. 5.

A man who left his native city when famine arose.

The initials of the following prove the name:—

1. One of the brothers of the king of Israel, famous for his commanding stature.
2. The original name of the city of Dan.
3. The district in Palestine likened to an ass bowing down between two burdens.
4. The burial-place of a patriarchal family.
5. An Ethiopian who delivered a prophet from danger.
6. The mountain which the Hebrew lawgiver prayed to see.
7. The seaport where a royal fleet was wrecked.
8. A king prophesied of by name.
9. The rebuilder of Jericho.

BIBLE CHARACTERS, NO. 6.

The politician who proved a traitor to his king and country.

The initials of the following prove the name:—

1. The only member of a royal family in Israel who was to be mourned for and buried.
2. A prophetess whose teaching proved a temporary check to idolatry in Judah.
3. One of whom it was prophesied, "He shall dwell in the presence of his brethren."
4. The burial-place of the great military leader of the children of Israel.
5. The minister of an Eastern king whose ambition resulted in his ruin.
6. The husbandman with the kingly heart.
7. The watery grave of a multitude.
8. The birthplace of Absalom.
9. A memorial of deliverance in battle.
10. The father of the second founder of the human race.

BIBLE CHARACTERS, NO. 7.

The godly governor of an idolatrous household.

The initials of the following prove the name:—

1. One who chose idolatry and home rather than suffer affliction with the people of God.
2. A city of Judah, for many years the abode of the Ark of the Lord.
3. The inspired herdsman of Tekoa.
4. A faithful servant of God, in whom was fulfilled the promise, "Them that honor me I will honor."
5. A giant, out of whose hands King David was delivered by one of his chief captains.
6. A wife promised and given as the reward of valor.
7. The builder of a city which lay under the curse of God.

BIBLE CHARACTERS, NO. 8.

Whose eagerness to secure a blessing for her son brought sorrow instead of joy?

The initials of the following prove the name:—

1. Whose rejection of faithful counsellors led to a national rebellion?
2. To whom was the charge of the tabernacle committed during the wilderness journey?
3. The ambitious prophet who perished among the enemies of the Lord.
4. The prophet who was a witness for God before multitudes, yet fled for his life at the threat of a woman.
5. What city did David deliver from the Philistines, but its inhabitants would not protect David from the anger of Saul?
6. At what place was Israel's army first defeated after entering Canaan?
7. Whose navy was celebrated in old times, and brought great riches to Jerusalem?

BIBLE CHARACTERS, NO. 9.

The loyal and attached subject of a fugitive king.

The initials of the following prove the name:—

1. The meeting-place of a king and patriarch.
2. The favorite child—a leader of revolt.
3. A people whose obedience was a subject of Divine commendation.
4. The person whose daughters were the first female inheritors of land in Palestine.
5. One of the grandsons of Eli.
6. The city where a king of Judah met with a violent death.
7. What tribe was prohibited from having any possessions in the land of Israel?
8. The prince and great warrior killed in revenge.
9. The faith of a son proved by the faith of a father.

BIBLE CHARACTERS, NO. 10.

What king set aside God's laws, and established laws of his own to gain the affections of his people?

The initials of the following prove the name:—

1. The father of a king beloved of God.
2. One of the river boundaries of the Promised Land.
3. The dwelling-place of one who served God and judged Israel all his life.
4. A deliverer and judge of Israel's people.
5. The mother of Israel's mightiest monarch.
6. The king of one of the nations destroyed by God's command when Israel entered Canaan.
7. One who took a principal part in bringing the Ark of God out of the Philistines' land.
8. A Jew who rose to great honors in a foreign court.

BIBLE CHARACTERS, NO. 11.

Whose covetous and deceitful conduct brought immediate and lasting punishment on himself and family?

The initials of the following prove the name:—

1. Where was the first memorial raised to tell of Israel's entrance into Canaan?
2. The meeting-place of a king and a wicked woman.
3. One of the supporters of Moses during the battle with Amalek.
4. Who alone escaped from the massacre of the priests of Nob?
5. Where was want changed to sufficiency in time of national distress?
6. The eastern boundary of the Persian empire.

BIBLE CHARACTERS, NO. 12.

A Gentile soldier who was fruitful in good works.

The initials of the following prove the name:—

1. Who gave largely of his substance to be counted a Roman citizen?
2. One who sought out and aided an imprisoned apostle.
3. From what city were all Jews expelled by law in the first century?
4. Where was a widow's heart turned from mourning to rejoicing?
5. A tempestuous wind to which St. Paul was exposed in one of his voyages?
6. A Christian church noted for its lukewarmness and self-righteous spirit.
7. In what country bordering on the Adriatic Sea did St. Paul preach the gospel?
8. One who assisted St. Paul in his missionary work.
9. Whose history is given us in the words, "She ministered to Christ of her substance?"

BIBLE CHARACTERS, NO. 13.

A great man who used his newly acquired power to help a fallen brother.

The initials of the following prove the name:—

1. What were some of the lowest of the Jews?
2. A garment used to promote a parent's comfort.
3. A sleepless occupant of a comfortable bed.
4. One of the offerings in the temple.
5. One of the plagues.
6. A country which sheltered both the type and the anti-type.
7. An herb of note among the Pharisees.
8. An object of regret.
9. A servant who betrayed a fugitive to his master.
10. A form of speech adopted by Job.
11. The innocent cause of a father's despair.
12. A man who, without being a king, may possess a crown.

BIBLE CHARACTERS, NO. 14.

A noted teacher of Jewish law, whose reasoning had great weight with the council at Jerusalem.

The initials of the following prove the name:—

1. The portion of Palestine which was the birthplace of many of the apostles.
2. An aged widow remarkable for a life of fasting and prayer.
3. A disciple of Cyprus, with whom Paul lodged during his last visit to Jerusalem.
4. The name of one whose sudden death brought great fear on all the church.
5. The only companion of St. Paul during his last imprisonment at Rome.
6. The city in Asia Minor from whence the Jews came who stoned Paul.
7. The village where our Saviour spent the first evening after his resurrection.
8. A city where the Apostle Peter ministered to the saints.

No. 15. What Scripture characters most strikingly illustrate the power of maternal influence for good or for evil?

No. 16. What Scripture characters show the danger and evil of self-trust?

No. 17. What Scripture characters exhibit the sin and punishment of irreverently treating holy persons and things?

No. 18. Who were those on whose devotion God put distinguished honor?

No. 19. What Scripture characters exhibit the power of faith?

No. 20. What Scripture characters illustrate the blessedness of early devotedness to the service of God?

BIBLE

STUDIES.

IN SACRED

History, Biography and Geography.

BIBLE STUDIES.

PERTAINING TO

History, Biography and Geography.

Answers page 123 *of Key.*

BIBLE STUDY, No. 1.

[Showing a possession lost for us by the first Adam ; regained for us by the second Adam.]

1. The name of one of the first seven deacons.
2. A man who, as a king, offered willingly land and goods to build an altar, and to offer sacrifice to God.
3. A family which earned the approbation and reward from God by their obedience to the command of their ancestor.
4. A maiden given to wife as a reward for capturing a city ; and who sought and obtained, of her father, land with springs of water.
5. The omitted tribe in the account, in the Revelation, of the sealing of the hundred and forty-four thousand.
6. The father of that prophet of the Lord who dared speak unpalatable truth to the wicked king to whom the rest of the prophets had spoken palatable falsehood.
7. A convert called by St. Paul "the first fruits of Achaia," and whose household that apostle baptized.
8. That prophet whose visions, in the Old Testament, are often much akin to those of St. John the Divine in the New.

The *initials* of the above will give the answer

BIBLE STUDY, No. 2.

1. What woman armies to the battle led?
2. In troubled times who gave God's prophet bread?
3. Who told a lie, to please his thirst for gain?
4. Whose house the holy ark of God received
5. Who early of her husband was bereaved?
6. Who felt a loving father's keenest pain?

In these *initial* letters find,
A precept all our deeds to guide,
That bids us think of others weal,
And cast all thoughts of self aside.

BIBLE STUDY, No. 3.

1. A name, the symbol of mere worldly gain;
   To love it and love God—the attempt is vain.
2. A vale Tobiah sought, with feigned alarm,
   To entrap there Nehemiah to his harm.
3. A plain where building projects of proud aim,
   By heaven confounded, soon was brought to shame.
4. A word of Christ, which ears fast chained unbound.
5. For incense, jewels, gold, a land renowned.

The *initials* of these words read downward and the *finals* upward and you have the names of two brothers.

BIBLE STUDY, No. 4.

1. The first duke on record.
2. The mount on which Aaron died.
3. Aaron's wife
4. An Apostle whom the Greeks took for their God, Jupiter.
5. The place where the Israelites murmured for water.
6. The father of Moses.
7. A ruler of the Jews, who secretly sought Jesus that he might be taught by him.
8. A name given to Simon Peter.
9. A prophet in the reign of King Asa.

The *initials* form one of the names of our Lord.

BIBLE STUDY, No. 5.

1. The prophet who was sent to tell David of the punishment he had incurred by numbering the people.
2. A man who "feared the Lord greatly."
3. The country where the gospel was preached by a man who once had been the terror of the inhabitants.
4. A man who plotted to destroy a whole nation for the offence of one man.
5. The only man who escaped the slaughter of the priests by Saul.
6. The mountain in whose neighborhood Sisera was defeated.
7. The prophet who reproved Asa for trusting to the king of Syria.
8. The name which Jacob gave to the place where the angels of God met him.
9. "A prince and a great man."
10. The king by whose decree the building of the second temple was finished.
11. The wife of Aaron.
12. The man to whom David showed kindness for Jonathan's sake.
13. A man who was spared by a king, and slain by a prophet.
14. The city of the priests.
15. The prophet who was slain by Jehoiakim.
16. Herod's brother.
17. The place where the Israelites fought their first battle after leaving Egypt.
18. The murderer of Gedaliah.
19. The Hebrew name of the place where our Lord was condemned.
20. The father of Lot.
21. The city to which Jehoshaphat attempted to send ships.

The *initials* of the above names (or words) form a statement which shows us that we are "very far gone from original righteousness."

BIBLE STUDY, No. 6.

1. The father, of Dathan and Abiram.
2. The beloved physician.
3. The surname of a traitor.
4. The name of a miraculous spring.
5. The mount of cursing.
6. Where a herd of swine perished.
7. A valley where a famous event took place.
8. A city of Phrygia, to which Paul addressed an epistle.
9. The place where a Syrian captain was defeated.

The *initials* of the answers will give the name of a sojourner in the land of Moab, and the *finals* that of his native town.

BIBLE STUDY, No. 7.

1. An Israelitish leader who conquered the host of Midian.
2. A cunning hunter.
3. A prophet, a native of Elkosh.
4. One whom the Lord refused for his anointed.
5. The wife of Zebedee.
6. The second son of Kohath.
7. The chief ruler of the synagogue at Corinth.

The *initials* and *finals* of the answers will give the names of two books of the Bible.

BIBLE STUDY, No. 8.

1. This *sacrifice* was offered at his birth.
   Who lived, despised and poor, upon the earth.

2. Calling the wise men (for he greatly feared),
   He asked of them what time the star appeared.

3, Warned by an angel, *thither* Joseph went,
   Ere the dark hours of night were fully spent.

4. He slept, and God, in pity and in love,
   Gave him, in this, a *glimpse* of heaven above.

5. The *tribe* of one who served God night and day,
And in the temple lived to watch and pray.

6. Take *it* upon you in your Saviour's might;
In youth 'tis easy, and 'tis rest at night.

7. Men saw *its* light, at heaven's eastern gate;
It passed before them, and their joy was great.

8. In haste *'twas* eaten, with the staff in hand;
For Israel's children sought a better land.

9. *Her* little ones as Christian martyrs slept,
She knows not, and refusing comfort wept.

10. The prophecy, a virgin shall conceive,
Will tell the name which she her *Son* should give.

11. 'Twas *here* in wisdom and stature too,
And grace with God and man, our Saviour grew.

12. The *place* where Christ bade his disciples stay,
Whilst he should leave them for a time to pray.

The initials give the whole.

Through God's great mercy, in sin's blackest night
It came from heaven to give his people light;
To bid our fears in death's dark shadows cease,
Guiding our feet into the way of peace.

BIBLE STUDY, No. 9.

1. The son of Phineas.
2. A city in central Palestine.
3. A name borne by one of the children of Anak.
4. One of the sons of Ashur.
5. An herb named by our Lord.
6. The builder of Jericho.

The *initials* and *finals* give the names of two great prophets.

BIBLE STUDY, No. 10.

1. A man who made a wretched choice.

2. A man raised up as a deliverer.
3. A woman beautiful and well-favored.
4. A woman called " a mother in Israel."
5. A king of Egypt who besieged Jerusalem.
6. A king of Israel rebuked by a prophet.
7. A queen who made a great feast,
8. A queen who saved her nation.
9. A city famous in the early history of the world.
10. A city in Asia mentioned in the New Testament.
11. A letter which commences no name in the Bible.
12. A letter of the earliest-named place in the Bible.
13. A nation often at war with the Jews.
14. A nation that had wars with Assyria.
15. A place mentioned in Paul's last voyage.
16. A place visited by Paul and Barnabas.
17. A mountain possessed by the Edomites.
18. A mountain where the Lord spake to Israel.

The *initials* give words spoken in a time of great peril.

BIBLE STUDY, No. 11.

1. *Whom* did his servants treacherously slay.
   As sleeping on his couch at noon he lay?
2. A *prince* who, with a missionary band,
   Went forth to preach throughout the Holy Land.
3. A *town* where mighty miracles were wrought,
   Which for its sin was to distruction brought!
4. Before *what idol* did a Syrian bend
   Lest he his heathen master should offend?
5. *Who* to withstand the Apostle's preaching.
   And on himself a fearful judgement brought?
6. *What* did once save from death the human race,
   And for a year was their sole dwelling-place?
7. A *prophet* who was called in early youth,
   And till old age he served the God of truth.
8. A *mother* who did early teach her boy
   The way that leads to everlasting joy.

9. What *king* against the tribes of Israel fought
   Because a passage through his land they sought?
10. A *word* inscribed in Babel's regal hall,
   Her impious king to penitence to call.
11. What *king* would not take counsel of the wise,
   But did his father's counsellors despise?
12. What makes the gold with purest lustre shine,
   And is an emblem of God's Word Divine?
13. What beauteous *creatures* dwell in heaven above,
   And visit earth on messages of love?
14. *Who* did, when Judah's tribe was borne away,
   The ruler of the remnant basely slay?
15. *Who* brought good news, the apostle's heart to cheer,
   When he was sore oppressed with grief and fear?
16. A blessed *emblem* of our Saviour dear,

For those that trust in Him need never fear,
In the *initials* of these words we read
A prayer for that which above all we need.
Without this gift the world would be most drear:
The next be viewed with overwhelming fear.
It casts its beams on every scene of woe,
And throws a radiance on our path below.

BIBLE STUDY, No. 12.

1. Who life and pardon for her nation won?
2, The name of noble Samuel's eldest son?
3. Who lost his two sons in a single day?
4. A king who captive led the Jews away.
5. An emperor to whom the world belonged.
6. A king who prayed and had his life prolonged.
7. Assyria's scornful messenger of pride.
8. The seer whose message all his threats defied.
9. Who curst King David as in grief he fled?
10. Who scarce believed Christ risen from the dead?
11. A man who lost, but got again his sight.
12. What Syrian had a dream from God at night?
13. Who brought on all mankind increasing woe?

14. A captain swift of foot as a young roe.
15. A mighty judge betrayed by woman's art.
16. What man did rashly with his birth-right part?
17. A noble monarch, warrior, poet, seer.
18. Who would not let King David taste his cheer?
16. A man who served the Lord in Ahab's court.
20. The place from which the finest gold was brought?
21. A faithful Archite, to King David dear.
22. Who said his wife, was not his wife, through fear?
23. From whom did Jesus seven devils cast?
24. The brother Joseph kept and bound so fast.
25. Who quickly for Rebecca water drew?
26. The famous mount where stately cedars grow.
27. Who in his prisoner no evil found;
And knew him innocent, yet left him bound?
By these *initials* you will plainly see,
To live like Christ, unselfish we must be.

BIBLE STUDY, No. 13.

1. Who like the lion seeketh to devour
The godly man in an unguarded hour?
2. Whose occupation did the apostle share,
When forced to labor for his daily fare?
3. In what did Ruth her present take away,
Which to her mother she did straight convey?
4. To what great sin was Israel's nation prone,
Which robbed their God of what was his alone?
5. Who was by faith enabled to despise
The lion's yawning jaws and glaring eyes?

Take the above initials, and you'll find
The nature of one most favored of mankind;
One from a number chosen by the Lord
To rule a nation by his sacred word.
Sweet were the sounds that issued from his songs
In praise of him to whom all praise belongs.
He, choosing in his youth the better part,
Was styled by God one after his own heart.

BIBLE STUDY, No. 14.

1. Who challenged Israel's hosts to single fight;
2. What prophets hid in caves as dark as night?
3. What poet sounded forth his Maker's praise
4. Who was expelled from his home in early days?
5. What king neglected and despised God's word?
6. What woman's heart "was opened by the Lord?"
7. What conquering king the towers of Shemer raised?
8. Who would not come to hear her beauty praised?
9. And who to heaven on fiery wheels was borne,
His mantle falling on his friend forlorn?

Take the initials, and in them you'll find
Wise words of counsel, for the young designed.

BIBLE STUDY, No. 15.

1. Whither did Jonah vainly try from God to flee?
2. Who once three angels entertained beneath a tree?
3. A noted brook that flowed beside Jerusalem?
4. A "ready scribe" who wrote the book that bears his name?

5. A judge who hoped to gain a bribe for Paul's release?
6. Who made a molten calf rebellious tribes to please?
7. A man that grossly mocked and cast stones at his king?
8. Whom did Paul ask his parchments, books, and cloak to bring?

9. Who unto Solomon for God's house workmen sent?
10. And where was it for precious gold his servants went?
11. Whom, four days dead, out of the grave did Jesus call?
12. Who loved this evil world, and hence deserted Paul?

13. On whose behalf did Paul an earnest letter write?
14. To whom was he conveyed a prisoner by night?
15. Whom did his godly father on an altar bind?
16. And for whose vineyard was it that a king repined?
17. A word th' Ephraimites could not pronounce aright?
18. Where Paul from Troas travelling, tarried for a night?

19. Where was the birthplace of the prophet Samuel?
20. Who touched God's ark, and instantly a victim fell?
21. Who cherished angry thoughts, and then his brother killed?
22. And into whose young mind were holy truths instilled?
23. A king's son on his bed once barbarously slain?
24. Who proved a friend to Paul, ashamed not of his chain?
25. A man that timidly, with deeply felt concern,
Came unto Christ by night, the way of truth to learn?

In the first letters of each name combined,
A gracious attribute of God you find.

BIBLE STUDY, No. 16.

1. Whose son was raised by Christ's almighty power?
2. What friend of God proved faithless for one hour?
3. Whose youthful life was saved for future fame?
4. Who cast a lustre on a mother's name?
5. On whose behalf did Paul the apostle plead?
6. O'er fall'n Jerusalem whose heart did bleed?
7. Whose life was saved that many might rejoice?
8. Who for the ruined temple raised his voice?
9. Who did with Baal's prophets long contend?
10. To whom did Abram prove the firmest friend?
11. Who feared to tell the king the prophet's word?
12. Where dwelt the judge so faithful to the Lord?
13. And who, though oft by Satan's wiles deceived,
A man of God's own heart the name received?

The initial letters form a Scripture exhortation.

BIBLE STUDY, No. 17.

1. In whom did Jesus say there was no guile?
2. What king did hinder Israel for awhile?
3. Who sought by letter Ezra's work to stay?
4. Whose fame for wisdom sounded far away?
5. Who called his wives to hear his doleful tale?

6. What friend of Paul in trouble did not fail ?
7. What was the faithful Abram s father's name ?
8. Who trembled at the Saviour's growing fame ?
9. Before whose bar did Paul most nobly plead ?
10. What warlike man for David's crime did bleed ?
11. What book shows forth the prophet's grief and pain ?
12. And by whose hands was Gedaliah slain ?
13. Whose vineyard did the wicked Ahab claim ?
14. And what blind man did Jesus not disdain ?
15. Where dwelt a patriarch of early date ?
16. Who owed to woman's hand his direful fate ?
17. What name proclaims the Saviour's ever near ?
18. What Ammonite made Israel's heart to fear ?
19. What faithful servant sought help from the Lord ?
20. Who, firm in faith, feared neither fire nor sword ?
21. Who, taking the infant Jesus in his arms,
Bade Mary's heart prepare for great alarms ?

These initials show, when read aright,
A precept wise and true,
To do with all thy power and might
Whate'er thou find'st to do.

BIBLE STUDY, No. 18.

1. What gates did Samson bear with ease away ?
2. Whose debt did Paul take on himself to pay ?
3. What god before the ark fell flatly down ?
4. Whose father died beneath God's angry frown ?
5. Whose servant bore an open letter forth ?
6. What Syrian's flocks were bless'd for Jacob's worth ?
7. Who by his brav'ry won his cousin's hand ?
8. Who boldly disobeyed her lord's command ?
9. What country nourished Israel's chosen race,
Till friendly kings to cruel ones gave place ?

Take now the letter that begins each name :
A very precious text you'll find the same.

BIBLE STUDY, No. 19.

1. What ruler of the Jews did Paul baptize?
2. Who saw a man of God to glory rise?
3. Who fell'd a bough to fire a city tow'r?
4. Who with great skill could speak of tree and flow'r?
5. What Hebrew bore a gift to Moab's king?
6. From whence did Solomon much treasure bring?
7. Whose threshing-floor stood on the temple's site?
8. Whose men did swear their king should no more fight?
9. Who forty years' repose for Israel gained?
10. What Moabitish king o'er them then reigned?
11. What queen in royal house a feast did make?
12. Who from a husband fond a wife did take?
13. Whose wordly choice became to him a snare,
    And says with warning voice to us, Beware?

You'll solve my rhyme, whate'er may be your age,
If well you search the Bible's sacred page;
Name after name must its initial give,
And if you heed the text your soul shall live.

BIBLE STUDY, NO. 20.

1. Who in a chariot preach'd with telling power?
2. Who met her future lord at eve's calm hour?
3. Who first was stoned with stones, then burn'd with fire?
4. What kind of pigeon did the law require?
5. From whence was cast a sinful queen to die?
6. Who had twelve sons, with towns and castles high?
7. Whence came one to plead with Israel's king?
8. A prophet's mother who with joy did sing?
9. Who built a town upon a hill he bought?
10. To whom was husbandry with pleasure fraught?
11. Where was a burning quench'd by earnest prayer?
12. Who drove three giants forth with courage rare?
13. A cunning hunter, to his father dear?
14. Who hired an army ere he fought with Seir?
15. What king, when wounded, ended his own life?

16. For whom did Eliezer seek a wife?
17. Who had a guileless heart, that priceless boon?
18. Where stood the sun, while also stayed the moon?

Your Bibles search (an act the Papist blames)!
These questions all must answer'd be by names.
The letter first of each place in a line,
To obey the words may God your heart incline!

BIBLE STUDY, NO. 21.

1. What Jew became a convert of our Lord,
   And with the seventy went to preach the word?
2. What name was given to Phinehas' infant son,
   Significant of Israel's glory gone?
3. Where David was compelled with foes to live,
   What city to him did king Achish give?
4. Who was a chosen vessel of the Lord,
   To guide his church and spread his name abroad?
5. Who was the victim spared by Saul's command,
   Who fell at length by Samuel's feeble hand?
6. What favored minion had a gallows made,
   And fell into the snare himself had laid?

The above initials will name a place
Whose story pleases every child of grace,
Since to a covenant God we there commend
The present and the future of our friend.

BIBLE STUDY, NO. 22.

1. On what high mountain were seven altars made?
2. Who was for her son's safety much afraid?
3. From what town were th' apostles forced to flee?
4. Whom did our Saviour 'neath the fig tree see?
5. Who to a king did tidings sad convey?
6. And who did once Goliath's brother slay?
7. Whose valor was rewarded with a wife?
8. Who trembled when Paul preached a future life?
9. What king to Abram did his wife restore?

10. Who was a ready scribe in Moses' law ?
11. A king of Judah in his chariot slain ?
12. A town where Jesus did some time remain ?
13. Who walked with God, and knew not death or pain ?

Take these initials, and a name they form
Of Him, who speaking, hushed the angry storm,
And where he walked, in gentleness and might,
A peaceful radiance shed, the Lord of light.
Oh may his reign within our hearts begin,
And his abounding grace prevail against our sin !

BIBLE STUDY, NO. 23.

1. The word whereby the test was once applied,
Where nations met beside the swelling tide ?
2. The portion of the day first named on earth ?
3. The power that gave created things their birth ?
4. The dried-up stem that blossomed like the rose ?
5. The number of the saints whose hands disclose
The Saviour's mark ? The prophet's earnest call
6. To take the water offered unto all ?
7. The twice-repeated words by God once spoken,
8. To save the house that all his laws had broken ?
9. What Christ is to his church ? The frame wherein
10. Time's cycles move ? In what should we begin
11. To worship God ? The word each one is bound
To speak, inviting others by the sound
12. To drink the living waters ? Christ's command—
What we should be who seek the better land ?
13. In what did the Creator fashion man,
Last of his works, yet chief in all the plan ?
14. The last bequest the Saviour gave to those
Who heard his voice in blessing when he rose ?
15. That which the lilies do not, and yet they
A glory greater than the king display ?
16. By what was judgment asked before the Lord,
When Joshua first assumed the leader's sword ?

17. What Christ declared the people went to see
Who waited on his herald's ministry?
18. How the rich man shall sadly go away?
19. What we shall be who loves the Lord's great day?

In one great precept the initials weave:
Obey, and you shall Christ himself perceive;
He spake the words, and all who seek his face
Shall find in them, full of truth and grace.

BIBLE STUDY, NO. 24.

1. The king whom Abram slew to save Lot's life?
2. The king whose son took Jezebel to wife?
3. The king whose pride by God was brought down low?
4. The king, who fearful, to a witch did go?
5. The king's son who was murdered on his bed?
6. The king who mourned in song his foe when dead?
7. The king who to Jehoiachin was kind?
8. The king who would not aged counsellors mind?
9. The king whose warlike help King Ahaz prayed?
10. The king who begged that God would grant him aid?
11. The king who cruelly died by Ehud's blade?
12. The king whose mother words of wisdom taught?
13. The king's court which the gentle Esther sought?
14. The king-built city where the king was slain?
15. The king's counsellor sent to ease his pain?
16. The king whose brothers twain their father slew?
17. The king, who more than any, heavenly wisdom knew?

Combine the initials of these royal names;
They give a text which man's poor splendor shames.
In summer glory God the earth arrays,
And crowns with beauty the succeeding days
Go, walk the fields and breathe the fragrant air
And mark the perfect wisdom everywhere:
What palace is there like the vaulted sky?
What king's attire can with these flowerets vie?
Oh thou, who clothest thus the verdant field,
To us the needed blessing daily yield.

BIBLE STUDY, NO. 25.

1. Who sheltered David in an hour of need?
2. Who died 'mid household grief and public gloom?
3. Who stained the young earth with a cruel deed?
4. Whose words averted Judah's coming doom?
5. Who through an erring monarch's treachery died?
6. Whose faltering conscience saved his brother's life?
7. Who did the toils of Nehemiah deride?
8. Who bore a gift and a distroying knife?
9. What infant's birth made glad a widow's heart?
10. Who for untimely forwardness was slain?
11. Who rashly with a God-sent gift did part?

Yet by his death a victory did gain?
In the initial letters see,
  A precept that 'twere well to heed,
For it imparts the cheering charm,
  Which in its turn each heart doth need.

BIBLE STUDY, NO. 26.

1. A doubter.
2. A proud courtier.
3. A scribe.
4. A king who remembered his mother's teachings.
5. The first judge of Israel.
6. A foolish young king who refused good counsel.
7. A heathen king who acknowledge the power of the true God.
8. A king's son, who was murdered in his bed.
9. One who tried craft to hinder a good work.
10. One who wished to entertain an angel.
11. A burden, which, when Christ's, is easy and light.
12. A selfish nephew of Abraham.
13. The assassin of one of Nebuchadnezzar's governors.
14. One who suffered for avarice and untruthfulness.
15. A man whose wife was more famous than himself.
16. A king of Assyria, at the time Pekah was king of Israel.

The *initials* give a saying of the Psalmist expressing faith and joy.

BIBLE STUDY, NO. 27.

1. The man whose name is first mentioned in connection with a victory over the Amalekites.
2. A prince of Midian slain by the Ephraimites.
3. The father of Jehu.
4. The captain of Absalom's host.
5. The only weapon used at the siege of Jericho.
6. A prophetess who foretold the evil that should come upon the kingdom of Judah.
7. The country to which the murderers of Sennacherib fled.
8. A king who was deprived of his dominion until he would acknowledge that all earthly power was the work of God.

The *initials* and *finals* of the foregoing names (or words) form the names of a father and son : the *initials* give us the son, who was sent to warn David of Absalom's intentions. The *finals*, the father, one of the priests in the reign of David.

BIBLE STUDY, No. 28.

1. A servant of God, who followed Him fully.
2. Another servant of God, who feared the Lord greatly.
3. The woman to whom Jesus first appeared after his resurrection.
4. A woman who is said to have been righteous before God.
5. The birth place of the father of the faithful.
6. A city where Jesus raised one from the dead.
7. A city in the wilderness, built by King Solomon.
8. A place from which gold was brought to King Solomon.
9. A prophet who lived in the reign of King Ahaz.
10. A prophet who lived in the reign of King Ahab.

The *initials* form a gracious invitation of the Lord Jesus.

BIBLE STUDY, NO. 29.

1. What office did our Lord fulfill in offering Himself a sacrifice for sin ?
2. What expression is used concerning Christ as of the house of David ?
3. In what term does St. Paul, in his epistle to the Corinthians, speak of the relation of Christ to the Father ?
4. What title of Christ, though given him in contempt by his enemies, was the fulfillment of a prophecy ?
5, A name of our Saviour that indicates his wisdom ?
6. In what prophetic language is the essential attribute of God ascribed to Christ.
7. A title by which our Lord's human descent is described ?
8. Under what designation does prophecy indicate Christ as cleansing from all iniquity ?
9. Name the grand office of Christ as our Divine Teacher.
10, What prophetic title of our Saviour shows Him to be both God and Man ?
11, One of our Saviour's names taken from the Greek alphabet ?
12. How does our Lord show himself to be the support of that temple built up of his elect ?
13, What is it that Christ's people find in him ?

From these *initials* you will find
The love of God to human kind.
As foretold by the prophet, what
Christ should be.

BIBLE STUDY, No. 30.

1. One whom Paul called his own son in the faith.
2. A king who helped Solomon to build the temple.
3. A prophet who was seen hundreds of years after he died.
4. The eldest sister of Rachel.
5. The grandfather of King David.
6. The eldest son of Jacob.
7. The youngest son of Jesse.

8. A distinguished teacher at Antioch.
9. A Roman officer who saved Paul's life.
10. A warrior who killed Goliath's brother.
11. A scribe who carried a message to Isaiah.
12. A king's son who killed his father.
13. One of the judges of Israel.
14. One of the best of the kings of Judah.
15. One of the ancestors of our Lord.
16. One of Job s comforters.
17. A great man among the Anakims.
18. A prophet who rebuked King David.
19. A prophetess who judged Israel.
20. The father of the first King of Israel.
21. The steward of Abraham's house.
22. The mother of Timothy.
23. The third Apostle called by Jesus.
24. An orator who accused Paul.
25. A king reproved by John the Baptist.
26. A false prophet who withstood Paul.
27. A true prophet in the land of Chaldea.

The *initials* express an affectionate wish and devout benediction.

BIBLE STUDY, NO, 31.

1. A servant who gained part of his master's property by slander and deceit.
2. A high priest who tried to hinder a great work of the Lord.
3. A title of honor which our Lord told his disciples to refuse when called by it.
4. One of those classes of people who shall be cast into the lake of fire, which is the second death.
5. The division of Palestine of which, at the beginning of John the Baptist's ministry, Philip, the husband of Herodias was Tetrarch.
6. The soldier who, when with David, took away Paul's spear and cruse of water, while his guards were asleep.

7. The cousin of a prophet who bought a field from him, as a token that the children of Israel should return from their captivity in Babylon.

The *initials* and *finals* give the names of two woman, sisters of a famous king of Israel. The first the mother of brave men, in connection with whom her name is often mentioned.

BIBLE STUDY, NO. 32.

1. A man whose end exemplifies that "the love of money is the root of all evil."
2. A man who "prepared his heart to seek the law of the Lord."
3. The town to which Elkanah belonged.
4. The country which bounded the dominions of Ahasuerus on the east.
5. The king of Elam who took Lot prisoner.
6. One of the prophets who incited the Jews to the building of the second temple.
7. The name which Joshua originally bore.

The *initials* of the above names form the name of a city taken by the Israelites where only one family was spared; the *finals*, of a city built by Omri, which was also his burial-place.

BIBLE STUDY, NO 33.

1. A tree with which a famous temple was built.
2. A tree under which idols were buried.
3. A prophet whom a king of Judah slew with the sword.
4. A city in Egypt, prophesied against by three prophets.
5. A tree into which one climbed to see Christ.
6. The place where the spies obtained the bunch of grapes.
7. One called "the beloved physician."
8. One whose heart the Lord opened.
9. One from whom our Lord was a descendant.
10. One who caused her son to deceive.

The above *initials* form a name by which our Lord was called in the Old Testament.

BIBLE STUDY, NO. 34.

1. The only queen that over Judah reigned,
And her brief reign with cruel murder stained?
2. Who for herself did carve a tomb on high,
Then died an exile 'neath a foreign sky?
3. A city where who once its portals gained
Protection from pursuing foes obtained?
4. Who nobly braved a wicked monarch's ire
And walked unhurt amid the blazing fire?
5. A symbol, first of God's forgiving grace,
That afterward showed the folly of our race?
6. A shapeless stone which did from heaven fall
On which for aid the heathen world did call?
7. An emblem of our Saviour's gentle sway,
Easy to those who do their God obey?
8. Who did the brother of Goliah slay,
And valiantly upheld king David's sway?
9. A beauteous type of Christ's life-giving power,
Who doth on earth the richest blessings shower?
10. Who, when a ruler was oppressed with care,
Assisted him to persevere in prayer?
11. Whose son taught men to strike the tuneful lyre,
And did their minds with harmony inspire?
12. Where did the patriarch a pillar raise
For visions sweet and bright his God to praise?
13. Who made a feast, that former friends might prove
The blessings of a Saviour's care and love?
14. What mighty empire o'er the earth bore sway
When here on earth our blessed Lord did stay?
15. Who, when a prophet was by grief oppresst,
Did come to aid him and procure him rest?
16. The land for Israel's sake supremely blest,
Type of the Christian's everlasting rest?
17. An altar raised, for Israel's sons to trace
That they belonged to that much favored race?
18. Who was the grandsire of a mighty seer
Who taught the Jews to overcome their fear?

19. A beauteous emblem in the temple riven,
    To show that Christ our Lord hath opened heaven?
20. The priest's son who Israel's thousands led,
    And before whom the waves of Jordan fled?

In these *initials* you will find
Precept and promise both combined.
If you, by grace, the first obey,
You then will find the heavenly way
That leads you to the realm above,
Where all is peace, and joy, and love.

BIBLE STUDY, NO. 35.

1. A word which signifies "peace."
2. A child who was born on the day of a great national calamity.
3. A city which was popularly supposed to produce nothing good.
4. A son of Saul who reigned over Israel for two years.
5. The father of Boaz.
6. An orator who accused St. Paul before Felix.
7. A king of Syria who was anointed by a prophet of Israel.
8. David's eldest brother.
9. The queen of Egypt in Solomon's time.
10. The town in which Samuel's house was.
11. The people who erected an altar "to the unknown God."
12. The only leper who was cleansed during the reign of Jehoram, King of Israel.
13. A conqueror whose death was more disastrous to his enemies than his life had been.
14. The country whence Elijah originally came.
15. A Moabitess who married into the tribe of Judah.
16. The Ethiopian eunuch who interceded for Jeremiah.
17. The mountain given to Esau for a possession.
18. The church to whom it was said, "Thou hast a name that thou livest, and art dead."

19. Leah's fifth son.
20. The conqueror of Chushan-rishathaim.
21. A servant whose master granted him leave of absence for twelve years.
22. A runaway slave who was sent back to his master by St. Paul.
23. The age of Moses when he visited his brethren.
24. Absalom's daughter.
25. An Egyptian slave who became the mother of a great nation.
26. The father of Bathsheba.
27. The well near which Isaac dwelt.
28. The tribe to whom it was said, "As thy days, so shall thy strength be."
29. A charge which was given to the disciples and to all Christians.

The *initials* of the above names (or words) give us a definition of sin.

BIBLE STUDY, NO. 36.

1. The tribe to which Korah belonged?
2. The son of Ruth?
3. That by which the sheep know the shepherd?
4. David's eldest brother?
5. The man whom Philip brought to Christ?
6. The father of Ahab?
7. The birthplace of St. Paul?
8. The man who "boasted himself to be somebody?"
9. The city given by Joshua to Caleb?
10. The prophet who said "I am not better than my fathers."
11. That which Pharaoh's daughter promised to Jochabed?
12. The man who was "blessed because of the Ark of God?"
13. The place where Elkanah lived?
14. That of which Jacob made pottage?
15. The man who was "greatly beloved?"

The *initials* form a precept much needed in this world.

BIBLE STUDY, NO. 37.

1. The prophet who "loved the wages of unrighteousness."
2. The native land of Ishmael's wife.
3. The man who would not part with the inheritance of his fathers.
4. The tenth part of an ephah.
5. The city to which Barnabas went to seek Saul.
6. The number of years that Moses sojourned in Midian.
7. The saint who, "being dead, yet speaketh."
8. The medium of communication between Joseph and his brethren.
9. St. Paul's "own son in the faith."
10. The father of King Manasseh.
11. Isaac's brother-in-law.
12. The prophet visited on his death-bed by King Joash.
13. The city where Omri was buried.
14. The Benjamite who cursed David.

These *initials* make a charge of our Saviour to His disciples.

BIBLE STUDY, NO. 38.

1. Whose faith and courage saved her people's life?
2 Who won a battle trusting in the Lord?
3. Who gained a sharp rebuke for jealous strife?
4. Who perished by a traitor's cruel sword?
5. Who checked his rage to prove a prophet's word?

The *initial* letters take—they form his name
Who did his foe's unwilling praise proclaim;
Then take the *finals*, and they give the same.

BIBLE STUDY, NO. 39.

1. A type of our Lord; one who entered the land of Egypt, and the house of bondage, and there saved his people.
2. One who preferred a present and temporal benefit, to that which was future and eternal, and repented, when too late.
3. The name of a King of Israel; also of one who, from a persecutor, became an apostle.
4. One who put out a rash hand, unauthorized by God, to

steady the ark, which he thought to be in danger, and received not praise, but punishment from God.

5. The name of that church of whose angel (or bishop) was said, "Thou hast a name that thou livest, and art dead."

The *first* letters of these make up the sweetest human name in the world.

"It makes the wounded spirit whole
It calms the troubled breast;
'Tis manna to the hungry soul,
And to the weary rest.

BIBLE STUDY, NO. 40.

Faith shall be swallowed up in sight,
Hope in fulfillment end,
When on our twilight life the light
Of heaven shall descend.

A sister grace to these, more great,
Shall brighten when they wane;
O let us more and more to this,
Even in *this* life, attain!

The initials of the following will give the name of this most excellent grace:

1. The grandmother of Timothy.
2. The good servant of a wicked king, who kept one hundred prophets of the Lord from the vengeance of the queen.
3. A queen who resisted her husband's command, and was deposed.
4. A good man, but a bad father.

BIBLE STUDY, NO. 41.

1. The father of the first artificer in brass and iron.
2. The man who said, "I thy servant fear the Lord from my youth."
3. The wise man's estimate of earthly pleasure.
4. The place where David slew Goliath.
5. Rehoboam's successor.

6. The people who stole the oxen of Job.
7. Herod's chamberlain.
8. The city where Jehu was anointed king.
9. The kingdom of Chedorlaomer.
10. Paul's amanuensis when he wrote the Epistle to the Romans.
11. The mother of Adonijah.
12. The wife of Mahlon.
13. The name of the altar that was built by the children of Reuben and Gad.
14. The younger son of Bilhah.

The initials give a loving command of Peter.

BIBLE STUDY, NO. 42.

The letters in the following words, when re-arranged, form the name of a false god, to whom human sacrifices were offered:

1. A man noted for wisdom.
2. An unclean beast.

BIBLE STUDY, NO. 43.

1. The hiding-place of Jonathan and Ahimaaz.
2. The prophet who was a herdman of Tekoah.
3. Cain's grandson.
4. The judge who succeeded Abimelech.
5. The prophet who foretold the destruction of Edom.
6. Hezekiah's name for the brazen serpent.
7. The place where Samson slew the lion.
8. Nehemiah's father.
9. Aaron's wife.
10. The city whence Sennacherib's ambassadors came.
11. The man of whom St. Paul says, "He was not ashamed of my chain."
12. The king of Syria who fought with Ahaz.
13. The tribe omitted when the rest are enumerated in the Book of Revelation.

The initials form an exhortation of the Psalmist.

BIBLE STUDY, No. 44.

1. Who prayed for death in dark despair?
2. To what did Christ himself compare?
3. What queen was fairest of the fair?

Now either way the *initials* place,
And still the selfsame name they give
Of one who sunk in deep disgrace,
Did yet a glorious hope receive.

BIBLE STUDY, No. 45.

1. First name a chief, the bitter foe
   Of Judah's Lord, and Judah's land.
2. A river next, whose waters flow,
   By old Damascus' heathen strand.
3. What did the Lord of Hosts o'erthrow,
   In pity to his chosen band?
4. What word is oft-times used to show
   The wonders of his mighty hand?
5. Next mark the name first borne in youth,
   By one, who in the cause of truth,
6. With manly courage risked his life,
   To still the murmuring people's strife.
7. And, last, his father's name set down,
   Known only by that son's renown;

The *initials* form a monarch's name,
Who, once a mighty empire swayed;
Yet are his exploits lost to fame,
And all his glory sunk in shade.
His captain's name the *finals* tell.

BIBLE STUDY, No. 46.

Six letters spell the name of one who was early dedicated to God. These six letters are the initials of six proper names which we will describe as follows:—

1. A quiet Prince.

4. A word which sealed the doom of an empire.

2. An Eastern River.
3. A priest of Baal.
5. A mighty man of valor.
6. A Levitical city.

The *final* letters of these six words either up or down, spell his mother's name.

Who was the boy? Who was his mother?

BIBLE STUDY, No. 47.

1. Whose mournful death made widows to lament?
2. What woman from her master's house was sent?
3. Who saw bright visions by a river's side?
4. What treach'rous servant to his master lied?
5. What warlike prince upon a rock was slain?
6. Who water sought when God withheld the rain?
7. Who came uninjured from the lion's den?
8. Who once near Lehi slew a thousand men?
9. Whose prayers and tears did a kind answer gain?
10. In what famed valley was a giant slain?
11. Who for his sin most bitterly did weep?
12. Where did his flock the son of Amram keep?
13. Who with a brother was at deadly strife?
14. What woman by her faith did save her life?
15. Who a fierce foe did in a monarch find,
But in that monarch's son a friend most kind?

Take the initials, and, as noonday clear,
A title of the Saviour will appear.

BIBLE STUDY, No. 48.

1. A little plant which grows upon a wall.
2. A tree of Bashan, strong and stout and tall.
3. Those which once sheltered a sad captive race.
4. In room of briars and thorns, this shall have place.
5. In figure, said to flourish, when men fail.
6. 'Mong presents, sent to Joseph to prevail.
7. They camped by Elim's wells, its palms close by.
8. When this puts forth its leaves, lo! summer's nigh.
9. 'Tis in the wilderness, from dwelling far.

10. Compared unto thy tens, these, Jacob, are.
11 By God's power flourishing when all is low.
12 A tree not known now by this name to grow.
13 The desert wild shall blossom like to this.
14 All things were perfect in this land of bliss,
15 On either side a river's brink it grew.
16. He shall resemble this, whose life's untrue.
17. Thus often, thou shall tithe thy fields and land.
18. Egyptian corn not smitten by Almighty hand.
19. This tree was asked o'er other trees to reign.
20. That which once budded, when man's words were vain.
21. No Nazarite with vow might eat of these.
22. Christ saw Zaccheus, passing 'neath this tree.

He that hath eyes to see, and heart to love,
Will quickly guess the *initials* writ above;
For day by day the earth repeats the same,
And bids us laud and magnify His name.

BIBLE STUDY, NO. 49.

1. What good physician was Paul's loving friend?
2. A place to which, for gold, they used to send?
3. What tree did Jesus with himself compare?
4. The vale whence finest fruits the spies did bear?
5. How oft might man approach the holy place?
6. His house where God's ark rested for a space?
7. Whom did God smite because he touched the ark?
8. Who, old and wise men's counsels would not mark?
9. A holy man of God who never died?
10. Who sought his coming unto Christ to hide
11. An Israelitish king, by Zimri slain.
12. Who over Judah reigned the longest reign?
13. Whom did his son deceive when old and weak?
14. What prophet dumb became, and could not speak?
15. Who owed to woman's wise advice his fall,
His head thrown lifeless from the city wall?

If men obeyed this precept more,
There soon would be an end of war,

For love would bid contention cease,
And give to all the nations peace.

BIBLE STUDY, NO. 50.

1. A woman who guarded the bodies of seven slain men.
2, A queen who was good and beautiful.
3. A Roman emperor who trembled under the reasoning of Paul.
4. A horned and untamable animal never used for sacrifice.
5. A climbing tree of rapid growth, under which the prophet Jonah once sat.
6. The name given to fierce wind mentioned in Acts.

The *initials* give that which Christ promised believers in time of trouble.

BIBLE STUDY, NO. 51.

1. Word that God alone can claim.
2. A slave who won a dearer name.
3. A holy woman raised to life.
4. A man who took a gleaner wife.
5. A feast of triumph after pain.
6. The robe that martyr myriads gain.
7. The name that "laughter" doth express
8. A bishop charged to faithfulness.
9. A counsellor and faithful friend.
10. A thing once yours, for ever gone.
11. A name of Christ that means "the end."
12. The light from Aaron's breastplate shown.

In these *initials* doth there lie,
The full form of the word good-by.

BIBLE STUDY, NO. 52.

1. The first military captain on record.
2. One who interceded with the king for the release of the prophet Jeremiah, when he lay in the dungeon of a prison.

3. The first man who was called a Hebrew.
4. The name given by Jesus to Simon when presented by Andrew.
5. An encampment of the Israelites where were twelve wells of water, and threescore and ten palm-trees.

The *initials* form the legacy Christ left his disciples.

BIBLE STUDY, NO. 53.

1. The founder of Samaria.
2. A prophet who was imprisoned because his prediction was displeasing to the king.
3. A distinguished soldier, and one in high favor with his king, yet who was afflicted with a horrible disease.
4. A son of Saul who was murdered in his bed.
5. A base time-server, who cursed King David in his adversity, and fawned upon him in prosperity.
6. Naomi's second son.
7. The town to which Paul and Barnabas went when driven from Antioch in Pisidia.
8. A village to which the diciples were going when Jesus joined them after his resurrection.
9. One who, according to the laws of Mosaic economy, separated himself unto the Lord by a vow.
10. The disciple who, not recognizing the risen Saviour, related to him the circumstances of his own death and burial.
11. A prophet whom the Jews expected would reappear upon earth.

The *initials* form one of the incommunicable attributes of the Deity.

BIBLE STUDY, NO. 54.

1. A teacher of the church of Antioch who ministered to the Lord.
2. A man who is mentioned by one of the apostles as being "subject to like passions as we are."
3. A wicked man who tried to prevent Paul from converting a deputy.

4. A man of Benjamin, whose son was a choice young man and goodly.

5. The time when it is good for a man to bear the yoke.

6. One who was said to be the first fruits of Achaia unto Christ.

7. A man who wrote one of Paul's Epistles.

8. A hill where David once hid.

9. One of the boundaries of King Ahasuerus' kingdom.

10. One of three women, who were fairer than any in the land.

11. A son of Amoz, who wrote a book.

12. A woman whose name signified pleasant.

13. A man who received a visit from an angel, while threshing corn.

14. One of the kings of Chaldea of the seed of the Medes.

15. A Moabitess, who married a man of the seed of the Ephrathites.

16. The name of a relation of a leader of the Jews.

17. A prophet to whom the Lord sent a vision concerning Edom.

18. One of the governers of Cæsarea.

19. One of the chief cities of the Philistines.

20. A place where the children of Israel pitched.

21. The wife of Felix.

The *initial* letters of the answers to the above questions give a Scripture exhortation of the highest importance.

BIBLE STUDY, NO. 55.

1. An element sometimes used as a symbol of the Holy Ghost.

2. The place to which he belonged who, together with Nicodemus, buried Christ.

3. A disciple whom Peter raised from the dead.

4. The father of Achan.

5. A river by the banks of which Daniel saw a vision.

6. An inspired herdman.

7. A prophetess who endeavored to intimidate Nehemiah when engaged in rebuilding the well of Jerusalem.

8. One who stirred up a revolt against Paul at Ephesus.

9. One who, for his godly zeal, had conferred upon him and his posterity an everlasting priesthood.

10. A king of Syria who drove the Jews from Elath.

11. A place of which it was proverbially said, in old time, "They shall surely ask counsel, and so end the matter."

12. That which is good for a man to bear in his youth.

The *initials* of the above words form a solemn admonition given by our Saviour.

BIBLE STUDY, NO. 56.

1. One who, when the evil deeds he subsequently committed were foretold by the prophet, was horrified at the recital.

2. One whose covetousness was punished with death.

3. One "who through faith subdued kingdoms."

4. A man who, when a woman threw a stone upon his head, begged his armor-bearer to slay him, that he might escape the reproach of being killed by a woman.

5. The city of waters.

The *initials* of the preceding words form the name of the first person on record to whom an angel appeared.

BIBLE STUDY, NO. 57.

1. To what doth God compare His holy Word?

2. What did a refuge to our race afford?

3. From whence was Paul compelled in haste to fly?

4. A city famed for cloth of choicest dye.

5. The haven where we all desire to go,
Reserved for those who serve their Lord below.

If these *initials* side by side you place,
You find what strengthens every Christian grace;
What doth this world of pomp and sin o'ercome.
And give us power to reach our heavenly home.

BIBLE STUDY, NO. 58.

1. That to which the trial of faith is compared.

2. That by which the Lord confirmed his promise to Abraham.

3. The wages of sin.
4. He who, according to Solomon, "shall suffer hunger."
5. An emblem to which our Saviour likens the righteous.
6. The mystic form in which the Saviour was seen by John in the Apocalyptic vision.
7. An animal with which Israel is unfavorably contrasted, for ever the dumb beast knoweth its owner.
8. That which at the crucifixion was torn asunder, as a sign that the Mosaic economy was superseded.
9. The bird to which David compared Saul and Jonathan in his lamentations for their death.

The *initials* form a statement which fills the heart of him who realizes it with adoration and joy.

BIBLE STUDY, NO. 59.

1. The name of one connected with another—
The eldest born of a great patriarch's brother.

2. In peace and purity her life was past,
Till entered sin, and sorrow came at last.

3. His daughters an inheritance was given,
Because a son had been denied by Heaven.

4. The mother of a minister of truth,
Who knew the sacred Scriptures from his youth.

5. They failed him in the day of his distress,
When sickness came, and none stood by to bless.

6. Faithful and true where'er the king might be,
A stranger in a foreign land was he.

7. The thing his mother valued most he took,
And straightway burnt, by Kidron's peaceful brook.

8. This man is known under two separate names;
He glorified his Maker in the flames.

My *final* letters of a sovereign tell
Who lost his eyesight when Jerusalem fell;
And my *initials* form another name,

To whom, in prayer, a gracious answer came.
Both bent in patience 'neath the chastening rod;
So must our wills before the will of God.

BIBLE STUDY, NO. 60.

1. The physician beloved by St. Paul.
2. The name which signifies "a prince of God."
3. The tree used as a figure of Christ and His people.
4. The place where there were twelve walls and seventy palm-trees.
5. The Church that ministered to St. Paul when he was in Thessalonica.
6. "A ready scribe in the law of Moses."
7. The prophet whose words were quoted by St. James, in his address to the apostles and elders at Jerusalem.
8. The province in which St. Paul was born.
9. The son of Josiah whose name was changed to Jehoiakim.
10. The captain of Saul's host.
11. The mother of Solomon.
12. The tribe that left the kingdom of Israel for that of Judah.
13. That time when it is good for man to bear the yoke.

The *initial* letters of these names compose a precept which, if obeyed, would cause "wars to cease."

BIBLE STUDY, NO. 61.

1. That which Saul called David, when dissuading him from encountering Goliath.
2. The father of Bathsheba.
3. The city to which Demas went when he forsook St. Paul.
4. The place where Zimri "slew his master."
5. The father of Milcah.
6. The native land of Ebedmelech.
7. The woman who was "justified by works."
8. The mother of David's sixth son.
9. The materials of which Jabin's chariots were made.
10. The ruler who was beaten before Gallio's judgment-seat.

11. The father of the man to whom Jehu displayed his zeal.
12. The rival of Tibni.
13. The child whose grandmother was his nurse.
14. The first word written on the wall of Belshazzar's palace.

The *initials* of these words make a sentence in one of the parables which suggests that the day of grace is not yet past.

BIBLE STUDY, NO. 62.

1. The first country visited by St. Paul after his conversion.
2. Saul's eldest daughter.
3. A judge of Israel during eight years.
4. A town of Crete, by which St. Paul passed.
5. The possession of the children of Lot.

The *initials* and the *finals* give the names of two captains unlike in birth and service, alike in their end.

BIBLE STUDY, NO. 63.

1. The city where Amaziah was slain.
2. The country which was a general resort in time of famine.
3. The rival of Omri.
4. The word which signifies "Thou art weighed in the balances and art found wanting."
5. The man who is emphatically called "the Jews' enemy."
6. The prophet who foretold the death of Ahab and Jezebel.
7. The mother whose love for her children, when they were dead, is without earthly parallel.
8. Sennacherib's successor.
9. The man whom God appointed to utter destruction.
10. The king of Moab whom Israel served eighteen years.
11. The tribe which was set apart to bear the ark of the covenant.
12. The prophet who foretold the discomfiture of Sennacherib.
13. The mountain where Saul was slain.
14. The father of the prophet Jehu.
15. The king of Assyria who distressed Ahaz.

The *initial* letters of these names form a command which illustrates in the most sublime manner the power of God.

BIBLE STUDY, NO. 64

1. The man who brought David before Saul with Goliath's head in his hand.
2. The disciple whose surname was Thaddeus.
3. The city where St. Paul was when the inhabitants attempted to worship him.
4. The King of Heshbon.
5. The man who said, "I will not eat till I have told mine errand."
6. The first born son of Seth.
7. The place where the spies were sent.
8. Absalom's daughter.
9. The woman who "lent her child to the Lord."
10. The prophet who was told to anoint Hazael king.
11. The band to which Cornelius belonged.
12. "The city of waters."
13. The country to which Jehoshaphat attempted to send ships for gold.
14. The place where Jonathan found honey.
15. The city where the angel appeared to the Virgin Mary.

The *initial* letters of these words show the universal selfishness of human nature.

BIBLE STUDY, NO. 65.

That which is the Christian's reproach and yet his glory.

That which is a burden to be carried, and yet as wings to bear him along.

That which upon his forehead, is either the badge of Christ's soldier, or the brand of the deserter may be discovered by the last letters of the following words :

1. One who digged again the wells of his father, which the enemy had stopped.
2. The mountain in which Esau dwelt.
3. A king of Egypt whose name consists of two letters.
4. The head of a household baptized by St. Paul.
5. The name of the Apostle who took the place of the traitor Judas.

BIBLE STUDY, NO. 66.

1. First name a woman whose heroic faith
Saved all her kindred from impending death.

2. A proposition next proceed to find,
Two words of gracious invitation joined.

3. Who judged God's people three-and-twenty years?
4. Who Abraham's brother's first born son appears?

The *final* letters form the name of one
Who was that first heroic woman's son.
The *initials* give his name (his willing bride)
Who was to her near kinsman first allied.
Both bride and mother came of heathen race,
Yet both were honored with special grace.

From them not kings alone may trace their birth,
But one far greater than the kings of earth.
When God vouchsafed to take our mortal frame,
Him as their child may both these woman claim

BIBLE STUDY, No. 67.

1. Go to the land of Uz; that tried one see;
Ask for his second daughter—lo! 'tis she.

2. Go to that mighty man, the third of three;
Ask for the Hararite—behold! 'tis he.

3. Go to Shusham, a proud man's sons there be;
Ask for the second, and behold! 'tis he.

4. Go to your tent; the childless patriarch see;
Ask for his steward, and behold! 'tis ne.

5. Go to Jerusalem: David's children see;
Ask for Bathshua's eldest—lo! 'tis he.

6. Go down where Moses and his people be;
Ask for the son of Raguel—lo! 'tis he.

The *initials* down, the *finals* upward trace,
And lo! the scene of Isreal's dire disgrace.

God said, "Go up, possess the land!"
But they drew back from his command.

There they rebelled. Through unbelief they fell.
If we their said example shun, 'tis well.

BIBLE STUDY, NO. 68.

1. The father of Shimei.
2. The man who took Kirjath-Sepher.
3. The wife who delivered her husband into the hands of his enemies.
4. A servent in the house of John surnamed Mark.
5. The only one of our great religious festivals that is mentioned in the Bible.
6. The name of the place of Artaxerxes.
7. The place to which Paul and Barnabas came when they were expelled from Antioch in Pisidia.
8. The wilderness between Elim and Sinai.
9. The birth place of St. Paul.
10. The man who in the most ungodly age of the world prophesied of the coming of the Lord with all his Saints.
11. An imposter who collected 400 followers, but was eventually slain.
12. The place which was built seven years before Zoan.
13. The place "whose merchants" were princes and "whose traffickers" were "the honorable of the earth."
14. The king of Judah who broke the brazen serpent in pieces.
15. The tribe to which Joshua belonged.
16. The man to whom Michal was given when Saul took him from David.
17. A mother who taught her son deceit.
18. The governor of Ahab's house.
19. The king of Judah who was struck with leprosy.
20. A mother in Israel.

The *initials* of these names or words form a statement showing us God's estimation of a sin the world thinks lightly of.

BIBLE STUDY. NO. 69.

1. A people who wept through unbelief in God's power to deliver.
2. A place where came destroying fire.
3. Another name for prophet.
4. The name of one to whom a certain leader said, "Thou mayest be to us instead of eyes."
5. A handsome but rebellious young man.
6. One who heard the gospel by a river-side.
7. An Evangelist who travelled with the Apostle St. Panl.
8. A place where lived one who forgot all care when listening to words of Jesus.
9. A valley around which Saul and his army gathered for battle.
10. What is better than rubies?
11. The name of one who saw wonderful visions by a river-side.
12. A son of Jacob and Leah.
13. The father of Noah.
14. Who journeyed far, carrying gifts to an infant?
15. The youth who nearly perished when cast out into the wilderness.
16. A mountain of Palestine.
17. Another mountain where God gave the Law to Moses.
18. The city of a woman who sold "purple."
19. One of the sons of Eli.
20. An ancient river whose name means "good and abounding."
21. A woman who tended sheep.
22. A patriarch who was deceived by his own son.
23. One afflicted through life for deceit and lying.
24. A king who watched a sun-dial with great anxiety.
25. A city over which Hiram once reigned.
26. A man of Bethlehem, Judah, who went to sojourn in Moab in times of famine.
27. A prophet who proclaimed the doom of Edom.
28. A sacred emblem worn by Aaron.

29. A word of gladness in the song of the redeemed.

The *initials* of these words give a truth known to those who place their trust in Christian righteousness.

BIBLE STUDY, NO. 70.

1. Where first did David seek his promised crown
2. Who won his wife by capturing a town?
3. Where fled a man before his brother's threat?
4. Who in a desert land three monarchs met?
5. Who seeking Canaan died upon the way?
6. Who killed his master that in sickness lay?
7. Name where an exiled king in sorrow trod
8. Whose son in cunning service wrought from God?
9. What prince was slain at noon upon his bed?
10. Say at whose threshing floor a priest fell dead.
11. Where first did Israel eat of Canaan's corn?
12. What son to Boaz was in gladness born?
13. Who sought to turn Paul's teaching into scorn?

Learn with the Psalmist, from whose words we borrow,
To serve the Lord and trust him for the morrow.

BIBLE STUDY, NO. 71.

1. An Edomite who was an adversary to Solomon
2. The birthplace of Apollos.
3. The city which St. Paul said he "must see."
4. The plain where the golden image was set up.
5. The valley where David slew Goliath.
6. Jereboam's successor.
7. The prophet that was honored by being left out of Adonijah's counsels.
8. The prophet who forbade the children of Israel to make slaves of their brethren.
9. St. Paul's secretary when he wrote to the Romans.
10. A word which is typical of dominion.
11. The sixth son of Jesse.
12. The man whom David killed with the sword of the children of Ammon.

13. The place where Amalek first fought with Israel.
14. Manasseh's mother.
15. The word which signifies "be opened."
16. The woman given to Joseph to wife.
17. The woman commended in the New Testament both for faith and works.
18. The Ephesian in whose school St. Paul disputed.
19. The people who carried off Job's oxen and asses.
20. Now take the *initials*, and you have my whole.

BIBLE STUDY, NO. 72.

1. "An eloquent man, and mighty in the Scriptures."
2. A woman of Athens who believed St. Paul's preaching.
3. The god of the Philistines.
4. The governor of the west of the Euphrates.
5. The man whose threshing-floor was the site of the Temple.
6. A manufacture imported by Solomon from Africa.
7. The prophet who foretold the destruction of Edom.
8. Job's native land.
9. One of the wells that Isaac's servants dug in Gerar.
10. The successor of Felix.
11. "A fellow soldier" of St. Paul.
12. A giant slain by Abishai.
13. The name of the tenth month.
14. The mother of Adonijah.
15. A type of the house of Israel.
16. The land that was made desolate as a punishment for rejoicing at the desolation of Israel.
17. The father of Hobab.
18. A king of Hamoth who sent presents to David.
19. A king of Judah in whose reign there was an earthquake.
20. The descendents of Esau.

The *initials* of the above names (or words) form a receipt which shows us that "faith without work is dead."

BIBLE STUDY, NO. 73.

1. Who through faith had sight restored?
2. Who through scorn lost sight deplored?

3. Seek from whence an angel went,
   Warning Israel to repent.
4. Where did sudden waters play?
5. Where did waters heaped, delay?
6. Where was once an image raised,
   Which a mighty nation praised.
7. Who to Gerar went for food?
8. Who a sinning king withstood?
9. Who, when bribed, refused his aid,
10. Who the temple vessels made?
11. What Moabite ruled Israel?
12. Where did Paul a cripple heal?
13. Who in camp received a crown?
14. Name Elkanah's native town.
15. Where did one, a Syrian king,
    Vainly send a seer to bring?

Find the *initials* and they will recall
The lessons of the mercies given to all.

BIBLE STUDY, NO. 74.

1. A holy woman famed for works of love.
2. The saint who was first called to heaven above
3. Who led a king his fearful love to see?
4. Who from his childhood home was forced to flee?
5. From whence with mighty signs was Israel brought?
6. What king was by his mother's wisdom taught?

In the *initials* you may trace,
A noble youth, who, by God's grace,
Was not ashamed his faith to own,
Before a heathen tyrant's throne.

BIBLE STUDY, NO. 75.

1. The most liberal contributor to the treasury of God.
2. Jesse's second son.
3. The place where God appeared to Samuel.
4. Queen Esther's other name.
5. The people who burned Ziklag with fire.
6. The sister of Tubal Cain.

7. The first city in which St. Paul preached Christ.
8 The king of whom Ahab said "he is my brother."
9. The city where Tyrannus lived.
10. The place where Nabal sheared his sheep.
11. St. Paul's hostess at Philippi.
12. Hagar's native land.
13. The prince who raised a monument to his own memory.
14. The idol in whose temple Sennacherib was slain.

The *initial* letters of these words show the remedy prescribed to a great captain who was suffering under a malady that only God could cure.

BIBLE STUDY, NO. 76.

1. The great apostle of the Gentile race?
2. The first man who in heaven found a place?
3. A youthful Christian in God's law well read?
4. The Lord's peculiar people by him led?
5. One who his birthright for a trifle sold?
6. An Israelite, indeed—one of Christ's fold?
7. The promised land with milk and honey blest?
8. A younger son by God beloved best?

The *initial* letters take and you will find,
One virtue of the lowly Christian mind.

BIBLE STUDY, NO, 77.

1. A wanderer guilty of his brother's blood?
2. The father of the seer who saw the flood?
3. 4. Cain's mother next, and then her husband take,
5. Then one who mourned in heart for Zion's sake,
6. A king whose sinning caused his early fall,
7. And one who toiled with the Apostle Paul.
8. Who wrote the long epistle unto Rome?
9. What hill did hunted David make his home?
10. What prophet pleaded for the captive race?
11. What priest made altars for his monarch base?
12. Who vainly sought to know an angel's name?
13. What altar knew no sacrificial flame?

14. Who left a prisoner bound to please the Jews?
15. What king did the council of the wise refuse?
16. What city, famed, to Joseph gave a wife?
17. What king, defeated, took a prince's life?
18. Who smiled contemptuous at an angel's word?
19. Whose bitter rage was calmed with flocks and herds?
20. What pagan prince was God's anointed named?
21. Whose family for temperance was famed?
22. What well did Isaac yield to those who strove?
23. Who would his faith by actual vision prove?
24. From whom did Paul to Cæsar's court appeal?
25. What soldier did the thing accursed steal?
26. Who sinned in fearing lest the ark should fall?
27. What man did Jesus from the grave recall?
28. Who vainly did the Apostle Paul accuse?
29. What seer a king's entreaty did refuse?

Range these *initials* and in all thy need,
Remember still this searching prayer to plead.

BIBLE STUDY, NO. 78.

1. The name of David's second son disclosed,
   A name a prophet afterward did bear.
2. Where was the son of Zedekiah killed?
3. Whose son was in the temple long concealed?
4. Where did a woman once two men bestow?
5. A priestly city Doeg filled with woe?
6. Name from what giant David once was saved.
7. And one whom none but he before had braved.
8. What seer did Asa into prison cast?
   Who told of wars throughout his life to last?
9. Where did a judge's son though conquering meet
   The death that did his shameful life befit?
10. Who grieved, though could not leave her widowed home!
11. Where did the legion-hunted maniac roam?
12. Who to a trembling monarch sold his land,
    While both beheld an angel near them stand?
13. Whence did a prophet lead a blinded band?

Learn the injunction which these *initials* give
And in their strict observance seek to live.

BIBLE STUDY, NO. 79.

1. He, loving rest, a double burden fears.
2. God's chief delight when He creation rears.
3. Him, in his blind old age, his son deceived.
4. They charge of God's most Holy things received.
5. The place where weapon small great carnage makes.
6. He, branded for his sin, God's presence fled.
7. Who hid and fed the prophets in a cave?
8. He who his blessing unto Abraham gave.
9. God's priest, yet his house could not command.
10. Whose counsel did his father's friend withstand?
11. A city overthrown for wicked deeds.
12. Once and again great tidings speeds?
13. The glory gone, the ark the Gentiles prize.
14. Where, Moses sees the goodly land and dies?

The *initials* manifest his promise dear,
Who ever lives our waiting hearts to cheer.

BIBLE STUDY, NO. 80.

1. A town where Peter performed a miracle, and afterwards saw a vision, the object of which was to teach him that he must preach the gospel to the Gentiles as well as to the Jews.
2. Naomi's husband.
3. David's fifth son.
4. A king who served God during the early part of his reign, which was consequently prosperous, but who, becoming self-confident, fell into error and was severely punished.
5. An Amanuensis, to St. Paul, and one whose house was said to have been the first fruits of Achaia.
6. One of the names of Christ.
7. David's eldest brother.
8. The birthplace of Rachel.
9. The father of Abraham.

The *initials* of the above names give an incident in the life of Christ which marks more impressively, perhaps, than any other, his perfect humanity.

BIBLE STUDY, NO. 81.

1. From whence did Israel precious metal bring?
2. Of what sweet tree did ancient prophets sing?
3. A holy seer who wondrous visions saw.
4. Whose children did obey their father's law?
5. What wicked man did take his father's life?
6. Who took a city to obtain a wife?
7. Seven of this name are found in holy writ.
8. The land which Israel once in haste did quit.
9. Who uttered forth a deep and bitter cry?
10. Whose son was sent the promised land to spy?
11. What aged saint with deepest grief opprest,
    Saw not that all was ordered for the best?
12. Who when on earth, his suffering meekly bore,
13. Then, led by angels, up to heaven did soar?
14. Who with a stone did once a conqueror slay?
15. Who sent his daughters from their home away?
16. What merchant city once was rich and great,
    But through it's sins was brought to low estate?
17. The mount from whence the blessing did proceed.
18. Who succored prophets in their greatest need?
19. The bird that sat on Babel's ruined towers.
20. A youth who served his God with all his powers.

In the *initials* of these names combined,
A heavenly receipt you will clearly find;
Which if we humbly from our hearts obey,
Will make us victors in the heavenly way.

BIBLE STUDY, NO. 82.

1. The name which Jacob gave to Luz, in memory of the Lord's appearing to him when he fled from Esau.
2. The wife of Moses.
3. A woman noted for her affection to her mother-in-law.

4. A man remarkable for his swiftness of foot.

The *initials* give the name of a priest and ready scribe.

BIBLE STUDY, NO. 83.

1. Three of the seven churches, deserts now,
   By man forsaken and by God laid low.
2. The ruler whom our Saviour taught by night,
   Because he feared to come when day was bright.
3. The man who ministered to Paul in need.
4. A youth who proved a man of God indeed.
5. Easy to bear if by our Saviour given.
6. The mount whence Christ ascended into heaven.
7. That which in every christian home should reign.
8. The blessed name our Saviour died to gain.
9. The wife whose prayer a child from heaven brought.
10. The Judge who watched her lips with evil thought.
11. A singer of sweet songs in David's time.
12. A place where refuge might be found for crime.
13. A lake enclosed by scenery sublime.
14. A pool where healing gifts were said to dwell.
15. A man who from an upper window fell.
16. An ancient town for commerce greatly famed.
17. The last who king of Syria was named.
18. A man who saved one hundred holy lives.
19. Then he who foremost in the battle strives.
20. Because his wife was deemed divinely fair.
21. The place which sheltered Jonathan's lame heir.
22. A queen who saved her race from death and shame.
23. A King who from our Saviour's parents came.

The *initial* letters of each name will show,
Dear words of comfort breathed by Christ below.

BIBLE STUDY, NO. 84.

1. The man from whose instruction St. Luke wrote.
2. The place where Miriam was smitten with leprosy
3. The word that signifies, "be opened."
4. A mighty nunter before the Lord.

5. The man that went out to meditate at Eventide.
6. Moses' eldest son.
7. The third river of the Garden of Eden.
8. The city where St. Paul left his cloak.
9. The place where Nathanael came.
10. The man who helped Ahab to seek pasture for his cattle.
11. Hezekiah's successor.
12. The place near Salem where John baptized.
13. The fellow-laborer to whom St. Paul said, "Let no man despise thy youth."
14. The father of Lot.

The *initials* suggest a solemn warning.

BIBLE STUDY, NO. 85.

1. The city in the siege of which Uriah the Hittite was killed ?
2. The place where Baal-zebub was worshiped ?
3. The metropolis of Ahab ?
4. The city built by Solomon in the wilderness ?
5. The Father of twelve princes ?
6. The invader from whom Saul delivered Jabesh Gilead ?
7. The place to which Jonah thought to flee ?
8. The re-builder of Jericho ?
9. The man who rescued Jeremiah from the dungeon ?
10. The author of the last chapter of Proverbs ?
11. The mountain ascended by David when he fled from Absalom ?
12. The mother of Armoni and Mephibosheth ?
13. The birth place of Abraham's steward ?

The *initials* will give a receipt of Consolation.

BIBLE STUDY, NO. 86.

1. My name a glowing gem of praise ;
2. A "nothing" graved by man's device !
3. What may not pass a needles eye ;
4. And what we call the showy sky ;
5. What all thing have when gone and past.
6. And a rich odorous ointment last.

The *initial* letters joined will tell.
What men so often love too well,
Yet lead down multitudes to hell.

BIBLE STUDY, NO. 87.

1. A place where the ark of God rested.
2. The Babylonian name of one of the months of the year.
3. A king one of whose governors wished to apprehend Paul, but failed to do so.

The *initials* both in order and *reversed* form the name of one who obeyed God, and caused others to do right. The *third* letters, with orders *reversed*, the name of one who disobeyed God and caused others to do wrong,

BIBLE STUDY, NO. 88.

1. Think of a precious sense in men ?
3. Its duplex organs think of them ?
3. What most befits the weary think ?
4. And into what the wicked sink ?
5. Think what will melt with fervent heat ?
6. What pierced the Saviour's hands and feet ?
7. What were his fellow sufferers tell ?

And mark the initial letters well.
These show who told the earliest lie,
And made our tempted parents die.

BIBLE STUDY, CHRISTMAS, No. 89.

Comes again the festive season ;
  Peals again the gladsome bell ;
Sounds again the wondrous story
  God with us is come to dwell :
Praise to Bethlehem's Babe we bring,
  Child of earth is heaven's King !

Listen to the joyful tidings :
  "Unto us a child is born !"
"Unto us a Son is given :"
Hail this happy Christmas morn !
Prophecy fulfilled we see,
Man enshrines the Deity.

1 Who foretold his humble birth,—
Crowned him "Prince of peace" on earth ?

2. Who supplied his wants—reproved,
Even as she served and loved ?

3. Who sat listening at his feet—
Attitude for woman meet ?

4. Who within the temple knew
Mary's babe as Christ the true ?

5. Who embalmed the Lord when dead,
Ere in Joseph's tomb he laid ?

6. Where dwelt he whose promised son
Typified th' anointed One ?

7. Where were they who mourned their Lord
Gladdened by himself restored ?

8. Who awoke and left his tomb,
Bid by Jesus rise and come ?

The initials of their name will make
His name of whom the prophet spake ;
A name to human hearts how dear,
For lo ! it brings the Godhead near.
Thrice welcome day when Christ was born,
Be God WITH US this sacred morn !

BIBLE STUDY, THE NEW YEAR, No. 90.

1. Who, by preaching of Paul knew the Lord, and with gladness his servants received?
2. Who, taught of Christ, his apostle sought out, and in time of sore trouble relieved?
3. Who, in the service of Master above, learned his duty to master below?
4. Who against God and his high priest rebelled, and met death in confusion and woe?
5. Who in the years yet to come saw his Lord, as the child unto us that is born?
6. Who came in secret to Jesus by night, nor could meet the Jews' hatred and scorn?
7. Who for the truth's sake in Christ was beloved by apostle most dear to the Lord?
8. Who in the pride of his heart forsook God, and was smitten a leper abhorred?
9. Who in his doubt went to Jesus, and found that from Nazareth came Israel's king?
10. Who, as a brother beloved in the Lord, did from Paul news to Ephesus bring?
11. Who in the fear of the Lord hid his saints from the wrath of an impious queen?
12. Who, when the mob to take Jesus drew near, in their front a lost traitor was seen?
13. Who by the aid of his God restored health to a leper reproving his pride?
14. Who bearing witness to Jesus was stoned, and forgiving his enemies died?
15. Whence came the patriarch, faithful when tried, and the pattern of all who believe?
16. Whom did our Saviour forewarn of the sin, over which he should bitterly grieve?

Join the initials of each of these names, and a motto they give for the year:

Heeding the which in our journey through life ever safe is our pathway and clear.

SCRIPTURE ENIGMAS.

(*Key Page* 161.)

SCRIPTURE ENIGMA, NO. 1.

Five hundred begins it; five hundred ends it;
  And five in the middle is seen;
The first of all letters, the first of all numbers,
  Have taken their stations between;
And if you correctly this medley can spell,
The name of an ancient king then it will tell.

SCRIPTURE ENIGMA, NO. 2.

I end as I began,
The weal and woe of man;
Yet do not harshly blame,
I bear my mother's name.

SCRIPTURE ENIGMA, NO. 3.

My centre is nothing;
  My first is my last;
And when the long ages
  Are over and past,
Then vengeance divine
  Shall devour me and mine.

SCRIPTURE ENIGMA, NO. 4.

Four heads have I, but body none,
And without any legs I run.
'Midst bliss supreme my lot was cast,
And joys that could not be surpassed.
Yet these delights did I forsake,
And far away my course I take;
Yet, while I wander far or nigh,
Still ever in my bed I lie.

SCRIPTURE ENIGMA, NO. 5.

In the water, in the air, and in the busy brain,
Busy once, but nevermore to hate or love again;
One of five, all like itself, in deadly deed united,
And yet delivering those in whom the Lord of Hosts delighted

SCRIPTURE ENIGMA, NO. 6.

Take from my whole my first away,
Behold it then our direst day,
Since Time his course began.
Restore again my several parts,
My whole brings peace to careworn hearts,
And rest to weary man.

SCRIPTURE ENIGMA, NO. 7.

Afar they watch my whole arise,
Its summit seems to touch the skies;
"When all is done," the crowds exclaim,
"Then shall we make ourselves a name!"

Remove a letter, and behold!
A shepherd issue from his fold,
With blood devoutly draws he nigh,
Himself, alas! how soon to die.

Remove a letter still, and now
Before an idol-god they bow;

To wood and stone is worship paid,
And men adore what men have made.
Remove a letter yet once more,
We see an altar stained with gore ;
And he who built it named it thus,
To teach a precious truth to us.

SCRIPTURE ENIGMA, NO. 8.

In many a bosom fondly nursed,
A fiery serpent is my *first*
When Jesus came for us to die,
He crushed this deadly enemy.
My *second* is a city's name,
Where Israel's host was put tc shame,
Because my *first* still unrevealed,
Was lurking in their camp concealed.
Upon my *whole*, pronounced by heaven,
The knowledge of my *first* was given.
The chosen people gathered round,
And trembled at the dreadful sound.

SCRIPTURE ENIGMA, NO. 9.

Earth revolves, and lo ! I come,
Out of darkness springing ;
Men and beasts their task resume,
Birds their carols singing ·
Glad my smiling face to see,
Earth wakes up to welcome me,
Earth revolves, and, like again,
Out of darkness beaming,
Shine I in Night's diadem,
On the wavelets gleaming ;
And my radiance dies away,
Only in returning day.

SCRIPTURE ENIGMA, NO. 10.

My *first* enjoins a watchful care,
To see and shun each lurking snare,
With earnest and unceasing prayer.

My *second* speaks a kingdom mine,
Where life and peace and joy divine
In uncorrupted glory shine.

My *third* would contradict my first,
'Tis watchful earnestness reversed,
By careless, prayerless folly nursed.

Faith is my *fourth*, of things not seen
While on the word of truth we lean,
Though clouds and darkness intervene.

These several subjects find in turn,
And as their primal signs you learn,
My *whole* in figure you discern.
This type of Jesus, and His saints
Their living, fruitful union paints,
And patient love that never faints.

SCRIPTURE ENIGMA, NO. 11.

In every clime, through every age,
In history's eventful page.
My *first* will always rise to view,
And wakes our love and hatred too
My *second* and my *third* will each
Express the self-same part of speech,
And, though two interjections brief,
May paint a world of joy or grief.
My *whole* most surely was my *first;*
But far more brave and firm in faith
His wife a mighty patriot nursed.
Who nobly died a hero's death.

SCRIPTURE ENIGMA, NO. 12.

My *first* is oft prefixed to words,
And signifies "beneath,"

My *second's* blessing is the Lord's.
To save from sin and death;
And planted oft on heathen soil,
It well repays the gracious toil.

When patient Job prepared his soul
To bow beneath the rod,
Without reserve he gave my *whole*
To meet the will of God.

SCRIPTURE ENIGMA, NO. 13.

Oh skillful the workers, oh mournful the day,
When within its recesses they hid him away,
So gracious, so noble, the pride of the State,
Their friend and their patron, the good and the great.

Oh wondrous the moment when forth from the land
They bore it, fulfilling the solemn command;
Still truly remembering the vows of the past,
And keeping the long-cherished promise at last.

Oh great the rejoicing when, after long years,
Its treasure unfolded still changeless appears;
Unfolded awhile, then for ever concealed
Till the day when the secrets of all are revealed.

SCRIPTURE ENIGMA, NO. 14.

My first descends
From Heaven, and tends
To make the gems of nature grow;
My second bends
And swiftly sends
Destruction to a distant foe;
My *whole* attends
Where wrath impends
God's covenant of peace to show;
And beauty blends,
And witness lends
Of God's good-will to all below.

SCRIPTURE ENIGMA, NO. 15.

My *first* is luscious, sweet, and round,
And pleasant to the taste is found;
My *second* in the forest grows,
And bears an acorn or a rose:
My *whole* may in a vineyard stand,
And well repay the planter's hand,
Or else seem flourishing and fair,
And yet stand profitless and bare,
And only mock the masters care.
So once when Jesus sought my first,
Sought vainly—he my second cursed;
And so my whole, with swift decay,
Stood withered on that solemn day,
That all might fear that passed that way.

SCRIPTURE ENIGMA, NO. 16.

It is a word I love to hear,
Though not of English birth;
A gentle word that fitly falls
From hapless sons of earth—
From patient souls that seek and love
The help which cometh from above.

No plainer words, no simpler words
To baby lips belong;
For turn this way, or turn it that
You cannot turn it wrong,
And yet the holiest lips were heard
To utter first this simple word.

Two letters make this simple word;
But oh! how much they mean,
They touch on earth, they soar to heaven
They span the gulf between;
And when its mission here is o'er,
This word shall reach the further shore.

BIBLE ACROSTICS.

(*Key Page* 163)

BIBLE ACROSTIC NO. 1.

1. The son of Zuph, an Ephrathite in the fourth generation ;
   The ancestor of one who gave two kings to Israel's nation.

2. The King of Zabath went to war with chariots and with horses ;
   But David smote and spoiled him and scattered all his forces.

3. The aged priest of Israel grieved by his son's backslidings,
   Fell down at last and perished, overwhelmed with evil tidings.

4. There, when God sent his Angels, to tell them of their failing ;
   All Israel wept and called it the place of tears and wailings.

5. The last of five great Princes who in Midian's country reigned,
   Whom Moses smote, and Reuben their fruitful land obtained.

6. The Ezrahite prophetic, who sang Jehovah's mercies,
   To David and his kingdom, in joyful, mournful verses.
7. The father of the officer who David made recorder,
   Then David judged the people to Canaan's farthest border.

8. The Horonite that envied the cities renovation.
   What time King Artaxerxes gave the Jews their restoration.

9. The place where they complained for Egypt's pleasures yearning,
But Israel's God was angry, and punished them with burning.

10. The second son of Jacob's heirs, from his chief place rejected,
Then to his birthright portion a younger was elected.

11. The city that was captured, and for their dwelling claimed it,
Who sprang from Bilhah's elder son, and after him they named it.

12. The lofty place in Canaan where Israel's bounds extended,
From the salt sea and onward its sunny side ascended.

13. The king who heard when David subdued a hostile nation,
And sent his son to bless him, with gifts and salutation.

14. The keeper of the household, beneath his royal master,
Then Judah's land was saved by Assyria's great disaster.

If the *first* and *final* letters from all these names be quoted,
You will find in two acrostics two wondrous things denoted.
The one was worn by Aaron four rows of jewels showing,
The other shone around it, with heavenly lustre glowing,
Oft as the priest was standing in service mediatorial,
The one he wore, the other bore his peoples bright memorial;
This well adorned his person upon his robes of glory,
That told in signs mysterious some glad or gracious story.
Some message from Jehovah, their God and King and Saviour,
To teach them his good precepts, and their behaviour,
And our High Priest in heaven, his robes of glory wearing
From richer gems reflected, a bright radiance bearing,
Still lives to make memorial of all for whom he suffered,

And bears their names upon him for whom his blood was
offered,
And those that trust his mercy nought from his love shall
sever,
He will guide them with his counsel, and lift them up forever.

AN EASTER ACROSTIC NO. 2.

1. The first of men who made and tasted wine,
2. He foretold the fall of Edom's line.
3. That which is due to none but God alone.
4. A judge, of whom but little now is known.

5. The place o'er which an ancient priest was king.
6. A town that oft Jesus' words did ring.
7. A prophet at the time of the return.
8. People from whom God told the Jews to learn.

9. A Gittite chieftain of King David's host.
10. Assyria's king, so fond of foolish boast.
11. An Ammonite who greatly vexed the Jews.
12. The place where Joshua Amalek subdues.

13. A son of Saul most treacherously slain.
14. A Seer who prayed for thunderings and rain.
15. The "stone of help" that Samuel once set up.
16. The man who handed Artaxerxes' cup.

17. A man who trembled at the words he heard.
18. The place where Samuel dwelt and was interred.
19. King Elah's chief who reigned a wicked reign.
20. A priest of Baal in his temple slain.

21. An orator who once accused Paul.
22. An envious man who compassed his own fall.
23. A man who rescue from a prophet sought.
24. A place from which the prophet he was brought.
25. An altar which at Shalem Jacob made.
26. A man who stole and dearly for it paid.
27. He who tries hard in sin to snare the soul.

Alphabet of Bible Proverbs.

A soft answer turneth away wrath. Proverbs. xv. 1.

Better is a little with righteousness than great revenues without right. Proverbs xvi. 8.

Commit thy words unto the Lord, and thy thoughts shall be established. Proverbs. xvi. 3.

Death and life are in the power of the tongue. Proverbs xviii. 21.

Even a child is known by his doings whether his work be pure or whether it be right. Proverbs xx. 2.

Fools make a mock of sin. Proverbs xiv. 9.

Go to the ant, thou sluggard ; consider her and be wise. Proverbs. vi. 6.

He that is soon angry dealeth foolishly. Proverbs xiv. 17.

If thine enemy be hungry, give him bread. Proverbs xxv. 21.

Judgments are prepared for scorners. Proverbs xix. 29.

Keep thy heart with all diligence, for out of it are the issues of life. Proverbs iv. 23.

Lying lips are an abomination to the Lord. Proverbs xii. 22.

My son, if sinners entice thee, consentthou not. Prov. i. 10.

A naughty person, a wicked man, walketh with a froward mouth. Proverbs vi. 12.

Only by pride cometh contention. Proverbs xiii. 10.

Poverty and shame shall be to him that refuseth instruction. Proverbs xiii. 18.

Remove far from me vanity and lies. Proverbs xxx. 8.

Say not I will do so to him as he hath done to me. Prov. 24 29.

The eyes of the Lord are in every place, beholding the evil and the good. Proverbs xv. 3.

Understanding is a well-spring of life unto him that hath it. Proverbs .xvi. 22.

Evil pursueth sinners, but to the righteous good shall be repaid. Proverbs. xiii. 21.

Whoso mocketh the poor reproacheth the Maker. Prov.xvii.5.

'Xalt her and she shall promote thee. Proverbs iv. 8.

Yet a little slumber, a little sleep, so shall thy poverty come as one that traveleth and thy want as an armed man. 24 34.

BIBLE ANAGRAMS.

(*Key Page* 165.)

BIBLE ANAGRAM, NO. 1

Six letters in one name appear,
As in the sequel will be clear !

And numbered thus in order due,
May be discovered by this clue :—
You find in six, five, one, two, three,
One hung on his own gallows-tree.

Three, four, five, six, his name compose,
From whom man's second lineage flows.

In six, two, one, his son you find,
The least beloved of all his kind.
In one, two, three, you clearly trace,
The name of our degenerate race.

From one, two, four, and three, you ken,
Of Judah's twos the first of ten.
Three, two, five, one, of Judah's tribes
The least of Caleb's sons describe.

Two old Egyptian cities see,—
This in three, four, and that four, three.
With all the six, describe at length,
The Father of the man of strength.

BIBLE ANAGRAM, NO. 2.

I am a word of fourteen letters.

My 9, 10, 14, will give the name of Saul's uncle.
10, 11, 14, 13, A godly scribe.
3, 2, 11, 10, 14, A city of refuge.
4, 11, The dwelling-place of a patriarch.
5, 7, 9, 13, A town of Galilee.
6, 4, 14, A friend of Moses.
7, 3, 13, 9, 7, A river of Damascus.
8, 7, 9, A tribe of Israel.
1, 4, 9, A father of a general.
2, 6, 4, 8, A judge of Israel.
11, 10, 2, 3, A prince slain at a wine press.
11 10, 3, 7, 6, A king of Midian.
13, 3, 1, 2, 14, A warrior.
14, 10, 4, 3, 2, 1, A son of Jacob.

The first letters of each of these names united will give the name of a proud imperious king.

BIBLE ANAGRAM, NO, 3.

I am a word of nine letters.

My 1, 6, 2, 7, will give the name of one mentioned in the Bible as "Blessed above women."
My 2, 7, 6, 9, The eldest son of Shem.
My 3, 6, 9, One of the sons of Hezron.
My 4, 3, The birthplace of Abraham.
My 5, 6, 9, 4, 8, 7, The last judge of Israel.
My 6, 3, The chief town of Moab.
My 7, 2, 9, 4, 8, 7, A king whose instructions are in the last chapter of the book of Proverbs.
My 8, 5, 6, 4, The father of the Edomites.
My 9, 6, 3, 5, A hill on which St. Paul preached to the people of Athens.
My whole is a city of ancient fame.

SCRIPTURE ALPHABETS.

(*Key Page* 166)

SCRIPTURE ALPHABET, NO. 1.

A was an emperor who gave a decree.
B was a blind man, anxious to see.
C was a brother who did a great wrong.
D was a teaser who weakened the strong.
E was a twin son, less loved by his mother.
F was a ruler, in place of another.
G was a province, quite frequently named.
H was a tyrant for cruelty famed.
I was a country of mountains and rocks.
J was a shepherd, possessor of flocks.
K was a place where the Ark did repose.
L was a mountain with turban of snows.
M was a priest, as a king also known.
N was a man, whose heart turned as stone.
O was a helper, whose service was kind.
P was a despot of changeable mind.
Q was a queen, as fair as you'll find.
R was a speaker, provokingly rough.
S was a wretch who was punished enough.
T was a disciple, raised from the dead.
U was a land whence came Israel's head.
V was a wife who refused one to be.
W was an animal, found in the sea.
Y was for youthful, and so let it be.
Z was for Zaccheus, who climbed a tree.

THE CHRISTIAN'S LEGACY.

Patrick Henry, a great statesman of Virginia, before he died made a *will* bequeathing all his property to his relatives; and at the close he wrote this true sentiment. "There is one thing more I wish I could leave you all, *the religion of Jesus Christ*—with this, though you had nothing else, you *could be* happy; without this, though you had all things else, you *could not* be happy."

SCRIPTURE ALPHABET, NO. 2.

A was a traitor found hung by his hair.
B was a folly built high in the air.
C was a mountain o'erlooking the sea.
D was a nurse buried under a tree.
E was a first-born, bad from his youth.
F was a ruler, who trembled at truth.
G was a messenger, sent with good word.
H was a mother, who loaned to the Lord.
I was a name received at the ford.
J was a shepherd in Arabian land.
K was a place near the desert of sand.
L was a pauper begging his bread.
M was an idol, an object of dread.
N was an architect, ages ago.
O was a rampart to keep out the foe.
P was an isle, whence a saint looked above.
Q was a Christian, saluted in love.
R was obscure, yet a mother of kings.
S was a Danite, who did wondrous things.
T was a city that had a strong hold.
U was a country productive of gold.
V was a Queen whom a king set aside.
Z was a place where a man wished to hide.

THE PRODIGAL'S RETURN.

FOUR STEPS REQUISITE TO SALVATION.

I. Conviction. "Came to himself," Luke xv. 17.
II. Contrition. "No more worthy," Luke xv. 19.
III. Confession. "I have sinned," Luke xv. 18.
IV. Conversion. "He arose and came," Luke xv. 20.

SCRIPTURE ALPHABET, NO. 3.

When you have found them, read and remember:
A was a monarch who reigned in the East.
B was a Chaldee who made a great feast.
C was veracious when others told lies.
D was a woman, heroic and wise.
E was a refuge where David spared Saul.
F was a Roman accuser of Paul.
G was a garden, a frequent resort.
H was a garden where David held court.
I was a mocker, a very bad boy,
J was a city preferred as a joy.
K was a father whose son was quite tall.
L was a proud one who had a great fall.
M was a nephew whose uncle was good.
N was a city long hid where it stood,
O was a servant, acknowledged a brother.
P was a Christian greeting another.
R was a damsel who knew a man's voice.
T was a seaport where preaching was long.
U was a teamster struck dead for his wrong.
V was a cast-off, and never restored.
Z was a ruin with sorrow deplored.

A CONCERT EXERCISE.

What Children should learn.

They should learn.

I. THE FIRST CHAPTER OF GENESIS. Why?
That they may know how the world was made.

II. THE THIRD CHAPTER OF GENESIS. Why?
That they may know how it fell.

III. THE FIRST CHAPTER OF JOHN. Why?
That they may know how it is to be redeemed.

IV. THE TWENTY-FIRST CHAPTER OF REVELATIONS. Why?
That they may know how it is to be reconstructed.

T. DEWITT TALMAGE.

Alphabet of Scripture Geography, No. 4.

A.-A river near which a heathen king met a prophet, whom he had sent to curse a nation.

B.-A town whose inhabitants received the word of God with gladness.

C.-A mountain where God asserted his own majesty by sending fire from heaven to consume the sacrifice.

D.-A place to which a youth followed his brothers, and met with evil treatment at their hands.

E.-A country famous for its horses.

F.-A stopping place on one of Paul's journeys.

G.-A city which Pharaoh gave as a present to his daughter Solomon's wife.

H.-A hill to which Saul went in pursuit of David.

I.-A town where St. Paul preached in its synagogue.

J.-A ford near which God wrestled with man and man prevailed and obtained what he sought.

K.-The place where Sarah, Abraham's wife, died.

L.-A forest whence wood was brought for the building of the temple.

M.-A place in the wilderness where the bitter water was made sweet by a miracle.

N.-A town where Jesus raised a dead man to life.

O.-A place where the Nethinims dwelt.

P.-The place where St. Paul sailed to Phœnicia.

R.-The place where Israel fought with Amalek and Israel prevailed Moses there built an altar to the Lord.

S.-A pool in which a blind man at our Lord's bidding washed and recovered his sight.

T.-A town built in the Wilderness by Solomon.

U.-The country whence God called Abraham.

V.-Where Jepthah slaughtered the children of Ammon.

W.-The abode of the children of Israel for forty years.

Z.-The coast to which the borders of Zebulun reached.

BLACKBOARD

OR

SLATE ILLUSTRATIONS.

CHALK TALKS

AND

OBJECT LESSONS.

A WORD TO THOSE HAVING THE CARE OF CHILDREN.

IF YOU CANNOT GET TO CHURCH,

If you cannot attend the

SABBATH SCHOOL,

Take this Book in hand, gather the CHILDREN about you

With SLATE, Or PAPER, And PENCIL;

Combine Bible object-teaching with the rudiments of ART in designing and sketching Scripture scenes,

SELECT ONE OR MORE OF THE FOLLOWING

PICTURE LESSONS.

Explain the Story thus Illustrated.

[With older children prove your statements by Scripture reference.]

Take pains in fixing the points to be learned, and so interest them that when you again call their attention to it, they may tell you something about it.

THE TWO EXTREMES IN THE LIFE OF CHRIST.

A Saviour Given.—LUKE ii., 11. A Saviour Risen.—MATT. xxviii., 6.

God forbid that I should glory save in the Cross of Christ.—ST. PAUL, GAL. vi., 14.

THE YOUNG BIBLE READER.

As you look upon the board, you see a very important *charge*, that was given by an *aged* servant of God, to a *youthful* disciple: "Give attendance to reading." Paul gave the charge, and Timothy received it. He wished Timothy to take his copy of the Old Testament Scriptures, and read *very* carefully and constantly. He urged him to *attend* to it. Mark the fact that this was not a *new* book to Timothy. He had *often* read it before, and understood it very well. Turn to 2 Tim. iii. 15, and you will see the proof: "*From a child* thou hast *known* the holy scriptures." But though he had *known* the book so well, and for so long a time, Paul did not excuse him from reading it. Many now excuse themselves from this duty, because the Bible is an old familiar book. They throw it aside for something *new*. What a mistake! Remember the *charge* to this young Bible reader. You may read papers, periodicals, and books on art, science, and literature, but do not neglect *the* book. "Give *attendance* to reading."

You also see the figure of a hand, having several words written upon it. On the palm is the word "Read," and on the fingers and thumb you see other words in the form of questions. Let us take these questions in their order, and see what answers can be obtained. The first is, "*Why*" should we read? *When? What? Where? How?* (Give answers, with Bible proof of each.) William King, the poet, was a great reader. It is said that when he was yet quite young "he had read over and made remarks upon considerably more than twenty thousand books and manuscripts."—*Buck.* He gave *attendance* to reading.

The Marquis of Lorne, now Governor-General of Canada, is a Bible reader, and recently published a metrical version of the Psalms of David.

You also see a book in the picture, and a statement written upon its pages. It is very positive and emphatic. "The Bible is the Book of Books." That is *true.* Think of its *Author.* "All scripture is given *by inspiration of God.*" 2 Tim. iii. 16. Think of its *teachings.* They make men "wise unto salvation." 2 Tim. iii. 15. Think of its *duration.* Not "one jot or tittle shall pass till all be fulfilled." Matt. v. 18. What book can compare with it? "When John Jay, at the age of eighty-two years, was urged to tell his children on what foundation he rested his hopes, and from what source he drew his consolation, his brief reply was, 'They have the book.'"—*Foster.*

Children, *you* also have the book. *Read it.*

If we do not see the golden thread through all the Bible marking out Christ, we read the Scripture without the key.—*Cecil.*

HOW TO SEARCH THE SCRIPTURES.

S-eriously........................Acts xvii. 11; 2 Tim. ii. 15.
E-arnestly ....Josh. i. 8; Ps. cxix. 12.
A-nxiously........................John xx. 31; Ps. cxix. 9.
R-egularly...........................Acts xvii. 11; Ps. i. 2.
C-arefully...................Luke xxiv. 27; 2 Tim. iii. 16, 17.
H-umbly.........................Luke xxiv. 45; Jas. i. 22.

LIGHT ON OUR PATHWAY. Ps. cxix. 105.

Here we have a picture which, at first sight, may not seem to be very interesting, and yet it is one of the most instructive that can be produced. Look at it for a moment, and see what it represents. You see, in part at least, the figure of a man, and he seems to be walking. You also see the outlines of a street, and at the corner you observe a lamp-post. In the man's hand you see a burning lamp, while the street-lamp also sends out its rays of light upon the darkness, thus enabling the man to see his way. Near the top of the picture you also see a book, which represents the Bible, the word of God. How beautifully the picture illustrates the Psalmist's declaration, "Thy word is a lamp unto my feet, and a light unto my path."

This man is carrying the light because he *needs it.* If the sun were shining, or the moon or stars, he might not need it. But it is *night*, and *so dark* that he must have the light. So we *need* the light of God's word. "It is not in man that walketh to direct his steps." Jer. x. 23. The way is dark, and he cannot tell where to go. He *wanders*, *stumbles*, and *falls.* But when he turns to God's word he finds "a lamp unto his feet, and a light unto his path." I have read of a traveller on the mountains who was for a time enveloped in a heavy mist, and could scarcely see his way from one rocky spur to another. Suddenly the mist rolled away, and to his surprise he found himself standing on the verge of a fearful precipice. The misty cloud was swept away just in time to show him his danger. So, when God's word becomes a "lamp to our feet," it shows us the perils of the way, and we walk in safety. "The entrance of thy words giveth light. Ps. cxix. 130. Let us remember that we are to *keep* this light with us wherever we go. A lamp will do us no good on a dark night if we leave it at home. What is this man, in the picture, doing with his light? You say, "Carrying it with him." Yes. And you are to take the word of God with you. Do you ask how? Carry it on the tablet of your *memory.* Keep it there. Do as the little boy did, who had to give up his Bible to the priest. The priest burned up the book, but the little boy said, "Thank God, you cannot burn up the twenty-eight chapters of Matthew that I have got in my head." He carried the light with him. We are *pilgrims.* Our *way* is *dark.* Let us take the light with us, and we shall walk in comfort, confidence, and safety.

WHY WE SHOULD TAKE GOD FOR OUR GUIDE.

1. Because as travellers we need a guide............Jer. iii. 4.
2. Because He knows the road....................Heb. iv. 15.
3. Because He has Himself encountered its dangers..Heb. ii. 10.
4. Because He goes with the traveller all the way. .Ps. xxiii. 4.
5. Because He cheers and supports when weary..Ps. xxxvii. 23.
6. Because as travellers we must follow our guide..1 Peter ii. 21.

WHAT IS HEAVEN ACCORDING TO THE BIBLE.

1. Our Father's house......John xiv. 2; Isa. lxiii. 15; 1 Kings viii. 30; Matt. xxiii. 9, Matt. vi. 9; Matt. vii. 11.
2. The home of Jesus......John iii. 13; John vi. 38; John xx. 17; Acts iii. 21; Heb. ix. 24; 1 Thess. i 10.
3. The future abode of believers....John xiv. 2, 3; 2 Cor. v. 1; Heb. xi. 10.

THE SPIDER'S WEB.

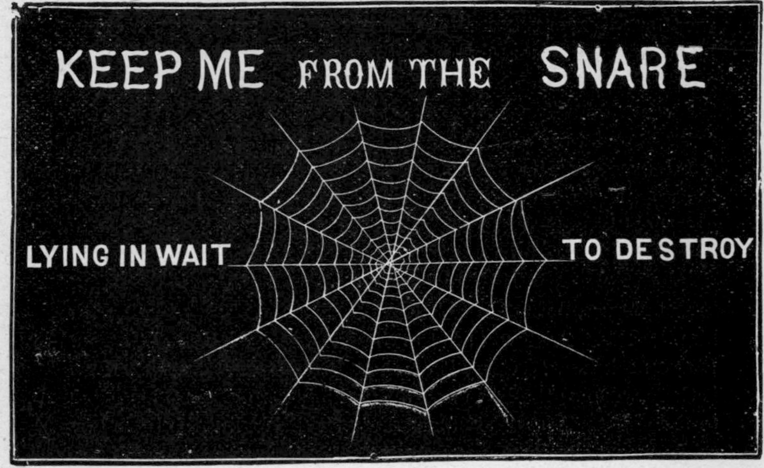

We have here the picture of a spider's web. The spider is a repulsive insect, and few, indeed, admire him. I have read of a man who had a "pet spider," and, when a tune was whistled, the little creature would instantly come out of its hole to listen. Few, however, would like such a "pet." We may dislike the spider, but we cannot fail to admire his work. See the delicate fibres, and the perfect form of this web. What ingenuity and skill it shows! But let us look a little more closely at the spider's work, and see if it has a lesson for us. See, first of all, how *orderly* and *systematic* it is. The lines running from the centre to the outer edge seem to be of equal length, and the distance between them seems to be equal also. Then, there are cords that cross the long threads, and these, too, are arranged with perfect order and system. Here is a lesson for us. We are not to work in a *hap-hazard* way. We are to have *order* in our plans and pursuits. We are to have "a place for everything, and everything in its place." "To everything there is a season." Eccl. iii. 1. The time to serve God is now. "Seek ye *first* the kingdom of God." That is the *order* we are to ob-observe.

See, again, how this work of the spider becomes an agency of *torture* and *destruction.* The chief mission of the spider seems to be to *ensnare* and *capture* other insects. Many a thoughtless fly comes buzzing along, and is hopelessly entangled in the web. It tries in *vain* to escape. It dies a slow, lingering death. How full of meaning are the words you see on the board: "Lying in wait to *destroy.*" Many things in this life become a *snare* to us; they *deceive* us and lead to *ruin.* The wineglass may seem tempting, but it carries *death* in its sparkling contents. "He that is deceived thereby is not wise." Prov. xx. 1. The saloon may be gilded, and the hall of revelry may be attractive; but beware of them, for, like the spider's web, they may become agencies of *destruction.* The prophet tells us that the "wicked may weave the spider's web." Isa. lix. 6.

What do you see written above the web? "Keep me from the snare." That is a prayer. Let us adopt it. This is a prayer for those who want to *keep out* of the snare. "Keep me *from* the snare." Some people run right into snares, and then wonder *why* they are caught. It is good to *get out* of the snare, but a thousand times better to *keep out.* "Watch and pray that ye *enter not* into temptation." Matt. xxvi. 41.

WHAT WE ARE BY NATURE.

1. Evil in our thoughts continually.............. Gen. vi. 5.
2. Unclean.................................... Job xiv. 4.
3. Shapen in iniquity.......................... Ps. li. 5.
4. Unclean and as filthy rags.................. Isa. lxiv. 6.
5. Deceitful and desperately wicked.... .... Jere. xii. 9.
6. All under sin............................ Rom. iii. 9–23.
7. The children of wrath........................ Eph. ii. 3.
8. Aliens from the commonwealth of Israel....... Eph. ii. 12.
9. Alienated from the life of God.............. Eph. iv. 18.
10. Dead in trespasses and sin................... Col. ii. 13.

THE DOOR OPEN OR SHUT.

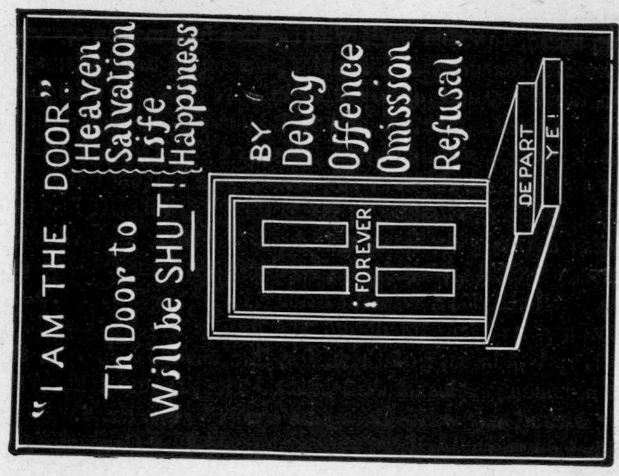

THE CLOSED DOOR.

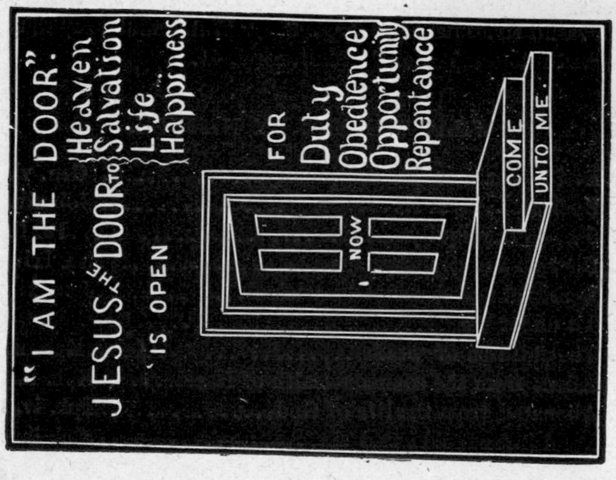

THE OPEN DOOR.

The term door literally means *entrance*, and denotes the way into a building. Jesus uses the term in a metaphorical sense, and applies it to Himself. "I am the door." John x. 9. He is the only way of entrance into spiritual life, into the church, and into heaven. Hence, his language is, "I am the way." John xiv. 6. How clearly did the ancient Fathers teach this truth, when they said, "Christ, from the foundation of the world, has been the Father's *way* to earth and the sinner's way to God."

That open door has a very *gracious* meaning. It means that Jesus is *now* ready to receive us. He is saying to us all, "*Come unto me.*" Matt. xi. 28. An open door invites us to enter, and so Jesus *waits* to receive us as we come to Him. Listen to His cheering words: "Him that cometh to me, I will in no wise cast out." John vi. 37. Enter the door *now*, while you are young. Many as young as you have done so. Polycarp entered when he was only *four years old.* At the age of ninety he said, "Eighty and six years have I served Him." Lady Huntington entered it when she was only *nine years old.* Bishop Hedding sought Christ at the age of *four* years. Alfred Cookman entered the door when he was *ten years old.* How true the promise: "Those that seek me early shall find me." Prov. viii. 17. Remember the door is open *now.* But the door that is shut has a very *sad and solemn meaning.* It means that Jesus, at the last, refuses to receive those who have refused Him. Can you pass through a doorway when it is *closed against* you? No. You turn away, and say the "door is shut." The foolish virgins found the "door was shut." Matt. xxv. 10. How terrible it will be for the soul to be *homeless* forever, and *unsheltered* amid the storms of eternity. If *this* door is shut against us, *no other* will open to receive us. *Wait*, and the door may be shut. Then you will *vainly* cry, "Lord, Lord, open unto us." Luke xiii. 25. "Too late, too late, ye cannot enter now."—*Tennyson.* A blacksmith, when he pulled his iron out of the fire, used to call out to his son, "Quick! quick! Now or never."—*Foster.* "Remember *now* thy Creator in the days of thy youth." Eccl. xii. 1. It may be now or never with us.

THE VINE AND ITS BRANCHES.

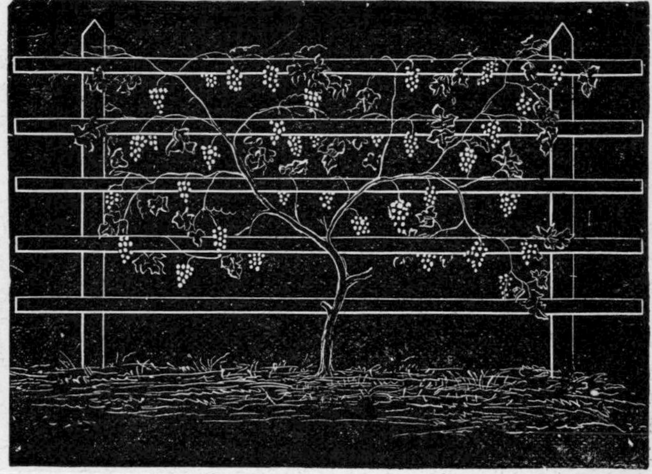

We have here a picture of a well-known vine. Let us see if we can learn a few lessons from it.

And, first of all, it does not claim to be anything but a *vine*—a grape-vine.

Look at it, and it *appears like one;* touch or test it in any form you please, and it always shows itself in its true character. It never tries to put on the appearance of some beautiful plant, nor look like some tall, stately oak. We, too, should always show ourselves to be *as* and *what* we are. *Bad* men often try to make others believe that they are *good.* They are ashamed to be known to others just as they are known to themselves. They claim to be what they are not. The vine, in this respect, *rebukes* them, for it *is* always just what it *seems* to be. Let all our boys and girls be *true,* and avoid deception of every kind. Henry Clay once said, "I would rather be *right* than to be President."

The vine also shows us the necessity of having some *suitable support.* Does this vine stand *alone*, or seem to hold itself in an upright position by its own strength? There is a trellis or frame to which it clings, and this frame gives it *support.*

Children, can we stand *alone* in life? Certainly not. We need each other's help. "Bear ye one another's burdens." Gal. vi. 2. We need Christ's help still more. He has said, "Without me, ye can do nothing." John xv. 5. Take away the trellis, and what would happen to the vine? Fall? Yes, it would fall to the ground. Many are in the dust to-day, because they have forsaken God, their only strength and support. "God is our refuge and *strength*, a very present *help* in trouble."

The vine also teaches us a lesson on *fruitfulness.* Some vines have perfect branches, heavy foliage, and pretty blossoms, but *no* fruit. The vine here represented is full of rich clusters. How fruitful it appears! Shall our lives be *barren?* If *vines* bear fruits, shall *souls* be unfruitful? Jesus once found a tree bearing upon its branches "*nothing but leaves.*" Mark xi. 13. What a disappointment? Nothing but leaves. Trees and vines all covered with rustling leaves and fragrant blossoms, may be very beautiful indeed, but to be *useful* they must bear *fruit.*

"In Eastern poetry they tell of a wondrous tree on which grew golden apples and silver bells, and every time the breeze went by and shook the fragrant branches, a shower of these golden apples fell, and the living bells chimed and tinkled forth their airy ravishment."—*Biblical Museum.*

Children, so live that the fruit of your lives may be more sweet, wholesome, and valuable than all the "golden apples and silver bells" that fancy ever painted.

GOD'S BEST GIFTS.

1. Joy in beileving.............................Ps. xxv. 9.
2. Rest..............................Matt. xi. 28; Jer. vi. 16.
3. Peace..........John xiv. 27; Isa. xxvi. 3, 4; Job xxii. 21.
4. Eternal life.........................John x. 28; John iii. 36.
5. The Holy Spirit.....John xiv. 16; Ps. li. 12; Titus iii. 5; 2 Cor. iii. 17; 1 Thess. i. 6.

SIN AND SALVATION.

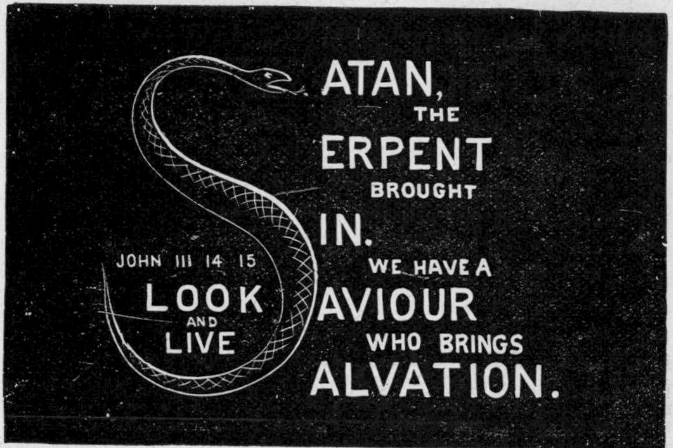

We have here the figure of a serpent. In Gen. iii. 1, we have the first scriptural mention of the serpent. The serpent represents Satan, and led Eve to disobey God in paradise. Said she, "The serpent beguiled me, and I did eat." Gen. iii. 13. How true, then, the words written upon the board: "Satan the Serpent brought Sin."

We are to remember that *sin* is a great *evil.* It is *here*—all around us and *within* us. What is the Bible definition of sin? "Sin is the *transgression* of the law." 1 John iii. 4.

If we break the law *voluntarily* and *knowingly*, then we are guilty of sinning. Have we not done *this* in some way and at some time? Yes. "For *all* have sinned." Rom. iii. 23. True, we may not have broken the *whole* law, but we are *no less sinners*, even though we have transgressed only a *small* portion of it.

"Whosoever shall keep the *whole law*, and yet offend in *one point*, he is *guilty of all.*" Jas. ii. 10.

Where is the person who has not transgressed "one point," at least, of God's law?

"We sprang from the men whose guilty fall,
Corrupts his race and taints us *all*."

This picture presents another great fact, and that is *salvation*. Salvation denotes *deliverance* from dangers or from enemies.

Turn now to the picture and read, "We have a *Saviour* who brings *salvation*." Satan brings sin, but the Saviour brings salvation. We have the *one;* shall we not have the *other?*

We brought with us into this world a *sinful nature*, *without our consent*, but we can have salvation only by choice. "*Choose* you this day whom you will serve." Josh. xxiv. 15.

Salvation never will be *thrust* upon us. Jesus is the "Saviour of all men, *specially of those that believe*." 1 Tim. iv. 10. Remember, then, though we have a Saviour, He will not save us, unless we "*believe* on Him."

We have Sunday schools, churches, Bibles, and Christian example, yet, if we do not love the Saviour, we shall be lost. "The saddest road to hell is that which runs under the pulpit, past the Bible, and through the midst of warnings and invitations."—*Ryle*.

Rev. John Newton, in his last moments, said that he remembered two things:

1st. That he was a great sinner.

2d. That Jesus Christ was a great Saviour.

"How shall *we* escape, if we neglect *so great* salvation." Heb. ii. 3.

WHAT THE BIBLE SAYS OF THE FOOL.

1. His belief....................Ps. xiv. 1. There is no God.
2. His walk......................Eccl. ii. 14—is in darkness.
3. His standing before God....Eccl. v. 4. No pleasure in him.
4. His heart.............Eccl. vii. 4—is in the house of mirth.
5. His food.....Eccl. x. 12. His life will swallow up himself.
6. His house..............Matt. vii. 26—is built on the sand.
7. His end..........................Luke xii. 20. Death.

THE BOW IN THE CLOUD.

(Draw the rainbow with pieces of colored crayons, held sidewise, and write the words heavily with white crayon. A beautiful effect may be produced if skilfully drawn.)

"And the bow shall be in the cloud; and I will look upon it, that I may remember the everlasting covenant between God and every living creature of all flesh that is upon the face of the earth." Gen. ix. 16.

State the facts of the flood, and so onward, until this covenant of God. Dwell on the shape and colors of the bow. These may be remembered by the initial word, "*Vib-gg or-y*," and these letters placed in the several spaces.

The bow is the *token* of God's promise. Explain the word "token" by instancing gifts of parents, teachers, etc. Explain covenant or *agreement*. The first covenant made by God with man. *God's* covenant, wherein the Lord agrees never again to destroy the world with a flood. Man is asked for no agreement in return. The Lord says, v. 13, "*My* bow." Token of God's *forbearance*. God *forbears* what He might justly do: drown the world again and again. His *condescension* is brought visibly to our minds when we see His bow in the clouds. He *condescends* to bind Himself by covenant promise, and to give us a token of it.

Thus He displays His grace, that source of all His blessings. 1 Cor. xv. 10.

These lessons are taught by His bow over *the world* (which write, as in diagram, under the bow). And the rainbow, this token of God's forbearance, condescension, and grace, surrounds *His throne* forever in heaven. Read Rev. iv. 3, and have the children repeat it in concert, as also the text which is the theme of the lesson.—From *Teacher and Class.*

WHAT CHRISTIANS HAVE.

Faith in God.................................Mark xi. 22.
Everlasting life..............................John iii. 36.
Light of life.................................John viii. 12.
My joy fulfilled in themselves...................John xvii. 13.
Hope toward God...............................Acts xxiv. 15.
A conscience void of offence......................Acts xxiv. 16.
Peace with God.................................Rom. v. 1.
Access by faith.................................Rom. v. 2.
Fruit unto holiness..............................Rom. vi. 22.
First fruits of the Spirit.........................Rom. viii. 23.
A building of God not made with hands...........2 Cor. v. 1.
These promises.................................2 Cor. vii. 1.
All sufficiency in all things.......................2 Cor. ix. 8.

COME TO JESUS FOR WHAT?

Pardon...........Eph. i. 5–7.	Peace...........John xiv. 27.
Comfort..........Isa. lxi. 2–3.	Joy..........John xv. 10, 11.
Health......Matt. viii. 16, 17.	Rest.............Matt. xi. 28.
Strength..........Phil. iv. 13.	Happiness...Prov. xiii. 17, 18.
Holiness ....John xv. 4, 5.	Eternal life......John vi. 47.

LIGHT FROM THE BIBLE.

In this picture you see a lamp, a torch, a rock, a ship, and a book. All these objects are *suggestive.* Lamps and torches are used to light up *dark places.* If we go down into deep mines, or caves, or into some dens of the city, what do we find? Darkness. Yes. The sunlight never enters these places, and so we must take the lamp or torch along to light up the way. Go down into the Mammoth Cave of Kentucky, and you must flash your torch upon the darkness if you would see.

There is darkness in the *spiritual* as well as in the natural world. Hence, Paul said of wicked men, "Their foolish heart was *darkened.*" Rom. i. 21. He also affirms that the Gentiles had "the understanding *darkened.*" Eph. iv. 18. Now, what do we need in this *darkness* of the soul? Light. Yes. Where shall we find it? In the Bible. Men who *follow* the Bible never go *astray.* It *banishes* their darkness. Hear what Peter says about it: "We have also a more sure word of prophecy; whereunto ye do well that ye take heed, *as unto a light* that shineth in a dark place." 2 Pet. i. 19.

This is the book we love to study Sabbath after Sabbath, and no other book can guide us to heaven. What would we do without it? "Rob us of our Bible, and our sky has lost its sun, and in the best of other books we have naught but the glimmer of twinkling stars."—*Guthrie.*

In the picture you also see a vessel and in the distance a rock. The vessel seems to be dashing right on toward the rock. But there is a chart on board, and this gives *timely* warning, and the vessel is saved. There are *rocks* in the current of your lives, children. Name some of them. Pride, Revenge, Falsehood, Disobedience, etc. Take the Bible for your chart. After one of the old Reformers had finished a controversy with an enemy of the truth, a friend begged to see the notes he had used in the discussion, and was surprised to find written there, many times in succession, the words, "More light, Lord—more light, more light!" Make this your prayer. "More light, more light!"

THE BIBLE MIRROR.

1. It is a wonderful mirror....................Ps. cxix. 129.
2. It shows us our own image..................Jas. i. 23–25.
3. It shows us what is wrong.....Luke vii. 40–47; Ps. cxix. 9.
4. It reveals a glorious light........John i. 14; 1 John i. 1, 2.
5. It reflects a light on those who look into it..Ex. xxxiv. 29, 30.
6. It should be used daily..........................Ps. i. 2.

HOW MAY WE GET TO HEAVEN?

1. Through our God, He will save us..........Isa. xxv. 8, 9.
2. By serving the Lord with all our heart..1 Sam. xii. 23, 24.
3. By following after righteousness.............Prov. xv. 9.
4. By doing the will of our Father.............Matt. vii. 21.
5. Through Christ, the door.........................John x. 9.
6. Through Christ, the way, the truth, and the life. John xiv. 4.
7. By access through Christ and the Spirit to the Father. Eph. ii, 18.
8. Through Christ bearing our sins...........Heb. ix. 27, 28.
9. By the blood of Jesus..........................Heb. x. 19.
10. Through the open door.......................Rev. iii. 8.

THE GREAT SHIP AND THE LITTLE HELM.

Turn to James, iii. 4, and you will read as follows: "Behold also the ships, which though they be so great, and are driven of fierce winds, yet are they turned about with a very small helm, withersoever the governor listeth." Now, look at the picture, and you will see the "*helm*" of which St. James speaks. Observe the fact that it is very *small* compared to the great size of the ship. The masts are tall and the body of the vessel seems large, but the "helm" is "*very small.*"

What power it exerts upon that huge ship! Here we learn the importance of *little* things. We read that the "Conies are but a *feeble folk*," Prov. xxx. 26; and we also read of the "*little* foxes that spoil the vines." Song ii. 15. The "tongue is a *little* member and boasteth great things." Jas. iii. 5. These expressions show the importance of *little* things. A clever Dutchman amused himself one day by cutting some letters of the alphabet on the bark of a tree. It was a very small thing, but out of that little thing came the art of printing. Little things often produce great results. "Who hath despised the day of small things?" Zech. iv. 10. But observe that while this helm is so very small, it *controls* the movements of the vessel. To this fact St. James here calls special attention. He reminds us that these "*great*" ships are "*turned about*" by the helm. "Turned about." They are *guided* and *kept* in their *proper* course by the helm. The vessel would *drift* along with the wind and tide if left to itself, but the pilot's hand is on the helm and that guides the ship to its destination. We are all out on the stormy ocean of life. We shall *drift* with the tide of evil influences and drift into ruin, unless we are *guided* in our movements. Let God be our *Guide*, and the promise is, "He shall *direct* thy paths." Prov. iii. 6. Said David, "Thou shalt *guide* me with thy counsel." Ps. lxxiii. 24. The ship never refuses to "*mind*" the helm. So let us *follow* our Divine Guide, and we shall reach the eternal harbor.

Then we will sing:

> "Drop the anchor, furl the sail,
> We are safe within the vale."

SIX COMMANDS OF CHRIST.

1. Turn from death .... Mark i. 14, 15.
2. Look for life .... John i. 29.
3. Come for rest .... Matt. xi. 28.
4. Abide for fruitfulness........................ John xv. 4.
5. Obey for friendship......................... John xv. 14.
6. Watch in readiness for His coming........ Mark xiii. 35-37.

INDISPENSABLE THINGS.

1. Without shedding of blood is no remission...... Heb. ix. 22.
2. Without faith it is impossible to please God...... Heb. xi. 6.
3. Without holiness no man shall see the Lord.. .. Heb. xii. 14.
4. Without works faith is dead.................... Jas. ii. 26.
5. Without love I am nothing................ 1. Cor. xiii. 1, 3.
6. Without chastisement ye are not sons .... Heb. xii. 8.
7. Without me (Jesus) ye can do nothing......... John xv. 5.

FIGS OR THISTLES—WHICH?

You see here a cluster of *grapes* and a branch of the *thorn-bush.* Then, in the words written upon the board, you see a reference to *figs* and *thistles.* The question relates to these *four* objects. We find it in Matt. vii. 16. Two of these objects, grapes and figs, are *useful;* the other two, thorns and thistles, are *worthless.* If we should ask, "*Which* do you prefer?" you would quickly answer, and not one of you would choose the *thorn* nor *thistle.* You would "gather" the grapes and figs. Let it be your aim always to choose the *good* in the moral world rather than the *evil.* Let the thistles, which *irritate* and *annoy*, and the thorns which *pierce* and *pain* be rejected. God offers you pleasant, palatable, healthful things in abundance. Take these, and let the *bad* and *barren* things alone. Be like Mary. "Mary hath chosen that *good* part." Luke x. 42.

But this question of the Saviour implies that fruit will always *harmonize* in its *essence* with the *nature* of the plant or tree that produces it. This is the chief point of the question. A certain tree or a plant has a *capacity* to produce a certain kind of fruit. It *cannot* bear anything else. A thorn cannot bear grapes, nor a thistle figs. The idea is that a *bad* life cannot produce *good* results.

Hence, said Jesus, "Neither can a *corrupt* tree bring forth *good* fruit." Matt. vii. 18.

"We cannot have *right* virtues without *right* conditions."—*Beecher*.

"A good man out of the good treasure of the heart, bringeth forth good things." Matt. xii. 35.

Let us strive to *be* good, and *do* good. How *little* good have we done! "A very *small page* will serve for the number of our good works when *vast volumes* will not contain our evil deeds." —*Bishop Wilson*. Let us be more fruitful in the gospel vineyard. The Egyptian fig-tree is said to bear fruit *seven times* every year. In Spain, it is said, there is nothing barren or not in some way useful. So may it be in *this* Sunday-school.

EXAMPLES OF PRAYER IN DANGER, AND BY WHOM.

1. Jacob, from his brother....................Gen. xxxii. 9–12.
2. Joshua, for deliverance of his people..........Jos. vii. 5–9.
3. Gideon, for deliverance of his people......Judges vi. 13–16.
4. Elisha, for deliverance from an army........2 Kings vi. 17.
5. Jehoahaz, for deliverance of his people......2 Kings xiii. 4.
6. Hezekiah, for deliverance of his people...2 Chron. xxxii. 20.
7. Josiah, for mercy..........................2 Kings xxii. 13.
8. Asa, for deliverance of his people.........2 Chron. xiv. 11.
9. Jehoshaphat, for deliverance of his people...2 Chron. xx. 4.
10. David, in fear......Ps. xxxii. 6, 7; Ps. lvi. 3; Ps. cxvi. 3–6.
11. Disciples in the storm.................... Mark iv. 37, *etc.*
12. Peter in prison............................Acts. xii. 5–17.
13. Paul and Silas in prison..................Acts xvi. 25–34.
14. Paul on his voyage........... ....Acts xxvii. 22, etc.

THE UPLIFTED SAVIOUR.

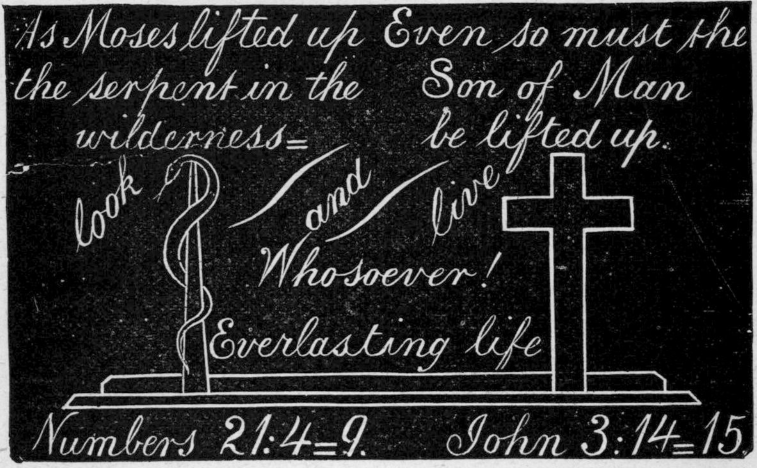

As Moses lifted up the serpent in the wilderness=
Even so must the Son of Man be lifted up.
look
and
live
Whosoever!
Everlasting life
Numbers 21:4=9.
John 3:14=15.

This picture recalls a very interesting event in the history of the Israelites. They were *journeying* through the wilderness. They suffered many painful *hardships*. Their trials overtaxed their patience, and at last they began to *murmur* and *complain* most bitterly. As a *punishment*, God sent serpents into their camp, and the murmuring people were bitten by them. "And the Lord sent fiery serpents among the people, and they bit the people; and much people of Israel died." Num. xxi. 6. God is never *at a loss* for means to punish the wicked. He can make the *winds* and the *waves* do His will. Here fiery serpents become the ministers of his wrath. Observe they did not enter the camp and bite simply *because* it was their nature to do so, for the "Lord *sent* fiery serpents among the people." Let us take care how we *provoke* Him. Moses was directed to "make a serpent of brass and set it up upon a pole," and the bitten ones looked upon it and were healed. They did not have to *go to it*, but only *look* upon it, and they lived. How *simple*, how easy the method of their cure. Now, this uplifted serpent reminds us of the uplifted Saviour. Read the words of Jesus: "As Moses lifted up the serpent in the wilderness, even so must the son of man be lifted up." John iii. 14, 15.

This refers to His crucifixion:

He *was* "taken, and by wicked hands crucified and slain." Acts ii. 23. He was "lifted up" upon the cross, and He *suffered for sins*, the just for the unjust, that He might bring us to God. 1 Pet. iii. 18. We *need a remedy* for sin as much as the Israelites needed one for the poisonous bite of the serpent. They found theirs in the uplifted serpent; we find ours in the uplifted Christ. They *looked* and lived. Are *you* "looking unto Jesus"? Heb. xii. 2. Hear the command of God: "Look unto me, and be ye saved." Isa. xlv. 22. This you *all* can do. How *simple* it is. "Here is one little word of four letter, and two of them are alike! *Look.*"—*Spurgeon.* Let us *look*, *believe*, and *live*.

WHAT CHRIST IS TO US.

The door....................John x. 9. Enter and be saved.
The Way....................John xiv. 6. Walk ye in Him.
The Light of the World....John viii. 12. Walk in the Light.
The Bread of Life..........John vi. 35. Eat and be satisfied.
The Smitten Rock....1 Cor. x. 4. Drink of the living streams.
Our Saviour....................2 Tim. i. 10. Receive Him.
Our Peace........................Eph. ii. 14. Rest in Him.
Our Shepherd..................John x. 11. Hear His voice.
Our Example...................John xiii. 15. Follow Him.
Our High Priest..............Heb. vii. 26. Look up to Him.
Our Lord.........................John xiii. 13. Obey Him.
The King of kings.....Rev. xix. 16. Wait for His appearing.

THE CHRISTIAN'S DEDICATION.

I take God the Father to be my God.............1 Thess. i. 9.
I take God the Son to be my Saviour..............Acts v. 31.
I take God the Holy Ghost to be my Sanctifier.....1 Peter i. 2.
I take the Word of God to be my rule........2 Tim. iii. 16, 17.
I take the people of God to be my people.......Ruth i. 16, 17.
I likewise dedicate my whole self to the Lord...Rom. xiv. 7, 8.
And I do this deliberately—Josh. xxiv. 15. Sincerely—2 Cor. i. 12. Freely—Psalm cx. 3. And forever—Rom. viii. 35-39.

SIGNALS OF DANGER.

In this picture you see a portion of a railroad track, and just at the curve you see a locomotive. You also see a line of telegraph-wires, and, located near them, is an electric battery, which is put in motion when the train passes, and thus gives notice of its coming. A person walking on the track or waiting at the station hears the alarm-bell ring and knows that the train is *near*. It is to him a signal of *danger*.

Our *pathway* in life is beset with many *dangers*, and there are *alarm-signals* out on every side. Dangers on the railroad are often met with at the *curves*. Persons walking there do not see the train, and it dashes upon them and destroys them. There is danger *at the curve*, and they must watch the signal. So there are curves or *turning-points* in every life. Be careful *how* you approach them—*how* you go around them. As you go out of childhood into youth, you pass a *curve* on life's pathway. As you go from youth into manhood you pass another. These are turning-points in your history. And just at these points life may become a *bane* or a *blessing*. Some round the curve with no thought of what they are to do as they pass it. Go around the curve with a *purpose.* Resolve to make all your *after-life* better than it was before. Some are in a feverish hurry to get around the curve. They want to press on to honor, pleasure, and wealth with *undue haste.* And here is their danger. They are *too eager*, too venturesome. Sometimes scholars decide to *leave* the school. Then they reach a *turning-point* in their history. There is danger before them. They are too hasty and inconsiderate. They may go astray, and never return to the right way. Let us look out for danger at these turning-points in life.

Signals of danger will be *useless* if we do not heed them. Let the whistle blow or the alarm-bell ring; but if the man on the track *does not heed it,* he will be destroyed. Let the mariner *ignore* the lighthouse, and his vessel will run upon the rocks, and all may be lost.

A bell was once so arranged that in a storm it would ring loudly, and thus warn mariners of their danger. Some pirates muffled the bell so that it would not ring out its alarm, hoping that, in its silence, some unfortunate vessel might be driven upon the rocks and become their prey. Strange to say, they themselves were the first to suffer. They had *silenced* the warning-bell, and all perished. Let us *never* muffle the bell of conscience. Let us *heed* the warnings of truth.

THE GOSPEL RAILROAD.

The graded road.... ....Isa. xl. 3–5; Isa. lxii. 10.
The track, Jesus..............................John xiv. 6.
The engine, Charity..........................1 Cor. xiii. 13.
The engineer, The Holy Spirit...........John xiv. 26; xv. 26.
The headlight, The Word of God...............Ps. cxix. 105.
The red lights, danger signals................Matt vii. 13, 14.
The car, our Saviour..........................John x. 9.
The conductor, our Heavenly Father........Ps. xxxiii. 18–20.
The travellers, Believers......................Rev. vii. 9, 10.
The destination Heaven..1 Peter i. 3, 4; Heb. xiii. 14; 2 Cor. v. i.

GAINING AND LOSING.

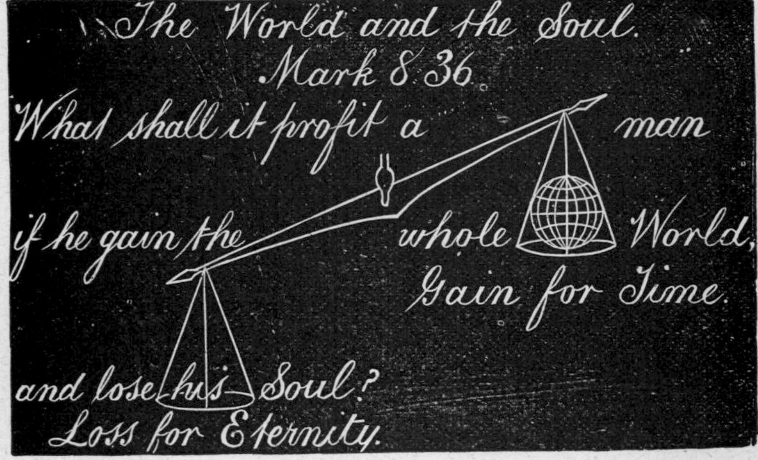

The World and the Soul.
Mark 8.36.
What shall it profit a man
if he gain the whole World,
Gain for Time.
and lose his Soul?
Loss for Eternity.

There you see a pair of scales. One side hangs down, as though it were heavily loaded, and the other rises upward, as though it had only a light burden to bear. On one side we see a representation of the World, and the other is supposed to be borne down by something more solid and valuable than the world itself—even a *soul*. A *soul* on one side, the *world* on the other. What a difference! Bear this in mind, and you will see the force of the question. "What shall it profit a man if he shall gain the whole world and lose his own soul!" Mark viii. 36. Your soul is greatly superior to the world, and should not be exchanged for it.

A little blind girl once asked, "What is soul?" Her instructor answered, "That which thinks, feels, hopes, loves." How little, how meagre, how trivial are all the pleasures, riches, honors, and glories of the world. "One soul *outweighs* them all." You have only one soul, and if you lose that, all is gone forever and ever. We sometimes lose *one* friend, but we have others left. Sometimes one portion of property will be taken away, but some other portion remains. Lose the soul, and *all* is gone. You cannot recall it, you cannot replace it. "He that is unjust, *let him be unjust still.*" Rev. xxii. 11. Your soul cost an immense price, and is valuable beyond all computation. "Ye are bought with a price." 1 Cor. vi. 20. That "price" is the blood of the Son of God. "We have redemption *through his blood.*" Eph. i. 7. Estimated by its cost, how valuable the soul is! What profit will it be for a man to lose his precious soul, and have nothing in exchange, but a *vain, worthless, decaying* world. That soul will live on forever and ever. Yea, it will live, "when the riches, powers, and pleasures of the world have passed away like a snow-wreath beneath a vernal shower."—*Rowland Hill.*

Gain as much of the world as you can *consistently*, but at the same time resolve to save your soul. A collegian, distinguished for his mathematical attainments, was fond of challenging his fellow-students to a trial of skill in solving difficult problems. One day a class-mate came into his study, and, laying a folded paper before him, said, "There is a problem I wish you would help me to solve," and immediately left the room.

The paper was eagerly unfolded, and there, instead of a question in mathematics, were traced the lines, "What shall it profit a man if he gain the whole world and lose his own soul; or what shall a man give in exchange for his soul?"

With a gesture of impatience he tore the paper to atoms and turned again to his books. But in vain he tried to shake off the impressions of the solemn words he had read. The Holy Spirit pressed home his conviction of guilt and danger, so that he could find no peace till he found it in believing in Jesus. He subsequently became a minister of the Gospel he had once despised, and his first sermon was from the words, so blessed to his own soul, "What shall it profit a man if he gain the whole world and lose his own soul?"

The apostles were very full, because very empty; full of the spirit of God, because empty of the spirit of the world.—*St. Augustine.*

THE CHRISTIAN'S DEFENCE—2 KINGS VI. 8-18.

Our lesson finds the man of God sore beset. Enemies are all around him, and there is no apparent escape. Yet how perfect is his security and safety. The one on his side is infinitely more than all his enemies. *If God be for us*, we have One who is more than all they that be against us.

Notice his perfect trust. While his servant is stricken with fear, his heart is calm. The plot of his wicked enemies seemed complete, but it had one fatal defect—God was not for them.

The true servant of God is surrounded by enemies—sin and temptation surround him. They are our foes, but we have a heavenly Defender. If God be for us, we shall surely *overcome*. To have God for us, we must be clearly and decidedly for God; we must be on the Lord's side.

There is no surrender in the fight with sin and Satan—no parleying or making terms with Satan. We are to "*fight the good fight.*" We are to resist the devil, if we would have him flee from us. If we had only our own strength to depend upon there would be but little hope of *victory;* but the weapons of our defence are heavenly. The shield of *Faith* is a sure defence. Trust in God never disappoints.

We are not only to fight, but to *conquer the evil one.* God will not only keep us through faith in Him, but he gives us a precious and priceless weapon of defence—"*the sword of the Spirit.*"

How necessary an acquaintance with its use—a knowledge of its power. The word of God should be "hid in our hearts" that we may delight in it and feel its power in our lives.

God is not only our Defender, but our *Reward.* Faithful here, victory will be sure, and the reward of His presence forever.

[Diagram by J. G. Phipps, Indianapolis.]

GOD IS ABLE.

Able to save.................................Jas. iv. 12.
" " " from the furnace heat.............Dan. iii. 13–18.
" " " " the lion's mouth.............Dan. vi. 18–24.
" " " " all uncleanness.............Ezek. xxxvi. 29.
" " " " our sins..........................Matt. i. 21.
" " " " death..............................Heb. v. 7.
" " " to the uttermost....................Heb. vii. 25.
Able to succor the tempted.......................Heb. ii. 18
" make us stand.........................Rom. xiv. 4.
" build us up............................Acts xx. 32.
" keep us from evil.....................2 Thes. iii. 3.
" keep us from falling...................Jude xxiv.
" keep that which we commit to Him......2 Tim. i. 12.
" perform His promises...................Rom. iv. 21
" do more than we ask....................Eph. iii. 20.
" make all grace abound..................2 Cor. ix. 8.
" subdue all things to Himself............Phil. iii. 21.
" raise us from the dead..................Heb. xi. 19.
" present us faultless.....................Jude xxiv.

THE TWO LADDERS.

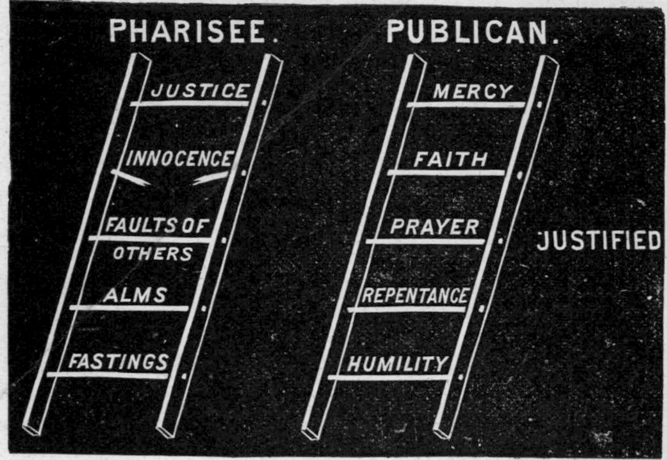

These two ladders are intended to represent the moral character and life of the Pharisee and the Publican. These characters differ very widely from each other, and the ladders drawn upon the board, with their peculiar inscriptions, make the difference between them all the more apparent. The parable is given by the Saviour in Luke xviii. 10–14. In the ladder which the Pharisee is represented as climbing, you see five rounds, bearing significant names, and these indicate the various *stages* or *steps* by which he hopes to reach heaven. The first round is *fasting*. See how he magnifies it. He is careful to mention that he fasts *twice* in the week. Will that make a man *good*, or *save* him? No. He might fast twice as often and yet be lost. Fasting is a Christian duty, but we cannot be saved by it. The second round is *alms*. That means gifts to the poor and needy. And this man was liberal, for he gave one-tenth of all he had. It is right to give to the destitute. Jesus said, "Ye have the poor always with you." Matt. xxvi. 11. We are to remember that "He that hath pity upon the poor, lendeth unto the Lord."

Prov. xix. 17. "A *miser* is a monster that no one can love."—*Dr. Thomas.*

The next round is described as the *faults* of *others.* He names a list of faults. How natural it is for us to see the sins of *other* people. It would be better to see *our own*, and forsake them. "If the best man's faults were written on his forehead, it would make him pull his hat over his eyes."—*Gaelic Proverb.*

The next round is a *broken* one. It is marked *innocence.* All the other rounds seemed strong enough to hold the Pharisee, but when he reached that round it gave way. He was far from being an innocent man. Every human scheme breaks down at this point. "*All* have sinned and come short of the glory of God. Rom. iii. 23.

The next round is *justice.* Of course he could not reach that, for the round below was broken, and his upward course was arrested. All this suggests one of the most striking utterances of the Saviour, "He that climbeth up some other way, the same is a thief and a robber." John x. 1.

Now look at the other ladder, which represents the course pursued by the Publican. You see the same number of rounds, and each one has a proper title. Name them. You see no *broken* rounds in this ladder. Each one is solid and strong. The Pharisee failed, but the Publican did not. Will *you* follow the Publican? He went down to his house justified. Be humble and prayerful, and ever trust in God. "The devil told St. Marcarius, "I can surpass thee in watching, fasting, and many other things; but humility conquers and disarms me."—*Foster.*

THE PATH TO ETERNAL LIFE.

1. Is a straight path..............Prov. iv. 25-27; Heb. xii. 13.
2. Is a narrow path..........................Matt. vii. 13, 14.
3. Is an upward path..............Prov. xv. 24; Isa. xl. 31.
4. Is an old path....................................Jer. vi. 16.
5. Is a pleasant path..............................Prov. iii. 17.
6. Is a light path...................................Prov. iv. 18.
7. Which leads to a glorious city.....................Ps. cvii. 7.

THE YOKE OF CHRIST—MATT. xi. 30.

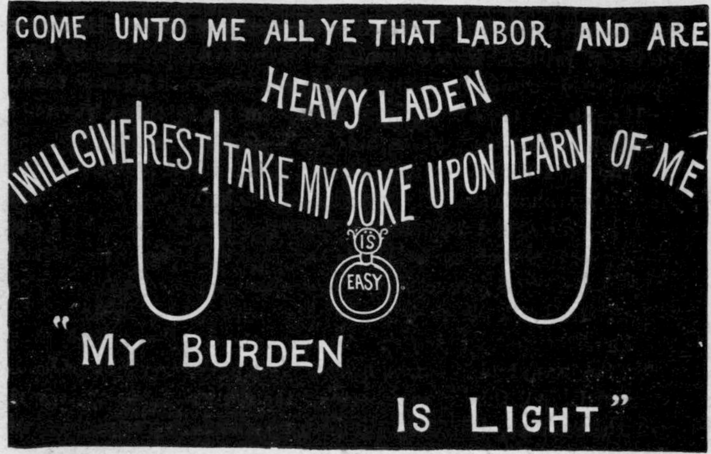

Having drawn the text upon the blackboard or slate, as explained above, call special attention to the fact that the yoke is intended for *use.*

It never is regarded merely as an *ornament*, but is designed for *service.* It may be very strong, and quite perfect in every respect; but unless it is *used* it will be almost worthless.

The yoke of Christ's teaching and example will be serviceable to us if we *use it.* He says to us: "*Take* my yoke upon you."

Did a yoke ever place itself upon the neck of the oxen?

No, it had to be put there by somebody. So, when you wear the yoke of Christ, it must be taken upon you. Remember, children, the Saviour asks you to *take it;* He does not try to *force it* upon you. Yokes sometimes seem heavy, because of the burdens that are attached to them. But Christ tells us that His yoke is *easy*, and His *burden* is *light.* Animals that bear the yoke have no rest until the yoke is removed. But the Christian has rest, even while he bears the yoke of Christ. Will you try it, children?

Mr. Moody tells us that "the service of Christ is the *only true liberty.*" The best time to bear the yoke is in *youth.*

It is a yoke of *restraint.* Learn *self-control now.* It is a yoke of *service.* Learn to render *service now.* It is a yoke of sacrifice. Learn to practise *self-denial now.*

The prophet tells us that "it is good for a man that he bear the yoke in his youth." Lam. iii. 27.

"Remember now thy Creator in the days of thy youth."

"COMES" OF THE OLD TESTAMENT.

Come into the Ark.................................Gen. vii. 1.
Come thou with us...........................Numbers x. 29.
Come, let us reason together.......................Isa. i. 18.
Come, return.......................................Isa. xxi. 12.
Come, my people, enter into thy chambers........Isa. xxvi. 20.
Come ye to the waters..... ....Isa. lv. 1.
Come unto me..Isa. lv. 3.

"COMES" OF THE NEW TESTAMENT,

Come unto me all ye that labor...................Matt. xi. 28.
Come, ye blessed................................Matt. xxv. 34
Come apart and rest. ....Mark. vi. 31.
Come down..Luke xix. 5
Come and see......................................John i. 39.
Come unto me and drink.........................John vii. 37.
Come forth ....John xi. 43.
Come and dine...................................John xxi. 12.
I will come again..................................John xiv. 3.
Come over and help us............................Acts xvi. 9.
Come out and be ye separate....................2 Cor. vi. 17.
Come boldly unto the throne of grace............Heb. iv. 16.
Come out of her, my people.....................Rev. xviii. 4.
Come, the Spirit and the Bride say.............Rev. xxii. 17.

THE CHRISTIAN'S CROWN.

We have here an object, at once beautiful and immensely valuable. It is a crown—the crown of life. In Rev. ii. 10, we read, "Be thou faithful unto death, and I will give thee a crown of life. Crowns are worn by earthly sovereigns to denote their royal character, official dignity, and dominion. On state occasions, crowns, sparkling with courtly splendor, deck the brows of princes, kings, and queens. The Christian has the promise of a crown. He is now a king in his *minority.* "There is *laid up for me* a crown of righteousness," is his triumphant utterance. 2 Tim. iv. 8. It is *waiting* for him in the "crown-chamber" above.

This crown will *never fade away.* The laurel wreath that rests upon the victor's brow withers, and he soon casts it aside as worthless. The brightest diadem of earth soon loses its lustre. But this crown always remains untarnished. "Ye shall receive a crown of glory that *fadeth not away.*" 1 Pet. v. 4. Try to win this crown. The worldling's crown is "corrupt-able," the Christian's "incorruptible." 1 Cor. ix. 25. This crown is invested with *great value.*

Many things in this world are prized because they are *rare* and *costly.* "The Queen of England wears a crown of gold, filled with diamonds and precious stones, worth $20,000,000."

One of the Queen's crown jewels alone is valued at $1,500,000. But here is a crown surpassing the value of all the crowns of earth combined. It *outshines* them, *outweighs* them, *outlasts* them.

Remember that the crown is to *follow* the cross. One has said, "After the cross cometh the crown." *Bear* the cross, if you would *wear* the crown. "Forty brave soldiers of the Thundering Legion were called to adjure Christ or die. One of them said, 'Let us forty ask God to send us to our crowns together.'"—*Foster.* They laid down forty crosses and took up forty crowns. A dying saint caught a glimpse of the crown-chamber, and shouted, "Crowns! crowns! crowns of glory shall adorn this head of mine ere long." Ask the question earnestly, "Shall the crown be mine?" "*Hold fast,* that which thou hast, that no man take thy crown." Rev. iii. 11.

"The crown that worldlings covet,
Is not the crown for me;
Its beauty fades as quickly
As sunshine on the sea."

"So run that ye may obtain." 1 Cor. ix. 24.

GOD'S WAY AND OURS CONTRASTED.

Pleasantness and peace..Prov. iii. 17.	Folly............Ps. xlix. 13.
Strength..........Prov. x. 29.	Wasting and destruction...Isa lix. 7.
Good and upright..Ps. xxv. 8.	Upside down.....Ps. cxlvi. 9.
Restful...........Jere. vi. 16.	Hard or weary...Prov. xiii. 15.
Righteousness and life...Prov. xii. 28.	Death..........Prov. xiv. 12.

THE FULL SURRENDER.

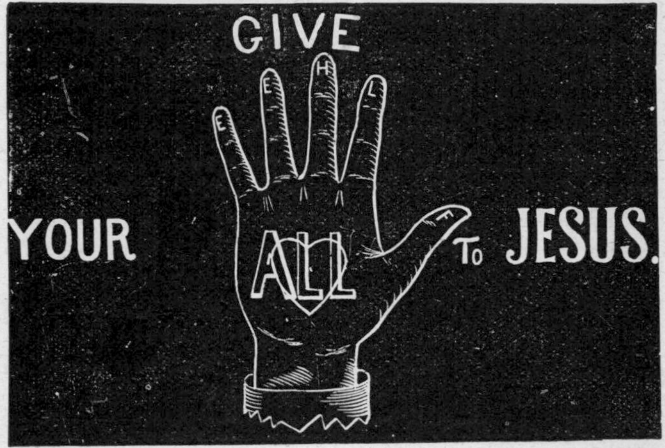

We have here the picture of a *hand*. It is *open*, thus showing that nothing is kept within its grasp, nor even concealed from sight. Some persons boast that they never "*Show their hands*" in what they do. They love to appear *shrewd* and *sly*. But Jesus wants boys and girls to *show* their hands in His service.

This open hand and the motto, and also the letters you see written upon the fingers, are intended to show that *all* we have should be given to the Saviour. It is said that, on the occasion of a missionary collection, a young man was so anxious to serve the Saviour that he wrote upon a card the single word "Myself," and dropped it into the basket. What a grand sentiment! *Myself for Jesus.* Nothing kept back—*all* given to Christ.

Children, open your hearts and give *all* the sympathy and love that throbs in them to the Saviour. Hear His voice, saying to you each: "Son, give me thy heart." Give it to Him *entirely*. Do not think that He will be pleased with just a little place in your heart, for He wants it *all*, and will have no rival. "The Roman soldiery chose Valentinian to be their emperor; afterwards they consulted how they might join a partner with him in the throne. On hearing this, the emperor replied, that, although it had been in their power to give him the empire, it was no longer in their power to give him a colleague."—*Biblical Museum.*

He wanted the *whole* empire under his rule. So Jesus wants the *whole empire* of the soul.

Children, go with *open* hands to Jesus, and *keep nothing back.* Can you tell me who tried to "keep back part of the price," and received a terrible punishment for the crime? Yes, Ananias and Sapphira. How dreadful their doom! Keep back nothing that the Lord claims. Let your *brains think* for Christ. Let your *hearts* beat with His love; let your *eyes* be fixed upon Him; let your *hands* bear His cross; let your *feet* walk in the "straight and narrow way." *All* your hearts for Jesus, *now* and *always.*

TEMPERANCE.

Bible proofs that strong drink leads to—

Shame........Example of Noah.................Gen. ix. 21.
Confusion.....   "   " Lot.................Gen. xix. 33.
Folly ....   "   " Ahasuerus.........Esther i. 10, 11.
Defeat........   "   " Benhadad......1 Kings xx. 16–20.
Poverty.......Warnings of Solomon..........Prov. xxiii. 21.
Trouble.......   "   "   "   ....Prov. xxiii. 29, 30.
Sacrilege......Example of Belshazzar...........Dan. v. 1–5.
Eternal rejection of God........................1 Cor. vi. 10.

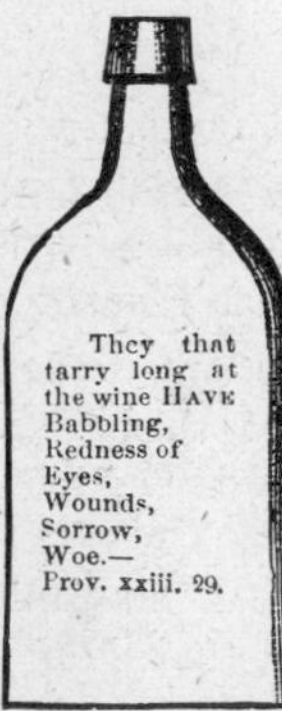

They that tarry long at the wine HAVE
Babbling,
Redness of Eyes,
Wounds,
Sorrow,
Woe.—
Prov. xxiii. 29.

Wine is a mocker, strong drink is raging, and whosoever is deceived thereby is not wise.—Prov. xx. 1.

Drink waters out of thine own cistern and running waters out of thine own well. —Prov. v. 15.

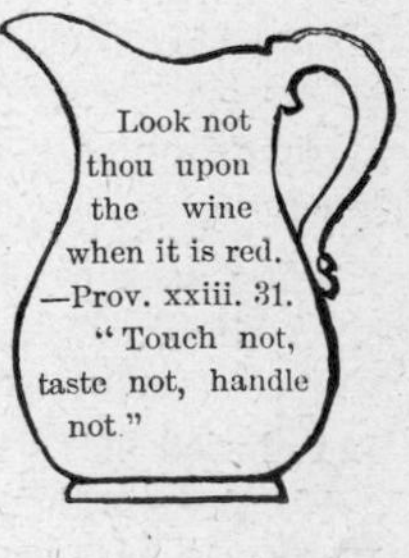

Look not thou upon the wine when it is red.
—Prov. xxiii. 31.
"Touch not, taste not, handle not."

THE CROSS OF CHRIST.

O
B X L
K
God forbid that I should Glory save in
THE CROSS OF OUR LORD JESUS CHRIST.
Gal. 6.14.

The cross here represented is surmounted with a crown, and there are written upon it four letters of the alphabet. These letters are intended to denote knowledge, belief, love, and obedience. You also see two arrows pointing towards a central letter X, and this letter is used to denote the word Christ. These letters suggest that we are to know, believe, love, and obey Christ. The arrow pointing towards the central letter indicates that Christ is the *centre of attraction.* "Jesus only." Matt. xvii. 8. At the foot of the cross you read: "God forbid that I should glory, save in the cross." Gal. vi. 14.

The *literal* cross was a gibbet made of two pieces of wood, crossing each other. The vilest criminals were put to death upon the cross. Hence it became a badge of shame. But Paul accepted it as though it were the highest badge of honor, and gloried in it.

We glory in the cross, because it is the symbol of Christianity. We see the zealous Jew bearing a *yoke* as the symbol of his faith, a heavy, burdensome yoke of rites and ceremonies; but the Christian finds his symbol of faith in the cross. "By the cross, then, we mean that which embodies the great doctrines of the Gospel, and presents them in all their clearness and force to the mind. Here the whole Deity is known. No wonder Paul glories in it. We glory in the cross, because it is an *independent* moral force. There is only *one* cross, and it stands *alone.* It does its own work and will win its way to universal triumph. "I would say to the insidious skeptic: Sir, Christianity asks no permission to live from either you or me—she draws her life from a higher source."—*Bishop Clark.*

Constantine looks up into the beautiful heavens at noon, and beholds, written upon a cross of wondrous beauty, the words, "In this sign conquer." Christianity will conquer by the cross —the cross alone. "There is none other name given under heaven among men, whereby we must be saved." Acts iv. 12. Take the cross and glory in it. "The old crusaders used to wear a cross upon their shoulders. This was their badge of service."—*Foster.* Jesus says, "If any man will come after me, let him deny himself, and *take up his cross,* and follow me." Matt. xvi. 24. Take the cross and let it *elevate* the soul. A heathen ruler, who had heard the story of the cross, was dying. He said to his attendants, "Make a cross, and lay me upon it." They did so, and as he lay there dying, he laid hold on the blood of Christ, and said, "It lifts me up; it lifts me; it lifts me; it lifts me."—*Bible Museum.* So may it lift us all into light and life.

John Newton, in commenting upon Paul's statement to the Corinthians concerning himself (1 Cor. xv. 10), says: "I am not what I *ought* to be; I am not what I *wish* to be; I am not what I *hope* to be. Yet though I am not what I ought to be, nor what I wish to be, nor what I hope to be, *I am not what I once was,* and 'by the grace of God I am what I am.'" How much of truth, thought, and experience in these few words!

THE TWO PATHS. PROV. IV. 10.-19.

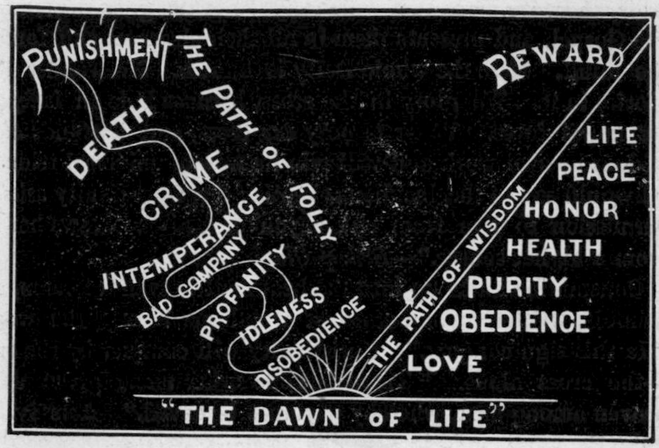

Commencing with the dawn of our lives, the beginning of our knowledge of right and wrong, we choose our own path in which we walk in this life. Two paths before each of us. The sin in our hearts will lead us in the path of *disobedience*, which through all its wanderings will lead at last to death and punishment.

Trace the steps in this "way of the wicked," writing them upon the board as in the diagram, enlarging and illustrating. The very first step in the "path of the just" is *love*.

Trace the progressive steps, and refer to the passages of Scripture indicating them. The end of the two ways. Practical and personal enforcement of the lesson: in which path am *I?*

Give familiar illustration of losing the way and taking the *wrong path*. In order to reach our home we must get in the right way. Our heavenly home. But one right way—the "path of wisdom." Not to love God and keep His law is wicked and foolish. The path of wisdom leads to heaven. The path of folly takes us farther and farther from God. Need of getting into the right path, in youth.—*J. B. Phipps.*

THE ALL-SEEING EYE.—A CHALK TALK.

"Thou, God, seest me," GEN. XVI. 23.

[Draw an eye on the board.] [Draw a window.]

Did you ever think how beautiful an eye is? How it will beam with love, or flash with anger. How it will laugh or cry. If you tell an untruth how do they look? *Ashamed.* Yes, and try to hide behind the lid, or turn away. And the eye of a Christian should look peaceful and happy.

The eye is sometimes called the "*window of the soul.*' What are windows for? *To see through and admit light.*

If in the evening it is not lit up, can you see anything? No, it is dark. [Pointing to window on board.] Does this window appear dark? *Yes.* Now watch me and see what I am going to do. Use your eyes. [Draw outline of heart around the window.] What have I just drawn? Where is the window now? *In the heart.* Now, children, God sees into our hearts, just as plainly as if we had a window there. When we are thinking and doing wrong things, the window of our hearts is dark all the time. And God has so wonderfully made these hearts of ours, that every time we do wrong, it is marked on our heart, to be accounted for at the Judgment day.

Then the rays of divine light from the All-seeing Eye [draw rays from eye] shining into our hearts, and lighting them up, will able us to light and help others.

THE FAMILY IN THE ARK.

We have here a picture of the ark. How long was Noah occupied in building it? One hundred and twenty years. How large was it? "If you should put it into one story and one floor, it would have been about sixteen feet high, two hundred and forty feet wide, and one thousand five hundred feet long."—*Moody.* God told Noah how large it must be. Gen. vi. 15. When God said to Noah, "Come thou and all thy house into the ark," the whole family marched in, and were safe while the deluge swept over the earth. That family consisted of eight persons—Noah and his wife, his three sons and their wives.

You see the word Christ written upon the ark in the picture. That shows that Jesus is the *soul's ark.* In him we find safety, happiness, and life eternal. God wanted the *whole* family of Noah saved. So to-day Jesus wants to get our families into the ark of salvation. How blessed it is for a whole family to be saved. How sad Noah would have felt, had any of his household been left out of the ark. It is a great joy to have *some* of the family in the ark, but we want them *all* saved. Some of you have parents in the ark, and they want you to join them. Some one has said, "Noah went in *first* and his children *followed* him." Follow your friends into the ark.

How *possible* it is for a whole family to be saved. There was room in the ark for Noah's family, and there is room in the loving heart of Jesus for us all. He takes the children of the family to His heart, and tells us that "Of *such* is the kingdom of heaven." Matt. xix. 14.

He also waits to welcome the older members of the home-circle. *All* may come. "Whosoever will, let him take the water of life freely." Rev. xxii. 17.

As the ark carried Noah to a happy destination, so will Christ, the spiritual ark, convey us home to heaven at last. Some are there *now*. They await us. A dying child, after exhorting her friends to meet her in heaven, said, "I'll be watching for you." Be anxious to get into the ark, every one of you. A little girl stood on the deck of a sinking vessel, and, when the life-boat came near, she sprang into the sea, crying, "Save me next! save me next." *Hasten* to the ark. Cry out, save *me*—save me *now*.

THE SIX ONE THINGS.

Sinner—One thing thou lackest............Matt. xix. 20, 21.
Blind man—One thing I know...................John ix. 25.
Mary—Hath the one thing needful...............Luke x. 42.
Christ—One is your Master...................Matt. xxiii. 10.
Paul—One thing I do..........................Phil. iii. 13.
Joshua—Not one thing has failed.............Josh. xxiii. 14.

D. L. Moody.

WHAT THE CHRISTIAN SOLDIER MUST DO.

1. Must fight..................................Tim. vi. 12.
2. Must obey his commander......Luke vii. 8; Acts xxvii. 23.
3. Must be armed for war....Eph. vi. 11-18; Ps. xviii. 34, 35.
4. Must never desert, but be ready to die in the service. Heb. xii. 4; 2 Tim. iv. 6, 7.
5. Must not engage in other service...2 Tim. ii. 4; Matt. vi. 24.
6. *Result*—victory and reward. Rom. viii. 36; 2 Tim. iv. 8; iii. 3.

LOVE NOT THE WORLD.

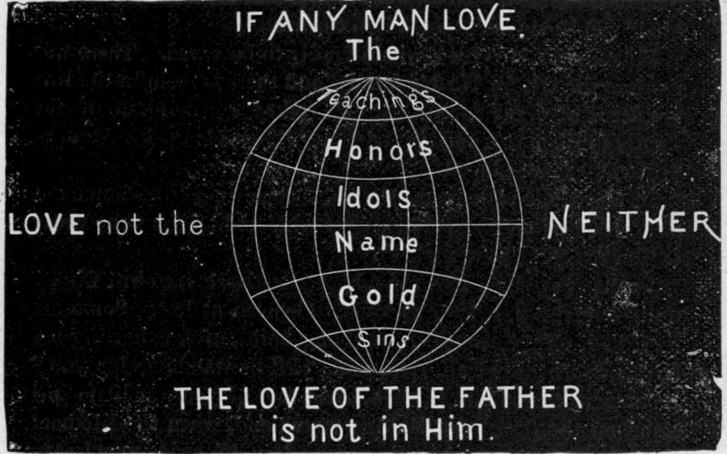

The picture of the world, here given, is designed to illustrate the meaning of the passage of Scripture written on the board, found in 1 John ii. 15. "If any man love the world, the love of the Father is not in him." This does not mean that we are not to love the *material* world: for its hills and plains, and mountains, and its rippling brooks and rolling oceans, its plants and trees and flowers, all are very beautiful, and challenge our love.

But we are not to love the *bad* spirit, nor follow the unchristian practice of the world. Paul speaks of it as "this present *evil* world." Gal. i. 4. Again, in Romans xii. 2, he admonishes his brethren against being "*conformed to this world.*" In the picture we have a reference to some of the things we are not to love. Its teachings, honors, etc. The man who loves these cannot have the love of the Father in him. There is not room enough for God and the world in any one heart. One or the other must be crowded out. "Ye cannot serve God and Mammon." Matt. vi. 24. Dr. Franklin once gave an apple to a very little child. The child could scarcely hold it in his hand; he then gave another, which occupied the other hand. Then choosing another, remarkable for its size and beauty, he presented that also. The child, after many ineffectual attempts to hold the three, dropped the last on the floor, and burst into tears. "See there," said Franklin, "there is a little man with more happiness than he can enjoy." If the world *fills* our hearts and hands, there will be *no room* for the Master. Let us be wise and give our love to the Father. Demas was charged with the crime of forsaking Paul, and the reason assigned was that he "*loved* this present world." 2 Tim. iv. 10. How many have given up their hope of heaven for the pleasures and follies of a sinful world. How disappointed they will be, when they find how insufficient and unsatisfactory the world is to the soul. It will allure you to its embrace, and promise you much pleasure; but remember that the "pleasures of sin" are but "for a season." Heb. xi. 25. "In St. Mark's Church, Venice, will be found the tomb of Duke Sebastian Foscarinus. Upon it are inscribed these words: 'Hear, O ye Venetians! and I will tell you which is the best thing in the world; it is to contemn and despise riches.'"—*Foster*.

WHAT IT IS TO BE A CHRISTIAN.

In faith, a believer in Christ.................... Mark xvi. 16.
In knowledge, a disciple........................ John viii. 31.
In character, a saint................................ Rom. i. 7
In influence, a light................................ Matt. v. 14
In conflict, a soldier.............................. 2 Tim. ii. 3.
In communion, a friend......................... John xv. 15.
In progress, a pilgrim............................ Heb. xi. 13.
In relationship, a child......................... Rom. viii. 16.
In expectation, an heir......................... Rom. viii. 17.

STEPS IN SIN. 2 Kings v. 20—27.

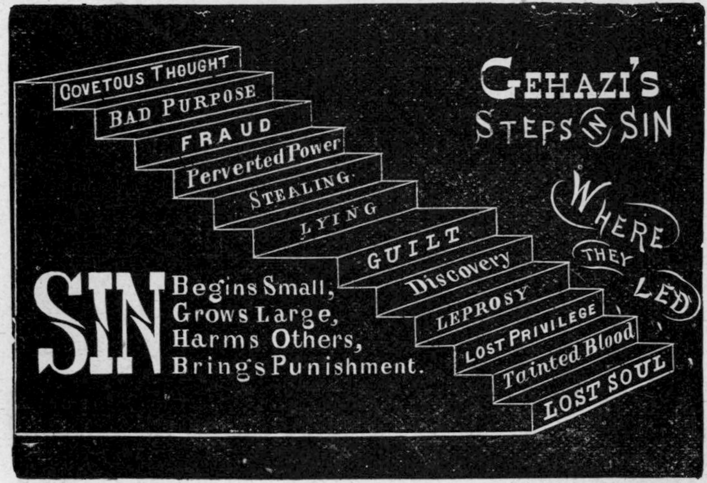

Draw a picture of steps, twelve in number, with the upper and lower pairs divided. The six upper steps are *Gehazi's steps in sin;* the six lower, the results to which they lead. He *took* the first six voluntarily, the other six necessarily.

Place in order the six sins of Gehazi; begin with the *Covetous Thought*, ending with *Lying*.

"Perverted Power" refers to the fact that he misused the spiritual gifts of Elisha for his own personal gain.

When a sinner begins, he knows not where he shall end. Having taken these steps, he was compelled to receive six consequences. Guilt, Discovery, etc. "Lost Privileges;" but for this sin he might have been Elisha's successor in the prophetic office.

"Tainted Blood ;" the leprosy extending to his seed after him.

On the margin (or other side of the board) write the four lessons as taught by this event, as per diagram.—*Rev. J. L. Hurlburt.*

THE TWO HANDS.

"The wages of sin is death, but the gift of God is Eternal Life through Jesus Christ our Lord. ROM. VI. 23.

See these two hands; the one reaches up to higher and heavenly things, the other down after the groveling things of time and sense. The one represents the Christian, the other the Sinner.

I. The one receives, the other grasps. As we stretch out the hand palm upward, in asking, so the Christian opens his soul toward God. We turn the hand downward to grasp.

So the sinner opens his hand towards the earth.

II. Notice the difference in what they receive. The one receives the Gifts of God—Life, Joy, Peace, Righteousness. The other may seize for a time Riches, Fame, Honor, Pleasure; but misfortune or death comes, and through the opening fingers all slip but Death.

Notice that Death is fastened by a band to the hand of "Greed," which band respresents the law of Justice.

A covetous man turns from the cry of distress by instinct; the hand of a kind man almost by instinct moves to his pocket, that he may relieve the suffering. C. W. B.

THE DOOR OF THE HEART—Rev. iii. 20.

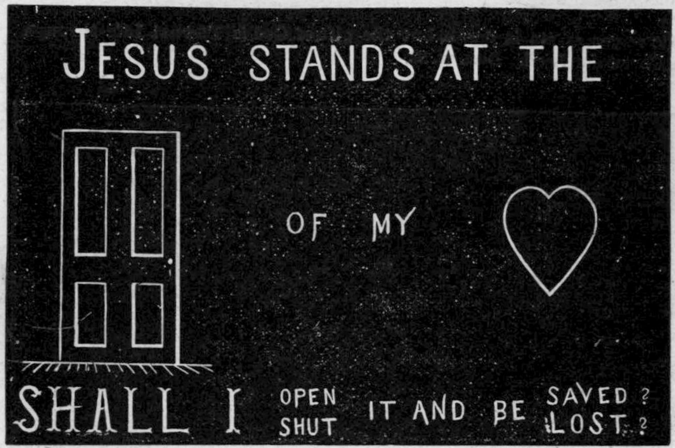

Jesus speaks of the soul as though it were a *house* into which He would like to enter, and abide as a *guest*. He calls it "The Door." His language is, "Behold, I stand at the door and knock." Your *heart* is the door. Did you ever think that the Saviour stands there *waiting* for you to open the door, so that He may come in and abide there? When some friend comes and knocks at the door of your house, you or some one quickly hastens to open the door, and let that friend come in. You do not keep your friend standing and waiting very long, if you can help it, but you throw open the door just as soon as possible. How do you treat the Saviour who comes and asks you to let Him come in?

How would your friends feel if they knew you were listening to their knocking, and yet would not let them come in? They would be *grieved*, and very likely would go away in great sorrow and anger. But do you not fear that the Saviour will become weary, and turn away and leave you all alone in your sins and sorrows? Sometimes you may not desire to have a person enter your house: but surely you would not feel like refusing to admit such a guest as the Saviour. It will make but little difference to you, sometimes, whether you open the door or not, when *some* persons are knocking, for you will be just as happy without their presence; but not so in this case.

It will make a great difference whether you open the door or keep it closed against the Saviour.

Open it, and He will come in, and help you and comfort you, and save you at last in His heavenly kingdom.

When the Prince of Wales came to this country, what a welcome he received; there wasn't anything too good for him. When the Prince of Russia came to this country, I saw him as he was escorted up Broadway, and cheer upon cheer went up all the way.—*Moody.*

But Jesus is the Prince of Life Eternal. Give Him a glad welcome.

WHAT WE DO BY FAITH.

We live.................................Gal. ii. 20.
We stand.................................2 Cor. i. 24.
We walk.................................2 Cor. v. 7.
We fight.................................1 Tim. vi. 12.
We overcome.................................1 John v. 4.
We die.................................Rom. vi. 11.
We sit with Him.................................Rev. iii. 21.

NEW THINGS OF THE BIBLE.

New birth (conversion).................................John iii. 3.
New nature (Christian life)..........2 Cor. v. 17; 2 Peter i. 4.
New heart (affections changed)................Ezekiel xi. 19.
New friends (Christians)........John xv. 15; Heb. xii. 22-24.
New name (Sons of God).1 John iii. 1; Rev. ii. 17; Rev. iii. 12.
New food (Heavenly Manna)......John vi. 48-51; Rev. ii. 17.
New tongue (To tell the story)........Mark xvi. 17; Acts ii. 4.
New song (Redemption).................................Rev. v. 9.
New home (Mansions above)..................Rev. xxi. 1-4.
All things new (in Christ)..........2 Cor. v. 17; Rev. xxi. 5.

GOD'S PROMISE IN THE RAINBOW.

When Noah left the ark, God gave him a promise not to destroy the race again with a flood. As a "token" of this covenant, He "set His bow in the cloud." Gen. ix. 13. Every time Noah saw the beautiful bow spanning the heavens he knew that God was keeping the promise, and he felt happy and secure. The bow was *silent*, and yet it *seemed to say*, "God is faithful to His promise."

Let us turn our attention to some features of the rainbow.

And, first, the rainbow is always associated with a storm. We do not see it when the noon-day sun is shining, but we must wait till the clouds gather and the rain-drops fall. Then the bow appears and delights our eyes. So in the storms of life, we see the beauty of God's promise shining through the gloom. The bow of His promise spans many a dark cloud of sorrow.

Again, the rainbow appears *very often.*

We suppose Noah saw it a great many times. Even some of our younger children have seen it quite often. God is never at a loss for a rainbow. He can make one at any time, and it would seem as though He had already made a great many. So many rainbows are so many *renewals* of His promise. And He has *many* promises for us all in the Bible. Some one has it that there are more than *thirty thousand* distinct promises in the Word of God. Think of it—thirty thousand *bows of promise* in the Bible. Take this one, children, as *your own:* "Those that seek me *early* shall find me." Prov. viii. 17.

The rainbow has all its *original beauty* unimpaired. It is just as brilliant to-day as when it first spanned the heavens. It has not changed its form, nor lost any of its bright colors. It is still God's token, *unchanged* and unchangeable. Some one has termed it "an *old* thing, invested with a *new* meaning." So His promises are *firm* and *true.* "All the promises of God in him are *yea*, and in him *Amen.*" 2 Cor. i. 20. "An old man once told me that he had marked at all the promises of God the letters 'P. T.'—which stood for 'Proved and Tried.' None of the promises of God ever will or can fail."—*Moody.*

Well may it be said, "The Lord is not slack concerning his promise." 2 Pet. iii. 9. What promise is written upon the bow in the picture? Will *you* try to obtain that rest?

THE APOSTLES' CREED.

I believe in God the Father ....Jer. xxxii. 17.
In Jesus the Son of God ....1 John iv. 9.
In His human birth..............................Rom. i. 3.
In His sufferings under Pilate..................John xix. 1.
In His crucifixion..............................Luke xxiii. 33.
In His death....................................John xix. 30.
In His burial...................................Matt. xxvii. 59, 60.
In His resurrection.............................Matt. xxviii. 5, 6.
In His ascension................................Mark xvi. 19.

W. F. C.

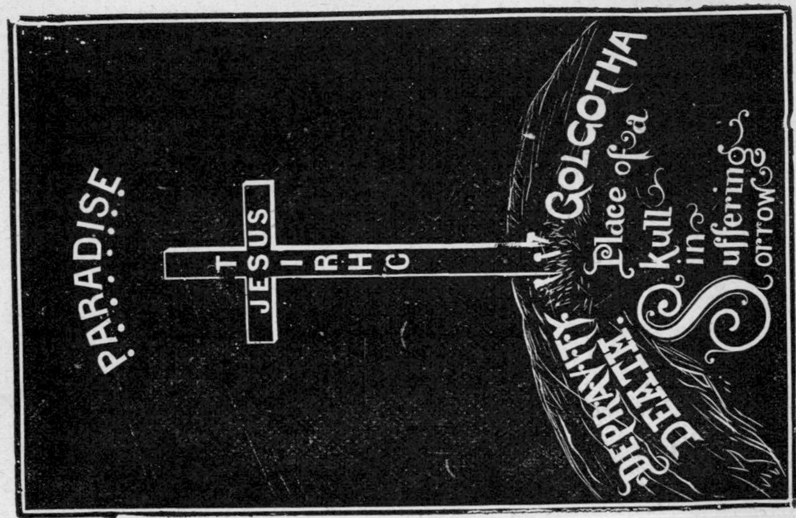
PARADISE
JESUS
CHRIST
GOLGOTHA
Place of a Skull
in Suffering Sorrow
DEPRAVITY
DEATH

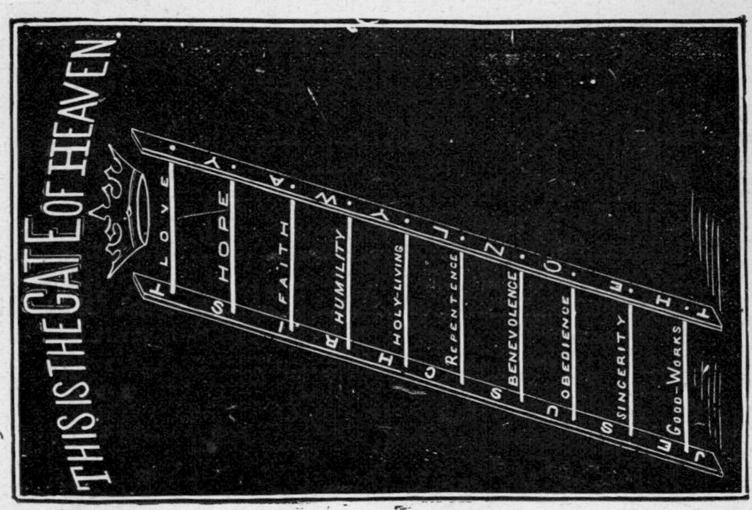
THIS IS THE GATE OF HEAVEN.
LOVE
HOPE
FAITH
HUMILITY
HOLY-LIVING
REPENTENCE
BENEVOLENCE
OBEDIENCE
SINCERITY
GOOD-WORKS

TRIUMPHS OF THE CROSS.

The cross upon which the crucified Redeemer suffered and died was placed on Golgotha, or Calvary, the place of a skull, so named from the sufferings and tortures of the wretched malefactors who were there crucified.

The gospel, with its plan of salvation, is based on human depravity. When this lost and ruined state is fully recognized in us and understood by us, then we can rightly appreciate the gospel message that comes to us through the cross, ever pointing heavenward to the Paradise of Saints; even to the throne of God.

Between earth and Paradise, Jesus Christ, the Saviour of the world, hung in agonies unutterable, and by His death He triumphed over *sin*, *suffering*, *sorrow*, and even *death*.

JACOB'S LADDER. Gen. xxviii. 10–23.

"This is none other but the house of God; this is the gate of heaven." Thus said Jacob as he awoke from his dream on the stony pillow at Luz (afterward called Bethel). The gate of heaven is nearer to each of us than we think. It is good to remember that God is always near; and this thought should be our guard against yielding to temptation and sin. Our loneliness and times of trial are often the occasions when God manifests Himself nearer and dearer to us, and gives us clearer and more precious views of His purposes concerning us. Jacob's pillow became a pillow of remembrance—a memorial; his lonely resting-place upon the plain, a Bethel—a House of God. Do we set up pillars of remembrance of His mercies to us? Jacob's ladder is emblematic of the way of salvation, which is like a ladder "set up on earth," its top reaching to heaven. Our *good works*, *sincerity*, *and acts* are like rounds or steps by which we hope to reach the heavenly home; these alone will not save us. Our only hope is through *Christ*. The rounds of a ladder are useless without sides. Let the sides represent Christ. If our desires, intentions, and acts are sanctified by resting in and through Christ, then we have that hope which is as an anchor to the soul, sure and steadfast. Without Christ all will be useless.

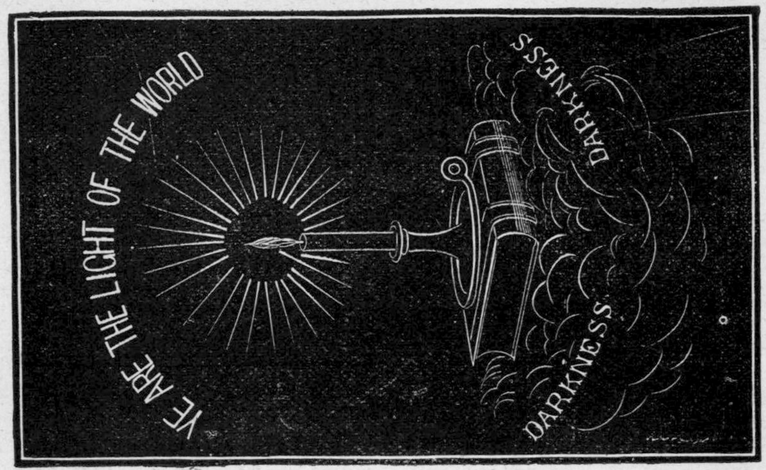
YE ARE THE LIGHT OF THE WORLD
DARKNESS
DARKNESS
DARKNESS

CHRIST
FAITH
VIRTUE
KNOWLEDGE
TEMPERANCE
PATIENCE
GODLINESS
CHARITY.

CHRISTIANS THE LIGHT OF THE WORLD.

Christ teaches us that he is represented in the moral world by His people, who are to let their "light *shine* before men." Matt. v. 16. This is *your* privilege, even though you are so young. The light often shines through young hearts just as clearly as it does from aged saints. You are to banish darkness from your homes and from the social circles in which you move. Keep the light shining in *your own* heart. Keep it shining on the pathway of *others*.

> "Let the lower lights be burning!
> Send a gleam across the wave!
> Some poor fainting, struggling seaman
> You may rescue, you may save."
>
> P. P. BLISS.

THE CROSS.

The chief idea conveyed by this illustration is that the Christian reaches heaven by the way of the cross. The word *Christ* stands out very prominently on this ladder, indicating that Christ is the source of its strength; while above it we have a glimpse of the sun, showing that it leads to a fair and sunny land. On the rounds of this ladder we see the words of Peter written in his 2d Epistle, 1st chapter, 5th and 6th verses. The order, however, seems to be reversed. Peter says: "Add to your faith, virtue," etc., and the most natural thought would be that "faith" should be at the *lower* round, and all the other virtues above it; and then *ascending* the ladder, we might "*add*" all other essential graces. But we see the wisdom of this order when we remember that the grandest exhibitions of *charity* are found in the lower realm of human life. He who is at the top of the ladder needs no charity for the angels nor the saints in light, but he does need it for those who are *below* him. Exercise charity. Let faith lift you up to Christ, and then you will have His spirit, and you will be true to yourselves and true to others.

CHRIST OUR GUIDING STAR.

Christ, the hope of the world, may be symbolized by a star, leading men to a better life, and pointing them heavenward. The magis and shepherds found Christ through the light and guidance of the star of Bethlehem. Christ is revealed in all the Scriptures, both Old and New Testament, as the Saviour for *All*, and *Forever*. The Bible has been, and is, such a star to-day, and by its light all men may be led to Christ which taketh away the sin of the world.

In 2 Pet. i. 19 reference is made to *the Word* as a light shining in a dark place, and to Christ as a *day Star.*

The points of the star, the lights and shadows composing it, all point to or centre in Christ.

In the diagram the various portions of the Bible that make up the grand luminary are indicated as follows: P. for Pentateuch; H. for Historical Books of the O. T.; Po. for Poetic Books; L. Pr. for five Longer Prophets; S. Pr. for Shorter Prophets; G. for Gospel; A. for Acts; E. for Epistles, and R. for Revelation. The whole Bible shining as one star, with the pre-eminent purpose of bringing all men to a saving knowledge of the truth as it is in Jesus; and to illustrate the universal reign of Christ and His salvation for the whole human family, we represent upon the outer points of the star the far-off nations or races of the world. C. for Caucasian, or white; A. for American or Indian; E. for Ethiopian or Negro; Ma. for Malay; Mo. for Mongolian. All of which, through the enlightening and converting influence of the gospel, are to be brought to know Christ as the Lord of lords and King of kings.

> "Jesus shall reign where'er the sun
> Does his successive journeys run;
> His kingdom stretch from shore to shore
> Till moons shall wax and wane no more."

"COMES" OF CHRIST.

1. Come unto me.................................Matt. xi. 28.
2. Come, ye blessed.............................Matt. xxv. 34.
3. Come apart and rest..........................Mark vi. 31.
4. Come down....................................Luke xix. 5.
5. Come forth...................................John xi. 43.
6. Come and dine................................John xxi. 12.
7. Come and see.................................John i. 39.
8. I will come again............................John xiv. 3.

LESSONS FROM THE LION.

The lion is the king of the forest, and from this proud, noble monarch of the animal kingdom we may learn some useful lessons.

The lion is *destructive* when enraged. A single stroke of his paw lays the strongest man in the dust. Satan, in this respect, is a being in the moral world that is compared to the lion. He "goeth about as a roaring lion, seeking whom he may *devour.*"

Beware of this lion of the *soul*, for he is *more* cruel than the lion of the forest.

The lion is *bold*. His eye never quails, his form never trembles with *fear*. The "righteous" are said to be as "*bold* as a lion." Will *you* also be "bold" in *opposing* the wrong, and in *defending* the right? *Cowards* are detestable. Be lion-like in *courage*. Learn to say *no* when necessary. "When sinners entice thee, consent thou not." Be *strong* and *bold*.

"The wicked flee when no man pursueth; but the righteous are bold as a lion." Prov. xxviii. 1.

SEARCHING THE SCRIPTURES.

We are to do this for various reasons. It would be sufficient to say that Jesus has commanded us to do so. "Search ye the scriptures, for in them ye think ye have eternal life." John v. 39. No book has been searched as the Bible has, from its origin to the present time. Foes have searched it with *evil* designs, but it *bears* their severest criticisms. Friends have searched it with sincere motives, and have found in it a *response* to all their *longings* and *hopes.*

How it *rewards* all who search it. It offers *light* for their darkness, and *truth* for error. It kindles *hope* in the soul, *comforts* it in sorrow, and reveals the way of *salvation.* Its teachings thrill the soul with *joy*, and lead to the precious boon of *peace*, here and hereafter. *Search* it, young and old. It is able to make us "wise unto salvation."

"All scripture is given by inspiration of God, and is profitable for doctrine, for reproof, for correction, for instruction in righteousness:

"That the man of God may be perfect, thoroughly furnished unto all good works." 2 Tim. iii. 16, 17.

THE WINE CUP.

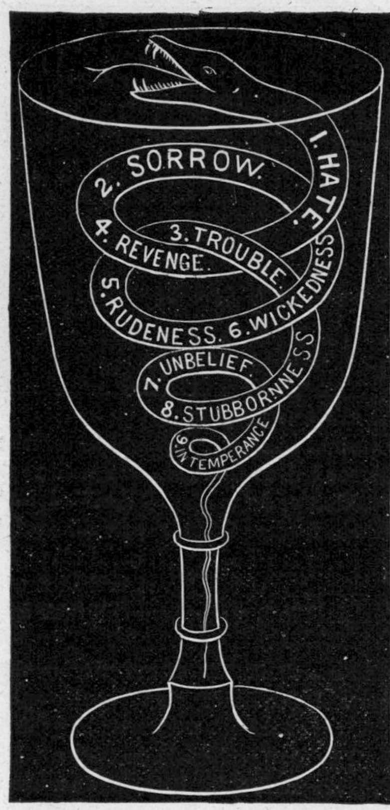

Behold the *ingredients* of the cup!

See the serpent coiled within the glass, waiting to fix his poisonous fangs upon the unsuspecting victim, and thrust the deadly poison through both body and soul. The glass may *seem* harmless, but it is *surcharged* with the elements of *destruction.* It may glow and sparkle, but the *hiss* of the serpent is in it. "At the last it biteth *like* a serpent." Prov. xxiii. 32. No wonder the Bible comes to us saying: "Look not thou upon the wine." Prov. xxiii. 31; xx. 1.

Children, beware of wine, and beware of *beer* as well. It is a very popular drink in America as well as in Europe, but it is a *dangerous, ruinous* beverage. Some say it is *nutritious.* How *false.* Liebig shows that "one must drink twenty-three barrels of it to get as much nutriment as there is in a five-pound loaf of bread." Try the *bread*, and shun the *beer.* Let this be our motto, "Touch not, taste not, handle not."

PRAYER.

A CHALK TALK.

"Ask, and it shall be open unto you; seek, and ye shall find; knock and it shall be opened unto you."—Matt. vii. 7.

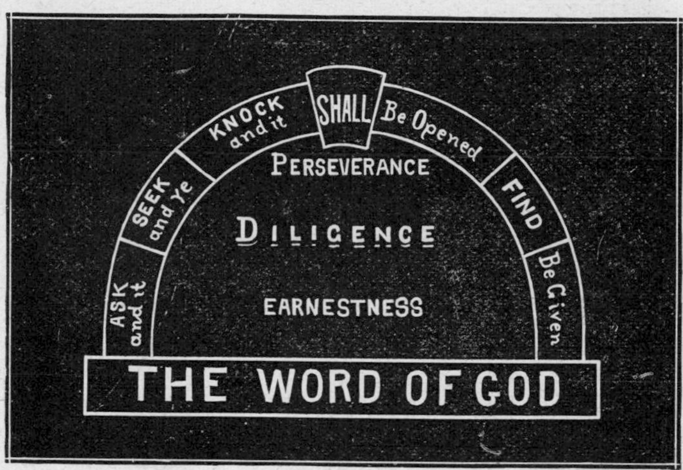

Have the children recite the verse in concert. Explain it as meaning, in all its directions, *Prayer*. Call attention to the fact that the initial letter of each direction themselves form a command to pray. Thus:

A-SK
S-EEK
K-NOCK

Ask the children to help you build an "Arch of Prayer." We learn how to pray, from God's Holy Word. It contains all the promises of God to us; all the encouragement to prayer.

We will build our arch, then, on the *Word of God*.

[Write, and enclose in lines as in diagram, for a foundation.]

The whole value of the promise depends upon this foundation. Remark upon God's omnipotence, love, &c., as being the qualities of this foundation stone.

Lay the first stone, and label it "*Ask*;" the opposite "*Given.*" Draw the others from the school, and place them as in diagram.

After the *third* block on each side is placed, call attention to the *space*. Show the importance of the *key ston* to the arch. It gives support and strength, and without it all the others are useless.

Point to the incompleteness of the sentence without one *word*. After they have named it, show its importance in binding the promise of God to the obedient, even though we are utterly unworthy of such a gracious pledge on the part of our Creator.

Show that these three words, *Ask*, *Seek*, *Knock*, indicate also different degrees of prayer. Commencing with an *earnest* desire, we inquire *diligently* after God's will, until our faith *perseveres* and conquers. [Illustrate by Scripture and familar example.]

This arch also illustrates the course of the returning sinner. He *asks* for the way, then *seeks* the door of salvation; having found it he knocks for admission.

We have no right to expect God's blessings until we comply with his conditions. We lay one stone, and immediately the opposite one is placed. When we do our part, God is faithful to His promise. Point to the positiveness of the promise in the key-stone word. Not *may*, but *shall*. Call especial attention to the fact that this promise is so framed as to be applicable to all—to *you*.

E. H. T.

Religious Emblems,

AND

ALLEGORIES,

AND

SEED THOUGHTS,

ILLUSTRATED.

True and false principles are here represented. The former are like the iceberg, brilliant, fascinating, ever changing, but cold, cheerless and melting before the sun. They cannot be trusted and will disappear before truth. True principles are like the rock, unchanged by years or storms and are worthy of confidence.—1 Pet. i. 25; Matt. xxiv. 35.

God's word is always good seed for the soil of man's mind and heart. It can be sown by the hand of every one. Sowing it, is the best employment in which any one can be engaged. This man is scattering this good seed, but birds, representing evil thoughts are ready to pick up and devour what he sows, and evil habits will trample on it. Matt. xiii. 3.

How many lives have been saved by a light-house which shows dangerous rocks or sand-bars in the sea, and the way into the harbor. The Bible is the great light-house of the world. Men are often in danger of drifting upon dangerous places in life, but those who have the Bible should warn the heedless to beware, and point out the narrow path which leads to heaven. Gen. xix. 7; Eph. ii. 2.

The self-confident proceed along the path of life as if there were no dangers ahead, when the experienced and observant know that fatal precipices may be reached at any time. But the conceited young man with a haughty air walks on, heeds not the warning voice that sounds in his ear, is deaf to every call although sudden destruction may come upon him. Prov. xxvi. 12.

The sea of life upon which fallen man now sails, is crested with billows threatening to engulf him, but Jesus is the Rock of salvation raising its head above every wave, and bearing upon its summit the cross, the emblem of atoning mercy, and complete salvation. Every sin-tossed soul may reach this Rock, cling to the cross and be safe. Ps. lxxii. 7.

The crowning graces of the Christian life are represented in this illustration. Faith in the cross of Jesus is the shield that wards off all the fiery darts of the enemy. Hope is the anchor which the Christian casts forward into the eternal world where there are no storms, and Charity which includes love to both God and man, crowns the whole and lasts forever. 1 Cor. xiii. 10.

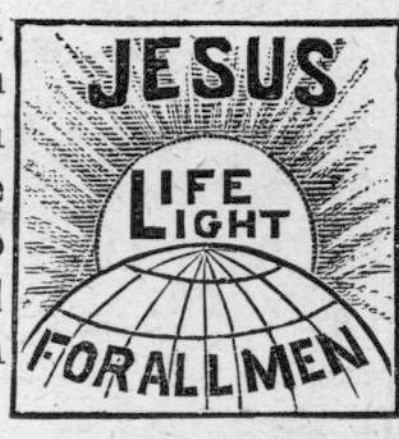

Darkness, because of sin, covers the earth and gross darkness the people. No created sun can enlighten this darkness. Jesus came from heaven, where all is light, to shed light upon the earth, and the knowledge of Him gives light to darkened minds and brings life to those dead in trespasses and sins. See how the earth brightens before Him. John ix. 6-9.

Folly, Solomon tells us, is bound up in the heart of a child and Paul writes that the world by its wisdom could not find God. But God's word is full of wisdom, profitable to man in every stage of his journey and in every circumstance of life. It enlightens him in his path, guides him in the way of peace and throws its brightness into the dark valley of death. Ps. li. 6; 2 Tim. iii. 17.

Man is in trouble and darkness because he is a sinner. He is often perplexed and in distress, and does not know which way to turn for relief or light. But rays of light and comfort come to him from Jesus who is the source of every good thing; these rays shine around his steps, cheer his heart, and puts new songs upon his lips. Ps. cxii. 4; xxiii. 4.

Heaven will admit nothing that is impure or earthly in its door. That door is therefore represented as strait and the way to it narrow. But a man who tries to carry his riches with him will find that his bags of gold must be left behind, and the man who is swelled with pride cannot crush through. There is room for nothing but a man himself. Mark vii. 14: Rev. xxi. 27.

Man becomes angry because he is a sinner. Sin excites the temper, inflames the passions, and dethrones the reason. When angry he is "beside himself," is ready to provoke others to wrath, to speak evil words and to commit evil deeds which may lead to disgrace and punishment. Therefore avoid anger and its attendant evils. Prov xv. 1; Eccl. vii. 9.

Who hast not seen a race where every one running was striving to be foremost? How unencumbered every runner appears! We are in the race of life and the prize to be won is eternal life. If we would win, we must not carry anything that will retard our steps; all weights must be thrown off. The man burdened with greed and selfishness cannot win. 1 Cor. ix. 24; Heb. xiii. 12.

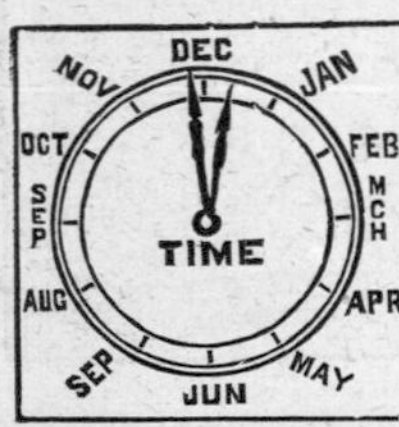

Time is divided into minutes, hours, months and years to help us improve it as it flies, and to warn us of the rapidity with which opportunities for becoming good and for doing good pass beyond our reach. As our eye catches the figures upon the dial-plate and we hear the tick of the watch or clock, we are reminded of the words, "Redeem the time." Eph. v. 16; Col. iv. 5.

Without Christian Hope we would be miserable in this life, being encompassed with trials here and without any bright prospect for another world. But faith in Christ supplies the believer with an anchor which keeps him steadfast, tends to cheer him in sorrow, and gives him promise of entering into a heaven of rest. Heb. vi. 19; Rom. viii. 24.

This illustration represents the same individual under different appearances—the one real and the other false. He is really cross, wicked and ready for every evil thing, but in his assumed character, with his mask upon him, he appears pleasant, and prepared for every good work. He is a wolf in sheep's clothing—a teacher of false doctrine—a hypocrite. Matt. vii. 15.

The currents of this world run so strong against the Christian that mere faith in Jesus as a Saviour will not avail him. If he does not ply the oar he will drift with the world, be caught in its eddying circles, dashed against its rocks or overwhelmed with its evil waves. His faith must be seconded by his works or he will be lost. James ii. 22.

"How false and yet how fair." is characteristic of many things in this world. Hence the danger that lurks beneath many of the bright, pleasant, and desirable objects of life. Luscious fruit may be attractive and tempting, but see the serpent behind ready to dart into that innocent, unsuspecting bird his poisonous fang! How blessed to have a deliverer. Matt. vi. 13.

This world is represented as a wilderness with dense forests, trackless wastes, pathless deserts and venomous animals. Man has to travel through it. He wants a light and a guide. God has given him these in the Bible. It is the only true light and sure guide. There are many false ones, but by using God's light he will reach home safely. Ps. cxix 105; 2 Pet. i. 19.

There is but one way to heaven and that is by the cross. It is the way of difficulty, of humility, of watchfulness, of perseverance in well-doing; but it is safe though encompassed with foes. It is marked with the footsteps of Jesus and every follower of Him, will find the cross easy, the burden light, the foes controlled by God and the crown sure. Mark viii. 38.

False religions abound yet in the world. But Christianity has the pledge of victory. The weapons of her warfare are God's word read and preached and made effectual by God's Spirit. Idolatory will vanish from the earth. The enemies of Jesus will be overthrown or converted into friends and Jesus will be crowned Lord of all. Rev. xix. 6.

And whosoever shall swear by the **altar** it is nothing; but whosoever swearest by the gift that is on it, he is guilty. Matt. xxiii. 18.

And the Lord said unto Noah, Come thou and all thy house into the **ark;** for thee have I seen righteous before me in this generation. Gen. vii. 1.

And when the **ark of the covenant** of the Lord came into the camp, all Israel shouted with a great shout, so that the earth rang again. I. Sam. iv. 5.

Is there no **balm in Gilead;** is there no physician there? Why then is not the health of the daughter of my people recovered? Jer. viii. 22.

And further by these my sons, be admonished; of making many **books** there is no end: and much study is a weariness to the flesh. Eccl. xii. 12. Many of them also which used curious arts brought their books together and burned them before all men. Acts xix. 19.

Stand therefore having your loins girt about with truth, and having on a **breast-plate** of righteousness. Eph. vi. 14. He put on righteousness as a breast-plate. Isa. lix. 17.

Whoso removeth stones shall be hurt therewith, and he that **cleaveth wood** shall be in danger thereby. Eccl. x. 9.

But God forbid that I should glory save in the **cross** of our Lord Jesus Christ; by whom the world is crucified unto me and I unto the world. Gal. vi. 14.

Who for the joy that was set before him, endured the **cross.** Heb. xii. 2.
Whosoever will come after me, let him deny himself, and take up his cross, and follow me. Mark viii. 34.

Behold, I come quickly: hold that fast which thou hast, that no man take thy **crown.** Rev. iii. 11.

Whose hope shall be cut off, and whose trust shall be a **spider's web.** Job, viii. 14.

The spider taketh hold with her hands as in kings' palaces. Job, xxx. 28.

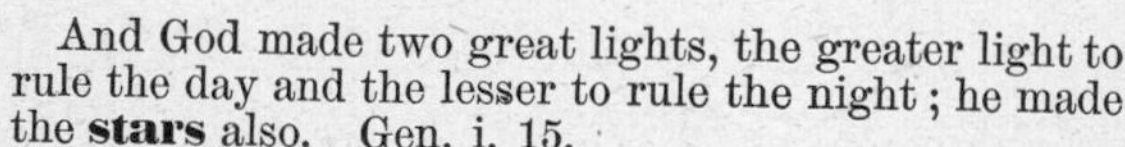

And God made two great lights, the greater light to rule the day and the lesser to rule the night; he made the **stars** also. Gen. i. 15.

But unto you that fear my name shall the **Sun** of righteousness arise with healing in his wings. And ye shall go forth and grow up as calves of the stall. Mal. iv. 2.

And they shall beat their **swords** into ploughshares, and their spears into pruning-hooks: nation shall not lift up a sword against nation, neither shall they learn war any more. Mic. iv. 3.

And the angel * * sware by him that liveth for ever and ever, that there should be **time** no longer. Rev. x. 6. And he cometh and findeth them sleeping and saith unto Peter, Simon, sleepest thou? couldst not thou watch one hour? Mark. xiv. 37.

Marvellous things did he in the sight of their fathers, in the land of Egypt. Psalm, lxxviii. 12.

I will make the land of Egypt utterly waste and desolate from the **tower** of Syene even unto the border of Ethiopia. Ezk. xxix. 10.

For among my people are found wicked men: they lay wait as he that setteth snares; they set a **trap,** they catch men. Jer. v. 26. A snare is laid for him in the ground, and a trap for him in the way. Job xviii. 10.

For what is a man profited if he shall gain the whole **world** and lose his own soul? Matt. xvi. 26.

Therefore shall ye lay up these my words, in your heart and in your soul, and bind them for a sign upon your head. Deut. ii. 18. Heaven and earth shall pass away, but my **word** shall not pass away. Mark, xiii. 31.

And the tables were the work of God, and the **writing** was the writing of God, graven upon the tables. Ex. xxxii. 16. But if ye believe not his writings, how shall ye believe my words? John, v. 47.

Thy word is a **lamp** unto my feet and a light unto my path. Psl. cxix. 105.

Cause the lamp to burn always. Exodus xxvii. 20.

Shall thy wonders be known in the dark? Psl. lxxxix. 12.

For thou art my **lamp,** O Lord; and the Lord wilt lighten my darkness. II. Sam. xxii. 29.

Take this book of the **law** and put it in the side of the ark of the covenant of the Lord your God, that it may be there for a witness against thee. Deut. xxxi. 36.

And the whole **world** was of one language and of one speech. Gen. ii. 1. The multitude came together, and was confounded because that every man heard them speak in his own language. Acts. ii. 6.

Ye are the **light of the world.** Matt. v. 14.

That ye may be blameless and harmless, among whom ye shine as lights of the world. Phil. ii. 15.

And all the people saw the thunderings, and the **lightnings,** and the noise of the trumpet, and the mountain smoking, and when the people saw it, they removed, and stood afar off. Ex. xx. 18.

And the second angel sounded, and as it were a great **mountain burning** with fire was cast into the sea. Rev. viii. 8. Let burning coals fall upon them: let them be cast into the fire. Ps. cxl. 10.

There shall the great **owl** make her nest, and lay and hatch, and gather under her shadow. Isaiah xxxiv. 15. I will make a * * * mourning as the owls. Micah i. 8.

Thou art weighed in the balance and found wanting. Dan. v. 27.

And I beheld, and lo, a black horse; and he that sat on him had a **pair of balances** in his hand. Rev. vi. 5.

And God shall wipe away all tears from their eyes; and there shall be no more death, neither **sorrow** nor crying; neither shall there be any more pain. Rev. xxi. 4.

Wherefore as by one man sin entered into the world and **death** by sin; and so death passed upon all men for that all have sinned! Rom. v. 12.

Draw nigh to God and he will draw nigh to you. Cleanse your hands, ye sinners; and purify your hearts, ye **double-minded.** Jas. iv. 8.

And they shall come from the **east** and from the **west,** and from the **north** and from the **south,** and shall sit down in the kingdom of God. Luke, xiii. 29.

As in water face answereth to **face,** so the heart of man to man. Prov. xxvii. 19.

A double-minded man is unstable in all his ways. Jas. i. 8.

As for man his days are as grass; as the **flower** of the field so he flourisheth. Psl. ciii. 15.

He cometh forth like a flower and is cut down. Job, xiv. 2.

So they hanged Haman on the **gallows** that he had prepared for Mordecai. Esther, vii. 10.

And they hanged Haman's ten sons. Esther. ix. 14.

Rechab said to him, Is thine heart right, as my heart is with thy heart? And Jehonadab answered, It is. If it be give me thine **hand:** and he gave him his hand; and he took him up to him into the chariot. II. Kings, x. 15.

When I consider thy **heavens,** the work of thy fingers, the moon and the stars which thou hast ordained, What is man? Psl. viii. 3.

Therefore when thou doest thine alms, do not sound a trumpet before thee, as the **hypocrites** do in the synagogues and in the streets, that they may have glory of men. Matt. vi. 2.

Solomon seeing the young man that he was **industrious,** he made him ruler over all the charge of the house of Joseph. I. Kings, ii. 28.

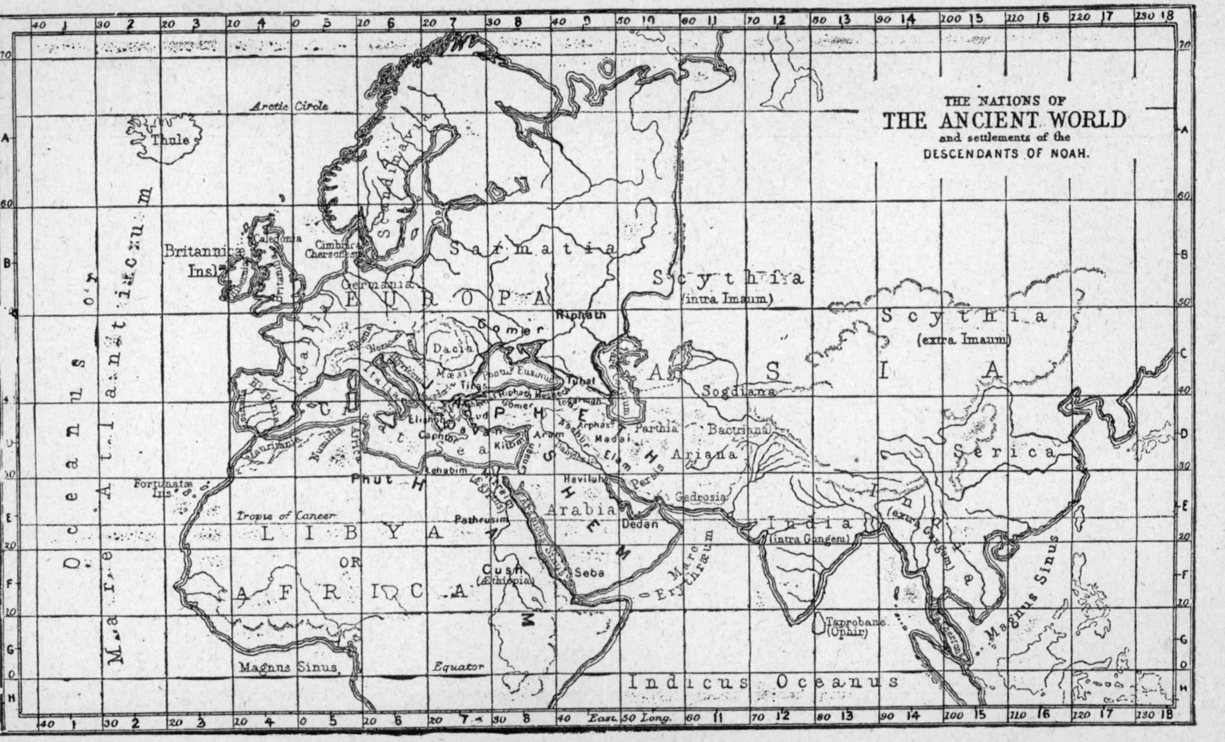
THE NATIONS OF
THE ANCIENT WORLD
and settlements of the
DESCENDANTS OF NOAH.
Arctic Circle
Thule
Britannicæ Insl.
Caledonia
Cimbrica Chersonesus
Scandinavia
Sarmatia
Germania
EUROPA
Scythia (intra Imaum)
Scythia (extra Imaum)
Riphath
Gomer
Dacia
Pontus Euxinus
Tubal
Togarmah
Tiras
Meshech
Italia
Hispania
Gallia
Mauritania
Numidia
Africa
Phut
Elishah
Caphtor
Kittim
Aram
Asshur
Arphax
Madai
Elam
Parthia
Bactriana
Sogdiana
Ariana
Persis
Gedrosia
Havilah
Arabia
Dedan
Seba
SHEM
JAPHETH
HAM
Pathrusim
Cush (Æthiopia)
LIBYA OR AFRICA
Tropic of Cancer
Fortunatæ Ins.
Oceanus Atlanticum
Mare Atlanticum
Magnus Sinus
Equator
Mare Erythræum
Indicus Oceanus
India (intra Gangem)
India (extra Gangem)
Taprobane (Ophir)
Serica
ASIA
Magnus Sinus
East. Long.

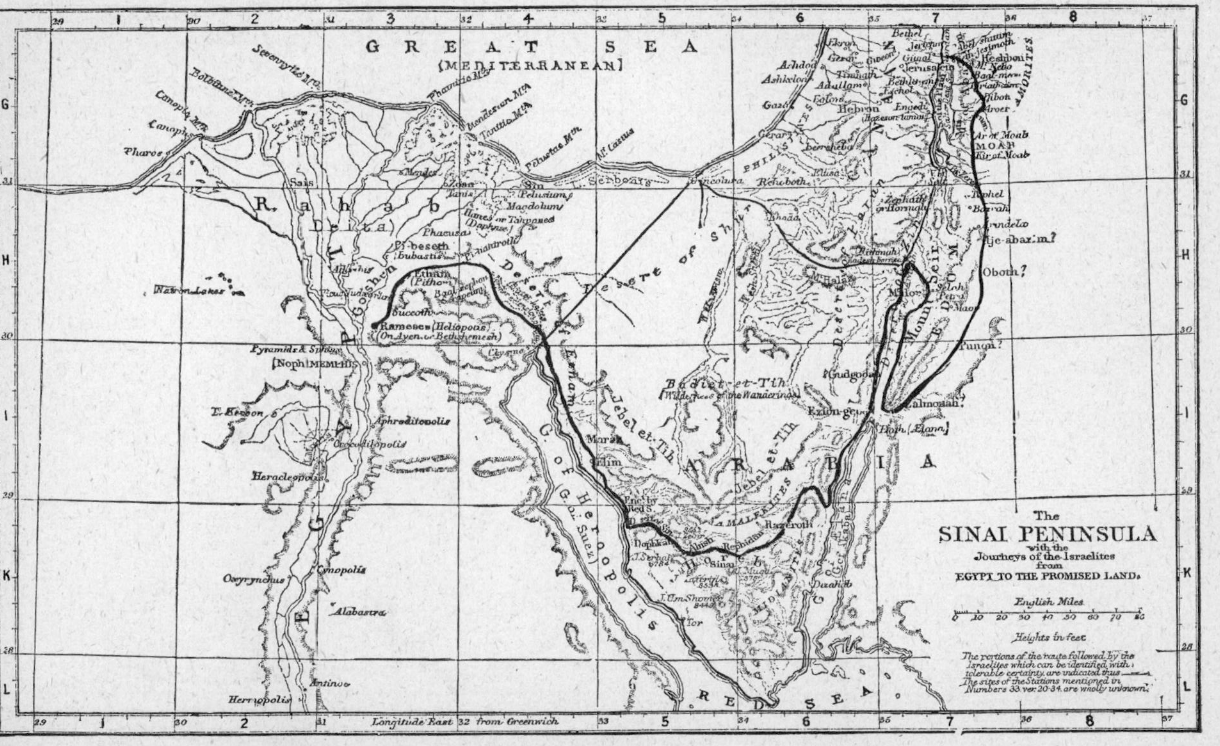
The
SINAI PENINSULA
with the
Journeys of the Israelites
from
EGYPT TO THE PROMISED LAND.
English Miles
0 10 20 30 40 50 60 70 80
Heights in feet
The portions of the route followed by the Israelites which can be identified with tolerable certainty are indicated thus
The sites of the Stations mentioned in Numbers 33 ver. 20-34 are wholly unknown.
GREAT SEA
(MEDITERRANEAN)
RED SEA
ARABIA
EGYPT
EDOM
MOAB
AMORITES
PHILISTINES
AMALEKITES
MIDIANITES
Rahab
(Delta)
Goshen
Desert of Shur
Desert of Etham
Badiet-et-Tih
(Wilderness of the Wanderings)
Jebel et-Tih
G. of Heroopolis
(G. of Suez)
Mount Seir
Rameses (Heliopolis)
(On Aven or Bethshemesh)
Succoth
Etham
(Pithom)
Baal-zephon
Marah
Elim
Dophkah
Sinai
Tor
Dizahab
Ezion-geber
Hebron
Gaza
Beersheba
Rehoboth
Gerar
Ashdod
Ashkelon
Adullam
Engedi
Jerusalem
Bethel
Heshbon
Nebo
Aroer
Ar of Moab
Kir of Moab
Oboth?
Punon?
Zalmonah?
Gudgodah
Hazeroth
Rhinocolura
Serbonis
Pelusium
Magdolum
Tanis
Zoan
Phacusa
Pi-beseth
Bubastis
Mendes
Sais
Canopus
Pharos
Natron Lakes
Pyramids & Sphinx
(Noph) MEMPHIS
Aphroditopolis
Crocodilopolis
Heracleopolis
Oxyrynchus
Cynopolis
Alabastra
Antinoe
Hermopolis
Longitude East 32 from Greenwich

PALESTINE
in the Time of Our Saviour
Roman Miles
English Miles
THE GREAT SEA
(MEDITERRANEAN)
SYRIA
DAMASCUS
Sidon
(Tyre) Tyrus
Ptolemais
Nazareth
CÆSAREA
Samaria
Sebaste
Sychar
Jerusalem
Hebron
Gaza
Ascalon
Azotus
Gadara
Gerasa
Decapolis
Philadelphia
Ammonitis
Trachonitis
Bostra
Moabitis
Idumæa
ARABIA
Longitude East from Greenwich

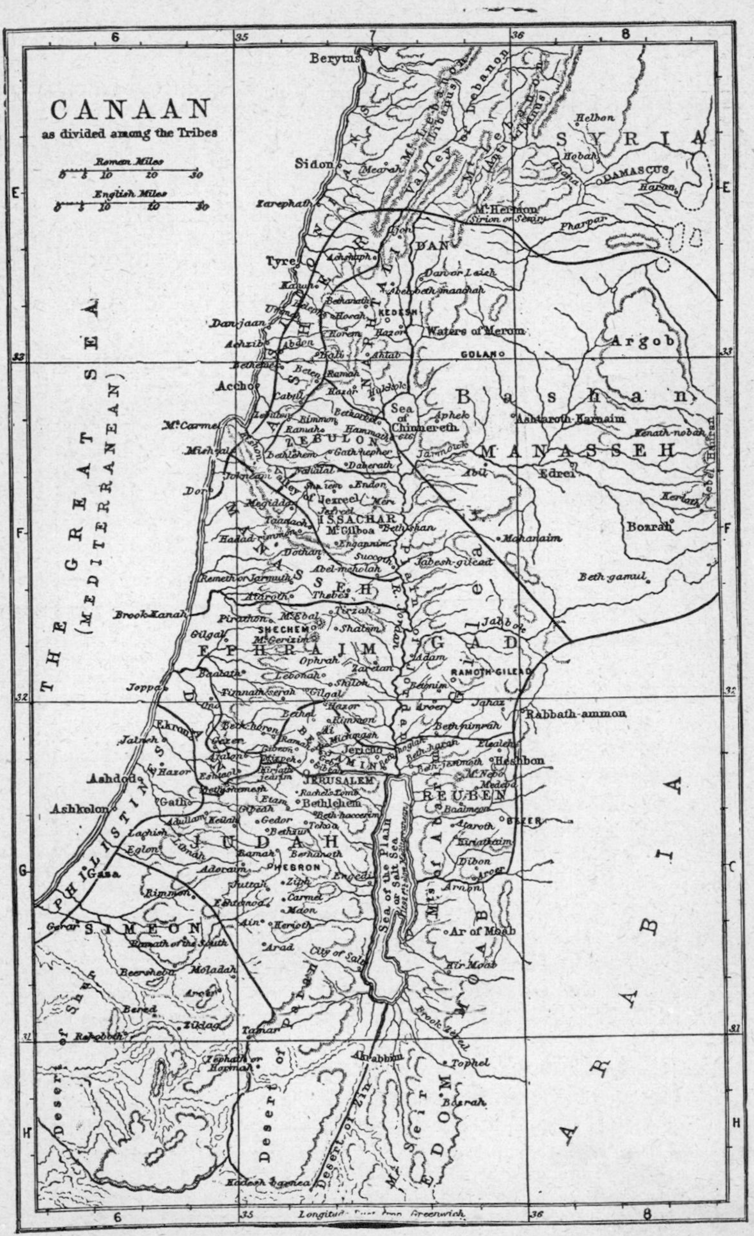

CANAAN
as divided among the Tribes
Roman Miles
English Miles
THE GREAT SEA (MEDITERRANEAN)
Berytus
Sidon
Zarephath
Tyre
Achzib
Accho
Mt. Carmel
Dor
Joppa
Ekron
Ashdod
Ashkelon
Gath
Gaza
PHILISTINES
SIMEON
Beersheba
JUDAH
HEBRON
JERUSALEM
Bethlehem
Jericho
BENJAMIN
EPHRAIM
SHECHEM
ISSACHAR
Mt. Gilboa
ZEBULON
Jezreel
Megiddo
ASHER
NAPHTALI
DAN
KEDESH
Waters of Merom
Sea of Chinnereth
GOLAN
Argob
Bashan
MANASSEH
Edrei
Bozrah
Mahanaim
GAD
Jabbok
RAMOTH GILEAD
Rabbath-ammon
Heshbon
REUBEN
BEZER
Arnon
Ar of Moab
MOAB
Sea of the Plain or Salt Sea
EDOM
Mt. Seir
Kadesh barnea
Desert of Zin
Desert of Paran
ARABIA
SYRIA
DAMASCUS
Mt. Hermon
Mt. Lebanon
Anti Lebanon
Pharpar
Longitude East from Greenwich

With Barnabas and John Mark. (Acts xiii. xiv.)

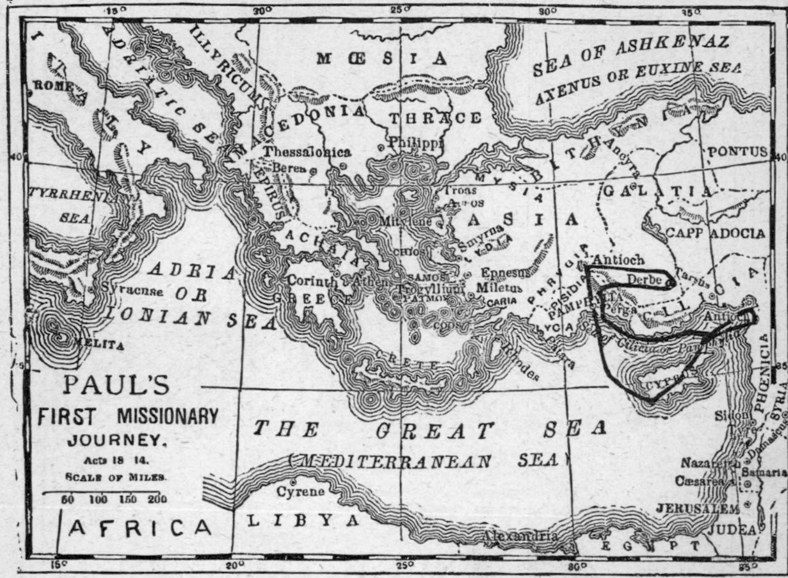

They start from Antioch, in Syria, the centre of Gentile evangelization, to go to Selucia, its seaport, whence they sail to the island of Cyprus, landing at Salamis. The Apostles preached in the synagogues there, then traversed the isle, 100 miles, to Paphos, its capital city, where Elymas was struck blind and Sergius Paulus, the Roman pro-consul, converted. They then crossed to the southern shore of Asia Minor and landed at Perga, where John Mark left them and returned home. The mountains were then crossed where they probably suffered the trials enumerated in II. Cor. xi., 26, 27, till they reached Antioch in Pisidia. Here they preached the first Sabbath in the synagogue to the Jews (Paul's first recorded sermon) and the second Sabbath to the Gentiles, but were subsequently ejected by the rulers. The great road was then followed to Iconium, the capital of Lycaonia, where they stayed a long time making converts, but were at length stoned and fled to Lystra. Here Paul healed a cripple and the multitudes treated them as gods, Jupiter and Mercury; but Jews from Iconium came and, declaring them impostors, had them stoned. They fled thence to Derbe where having rested awhile they returned through Lystra, Iconium and Antioch to Perga. Having here but little success they sailed back to Antioch where they reported their work to a full assembly of disciples and abode probably six or seven years.

With Silas. (Acts xv. 36; xviii. 22.)

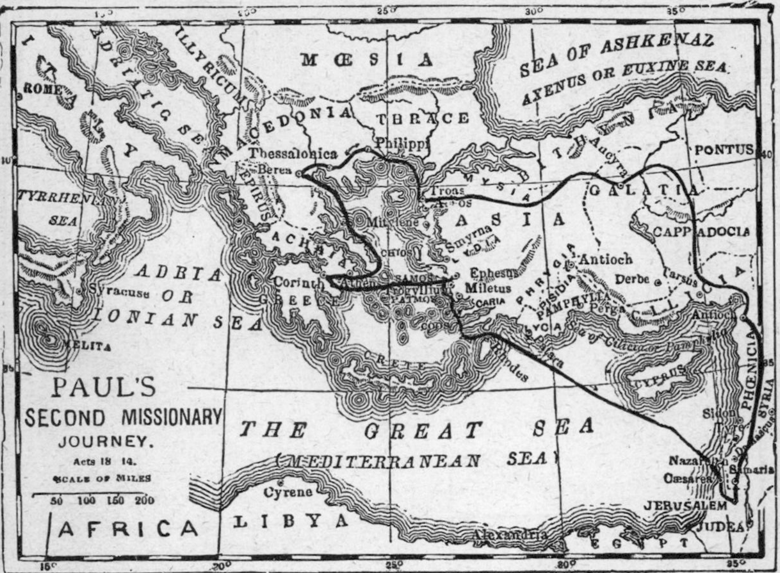

Antioch, in Syria, the starting-point, whence through Syria and Cilicia, confirming the churches and delivering the decrees of the council of Jerusalem. Thence across the mountains to Derbe and Lystra, where Timothy joined Paul. They then went through Phrygia and Galatia, where Paul fell sick (Gal. iv., 13), then into Mysia, thence were divinely guided to Troas, where Paul met with Luke and had a vision inviting him to Macedonia. Here they embarked, touched at Samothracia and landed at Neapolis. Thence they crossed the Pharsalian Plain to Philippi, where Lydia and the jailer with his household were converted and baptized, the sorceress exorcised, the Apostles scourged, imprisoned and miraculously released. Paul, leaving Luke and Timothy here, passed through Amphipolis and Apollonia to Thessalonica, where he stayed three Sabbaths, was assailed by a Jewish mob, and escaped to Berea. Thence he was sent by the brethren probably by sea to Athens, where he disputed with the Jews and made his memorable address on Mars' Hill. Then he retired to Corinth; from this, as his head-quarters, he evangelized in Achaia; was joined by Silas and Timothy, wrote two Epistles to the Thessalonians, was brought before Gallio, and sailed with Aquila and Priscilla, two converts, from Cenchrea to Ephesus, where he left Aquila and Priscilla and went on to Cæsarea, thence to Jerusalem to keep the feast of Pentecost and returning to Antioch, where he remained a year.

With Timothy. (Acts xviii. 23; xxi. 33.)

Antioch, in Syria, again the starting-point, thence through Galatia and Phrygia to Ephesus, where they stayed three years. Here Paul refuted false philosophers, exposed the sorcerers, who burnt their books, taught in the school of Tyrannus, was opposed by Demetrius, and sent away by friends to Macedonia where he visited his converts, then passed on into Greece and probably visited the churches at Corinth and Achaia. Being waylaid by the Jews, he sent his companions forward to Troas, and by some secret route reached Philippi himself, where he was joined by Luke. They sailed thence and arrived at Troas in five days, where Paul preached and Eutychus fell from the window. From this they travelled by land to Assos, where Paul embarked, touched at Mitylene, anchored the next day off Chios, put in the day after at Throgyllium and the following day touched at Miletus, where Paul probably remained for two days, sent for the presbyters of Ephesus and bade them farewell. They sailed past Coos and Rhodes to Partara, changed vessels, sighted Cyprus, landed at Tyre, where Paul was warned not to go to Jerusalem. Here the Christians accompanied him to the ship, knelt on the shore and prayed. Then Paul proceeded to Ptolemais, thence to Cæsarea, where he remained many days with Philip and Agabus foretold his imprisonment. Then, accompanied by Mnason, they went by land to Jerusalem, where he was put in prison and sent to Cæsarea to the governor Felix.

With Aristarchus and prisoners under charge of Julius a centurion of the Augustan cohort. (Acts xxvii. xxviii.)

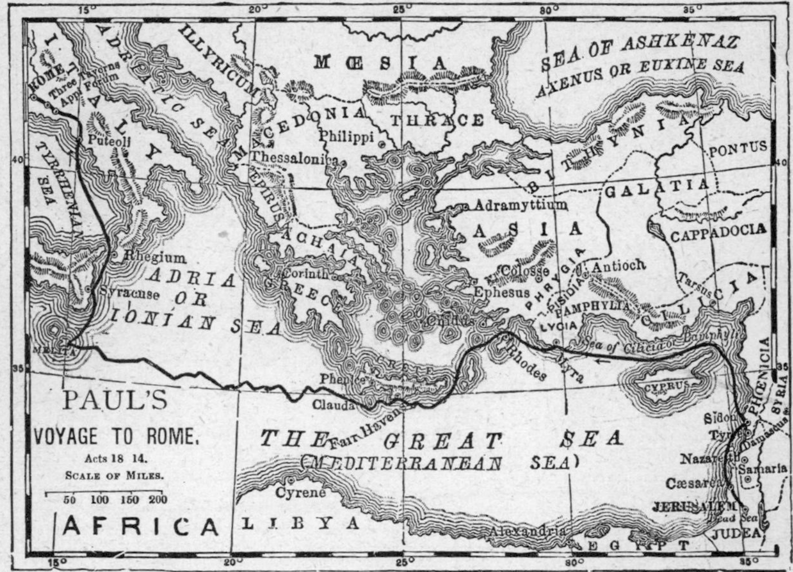

Paul sailed from Cæsarea in a vessel bound for Adramyttium, touched at Sidon, where he visited friends, sailed north of Cyprus to Myra, where they were transhipped to an Alexandrian corn-vessel which coasted for about 130 miles along the southern shore of Asia Minor and Cnidus, where the wind and current drove the ship southward to Crete; rounding Cape Salmore they made for Fair Havens, where Paul advised them to winter. But the harbor being incommodious, they tried to reach Phenice, which had a sheltered harbor, and were caught by the wind Euroclydon from the North-west. Under shelter of Clauda, an island south of Crete, they prepared for a tempest, struck sail, undergirded the ship, turned her head to the wind and lay to; during the next fourteen days they drifted 486 miles and ran the ship aground in a creek of Melita (Malta) where they landed by various means. Here Paul shook a viper from his hand, healed Publius, the chief man of the island, of fever, and abode three months. Sailed thence in an Alexandrian corn-ship to Syracuse (Sicily), then making a circuit, they came to Rhegium, Italy; after one day reached Puteoli, in the bay of Naples, where they rested seven days; thence went by the Appian Way to Appii Forum, where brethren met him and accompanied him to Rome, there he remained in custody of a soldier two years in his own hired house.

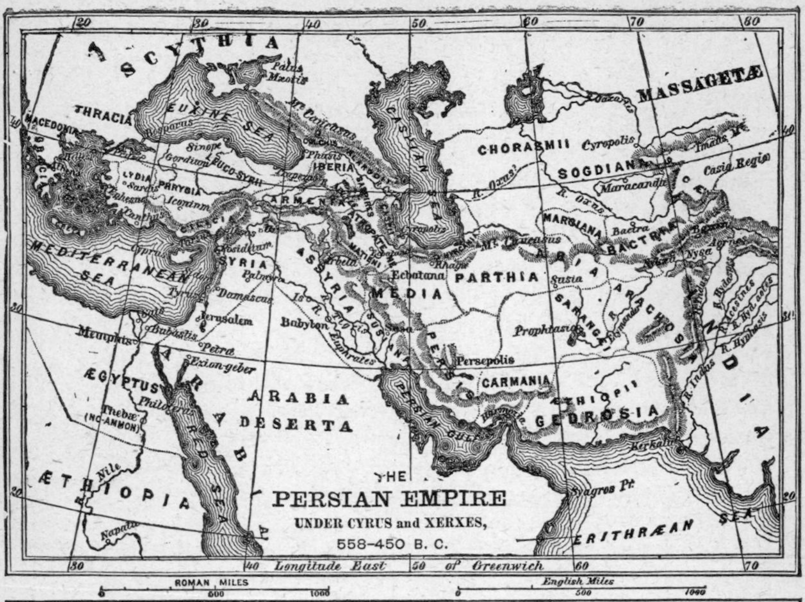

THE
PERSIAN EMPIRE
UNDER CYRUS and XERXES,

558-450 B. C.

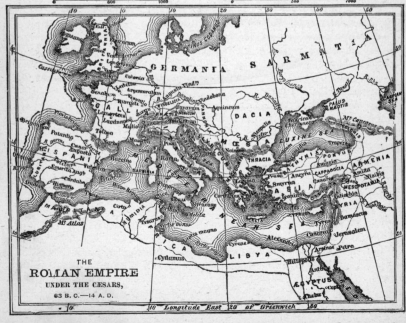

Longitude East of Greenwich

ROMAN MILES 0 500 1000

English Miles 0 500 1000

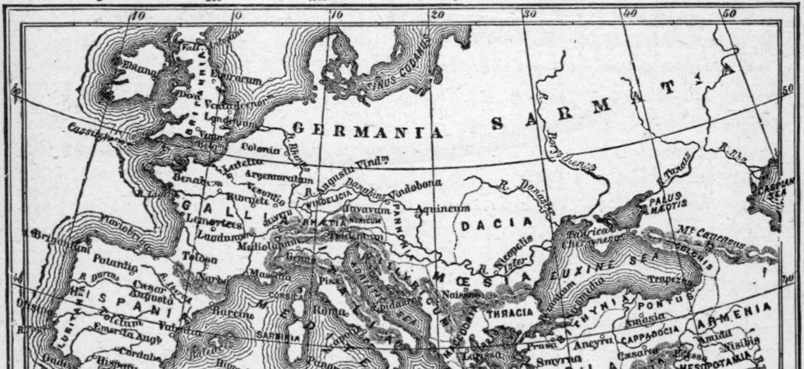

THE
ROMAN EMPIRE
UNDER THE CÆSARS,

63 B. C.—14 A. D.

Longitude East of Greenwich

PRAYER MEETING TALKS.

HOW TO MAKE PRAYER MEETINGS INTERESTING.

1. Get all the people close together, Ezra iii. 1 ; Neh. viii. 1 ; Matt. xviii. 20 ; Acts xii. 12 ; Acts ii. 1.

2. The leader should simply direct the minds of those present to something definite for prayer and meditation.

All talks should be short, Ecc. v. 2 ; 1 Cor. ii. 1-5, etc.

3. All prayers should be short and to the point ; avoid repetition, Matt. vi. 7-13. Short prayers the rule of the Bible.

Illustrations : Moses—Deut. ix, 26-29 ; Solomon—1 Kings iii. 6-9 ; Elisha—2 Kings vi. 17, 18 ; Hezekiah—2 Kings xix. 15-19 ; Jeremiah—xxxii. 16-25, etc.; Paul—Eph iii. 14-21 ; Our Saviour—Matt. xxvi. 39 ; John xvii.

4. There should be special prayer for special cases, Acts xii. 5 Christ encouraged specific prayer, Mark x. 46-51.

Have requests, 1 Thess. v. 25 ; 2 Thess. iii. 1.

5. Have good appropriate singing, Psa. lvii. 7-9 ; lix. 16 ; lxxxix. 1 ; ci. 1 ; civ. 33 ; 1 Cor. xiv. 15. Use an organ or piano to lead ; 2 Chron. xxx. 21 ; Psa. lxxxvii. 7. Avoid formal prayers addresses. They will kill a meeting.

6. Hints as to how we should pray :

(*a*) Reverently, Isa. vi. 2-3.

(*b*) In humility, Psa. ix. 12.

(*c*) In faith, believing, Heb. xi. 6.

(*d*) In reliance on Holy Spirit for help, Rom. viii. 26.

(*e*) Fervently ; earnestly, James v. 16.

(*f*) Importunately, Luke xi. 7, 8.

(*g*) Heartily, Matt. xv. 8.

(*h*) With expectation, 1 Peter iii. 12.

(*i*) With argumentative power, Job xxiii. 4.

(*j*) In accordance with God's will, Matt. 24, 39 ; 1 John v. 14.

(*k*) In a forgiving spirit, Mark xi. 25, 26.

(*l*) With confession, Dan. ix. 4, 5 ; 1 John i. 9.

(*m*) With thanksgiving, Phil. iv. 6.

(*n*) Ask in Christ's name, John xiv. 14.

Let us be always in the Spirit of prayer, Eph. vi. 18.

THE SWEET WORD "COME."

The first "Come" in the Bible is a "Come of Salvation," when God invited Noah and his family into the ark (Gen. vii, 1). The last "Come" in the Bible is a "Come of Salvation," too. "The Spirit and the bride say come" (Rev. xxii. 17). After John had seen all the glories of heaven, the Lord Jesus Christ sent him the message: "Come"—the last message Jesus sent from heaven to this earth. Luke xix. 5; "Make haste and come down, for to-day I must abide at thy house." People say Zaccheus was very much in earnest, but if he was he would have been like the woman who pressed through the crowd to touch Jesus, instead of hiding himself up in a tree. We do not read that Zaccheus saw Jesus, but Jesus saw Zaccheus. We are naturally proud, and, like Zaccheus, we wish to exalt ourselves, but before Jesus can do us any good, we must come down. Matthew xi. 28: "Come unto me all ye that labor and are heavy laden, and I will give you rest." This is a very important "Come;" there must be a coming unto the person of the Lord Jesus Christ.

Many people think salvation depends on receiving the doctrine of the Bible; but we may receive every doctrine in the Book and not be a Christian. A sinner wanted to prove that he was as good a Christian as anybody, because he believed all that was in the Bible. [He was too smart for me, and I could not argue with him, but I said: I have been to America three times. I have gone right from New York to California and back again. If you were to ask me my opinion of America, suppose I should say it was just as good as yours, and that I was as much an American as you?] Views about Christ do not make us Christians; we must come to Him as a person; "Come unto me."

In 2 Cor. vi. 17, we have another "Come" from the lips of God; "Come out from among them, and be ye separate." Some people think that should be the first "Come," that coming out and being separate makes them Christians. But this is Jesus' message to His people. I do not come out—come out to make myself a Christian, but because I am a Christian.

John xxi. 12 : "Come and dine." As soon as we cease to let the world satisfy us, God satisfies us. These are three sweet words of the Savior to Peter in this chapter : "Come and dine," "Feed my sheep," "Follow thou Me." God never sends a hungry Christian to feed his sheep ; they must themselves first be fed. If we dine with the Master, we are able to go and satisfy some one else. Therein we shall follow Him. John xi. 42 : "Lazarus, come forth !" Jesus had but to speak the word, and the dead will live. Ah, but that was Jesus, you say. "Greater things than these shall ye do." We have not got this power, simply because we have not the other "Comes" that go before.

Another sweet "Come" (Mark vi. 31) : "Come ye yourselves apart into a desert place and rest awhile. The disciples had received power to cast out devils ; they had come back and told Jesus of the sermons they had preached and the mighty deeds they had done, expecting Him to pat them on the back, and say, "Ye did well." There is something we need just as much, and that is to be with Christ. Notice one point ; Christ did not say : "Go into a desert place." He never sends us into the desert ; He takes us there. The desert is a sweet place when the Master is with us. God sends us these seemingly mysterious visitations of His providence that we may "come apart." John xiv. 3 : "I will come again and receive you unto myself." Christ said He would go away, and He did. He has promised to come back, and this word is as sure as the other. Then His word will be : "Come home." Salvation begins with "Come down," and ends with "Come home." Put these seven sweet "Comes" together : "Come down;" "Come to Me ;" "Come out ," "Come and dine ;" "Come forth ;" "Come apart ;" "Come home." And may God open our ears to hear the Master's voice.—HENRY MOORHOUSE, in outline "Bible Studies."

THE LIFE AND TIMES OF ST. PAUL.

The apostle himself holds up his own example as a model, therefore we do well to search closely his statements concerning himself and his relations to the church and to the gospel. These are expressed in the comparisons of which he makes use, each giving us a distinct lesson.

A DEBTOR, Rom. i, 15. He regards himself as a debtor. It is an act of simple honesty to pay one's debts, fully, promptly, cheerfully; and after all, one has only done a duty. Thus St. Paul looked on Jews and Gentile as his creditors to whom he owed preaching of the gospel.

AN AMBASSADOR, 2 Cor. v, 20. He represents his Sovereign, the most High, pleading with men to be reconciled to Him. The thought is of dignity and responsibility. An Ambassador has at all times to maintain the dignity of his position, whether engaged in delivering his message or not. The first Ambassador from England to China, found that he could only obtain an audience of the Emperor on condition of prostrating himself in his presence. The thought was inadmissible. The honor of England would be compromised. He returned home without even presenting his credentials and his king and country approved the conduct of their Ambassador.

AN AMBASSADOR IN BONDS, Eph. vi, 20. This gives us an additional thought, oppressed, imprisoned, bound with chains, an Ambassador still. As such he pleaded with Agrippa (Acts xxv, 29,) not as prisoner before a judge, but as "Ambassador in bonds."

AN EARTHEN VESSEL, 2 Cor. iv. 7. Formed by God, his maker for a purpose utterly dependant on Him; without Him, base and worthless, and needing constant in-filling from the Divine Treasury.

A LANTERN, 2 Cor. iv. 6. Here he is illuminating the surrounding darkness because He has himself received light from on high, unless if his light grow dim or be extinguished.

A LABORER, 2 Cor. iii. 9. Whose wages depend on his work being well done, but to whom no glory or applause is due.

A SOWER, 1 Cor. ix. 11. Rejoicing in Hope, knowing that though others reap the fruit of his labors, all are under the same Lord of the harvest and one day "Sower and reaper shall rejoice together." Diversities of gifts but the same Lord.

A STEWARD, 1 Cor. iv. i. Entrusted with his Lord's goods for the benefit of others, and earnestly endeavoring to be found faithful in all things as "a good steward of the manifold grace of God."

A FATHER, 1 Thess. ii. 11, 12. To the young church, tenderly solicitous for its welfare, its health, its growth, not only for the church or congregation as a whole, (many are full of genuine affection and tenderness in the pulpit on Sabbath) but for each individual member, exhorting and consoling *each one.*

An ARCHITECT, 1 Cor. iii. 10. Who has well laid the foundation of a building, or perhaps rather who has commenced an edifice on the only sure foundation, the Rock Christ Jesus, and who anxiously warns those who are to continue His work, to put into it none but good material and good workmanship.

A RUNNER, 1 Cor. ix. 25, 26. His thoughts are in the Grecian games so well known to the Corinthians, running steadily, his eye fixed on the goal, where awaits him an incorruptible crown ; the thought of that crown giving him courage not only to run, but "to be temperate in all things."

A WRESTLER, 1 Cor. ix. 25, 27. He is more even than a runner, he is earnestly contending in desperate conflict with the "flesh" as with an invincible adversary ; who has a charmed life, who can be kept in subjection but not killed ; fearing to give him a moment's repose or an inch of foothold, least having preached to others Paul should be cast away.

A SOLDIER, 2 Tim. iv. 7. He has "fought a good fight" and knows that his Commander is satisfied with him.

A VETERAN, 2 Tim. ii. 4. He counsels his young comrade Timothy to "endure hardness as a good soldier of Jesus Christ" and not to "entangle himself with the affairs of this life," but to seek only to "please Him who has chosen him to be a soldier.

A VICTOR, 2 Cor. ii. 14. A soldier still, he is led in triumph, his Prince has triumphed and he who has shared the toil and the battle shares also the glory. S. R. GELDARD.

MAN AND THE WATCH.

TEXT — "I am fearfully and wonderfully made." — Ps. cxxxix. 14.

I. The watch has a maker. So man has a Maker (Isa. lxiv. 8 ; Job. xxxv. 10). If a man said a watch had no maker, you would call him a fool. That is just what the Holy Spirit says about such men who say we have no Maker. "The fool hath said in his heart there is no God" (Ps. xiv. 1). The Heavens declare the Glory of God, and the firmament showeth His handiwork. (Ps. xix. 1 ; Rom. i. 20).

II. Watchmakers name the watch by three principal parts, 1. The movement. 2. The plates. 3. The case that holds them. So man has a body, soul and spirit. (1 Thess. v. 23). And like his Maker, he is a trinity. (John xiv. 9, 11 ; Gen. i. 26).

III. Although you take the movement out of the case, it will go all the same. So with man, "whether in the body or out of the body." Absent from the body, the believer is present with the Lord. (2 Cor. v. 8, 12 ; 1, 4). The watch don't go to sleep because out of the case ; neither does man. (Acts vii. 59). The body sleeps, but the spirit goes to God that gave it, if a believer, and to his own place like Judas if an unbeliever. Eccl. iii. 21 ; xii. 7 ; Acts i. 25 ; Luke xvi. 22, 23.

IV. By looking at the face of the watch, you can generally tell whether it is right or wrong, when fast or slow. So with man ; when sorrowful, the face tells it (Neh. ii. 2) ; when joyful, the same (Prov. xv. 13) ; when sinful, (Mark vii. 20, 23 ; 2 Chron. xxvi. 19. The sinner runs *fast*, (Rom. iii. 15). The Christian runs with *patience*. (Heb. xii. 1 ; 2 Cor. v. 7). The sinner's end, "death." Rom. vi. 21 ; Prov. iv. 12. The Christian's end, everlasting life and "pleasures for evermore." Rom. vi. 22, 23 ; Ps. 16, 11.

V. All the works are run by the mainspring. Take that away and it stops. So God is man's mainspring. A believer can say "All my springs are in Thee," as he is a being of both worlds—the material and the spiritual worlds. "In Him we live and move and have our being." (Ps. lxxxviii. 7 ; Rom. i. 20 ; Acts xvii. 28 ; Col. i. 16, 17 ; 1 John i. 4, 10 ; John v. 12).

VI. They make seven, nine and sixteen jewelled watches. We have seen seven and nine jewelled Christians ; we have no doubt of it, but nine jewelled ones are very rare. Gal. v. 22, 23, speaks about the nine we ought to have. There never was a sixteen jewelled one but Christ. (Heb. vii. 26 ; 1 Pet. ii. 21, 23).

Lately there are some trying to make us believe they are sixteen jewelled, and capped at that ; read Prov. xxx. 12, 13, and see what generation they have sprung from ; and Heb. v. 12, 13, the trouble ; and in John i. 8, the cause. Beware of sounding brass and tinkling cymbal watches.

VII. The maker gives the watch to the one that can pay his price for it. So the believing sinner has been given to Jesus. (John vi. 37 and xvii. 2, 11). He has paid the price for the sinner. (1 Pet. i. 18, 19 ; Acts xx. 28). So now he is not his own but bought with a price. (1 Cor. vi. 19, 20 ; Gal. ii. 20). Every sinner may come to Christ and He will in no wise cast out. John vi. 37.

VIII. The watch, after running a while, needs cleaning and oiling. So the Christian needs cleaning and oiling all through life to keep him in good running order. We have heard some tick and point the hours irregularly ; a little cleaning and oiling would do them much good. 1 John 1, 7, 10, 2, 1 ; James v. 16 ; Heb. iv. 14, 16.

IX. The watch has a regulator to correct it if wrong. So God has given every man a regulator, and that is conscience ; Rom. ii. 13, 16 ; but some have their consciences seared, as with a hot iron, so it is no longer a trustworthy regulator. "And now God by His word commands men everywhere to repent, and believe in the gospel," and if he don't the word shall judge him in the last day. "Search and see." 1 Tim. iii. 2 ; Acts xvii. 30 ; Mark i. 14, 15 ; John 1, 9 ; 12, 46, 50.

X. Finally the watch accomplishes what it was made for. So every man was made for a purpose and that is to "glorify God his Maker here, and enjoy him forever." Eccl. xii. 1 ; 1 Cor. x. 31 ; Luke xix. 12, 27 ; Matt. xxv. 14, 46. May God bless this truth to every soul who reads it, is the prayer of a brand plucked from the burning. Zec. iii. 1, 5.

—John Currie in "The Evangelistic Record."

PRAYER MEETING TALKS.

I. FAITH. 2 Peter, 1: 5-7.

THE CHRISTIAN GRACES.

Every grace has its own sphere in which it manifests itself, and in which it exercises its specific virtue. It has its own office in the economy of salvation. Faith is the first and fundamental grace. It underlies every other grace. It makes them possible. It brings them forth as its own children. Its sphere therefore, is an universal one, because it is necessary in every part of the Christian life. "Whatsoever is not of faith is sin." Rom. 14 : 23. "Without faith it is impossible to please God." Heb. 11 : 6.

I. ITS ORIGIN. 1. *God.* Rom. 12 : 3; Eph. 2 : 8.
" " 2. *Holy Ghost.* 1 Cor. 12 : 9; Gal. 5 : 22.
" " 3. *Jesus Christ.* Heb. 12 : 2.

II. ITS OBJECT. Being in the soul it speeds back to its source. It it therefore, *the Couplet*, the band of gold uniting the soul to all that is endearing and eternal. 1st, *God.* Jno. 14 : 1; 2nd, *Christ*, Acts 20 : 21; 16 : 31.

III. ITS CHARACTER. This is taken from what it deals with. Its essential character is given in the word "reliance," "trust." Prov. 3 : 5: Ps. 37 : 5. It is precious. 2 Pet. 1 : 1. Most holy. Jude 20. Fruitful, 1 Thess. 1 : 3; 2 Thess. 1 : 11. An evidence of regeneration. 1 John 5 : 1.

IV. ITS EFFECTS. In its effects it attaches itself to everything in the Christian's way and warfare. If it does not "work by love." Gal. 5 : 6. It is dead, being alone. Jas. 2 : 17. Wherever it is a true living grace, there it justifies. Rom. 5 : 1. Sanctifies. Acts 15 : 9. Edifies. 1 Tim. 1 : 4. Preserves. 1 Pet. 1 : 5. Gives Hopes. Rom. 5 : 2. Joy. 1 Pet. 1 : 8. Peace. Rom. 15 : 13. Confidence. Isa. 28 : 16. Spiritual light. Jno. 12 : 36-46. Salvation. Mark 16 : 16.

No Faith—no Spiritual Life:—no Salvation.

In temptation, tribulation, and adversities we should have perished, except faith went with us to deliver us.—TYNDALE.

"If our faith were but more simple,
We should take him at His word,
And our lives would be all sunshine
In the sweetness of our Lord."—FABER.

II. VIRTUE.—2 Peter i. 5, 7.

THE CHRISTIAN GRACES.

"Giving all diligence, add to your faith virtue;" or as it may be rendered "Courage." This grace is a soldierly virtue, and its sphere is the battlefield of faith. This is the first-born grace of a living faith. Faith arms the soul with manly vigor through laying hold of God. It is especially needed for contention with the evils that come of sin within, and the temptations that way-lay the Christian without. The Christian needs a holy bravery and an heroic daring to go forward in the way of righteousness. He must be no coward. He must quit himself like a man and be strong. 1 Cor. xvi. 13.

I. The Godly are called to Courageous Action. Josh. i. 7; Deut. 31: 6; 7: 23; Num. 13: 20; 2 Sam. 10: 12; 1 Chron. xxii. 13; 28: 20; Ezra x. 4;2 Sam. 12: 28.

II. This Action is associated with Prayer. Psa. xxvii. 14, xxxi. 24; Joshua x., Judges 6.

III. It Draws its Vigor from the Promises. 1 Cor. xvi. 13; Acts xxviii, 15; comp. with Acts xxiii. 11; Deut. xx.3, 4.

IV. There is no Christian Enterprise without Courage. Fear ever brings failure. 1 Sam. xv. 24; Luke xix. 21; John ix. 19, 22.

Virtue wraps a nation in moral grandeur which no despotism can overthrow.—J. Linero.

Virtue maketh men on earth famous; in their graves, illustrious; in the heavens, immortal.—Chilo.

I would be virtuous for my own sake, though nobody were to know it, as I would be clean for my own sake, though nobody were to see me.—Shaftesbury.

Virtue consists in doing our duty in the several relations we sustain in respect to ourselves, to our fellowmen and to God, as known from reason, conscience and revelation.—Sir W. Alexander.

Virtue, according to my idea, is the habitual sense of right, and the habitual courage to act up to that sense of right, combined with benevolent sympathies, the charity which thinketh no evil. The union of the highest conscience and the highest sympathy fills my notion of virtue.—Mrs. Jameson.

III. KNOWLEDGE.—2 Peter i. 5-7.

THE CHRISTIAN GRACES.

This comes of faith, because faith is the *open* eye to see Jesus, and the *open* ear to hear Him speak. The Christian life has both teaching, and teaching embodied in an example. Its truth is not entirely abstract, it is concrete. It is full of intelligence, and therefore feeds upon and grows strong by knowledge. It is an emotional life because it centres itself in the affections, but it is in the affections because it is first of all intelligently apprehended. Christians give this account of themselves "we have known and believed the love that God hath to us." 1 Jno. iv: 16. "We love Him because He first loved us." *v.* 19. The sphere of knowledge therefore is to keep alive the soul through communion with the truth.

I. We are urged to grow in knowledge. 1 Pet. ii. 2; 2 Pet. iii. 18; Col. i. 10; Eph. i. 17; Eph. iv. 13.

II. Knowledge increases confidence in God. Ps. ix. 10; Ps. v. 11; Ps. lvii. 1.

III. Knowledge enlarges our love. 1 Jno. iv. 16-19; Gal. v. 16; Jude 20. 21; 1 John v. 1, 2.

IV. Knowledge arouses the soul to manifold activity. Acts iv. 20; Jer. xx. 9; Jno. i. 40-46; Rev. xxii. 17.

V. The knowledge of Christ prized above every other thing. Phil. iii. 8.

It is the property of all true knowledge, especially spiritual, to enlarge the soul by filling it. T. Sprat.

Knowledge is estatic in enjoyment, perennial in fame, unlimited in space and infinite in duration. De Witt Clinton.

The first step of knowledge is to know that we are ignorant. We can form no other knowledge of spiritual things, except what God has taught us in His word, and where He stops we must stop. Burleigh.

Our infallibility and shortness of knowledge should make us peaceable and gentle, because I *may* be mistaken I must not be dogmatical and confident, peremptory and imperious. I will not break the certain laws of charity for an uncertain doctrine. Whichcote.

IV. TEMPERANCE.—2 Peter 1 : 5, 7

THE CHRISTIAN GRACES.

Temperance here means self-control. In other words, the supremacy of the reason and conscience over the senses of the body and the faculties of the soul. It is the reign of God's Spirit through these and the consequent regulation of the life by them. Temperance is not to be taken in the narrow sense usually given to it to-day, but in the broad and comprehensive sense of the New Testament embracing the whole man, in all his power. He is to be like Paul keeping his body under, lest he should be a castaway. 1 Cor. ix, 27. It is :

I. Control of the thoughts of the heart. 2 Cor. x. 5 ; Prov. xxiv. 9 ; Deut. xv. 9 ; Ezek. xxxviii. 10 ; Heb. iv. 12 ; 1 Cor. xiii. 5 ; Matt. xv. 19 ; Ps. cxix. 13 ; Prov. xv. 26 ; Isa. lv. 7.

II. Control of the tongue. Matt. xii. 37 ; Jas. i. 19, 20 ; Prov. x. 19 ; Eccles. v. 2, 3 ; Matt. xi. 7 ; Prov. x. 19 ; Eccles. xii, 11.

III. Control of the appetite. 1 Cor. vi. 12, 13 ; 1 Cor. ix. 22 ; Rom. xiv. 17-23 ; 1 Pet. ii. 11 ; 1 Thess. iv. 3 ; Prov. xxiii. 20 ; Prov. xxxi. 4-7.

IV. Control of the way of life. 1 Thess. v. 22 ; Isa. xxxiii. 14-17 ; Ps. ci. Prov. i. 10-16 ; 1 Cor. x. 32, 33 ; Prov. vii. 1-3.

Temperance is corporeal piety ; it is the preservation of divine order in the body.—T. Parker.

Temperance is reason's girdle and passion's bridle, the strength of the soul and the foundation of virtue.—Jeremy Taylor.

Temperance is the preservation of the dominion of the soul over sense, of reason over passion ; the want of it destroys health, fortune and conscience.—W. Dodd.

Our physical well-being, our moral worth, our social happiness, our political tranquility all depend upon the control of all our appetites and passions which the ancients designed by the cardinal virtue of temperance.—Burke.

V. PATIENCE.—2 Peter. i. 5, 7.
THE CHRISTIAN GRACES.

The sphere of patience is that of trial, affliction, persecution. There it does its work in the maintenance of Christian integrity and nobleness of character. There it is called into play; "the trial of your faith worketh patience," Jas. i. 3; "Tribulation worketh patience" Rom. v. 3. There it shines forth in its Divine beauty, for so it is written of Christ: "He was oppressed and He was afflicted, yet He opened not His mouth: He is brought as a lamb to the slaughter and as a sheep before her shearers is dumb, so He openeth not His mouth" Isa. liii. 7. "Who when He was reviled, reviled not again; when He suffered, He threatened not, but committed Himself to Him that judgeth righteously." 1 Pet. ii. 23. [Matt. x. 23.

I. It is a Perfecting Grace. Jas. i. 4; 1 Pet. v. 10;

II. God's Plan is accomplished in us through our Patience. Jas. v. 7, 8; Ps. xxxiii. 7; Hab. ii. 2, 3.

III. A Grace that adhered to every Christian Work. Rom. ii. 7; Heb. vi. 12; x. 36, 12, 1; Luke xxi. 19.

IV. It is Necessary to our Receiving Answers from Prayer. Ps. xl. 1, 3; Ps. cxxx. 5, 8; Lam. iii. 25, 26; Micah vii. 7. [xlii. 10.

V. He Rewards Patience. Heb. vi. 15; Jas. i. 12; Job.

VI. Examples of Patience. 2 Thess. i. 4; Gen. xlix. 18; Jas. v. 10, 11.

Patience is one of the few virtues that can only be manifested in this world.—J. R. Macduff.

Be patient and long suffering toward sinners; the Lord waits with patience on sinners and so may you.—Flavel.

Patience is a most precious jewel, radiant with imperishable beauty; its brightness remaining even in the deep night.—Krummacher.

Patience adorns the woman, approves the man, is loved in a child, praised in a young man, admired in an old man. She is beautiful in either sex and every age.—G. Home.

True resignation consists in a thorough conformity to the whole will of God. In order to do this, we have only to embrace all events, good and bad, as His will.—Wesley.

VI. GODLINESS.—2 Peter i. 5, 7.

THE CHRISTIAN GRACES.

This is a very choice grace. It shines like the golden crown on the brow of the Sainted ones. It allies a man to God, and binds him over to Him. BENGEL gives us this as its meaning, "Godliness—by which the faithful look to God above all things." Alford defines it as "*God trusting.*" It is that habitual reference to God, and that conscientious regard for His will, His law, in every individual thing, which belongs only to a truly gracious spirit. It is like the fragrance of the rose, it gives a graciously potent charm to the soul, and it cannot be separated from it. It adheres in the depths of its nature as renewed. It is at the same time the strength, and the joy and sweetness of the believer's life. It fills the heart with a brave spirit, and the life with a beneficent grandeur. It is the true spirit of conquest. It is marked by:

I. *A life in God, and with God.* Gen. v. 24: xxxiii. 14-17; 1 Tim. ii. 1-4; 2 Peter iii. 11.

II. *It has rich rewards.* 1 Tim. vi. 6.

(1). *Peace* of mind. Phil. iv. 6; Isa. xxvi. 3.

(2.) *Protection.* Psa. xci. 9-13; Prov. xii. 21; Isa. xxvi. 4.

(3.) *Deliverance.* Psa. xci. 14; xxxiv. 7, 17-19; xcvii. 10.

(4.) *Guidance.* Psa. lxxiii. 23-25; xlviii. 14; xxxii. 7, 8.

(5.) *Instruction.* Psa. xxv. 9-12.

(6.) *It lacks nothing.* Psa. lxxxiv. 11; 1 Tim. iv. 8.

He that lives in Godliness cannot be weary of his life.—R. HALL.

Godliness is that outward deportment which characterises a heavenly temper.—G CRABB.

God throws many sweet allurements around the man who lives a godly life, and places before him many useful and needful acts that he may seek and perform them.—BISHOP HOPKINS.

Godliness is to act with a pious spirit toward God and includes the whole of practical religion.—A. RITCHIE.

He who traffics in Godliness derives a sure and constant interest which tells upon name, character, relations, business, prospects. It yields a gain for this world, and for that which is to come.—JOHN BATE.

VII. BROTHERLY KINDNESS.—2 Peter i. 5, 7.

THE CHRISTIAN GRACES.

When we have found "The Father" we quickly discover "The Brethren," those who are members of the family of God. And as John assures us, "every one that loveth him that begat, loveth him also that is begotten of him." If we instinctively love our brothers and sisters by natural affinity, how much more should we love those who are of the household of God, our brethren by spiritual generation? In our human relations we find a widely different spirit often dwells in different members of the family, but in the family of God one spirit dwells, one spirit reigns. "By one spirit we are all baptized into one body, whether we be Jews or Gentiles, whether we are bond or free; and have all been made to drink into one spirit." There is but one spirit in all the household of God. And that spirit breathes the tenderest affection to all its kin. Hence we note:

I. BROTHERLY KINDNESS IS SHOWN BY MANY TOKENS. (1.) *Hospitality.* Acts xvi. 15; 1 Tim. iii. 2; v. 10. (2.) *Providing for necessities.* Phil. iv. 10-17; Gen. xlii. 25; xliii. 31; xlvii. 11. (3.) *Prayer.* Col. i. 9-11; Eph. i. 16-23; iii. 14-21; 3 John ii. (4) *Giving honor that is due.* Phil. iv. 16. (5.) *Fellowship.* 2 Tim. iv. 9. (6.) *Submiting to one another.* Eph. v, 21.

A brother's sufferings should ever claim a brother's pity.—ADDISON.

The word of a brother pronounced from Holy Scripture in a time of need carries an inconceivable weight with it.—M. LUTHER.

A brother is born for adversity and not only should Christian be to a Christian, a friend that sticketh closer than a brother, but he should exemplify the loveliness of his religion to them that are without.—J. M. MASON.

Bind to your bosom your brothers and sisters, cherish them as your dearest and best companions through the journey of life.—J. GREY.

VIII. CHARITY.—2 Peter i. 5-7.

THE CHRISTIAN GRACES.

Charity is the crowning grace. It is the end, or the fulfilment of the commandment or the law. Brotherly kindness is love to our fellow Christian, but charity is love to God and love to men. It is an all-compassing grace. It is delineated grandly in the 13th chapter of 1 Cor., so grandly that many have regarded it as a portraiture of Jesus himself. The graces of the Spirit reach their highest perfection in this Divine love, and yet it is not a grace that we are to wait years for. It is awakened in the first stirring of the Holy Ghost in our hearts. But it is to grow and enlarge in us. It is to become the prevailing power in the heart, that by which faith is to effect its ends. "Faith worketh by love." Without this charity, the Christian life is simply impossible, for we have no evidence of possessing the Spirit, of whose presence in the soul this is the first fruit. Having charity, it leads us to—

I. Self Sacrificing Action. 2 Cor. viii. 9; 1 Cor. xiii. 5; Phil. ii. 25–30; 1 Cor. xvi. 14, 15; Rom. 9. 1–3; Exod. xxxii. 31, 32.

II. Hate Evil and Unjust Thoughts. 1 Cor. xiii. 5. Prov. v. 16–19; Prov. xii. 5; Deut. xv. 9; Prov. xxiv. 9; Ezek. xxxviii. 10; 2 Cor. x. 5; Ps. cxxxix. 23.

III. Abstain From and Avoid Unrighteous Action. 2 Tim. ii. 9; Ps. xcvii. 10; Prov. viii. 13. Delights not in iniquity. 2 Sam. iv. 10, 12; 1 Cor. xiii. 6.

IV. Suffers Long with Evil. 1 Cor. xiii. 4; 2 Pet. iii. 9; Rom. xii. 19–21.

Charity is a universal duty.—Dr. Johnson.

Charity is the first-born of religion.—Frazer.

Charity is the very livery of Christ.—Latimer.

Charity is an angel breathing on riches.—Hale.

The charities of life are scattered everywhere, enamelling the vales of human beings as the flowers paint the meadows.—G. Bancroft.

Faith is the root, the works of charity are the branches bearing fruit.—Matt. Elendues.

Alas for the rarity of Christian charity under the Sun! [—Thos. Hood.

WHAT IS A CHRISTIAN?

First. In faith he is a believer in Jesus Christ. "God so loved the world that He gave His only begotten Son, that whosoever believeth in Him should have everlasting life. . . He that believeth on Him is not condemned, but he that believeth not is condemned already, because he hath not believed in the name of the only begotten Son of God." (John iii. 16, 18). "He that believeth on the Son hath everlasting life, and he that believeth not the Son shall not see life; but the wrath of God abideth on him" (John iii. 36). "This is the work of God, that ye believe on Him whom He has sent" (John vi. 29). "This is the will of Him that sent me, that every one which seeth the Son, and believeth on Him, may have everlasting life, and I will raise him up at the last day" (John vi. 40). See also John xi. 25; Acts x. 43; xiii. 39; xvi. 31; 1 John v. 13.

Second. In relationship he is a child of God. "As many as received Him, to them gave He power to become the sons of God, even to them that believe on His name, which were born not of blood, nor of the will of the flesh, nor of the will of man, but of God" (John i. 12, 13). "Ye are all the children of God by faith in Jesus Christ" (Gal. iii. 26). When the fulness of the time was come, God sent forth His Son, made of a woman, made under the law, to redeem those that were under the law, that we might receive the adoption of sons. And because ye are sons God has sent forth the Spirit of his Son into your hearts, crying, Abba, Father" (Gal. iv. 4-6). "Beloved, now are we the sons of God, and it doth not yet appear what we shall be, but we know that when He shall appear, we shall be like Him, for we shall see Him as He is" (1 John iii. 2). "Whosoever believeth that Jesus is the Christ is born of God" (1 John v. 1).

Third. In communion he is a friend of God. "Henceforth I call you not servants, for the servant knoweth not what his lord doeth; but I have called you friends, for all things that I have heard of my Father I have made known unto you" (John xv. 15). "Go to my brethren and say unto them, I ascend unto my Father and your Father, and to my God and to your God" (John xx. 17). "Both He that sanctifieth and they who are sanctified are all of one, for which cause he is not ashamed to call them brethren. Forasmuch then as the children are partakers of flesh and blood, He also Himself likewise (the word likewise means "close by the side of") took part of the same, that through death He might destroy him that had the power of death, that is, the devil. . . . For verily he took not on Him the nature of angels; but He took on Him (the same word is translated *caught*, when Jesus caught Peter sinking in the waves) the seed of Abraham" (Heb. ii. 11-16). "Truly our fellowship is with the Father, and with His Son, Jesus Christ" (1 John i. 3). "And there is a friend that sticketh closer than a brother" (Prov. xviii. 24).

Fourth. In character he is a Saint, or sanctified, or separated one. "To all that be in Rome, beloved of God, called to be saints" (Rom. i. 7). "Wherefore Jesus also, that He might sanctify the people with His own blood, suffered without the gate" (Heb. xiii. 12). "As He which hath called you holy, so be ye holy in all manner of conversation; because it is written Be ye holy, for I am holy" (1 Peter i. 14, 15). "We thus judge, that if one died for all . . . that they which evil should not henceforth live unto themselnes, but unto Him which died for them and rose again" (2 Cor. v. 14, 15). "To me, to live is Christ" (Phil. i. 21). "And the very God of peace sanctify you wholly; and I pray God your whole Spirit and soul and body be preserved blameless unto the coming of our Lord Jesus Christ." (1 Thess. v 23).

Fifth. In conflict he is a soldier. "Thou, therefore, endure hardness as a good soldier of Jesus Christ. No man that warreth entangled himself with the affairs of this life, that he may please Him who hath chosen him to be a soldier (2 Tim. ii. 3, 4). "Fight the good fight of faith; lay hold on eternal life, whereunto thou art also called, and hast professed a good profession before many witnesses" (1 Tim. vi. 12). "Watch ye; stand fast in the faith; quit you like men; be strong; (2 Cor. xvi. 13). "Wherefore, take unto you the whole armor of God, that ye may be able to withstand in the evil day, and, having done all [margin overcome], to stand" (Eph. vi. 13). "Be thou faithful unto death, and I will give thee the crown of life" (Rev. ii. 10.)

Sixth. In the world he is a stranger and pilgrim. "Dearly beloved, I beseech you as strangers and pilgrims, abstain from fleshy lusts which war against the soul" (1 Pet. ii. 11.) "For our conversation [or citizenship] is in heaven, from whence also we look for the Savior, the Lord Jesus Christ" (Phil. iii. 20). "They are not of the world even as I am not of the world" (John xiv. 16). "Behold, what manner of love the Father hath bestowed upon us, that we should be called the sons of God; therefore, the world knoweth us not, because it knew him not" (1 John iii. 1). "God forbid I should glory, save in the cross of our Lord Jesus Christ, by whom the world is crucified unto me, and I unto the world" (Gal. vi. 14).

Seventh. In expectation he is an heir. "If children, then heirs, heirs of God and joint heirs with Christ; if so be that we suffer with Him, that we may be also glorified together" (Rom. viii. 17). "If ye be Christ's, then are ye Abraham's seed, and heirs according to the promise" (Gal. iii. 29). "Wherefore thou art no more a servant, but a son; and if a son, then an heir of God through Christ" (Gal. iv. 7). "That, being justified by His grace, we should be made heirs according to the hope of eternal life" (Titus iii. 7). "Blessed be the God and and Father of our Lord Jesus Christ, which, according to His abundant mercy, hath begotten us again unto a lively hope by the resurrection of Jesus Christ from the dead to an inheritance incorruptible and undefiled, and that fadeth not away reserved in heaven for you" (1 Pet. i. 3, 4).—*The Truth.*

RULES FOR THE CHRISTIAN RACE.

I. "I will run in the way of Thy commandments," Ps. cxix. 32.
II. "Run after Thee," Song of Solomon, i. 4.
III. "Run well," Gal. v. 7.
IV. "Run not uncertainly," 1 Cor. xi. 26.
V. "Run with patience," Heb. xi. 1.
VI. "Run and not be weary," Isa. xi. 31.
VII. "Not run in vain," Phil. ii. 16.

WHAT FAITH IS AND DOES.

FAITH DEFINED; Heb. xi. 1. Now faith is the substance of things hoped for, the evidence of things not seen.

FAITH, ITS FRUITS; Heb. xi. 3—40.

1. Faith grasps the gospel promise of salvation in and through Jesus Christ. 1 John ii. 25.
2. Faith views God in Christ at the helm in the greatest storm. Heb. xi. 28.
3. Faith casts the Soul's Anchor on the Rock of Ages. Heb. vi. 19, 20.
4. Faith brings new strength and auxiliary supplies of Grace from heaven. Deut. xxxii. 25.
5. Faith keeps the soul from sinking under heavy trials. Acts xxvii. 25.
6. Faith supports the soul, from the pleasure it gives of a pleasant view and prospect of a happy release from all troubles. Heb. xi. 26.
7. Faith gives support by the encouraging representations it makes of Christ. Heb. xii. 2.
8. Faith represents Christ as putting His Almighty arm under the believer's head. Song of Sol. ii. 6.
9. Faith represents Christ as pleading the afflicted believer's cause with God. Heb. vii. 25.
10. Faith represents Christ as standing by the furnace, as a refiner where his gold is melting. Mal. iii. 3.
11. Faith represents Christ as smiling on his people under the cross, whispering peace unto our ears, and saying, Well done, good and faithful servant. Acts vii. 55.
12. Faith secures eternal life by taking hold of Christ. John iii. 15.
13. Faith enables the possessor to overcome difficulties, by holding up the rewards of victory. Heb. xi. 25, 26.
14. Faith encourages the dying believer by giving the assurance of the crown of righteousness awaiting him. 2 Tim. iv. 7, 8.

CHRIST'S METHOD OF TEACHING.

"Never man spake like this man."—(John vii. 46).

All believers should preach, teach, or talk the Gospel, and Christ is our model in matter and manner.

The characteristics of his methods are :

1. He spoke with the authority of the divine majesty (and so may we, in His name), and the assurance of absolute and positive truth.

He was a personal witness concerning divine and unseen things. He was not a debater nor reasoner. Isa. lv. 4 ; Matt. v. 21, 22 ; vii. 29 ; John iii. 11.

2. He taught much in parables, similitudes and illustrations. Matt. xiii. 1 ; vii. 24-27 ; v. 14, 15 ; Luke vii. 31-35.

The Old Testament Scriptures, all nature, and all the occupations of man, constituted His cyclopædia of illustrations.

3. He was frank and free from sophistry, and exposed the shams, hypocrisies and wiles of His enemies. Matt. xxii. 15-46 ; and xxiii. 14.

4. He did not seek to excite sensation, or gratify idle curiosity. Matt. xii. 39 : xiii. 23, 24 ; Luke vii. 24-26. Let this apply to "curious questions" about Old Testament history.

5. He used wisdom and fact in dividing the Word of God to different classes, even revealing truth to one class and concealing it from another, in the same assembly, by the use of parables. John iv. 14 ; xvi. 12 ; Matt. xiii. 10-16. Luke iv. 16-19.

6. He sought no applause from His hearers. John v. 41 ; Rom. xv. 3. The motto of the play-actor is, "We study to please," but of the preacher, "We study to save."

7. He preached with boldness, regardless of the fear or favor of man. Matt. xi. 20-24 ; xxiii. 33 ; Luke xi. 33 ; Luke xi. 38-47 ; xii. 49 ; xx. 33. Men who want us to "preach as Christ did," are unwittingly asking for almost unparalleled severity.

8. He taught with patience, repetition, self-control, meekness and kindness. Matt. vii. 7, 8 ; ix. 36 ; xi. 29 ; xxiii. 37 ; Mark ix. 43 ; Luke xix. 41. F. P. M.

GOOD NEWS.

HAVING SINNED.

..ere is none righteous—no, not one.—Roman iii. 10.

..here is no difference, for all have sinned, and come short ..he glory of God.—Roman iii. 23.

.. we say that we have not sinned, we make Him a liar, and .. word is not in us.—1 John i. 17.

YOU MAY BE SAVED.

..r God sent not His Son into the world to condemn the .. ; but that the world through Him might be saved.— ..ohn iii. 10.

The blood of Jesus Christ His Son, cleanseth us from all sin.—1 John i. 7.

Believe on the Lord Jesus Christ, and thou shall be saved. —Acts xvi. 31.

NOW.

Behold, now is the accepted time; behold, now is the day of salvation.—2 Corinthians, vi. 2.

Boast not thyself of to-morrow; for thou knowest not what a day may bring forth.—Proverbs, xxvii. 1.

Seek ye the Lord while He may be found; call ye upon Him while he is near.—Isaiah, iv. 6.

AND LIVE.

He that believeth on the Son hath everlasting life.—John iii. 36.

Verily, verily, I say unto you, he that heareth My word, and believeth on Him that sent Me, hath everlasting life, and shall not come into condemnation, but is passed from death unto life.—John v. 24.

And by Him all that believe are justified from all things, from which ye could not be justified by the law of Moses.— Acts xiii. 39.

SPIRITUAL WEATHER.

PROBABILITIES AND WARNINGS.

[*Suggestive Thoughts for the First Prayer Meeting of Each Month.*]

ANUARY. Now is the time to make good the fading leaves of the old year, by turning over new ones. Ps. 116 : 18, 19. If you want continual sunshine, live in Isa. 60 : 20. Prevent quinsy throat and evil tongue by obeying Ps. 34 : 13; Phil. 2 : 11. Renew your youth by enjoying the good things spoken of in Ps. 103 : 5. Only the evergreen religion of Ps. 1 : 1-4 will survive the storms of winter.

EBRUARY. Look out for cold waves this month. Matt. 24 : 12. Holy Ghost fires rekindled at the week of prayer, need prayerful attention. Acts 2 : 46, 47. You need not emigrate if you will bask in the sunshine of God's love. Ps. 84 : 11. For heavenly power consult and follow Acts 1 : 14 ; 2 : 1-4. Spiritual warmth is enjoyed at all seasons by the upright in heart. Ps. 140 : 13 ; Ps. 16 : 8.

ARCH. To avoid sudden changes, squalls and storms, abide under the shadow of the Almighty. Ps. 91 : 1. Souls in Canaan are not affected by equinoctials. Deut. 33 : 26, 27. Those not well grounded in the faith should give heed to danger signals. Heb. 2 : 1. Those who have not built their hopes on Christ must apprehend ruin in the season of storms. Matt. 7 : 26, 27.

PRIL. Look out for early frosts that kill tender plants. Song of Solomon 2 : 15. Be prepared for the following changes as the busy season approaches—no time for family worship—too tired to go to prayer meeting—disposition to find fault—lack of spiritual interest. Song of Solomon 4 : 16; Ps. 78 : 47; Rom. 12 : 11. The heart should be filled with the good seed of the kingdom. Jer. 4 : 3 ; Ps. 119 : 11.

AY. The growing season is upon us. "Showers of grace" are in constant demand. These with the sunshine of His love and the needful pruning, plowing and culture of grace in the soul, will make it bloom like Eden. Ezek. 34 : 26, 27; John 15 : 2. For spiritual growth take Paul's advice. II. Cor. 9 : 6-11: I. Pet. 2; 2. A happy life is the fruit of holy living.

UNE. Buds of promise, flowers of affection and singing birds should abound this month. Ps. 138: 5. Keep in the reckoning of Rom. 6: 11 if you would avoid storms of passion and cyclones of anger. If prone to wander, strive to keep in the better way of Isa. 35: 8–10, looking unto Jesus. Heavenly manna is always to be found in Canaan latitudes. Ps. 111: 5; Hos. 11: 4.

ULY. Prayer and faith will bring spiritual showers when there is need of moisture. I. Kings 18: 1–45. Fog horns should be heard as cautionary signals in the region of icebergs and sleepy pew-holders these hot days. Isa. 58: 1. Keep close to Jesus and you need not flee to the mountain or seaside to keep cool. Isa. 25: 4; 32: 2; Song of Solomon 2: 3.

UGUST. Avoid low spirits during "dog days" by looking unto Jesus. Heb. 12: 1, 2. If you lack appetite give more time to knee drill and look often in the mirror mentioned in James 1: 25. Hereditary and chronic diseases are only cured at the fountain of life. Zech. 13: 1. Sun-stroke from prosperity may be avoided by sitting under Christ's shadow. Isa. 32: 2.

EPTEMBER. Look out for a cold snap after the Fall equinox which will drive the prodigals in Egypt home, where they have spent the summer and mingled with the heathen contracting malaria and tongue paralysis. Luke 15: 13–18. Keep the Salvation Hospital in good order for their benefit. Luke 15: 22–24. Encourage them with such promises as Ezek. 36: 11.

CTOBER. Killing frosts this month, coldness and indifference follow unchristian amusements and Sabbath desecrations; also heart-burns and general good for nothingness for God. Frost-bitten leaves wither and fall; so do hopes chilled to death by back-sliding. For all heart aches consult Matt. 11: 28, and for the renewal of vows adopt the words of Ps. 116: 12–19.

OVEMBER. This month will be like last month if you don't get nearer to God. Luke 22: 54. Blue Mondays and Down in the Valley days will prevail, if the advice of the Great Physician is not closely followed. John 8: 12. Avoid bad spells of inherited depravity and carnal nature by giving heed to Mark 9: 42–47. Have a Thanksgiving of your own. Ps. 116: 1, 2; 103: 1–4.

ECEMBER. Variable weather this month, though bright and pleasant to those walking in the light of I. Jno. 1: 7. Chilly and disagreeable atmosphere may be expected in the region of fairs, sociables and holiday festivities. I. Pet. 2: 13; Jude 12; Rev. 3: 15, 16. Keep close to God for spiritual warmth. Ecc. 4: 11. Discharge duties prayerfully and await the end in faith and hope. Dan. 12; 13.

ARE YOU INSURED?

Reasons for insuring in the Kings Insurance Co.

1. It is the oldest Insurance Company in the world, having been in succcessful operation thousands of years. Rev. xiii. 8.

2. The only Company Insuring against Loss in the Great Judgment Day Fire. 2 Thess. iv. 14-17. 2 Peter iii. 10-13.

3. The only Company Insuring against Shipwreck in the RIVER OF DEATH. Isa. xliii. 2.

4. Its Policies never expire, giving to the faithful holder Eternal Life. John x. 28; Romans vi. 23.

5. It has never changed its management. Heb. xiii. 8.

6. It insures a man for more than he is worth. Ps. xcvii. 10. Persons claiming to have No Souls need not apply. Applicants come directly to the PRESIDENT. John xiv. 6. All Companies offering to issue Policies after death are a fraud. Eccle. xi. 3; Rev. xxii. 1.

The King's Insurance Co.

GREATEST, OLDEST AND ONLY

ABSOLUTELY RELIABLE

Fire, Marine and Life Insurance Co.

IN THE WORLD.

CASH CAPITAL.

"The unsearchable riches of Christ." Eph. iii. 8

ASSETS.

Real Estate.—"An inheritance incorruptible undefiled and that fadeth not away."
1 Peter i. 4.

Cash in Bank.—"Gold tried in the fire."
Rev. iii. 18.

LIABILITIES.—"Whosoever will may come."
Rev. xxii. 17.

Surplus Over All Liabilities.
"Able to do exceeding abundantly above all that we ask or think."
Eph. iii. 20.

Condition of Policy.
"Repentance toward God, and faith in our Lord Jesus Christ." Acts xx. 21.

PRESIDENT - **"KING OF KINGS."**

From "*The Highway.*"

PRAYER MEETING SUBJECTS

AND

DAILY READINGS.

1. Glad Tidings.—A Savior Born. Luke ii. 8-20.

M. Predicted by Isaiah .... Isa. ix. 1-7.
T. Predicted by Daniel .... Dan. ix. 20-27.
W. Predicted by the angel .... Luke i. 26-35.
T. The visit of the wise men .... Matt. ii. 1-12.
F. The visit to the temple .... Luke ii. 21-38.
S. The flight into Egypt .... Matt. ii. 13-23.

2. The Gracious Invitation.—Isa. lv. 1-11.

M. To sinners .... Luke v. 18-32.
T. Saved through Grace .... Eph. ii, 1-10.
W. According to his mercy .... Tit. iii. 1-7
T. All things are ready .... Luke xiv. 15-24.
F. The call urged .... Rev. xxii. 13-21.
S. The call accepted .... Josh. xxiv. 14-28.

3. Jesus Only.—Acts iv. 1-14.

M. Confession of Christ .... Luke xii. 1-12.
T. The corner-stone .... Psa. cxviii. 19-29.
W. The foundation-stone .... Eph. ii. 11-22.
T. The precious stone .... 1 Peter ii. 1-10.
F. The only foundation .... 1 Cor. iii. 1-15.
S. Building on the rock .... Matt. vii. 13-27.

4. Nicodemus and the New Birth.—John iii. 1-18.

M. Born of the will of God....................John i. 1-13.
T. Born new in Christ....................2 Cor. v. 14-21.
W. Born unto good works....................Eph. ii. 1-10.
T. Born unto righteousness................Eph. iv. 17-25.
F. Born of the word of truth..................Jas. i. 1-18.
S. Born by the word of God................1 Pet. i. 13-28.

5. The Christian's Model.—1 Peter ii. 19-25.

M. The pattern of lowliness................Matt. xx. 20-29.
T. The compassionate Christ................Luke vi. 11-17.
W. The pattern of suffering..................Isa. liii. 1-12.
T. The pattern of purity....................Heb. iv. 9-16.
F. The forgiving Christ..................Luke vii. 36-50.
S. The pattern of love.....................John xv. 9 16.

6. Answered Prayers.—2 King xx. 1-17.

M. The prayer of Abraham..............Gen. xviii. 16-33.
T. The prayer of Lot....................Gen. xix. 12-22.
W. The prayer of Gideon..................Judg. vi. 36-40.
T. The prayer of Hannah..................1 Sam. i. 9-28.
F. The prayer of Jonah....................Jon. ii. 1-10.
S. The prayer of Peter....................Acts ix. 36-43.

7. Help for the Faithful.—Dan. i. 8-17.

M. The captive children..........................Dan i. 7.
T. Blessings for obedience..............Deut. xxviii. 1-9.
W. Elisha's experience..................2 Kings vi. 8-17.
T. Daniel's experience....................Dan. vi. 19-24.
F. God's care for his people................Deut. viii. 1-11
S. The result of obedience.......................Psalm 23.

8. Comfort in Trouble.—Jer. xxxiii. 1-9.

M. Joseph in prison..........................Gen. xl. 1-15.
T. John the Baptist in prison..............Matt. xiv. 1-12.
W. Peter in Prison..........................Acts xii. 1-12.
T. Paul and Silas in prison................Acts xvi. 16-31.
F. Paul's comforter....................Acts xxvii. 18-26.
S. Visiting the prisoners................Matt. xxv. 34-40.

9. Sanctified Afflictions.—Job xxxiii. 14-30.

M. The affiictions of Joseph.............. Gen. xlv. 1-15.
T. The afflictions of the Isrealites..........Deut. viii. 1-20.
W. The afflictions of Hezekiah.......2 Chron. xxxii. 24-33.
T. The afflictions of Manasseh... ....2 Chron. xxxiii. 1-17.
F. The afflictions of Jonah.. ....Jonah ii. 1-10.
S. The afflictions of the Apostles.... ......2 Cor. vi. 1-10.

10. Pentecostal Blessing.—Act ii. 1-16.

M. The Holy Spirit foretold............Ezek. xxxvi. 23-30.
T. The Holy Spirit promised...............Matt. iii. 1-17.
W. The Holy Spir.t's work... ....John xvi. 1-14.
T. The Holy Spirit's leading.......... ......Rom. viii. 1-17.
F. The Holy Spirit's fruits......................Gal. v. 16-25.
S. The Holy Spirit's invitation............Rev. xxii. 16-21.

11. Faith and Works.—James ii. 14-26.

M. Faith essential...................... Matt xvii. 14-21.
T. Faith commended.......................Luke vii. 1-10.
W. Faith honored..........................John iv. 43-54.
T. Works essential.........................Luke vi. 27-36.
F. Works commended.....................Luke vi. 43-49.
S. Works profitable......... ....Titus iii. 1-8.

12.. Sowing and Reaping.—John iv. 27-42.

M. The Plenteous Harvest.................Matt. ix. 27-38.
T. Parable of the Sower....................Matt xiii. 1-23.
W. Parables of the Harvest................Matt. xiii. 24-32.
T. The laborers in the Harvest...... ... ... 1 Cor. iii. 1-9
F. The contributors to the Harvest.........John xv. 1-16.
S. The source of the Harvest..............Johnxii. 23-36.

13. Watching and Waiting.—Mark xiii. 21-37.

M. The parable of the virgins...............Matt. xxv. 1-13
T. The parable of the talents........... ... Matt. xxv. 14-30.
W. The coming of the Son.. ....Matt. xxv. 31-46.
T. A lesson of warning.................1 Kings xx. 28-43.
F. The watchman's warning... ....Ezek. xxxiii. 1-11.
S. The reward of waiting.................Psa. cxxvi. 1-6.

14. Christian Humility.—Psalm li. 1, 12.

M. Transient repentance..................Exod. x. 16, 29.
T. Repentance of the head..............Num. xxii. 22, 35.
W. Private repentance... ....1 Sam. xv. 10, 31.
T. After repentance.......................Josh. vii. 10, 26.
F. Repentance of despair ....Matt. xxvii. 1, 10.
S. True repentance ....Luke xv. 11, 24.

15. Confidence in God.—Luke vii. 1, 10.

M. The faith of the blind men.............Matt. ix. 27, 38.
T. The faith of the Syro-phenician........Matt. xv. 21, 28.
W. The faith of Bartimeus..................Mark x. 46, 52.
T. Faith and works........ ....James ii. 14, 26.
F. The power of faith...................Matt. xvii. 14, 21.
S. The victories of faith....... ....Heb. xi. 32, 40.

16. Christian Courage.—Acts iv. 18, 31.

M. The courage of Abraham.... ....Gen. xviii. 20, 33.
T. The courage of Gideon...............Judges vii. 15, 22.
W. The courage of Elijah.............1 Kings xviii. 21, 39.
T. The courage of the three Hebrews........Dan. iii. 8, 27.
F. The courage of Paul.................Acts xxvii. 15, 26.
S. Courage commanded....................Josh. i. 1, 19.

17. Sin Reproved.—2 Chron. xix. 1, 9.

M. Moses reproved.........................Num. xx. 1, 13.
T. Eli reproved...........................1 Sam. ii. 27, 36.
W. Saul reproved.........................1 Sam. xiii. 7, 14.
T. David reproved....................2 Sam. xxiv. 10, 25.
F. Solomon reproved ....1 Kings xi. 9, 13.
S. Hezekiah reproved..................2 Kings xx. 12, 18.

18. The Wanderer Welcomed.—Luke xv. 11, 24.

M. God our Father.........................Isa. lxiii. 7, 16.
T. A bountiful Father..................Deut. xxxii. 6, 14.
W. An offended Father. ....Isa. i. 1, 9.
T. A suffering son............................Jer. ii. 9, 19.
F. A returning son...........................Jer. 31. 9, 21.
S. Joy in heaven.........................Luke xv. 1, 10.

19. The Way of the Righteous.—Psalm i. 1-6.

M. The duty of the righteous... ....Deut. vi. 1-25.
T. The growth of the righteous............Heb. vi. 1-20.
W. Comfort for the righteous.............1 John ii. 1-17.
T. Joy for the righteous..................John xv. 1-11.
F. Blessings for the righteous.........Psalm cxxviii. 1-16.
S. Heaven for the righteous..............Rev. xxi. 14-27.

20. The Christian Warfare.—Eph. vi. 10-20.

M. The Christian's warfare.................2 Cor. x. 1-18.
T. The Christian's leader...................Heb. ii. 1-10.
W. The Christian's strength................Heb. xi. 32-40.
T. The Christian's prayer..................Psa. xxxv. 1-9.
F. The Christian's song................2 Sam. xxii. 31-51.
S. The Christian's victory.................2 Tim. iv. 1-8.

21. THE MISSION OF THE TWELVE.—Mark vi. 1-13.

M The charge to the twelve..............Matt. x. 16-32.
T. The need of the Gospel...... ....Rom. x. 1-18.
W. Preaching the Gospel.................Acts xvi. 6-15.
T. The privileges of the Gospel............Luke x. 17-24.
F. Fate of God's enemies.............. .Gen. xix. 15-29.
S. The followers of the Lord............Ps. lxxxiv. 1-12.

22. MIRACULOUS HEALING.—Acts iii. 1-11.

M. The paralytic healed......................Mark ii. 1-12.
T. The people healed.......................Num. xxi. 1-9.
W. The cripple at Lystra healed...... .....Acts xiv. 5-20.
T. The cripple at Bethesda healed.... ......John v. 1-15.
F. The leper healed.......................2 Kings v. 1-14.
S. The mighty Healer.......... ....Mark i. 29-39.

23. CONFESSING CHRIST.—Mark viii. 22-33.

M. John the Baptist's confession...........John i. 19-36.
T. The first disciple's confession............John i. 37-51.
W. The Samaritan's confession..............John iv. 19-42.
T. The blind man's confession...............John ix. 17-38.
F. The apostle's confession..................Acts iv. 1-21.
S. Paul's confession......................Acts xxiv. 10-27.

24. CHRISTIAN CONTENTMENT.—Phil. iv. 1-13.

M. Rejoicing evermore..................1 Thess. v. 1-13.
T. Rejoicing in Hope.................. ... Rom. xii. 1-16.
W. Rejoicing in the Lord....................Ps. xxxii. 1-11.
T. Rejoicing in suffering.................1 Pet. iv. 12-19.
F. Rejoicing in Sorrow....................2 Cor. vi. 1-10.
S. Rejoicing in Trials.........................James i. 1-4.

25. THE FRUIT OF THE SPIRIT.—Gal. v. 22-26 ; vi. 1-9.

M. The source of character.................John xv. 1-11.
T. The formation of character.................Jas. i. 1-25.
W. The test of character............ .....Matt. vii. 15-23.
T. The endurance of character.............Psa. xcii. 1-15.
F. The result of character................Matt. xiii. 24-43.
S. The blessedness of character..............Matt. v. 1-12.

26. THE FAITHFUL SAYING.—1 Tim. i. 15-20 ; ii. 1-6.

M. Coming to Call Sinners.................Luke v. 17-32.
T. Coming to save the lost.................Luke xix. 1-10.
W. Coming to give His life...............1 John iii. 13-24.
T. Coming to give life.....................1 John iv. 1-21.
F. Coming to save the world...............John iii. 1-17.
S. Coming to die for sinners...............Rom. v. 1-10.

27. THE GREAT COMMANDMENT.—1 Cor. i. 13.

M. Christian love.........................Matt. xxii. 34-40.
T. Illustrated... ....Luke x. 25-37.
W. Evidenced.............. ....1 John iii. 10-24.
T. Commanded........................1 John iv. 7-21.
F. Rewarded..........................Matt. xxv. 31-46.
S. Taught by Christ.....................Luke vi. 27-36.

28. CHRIST, OUR EXAMPLE.—Phil. ii. 5-15.

M. Learning of Christ... ....Matt. xi. 25-30.
T. Serving with Christ... ....John xiii. 1-15.
W. Following Christ's steps. ....1 Pet. ii. 11-25.
T. Walking as Christ Walked.............1 John ii. 1-16.
F. Living as Christ lived....... ....1 Pet. i. 1-16.
S. Loving as Christ loved........... ....John xiii. 20-35.

29. THE GOSPEL FEAST.—Luke xiv. 15-24.

M. A free invitation........................Isa. lv. 1-13.
T. An abundant supply.................. ....Rom. v. 1-21.
W. An easy condition ....Rom. x. 1-13.
T. A willful refusal....... ....John iii. 11-21.
F. A royal feast...........................Matt xxii. 1-14.
S. A marriage supper......................Rev. xix. 4-16.

30. WORKING FOR GOD.—2 Chron xxiv. 4-13.

M. The tabernacle..........................Exod. xl. 17-38.
T. The first temple.......................1 Kings viii. 1-11.
W. The second Temple....... ....Ezra vi. 16-22.
T. No temple on earth......................1 Cor. iii. 11-17.
F. The Christian temple....-.............John iv. 19-29.
S. No temple in heaven............ ....Rev. xxi. 10-27.

31. THE FRIEND OF SINNERS.—Luke vii. 40-50.

M. A needed friend..........................Matt. ix 1-13.
T. A strong friend.........................Matt. viii. 22-31.
W. A protecting friend......................John x. 7-18,
T. A loving friend... ....John xv. 9-17.
F. A constant friend ....Rom. viii. 31-39.
S. An eternal friend ....1 Thess. iv. 13-18.

32. THE GOOD SAMARITAN.—Luke x. 30, 37.

M. The command to beneficence..............Deut. xv. 1-11.
T. Job's beneficence.......................Job xxxi. 16-28.
W. Isaiah's warning......... ....Isa. lviii. 1-11.
T. Blessings for the merciful.............. Psa. cxii. 1-10.
F. The source of kindness ....1 Cor. xiii. 1-13.
S. The reward of mercy ....Matt. xxv. 34-40.

33. THE MISUSE OF RICHES.—Luke xii. 13-23.

M. Covetous Achan................ ....Joshua vii. 16-26.
T. Covetous Nabal ....1 Sam. xxv. 4-13, 36-38.
W. Covetous Ahab........................1 Kings xxi. 17-24.
T. Covetous Gehazi.......................2 Kings v. 20-27.
F. Covetous Ananias and Sapphira ....Acts v. 1-11.
S. Covetousness accursed.................. James v. 1-9.

34. THE FALL OF JERICHO.—Josh. v. 10-15; vi. 1-5.

M.	The fall of Jericho	Josh. vi. 11-27.
T.	The manna in the wilderness	Exod. xvi. 11-31.
W.	The spiritual warfare	Eph. vi. 10-20.
T.	Conquest by the Lord	Psa. xliv. 1-8.
F.	Weak things mighty	1 Cor. i. 18-31.
S.	The triumphs of faith	Heb. xi. 24-40.

35. THE CITIES OF REFUGE.—Josh. xx. 1-9.

M.	The law of the refuge	Num. xxxv. 16-34.
T.	A refuge needed	Psa. cxlii. 1-7.
W.	A refuge provided	Psa. xlvi. 1-11.
T.	A refuge accessible	Heb. vi. 10-20.
F.	A secure refuge	Psa. xci. 1-16.
S.	A refuge for the righteous	Isa. xxxiii. 15-24

36. GIDEON'S BAND.—Judg. vii. 1-8.

M.	The Midianite oppression	Judg. vi. 1-10.
T.	The call of Gideon	Judg. vi. 11-24.
W.	Gideon's fleece	Judg. vi. 25-40.
T.	Gideon's victory	Judg. vii. 16-25.
F.	Gideon's pursuit	Judg. viii. 4-21.
S.	Strength for the upright	Psa. xxxvii. 23-40.

37. FOUND WANTING.—Dan. v. 22-31.

M.	The handwriting	Dan. v. 1-9.
T.	The interpreter	Dan. v. 10-21.
W.	Israel found wanting	Num. xiv. 11-24.
T.	Saul found wanting	1 Sam. xv. 10-23.
F.	Sardis found wanting	Rev. iii. 1-6.
S.	The hidden talent	Matt. xxv. 14-30.

38. KEEPING THE SABBATH HOLY.—Neh. xiii. 15-22.

M.	Its holiness	Matt. xii. 1-13.
T.	Its observance	Isa. lvi. 1-12.
W.	Its duties	Jer. xvii. 19-27.
T.	Commanded by God	Exod. xxxi. 12-18.
F.	A memorial of creation	Gen. i. 26-31; ii. 1-3.
S.	A type of heavenly rest	Heb. iv. 1-11.

39. The Spread of the Gospel.—Acts xi. 19-30.

M. A scattered Church....................Acts viii. 1-8.
T. A working Church....................1 Thess. i. 1-10.
W. An endowed Church....................Eph. iv. 1-16.
T. A complete Church....................Col. ii. 1-15.
F. A generous Church....................2 Cor. ix. 6-15.
S. A rejoicing Church....................Phil. iv. 1-19.

40. Communing with God.—Ps. lxxxiv. 1-12.

M. The Church formed....................Matt. xvi. 13-20.
T. The design of the Church....................Matt. v. 1-16.
W. The power of the Church....................Matt. xviii. 15-22.
T. The duties of the Church....................Titus iii. 1-14.
F. Christ its head....................Eph. iv. 1-16.
S. Desire for God's house....................Psalm xxvii. 1-14.

41. Home Religion.—Mark x. 1-16.

M. Practical religion....................Col. iii. 16-25.
T. The first marriage....................Gen. ii. 15-24.
W. Isaac and Rebekah....................Gen. xxiv. 50-67.
T. The social relations....................Eph. v. 22-33.
F. The duties of home....................1 Pet. iii. 1-12.
S. The psalm of home....................Psa. cxxviii. 1-6.

42. The Triumphs of Faith.—Heb. xi. 1-10.

M. Abraham's faith....................Gen. xxii. 1-19.
T. The faith of the Patriarchs....................Heb. xi. 24-40.
W. The Hebrew children's faith....................Dan. iii. 8-28.
T. The faith of Caleb....................Num. xiv. 1-10.
F. Nathanael's faith....................John i. 43-51.
S. The Ethiopian's faith....................Acts viii. 27-40.

43. Saul's Conversion.—Acts ix. 1-18.

M. Paul's story....................Acts xxvi. 1-18.
T. Christ seen by Paul....................1 Cor. xv. 1-11.
W. From darkness to light....................Isa. xxix. 10-24.
T. Giving up all for Christ....................Phil. iii. 1-14.
F. The new creation....................Rom. viii. 1-17.
S. The revelation of the Gospel....................Eph. iii. 1-13.

44. Forgiveness for the Penitent.—2 Chr. xxxiii. 9-16.

M. The repentance of Israel................Judg. x. 6-18.
T. The repentance of David............2 Sam. xxiv. 10-17.
W. The repentance of Nineveh.............Jonah iii. 1-10.
T. The repentance of Judas.............Matt. xxvii. 3-10.
F. The repentance of Peter..............Matt. xxvi. 69-77.
S. The repentance of the Corinthians......2 Cor. vii. 1-11.

45. God's Work and Word.—Ps. xix. 1-14.

M. God's handiwork.......................Gen. i. 14-19.
T. It obeys God............................Josh. x. 6-14.
W. God's Perfect Teaching................2 Tim. iii. 10-17.
T. The Fear of the Lord....................Prov. ix. 1-11.
F. The Everlasting Word...................Matt. v. 13-20.
S. The Final Word.......................Rev. xxii. 16-21.

46. The Transfiguration.—Mark ix. 2-13.

M. The voice of God.........................2 Pet. i. 1-18.
T. Moses on the Mount.....................Exod. iii. 1-15.
W. God's glory on the Mount...............Exod. xxiv. 1-18.
T. Elijah on the Mount.................1 Kings xix. 1-18.
F. The vision of Isaiah.......................Isa. vi. 1-13.
S. The testimony of God..................Matt. iii. 1-17.

47. Early Piety.—1 Sam. iii. 1, 19.

M. Josiah's early piety..............2 Chron. xxxiv. 1-8.
T. Joseph's early piety...........Gen. xxxix. 1, 6; 20-23.
W. Samuel's early piety...................1 Sam. iii. 1-21.
T. Solomon's early piety.................2 Chron. i. 7-17.
F. Moses' early piety......................Exod. ii. 1-10.
S. Timothy's early piety...................2 Tim. i. 1-18.

48. The Presumptuous Punished.—2 Chron. xxvi. 16-21.

M. Pharaoh's presumption................Exod. x. 16-29.
T. Korah's presumption..................Num. xvi. 28-35.
W. Saul's presumption.................1 Sam. xiii. 8-14.
T. Nebuchadnezzar's presumption.........Dan. iv. 28-37.
F. The rich man's presumption...........Luke xii. 13-21.
S. Herod's presumption...................Acts xii. 19-23.

49. The Christian's Lost Victory.—1 Cor. xv. 50-58.

M. Power from Christ.................. Matt. xvi. 17-28.
T. Christ's resurrection.................. John xx. 1-18.
W. Its Power.................. Phil. iii. 10-21.
T. Christ the first fruits.................. 1 Cor. xv. 1-26.
F. The Spiritual Body.................. 1 Cor. xv. 35-40.
S. The End of Death.................. Rev. xx. 1-15.

50. Here and Hereafter.—Luke xvi. 10-31.

M. The ungodly prospered.................. Psalm lxxiii. 1-17.
T. The saints afflicted.................. Heb. xii. 1-13.
W. Compensation hereafter.................. 2 Thess. i. 1-12.
T. Sin in high places.................. 1 Kings xii. 25-33.
F. The end of the wicked.................. Job. xxvii. 11-23.
S. The hope of the righteous.................. 2 Cor. v. 1-9.

51. The Saints in Heaven.—Rev. xxi. 10-20.

M. Hungering no more.................. Rev. vii. 9-17,
T. Sitting down in the Kingdom.................. Matt. viii. 5-13.
W. Singing a new song.................. Rev. xiv. 1 5.
T. At the Marriage Supper.................. Rev. xix. 1-10.
F. Sorrowing no more.................. Rev. xxi. 1-7.
S. Night no more.................. Rev. xxii. 1-14.

52. Easter Meditations.—Matt. xxv. 1-13.

M. The Risen Saviour's Message.................. Mark xvi. 1-8.
T. The ascension foretold.................. John xx. 1-17.
W. The ascending Lord.................. Acts i. 1-14.
T. His heavenly work.................. John xiv. 1-17.
F. His second coming.................. 1 Cor. iv. 9-18.
S. The Risen Saviour and our resurrection. 1 Cor. xv. 45-58

WHAT CHRISTIANS SHOULD BE.

ACCORDING TO THE BIBLE.

[*Prayer Meeting Topics and Daily Thoughts.*]

Abhorring that which is evil.................. ....Rom. xii. 9.
Abstaining from all appearance of evil........ 1 Thess. v. 22.
Always abounding in the work of the Lord......1 Cor. xv. 58.
Always confident........................... ...2 Cor. v. 6.
Approving things that are excellent.............. Phil. i. 10.
Asking and receiving ....1 Jno. iii. 22.
Avenging not themselves..........................Rom. xii. 19.
Avoiding profane and vain babblings...........1 Tim. vi. 20.
Awaking to righteousness........................1 Cor. xv. 34.
Bearing one another's burdens ....Gal. vi. 2
Believing to the saving of the soul ....Heb. x. 39.
Bewareing of covetousness.......................Luke xii. 15.
Blameless and harmless, the Sons of God..........Phil. ii. 15.
Blessing them which persecute us......... .....Rom. xii. 14.
Boldly saying the Lord is my helper.............Heb. xiii. 6.
Bringing forth fruit unto God.......... ....Rom. vii 4.
Calling upon the name of Jesus Christ our Lord ...1 Cor. i. 2.
Careful for nothing...............................Phil. iv. 6.
Careful [only] to maintain good works.............Tit. iii. 8.
Casting all your care upon Him...... ....1 Pet. v. 7.
Circumcised without hands.. ....Col. ii. 11.
Cleansed from all filthiness......................1 Cor. vii. 1.
Cleansed with the blood of Christ from all sin .....1 John i. 9.
Cleaving to that which is good........ ....Rom. xii. 9.
Clothed with humility ... .1 Peter v. 5
Coming continually unto Christ...................1 Pet. ii. 4.
Considering Christ Jesus ....Heb. iii. 1.
Content with such things as we have............Heb. xiii. 5.
Continuing constant in prayer..................Rom. xii. 12.
Crucified by the cross unto the world............Gal. vi. 14.
Dead to sin..... ... .Rom. vi. 2.
Dead to the law ....Rom. vii. 4.
Declaring plainly that we seek a country..........Heb. xi. 14.
Delivered from the power of darkness..............Col. i. 13.

Denying self, or the old nature .... Matt. xvi. 24.
Discerning both good and evil .... Heb. v. 14.
Distributing to the necessity of saints............ Rom. xii. 13.
Dwelling in love and in God................... 1 John iv. 16.
Earnestly contending for the faith... .... Jude 3.
Earnestly desiring our house from heaven......... 2 Cor. v. 2.
Edifying one another .... 2 Thess. v. 11.
Endeavoring to keep the unity of the Spirit........ Eph. iv. 3.
Enduring hardness....... .... 2 Tim. ii. 3.
Entering with boldness into the holiest .... Heb. x. 19.
Espoused to one husband.......................... 2 Cor. xi. 2.
Excelling to the edifying of the Church........ 1 Cor. xiv. 12.
Exhorting one another as the day approaches...... Heb. x. 25.
Faithful stewards.............. .... 1 Cor. iv. 2.
Fearing God.................................... 1 Pet. ii. 17.
Fervent in spirit.............................. Rom. xii. 11.
Fervently loving one another with a pure heart ... 1 Pet. i. 22.
Filled with all the fulness of God................ Eph. iii. 19.
Filled with the spirit......... .... Eph. v. 18.
Filled with the fruits of righteousness.. .... Phil. i. 11.
Following peace with all men, and holiness....... Heb. xii. 14.
Following the steps of Jesus .... 1 Pet. ii. 21.
Forbearing one another in love .... Eph. iv. 2.
Forgiving one another .... Col. iii. 13.
Fruitful in every good work...... .... Col. i. 10
Gentle unto all men .... 2 Tim. ii. 24.
Glorifying God in body and in spirit........... 1 Cor. vi. 20.
Given to hospitality.... .... Rom. xii. 13.
Giving diligence to make our calling and election sure...... .... 2 Pet. i. 10.
Giving thanks always for all things.............. Eph. v. 20.
Giving not grudgingly, or of necessity........... 2 Cor. ix. 7.
Grieving not the Holy Spirit of God.............. Eph. iv. 30.
Growing in grace and knowledge of Christ....... 2 Pet. iii. 18.
Happy in bearing reproach for Christ............ 1 Pet. iv. 14.
Hastening the coming of the day of God......... 2 Pet. iii. 12.
Having promise of the life that now is and that to come.................... .... 1 Tim. iv. 8.

Holding fast that which is good... ....1 Thess. v. 21.
Holding fast the form of sound words............2 Tim. i. 13.
Holding fast the faithful word......................Tit. i. 9.
Holy in all manner of conversation...............1 Pet. i. 15.
Hoping to the end..................................1 Pet. i. 13.
Humbling self under the mighty hand of God......1 Pet. v. 6.
Hungering and thirsting after righteousness.......Matt. v. 6.
Illuminated... ....Heb. x. 32.
Increasing in the knowledge of God................Col. i. 10.
Inheriting all things.................................Rev. xxi. 7.
Instant in season, out of season..................2 Tim. iv. 2.
Joined unto the Lord.......................... 1 Cor. vi. 17.
Joying in God through our Lord Jesus Christ.....Rom. v. 11.
Judging one another no more................ Rom. xiv. 13.
Keeping the commandments of Christ..........John xiv. 21.
Keeping that which is committed to our trust....1 Tim. vi. 20.
Keeping yourselves unspotted from the world.....James i. 27.
Keeping yourselves from idols..................1 John v. 21.
Keeping ourselves in the love of God...............Jude xxi.
Kind to one another, tenderhearted..............Eph. iv. 32.
Kindiy affectioned one to another...............Rom. xii. 10.
Knit together in love............. ....Col. ii. 2.
Knowing that we have eternal life ....1 John v. 13.
Laboring to enter into th it rest...................Heb. iv. 11.
Laying aside all malice and all guile...............1 Pet. ii. 1.
Laying up for ourselves treasures in Heaven......Matt. vi. 20.
Led by the Spirit of God.........................Rom. viii. 14.
Letting no corrupt communication proceed out of the mouth.................... ....Eph. iv. 29.
Like minded, having the same love................Phil. ii. 2.
Living henceforth not unto ourselves, but unto Him....................... ....2 Cor. v. 15.
Looking not at the things which are seen........2 Cor. iv. 18.
Looking for the Savior............ ....Phil. iii. 20.
Looking for that blessed hope.......................Tit. ii. 13.
Looking for Him that shall appear ....Heb. ix. 28.
Looking off unto Jesus...........................Heb. xii. 2.
Loving God because He first loved us...........1 John iv. 19.

Loving Christ whom we have not seen............1 Pet. i. 8.
Loving one another, and thus showing that we are His....................................John xiii. 35.
Made meet to be partakers of the saints' inheritance...Col. i. 12.
Meek, and inheriting the earth..................Matt. v. 5.
Merciful, and obtaining mercy...... ....Matt. v. 7.
Mindful of the words recorded in the Scriptures...2 Pet. iii. 2.
Mortifying our members which are on the earth... Col. iii. 5.
Not pleasing ourselves........................... Rom. xv. 1.
Not resisting evil..................................Matt. v. 39.
Not taking anxious thought about our life........Matt. vi. 25.
Not judging, that we be not judged.............Matt. vii. 1.
Not fearing them which kill the body............Matt. x. 28.
Not of the world ....John xvii. 16.
Not conformed to this world.......................Rom. xii. 2.
Not wise in our own conceits....................Rom. xii. 16.
Not our own............................... 1 Cor. vi. 19.
Not children in understanding................1 Cor. xiv. 20.
Not equally yoked together with unbelievers.....2 Cor. vi. 14.
Not entangled again with the law..................Gal. v. 1.
Not weary in well-doing............................Gal. vi. 9.
Not sleeping, as do others.......................1 Thess. v. 6.
Not self-willed, not soon angry......................Tit. i. 7.
Not forsaking the assemblage of ourselves together.Heb. x. 25.
Not despising the chastening of the Lord....... ..Heb. xii. 5.
Not carried about with divers and strange doctrines...... ....Heb. xiii. 9.
Not rendering evil for evil............. .. ....1 Pet. iii. 9.
Now past all condemnation.......................Rom. viii. 1.
Now made nigh by the blood of Christ...........Eph. ii. 13.
Now the Sons of God................ ....1 John iii. 2.
Obedient children...... ....1 Pet. i. 14.
Occupying till Christ comes.....................Luke xix. 13.
Ordained unto eternal life........................Acts xiii. 48.
Overcoming by the blood of the Lamb............Rev. xii. 11.
Passed from death unto life.....................John v, 24.
Patient in tribulation..........................Rom. xii. 12.
Patient toward all men..........................1 Thess. v. 14.

Patiently waiting for Christ....................2 Thess. iii. 5.

Peacemakers....................................Matt. v. 9.

Perfectly joined together in the same mind.. .....1 Cor. i. 10.

Pitiful and courteous..............................1 Pet. iii. 8.

Praying without ceasing.......................1 Thess. v. 17.

Praying always in the spirit, for all saints........Eph. vi. 18.

Proving what is acceptable unto the Lord.........Eph. v. 10.

Purchased with blood....... ....Acts xx. 28.

Purifying ourselves even as He is pure..........1 John iii. 3.

Putting away all bitterness and wrath............Eph. iv. 31.

Putting on the new man..........................Eph. iv. 24.

Putting on the whole armor of God..............Eph. vi. 11.

Putting on love above all these things.............Col. iii. 14.

Quenching not the spirit.......................1 Thess. v. 19.

Reaching forth unto those things that are before..Phil. iii. 13.

Ready to every good work............. ....Tit. iii. 1

Receiving a kingdom...........................Heb. xii. 28.

Receiving the promise of the Spirit...............Gal. iii. 14.

Reckoning ourselves dead unto sin.... ....Rom. vi. 11.

Redeeming the time.............................Eph. v. 16.

Refraining the tongue from evil................1 Pet. iii. 10.

Rejoicing in the Lord always.... ....Phil. iv. 4.

Returned into the Shepherd and Bishop of our
Souls........................ ....1 Pet. ii. 25.

Running with patience the race set before us......Heb. xii. 1.

Sanctified through the offering of Christ ....Heb. x. 10.

Saved by grace through faith......................Eph. ii. 8.

Sealed with that Holy Spirit of promise ....Eph. i. 13.

Searching the Scriptures.........................John v. 39.

Seeking not our own, but the welfare of others...1 Cor. x. 24.

Separated from the world......................2 Cor. vi. 17.

Serving one another by love.................... ......Gal. v. 13.

Sincere and without offence till the day of Christ...Phil. i. 10.

Sounding out the word of the Lord.............1 Thess. i. 8.

Speaking the truth in love........................Eph iv. 15.

Speaking not evil one of another...............James iv. 11.

Stablished in the faith.......................... Col. ii. 7.

Striving together for the faith of the gospel ....Phil. i. 27.

Taking heed to an evil heart of unbelief...........Heb. iii. 12.
Taught of God to love one another]..............1 Thess. iv. 9.
Teaching and admonishing one another ....Col. iii. 16.
Thankful.......................... ....Col. iii. 15.
Thinking no evil............... ....1 Cor. xiii. 5.
Transformed by the renewing of the mind ....Rom. xii. 2.
Trusting in the living God......................1 Tim. iv. 10.
Using this world as not abusing it ....1 Cor. vii. 31.
Victorious through faith.........................1 John v. 4.
Vigilant against our adversary the devil...........1 Pet. v 8.
Waiting for the Son of God from Heaven.........1 Thes. i. 10.
Walking in the light, as He is in the light ... .1 John i. 7.
Wanting nothing ....James i. 4.
Watching and standing fast in the faith........1 Cor. xvi. 13.
Weeping with them that weep..... ....Rom. xii. 15.
Wise unto that which is good ....Rom. xvi. 19.
Working out our own salvation ....Phil. ii. 12.
Worshipping God by the Spirit....... ....Phil. iii. 3.
Yielding ourselves unto God ....Rom. vi. 13.
Zealous of good works................ ....Tit. ii. 14.

THE GOSPEL SHIP.

Emigrants for Emmanuel's Land should lose no time in having their places secured, as only one voyage is made from our shores to that happy country.

The vessel's name—**The Gospel Ship.** Matt viii. 23.

Port from which it sails—**The City of Destruction.** Ps. cxiii. 4 ; Isa. xix. 18.

Destination—**Emmanuel's Land.** Isa. viii. 8 ; Heb. x. 14.

Time of sailing—**To-day.** Heb. iv. 7 ; 2 Cor. vi. 2.

Price of passage—**Without money**. Isa. lv. 1 ; Rev. xxi. 17.

Captain's name—**Jesus Christ.** Matt. xiv. 25 ; Mark iv. 37.

Crew—**Converts and ministers.** Matt. xiv. 23 ; Eph. iv.

Passengers—**Sinners saved by grace**. 1 Cor. 1, 2; Acts 6.

Sea over which it passes—**Time.** James iv. 14 ; Rev. x. 3.

Light-house—**The Holy Scriptures.** 2 Cor. vi. 4 ; Isa. 58.

Compass—**Truth.** Ps. xliii. 3.

Sails—**Faith and love.** 1 Thess. i. 3.

Wind—**The Holy Spirit.** John iii. 8 ; Gal. v. 22, 23.

Helm—**Grace.** Eph. iv. 5 ; 2 Thess. ii. 16.

Anchor—**Hope.** Heb. vi. 19.

Passengers are supplied with everything on the voyage.

"*My God shall supply all your need.*"—Phil. iv. 19.

"*And yet there is room.*"—Luke v. 22.

THE GOSPEL RAILROAD.

1. Road bed. **The Bible.** Ps. cxix, 105; Heb. iv, 12; 2 Tim. iii. 16 ; 1 Peter i. 25.

2. Engine. **Love,** 1 John iv. 16 ; John iii. 16 ; Deut. vi. 5 ; 1 John ii. 5 ; iv. 19 ; Rom. xiii. 10.

3. Engineer. **God,** Ps. xlvi. 1 ; xlviii. 3 ; Matt. xix. 17 ; John xvii. 3.

4. Conductor. **Jesus Christ,** Rom. v. 8; Heb. xiii. 8; Rom. viii. 1 ; Col. iii. 1-4.

5. Train. (Made up of) **Believers,** Acts xvi. 31; 1 Tim. iv. 12 ; Mark ix. 23, 24.

6. Destination. **Heaven,** 2 Cor. v. 1 ; 1 Peter i. 3, 4 ; John xiv. 1-3 ; Rev. viii. 9-17.—*Y. M. C. A. Watchman.*

WHAT A PRAYER MEETING SHOULD BE.

1. Regular and punctual attendance....Heb. x. 25; Ps. lxxxiv. 1, 4; Acts ii. 1, 6.
2. Bring others...........Num. x. 29; Ps. xlii. 4; Dan. xii. 3.
3. Come praying....................John xii. 21; John xv. 5.
4. Continue in prayer..Phil. iv. 6; Gen. xxxii. 26; Eph. vi. 18.
5. Avoid criticism..Ps. cxxxiii. 1; Rom. xii. 10; John xvii. 23.
6. Participate promptly and heartily...Col. iii. 16; Heb. iv. 16.
7. Let all exercises be brief..........Eccles. v. 2; Matt. vi. 7.
8. Keep in mind that we speak and sing before God.....2 Cor. xii. 19; 1 Sam. xvi. 7.
9. Christian testimony.....Ps. xl. 10; Ps. li. 15; Ps. lxiii. 3–5; Mal. iii. 16, 17; Heb. iii. 13; James v. 16.—W. F. C.

CHARACTERISTICS OF GOD'S PEOPLE.

Ye are a P-raying..............................Eph. vi. 18.
E-arnest..............................Jude iii.
C-onsecrated..............................1 Cor. i. 8.
U-nited..............................Eph. iv. 13.
L-oving..............................Rom. xiii. 8.
I-mmortal..............................Ps. xxxvii. 29.
A-ctive..............................2 Peter i. 5.
R-ighteous..........PEOPLE...........Isa. lx. 21.

Ye are a chosen generation; a royal priesthood; a holy nation; a peculiar PEOPLE..................1 Pet. ii. 9.—J. B. A.

THE TWO MASTERS.

The work of

The D-eceives, Rev. xii. 9......	But J-ustifies, Rom. iii. 26.
E-ntices, 2 Tim. ii. 26.....	E-levates, Matt. xxv. 23.
V-itiates, 2 Cor. iv. 4......	S-anctifies, 1 Cor. vi. 11.
I-nfatuates, John xiii. 2...	U-nites to God, Eph. ii. 14.
L-eads to hell, Matt. xxv. 41; 1 John iii. 8.......	S-aves, John iii. 17.
	S. W. M.

HOW SHALL I APPROACH THE MERCY-SEAT—
HEB. IV. 16.

B-elieving God........................Matt. xxi. 22.
O-beying God........................Heb. v. 9.
L-oving God........................Gal. v. 6.
D-epending on God........................Jas. i. 17.
L-ooking to God........................Heb. xii. 2.
Y-ielding to God........................Rom. vi. 13.

J. B. A.

WHAT SHALL I DO WITH JESUS?

Prove Him........................Mal. iii. 10.
Prize Him........................Eph. i. 21.
Praise Him........................Ps. c.
Preach Him........................2 Cor. iv. 5.
Pray to Him........................John xiv. 14.

J. B. A.

HOW SHALL I FIND JESUS?

I' I S-incerely........................Phil. i. 10.
E-arnestly........................Heb. ii. 1.
A-ttentively........................Luke xix. 48.
R-epeatedly........................Phil. vi. 18.
C-arefully........................1 Peter iv. 7.
H-onestly........................1 Tim. ii. 1–3.

Seek HIM while He may be found.
Call upon HIM while He is near..........Isa. iv. 6.

TO WHOM SHALL WE GO FOR SAFETY?

Flee to C-aptain of our salvation........................Heb ii. 10.
H-orn of salvation........................Ps. xviii. 2.
R-oot of Jesse........................Isa. ii. 10
I-mmanuel........................Isa. vii. 14.
S-hepherd of Israel........................Ps. lxxx. i.
T-rue God........................1 John v. 20.

W. F. C.

SEVEN CONFESSIONS OF THE BIBLE.

"*I have sinned*"—By whom and the motive of each.

1. Pharaoh, from slavish fear..............Ex. ix. 27; x. 16.
2. Balaam, for a reward.........................Num. xxii. 34.
3. Achan, being detected of God...............Joshua vii. 20.
4. Saul, from cowardice.........................1 Sam. xv. 24.
5. David, being reproved ....2 Sam. xii. 13.
6. Judas, from despair.........................Matt. xxvii. 4.
7. Prodigal Son, from an honest heart...... .Luke xv. 18, 21.

GOD'S PROVIDENCE.

Mysterious.........................Psalm x. 5; Job xi. 7–9.

Seems sometimes not to regard the right.......Ps. lxxiii. 2–16:

But really upholds the right..Ps. lxxiii. 17–20; Eccl. viii. 12, 13.

Brings good out of evil...Gen. l. 20; Ex. xiv. 4; Deut. xxiii. 5.

Directs events...........Ezra v. 5; Prov. xvi. 9; Prov. xxi. 1.

THE ATONING SAVIOUR.

CHRIST DIED FOR THE

U-NWORTHY, Acts xiii. 46.
N-EEDY, Matt. ix. 12.
G-UILTY, Rom. iii. 19.
O-LD, Ps. xxxvii. 25.
D-RUNKARD, 1 Cor. vi. 10.
L-OST, Luke xix. 10.
Y-OUNG, Eccl. xii. 1.

C. N. P.

ALL THINGS THROUGH CHRIST.

WE KNOW THAT

ALL

T-RIALS, 2 Cor. iv. 17.
H-ATRED OF FOES, Gen. xl. 5.
I-NFIRMITIES, Acts iii. 11.
N-ECESSITIES, Ps. xxxvii. 25.
G-RIEFS, Heb. xii. 11.
S-UFFERINGS, 2 Cor. xi. 23–28.

WORK

Together for Good to Them that love GOD. Rom. viii. 28.

J. B. A.

SEVEN THINGS TO HOLD FAST.

1. That which is good........................1. Thess. v. 1.
2. The faithful word............................Titus i. 9.
3. The form of sound words....................2 Tim. i. 13.
4. The confidence and rejoicing of the hope.........Heb. iii. 6.
5. The profession of our faith......................Heb. x. 23.
6. That we have, that no man take our crown......Rev. iii. 11.
7. The unfaithful, hold fast and repent............Rev. iii. 3.

THE SEVEN "MUSTS."

1. What MUST I do to be saved?.................Acts xvi. 30.
2. Ye MUST be born again........................John iii. 7.
3. No other name under heaven, whereby we MUST be saved. Acts iv. 12.
4. So MUST the Son of man be lifted up...........John iii. 14.
5. As thou hast said so MUST we do................Ezra x. 12.
6. Zacchæus, To-day I MUST abide at thy house....Luke xix. 5.
7. For we MUST all appear before the judgment seat of Christ. 2 Cor. v. 10.

THINGS TO WHICH WE SHOULD TAKE HEED.

That no man deceive us....Mark xiii. 33–37; 1 Cor. i. 7; Titus ii. 13; Heb. ix. 28.

What we hear.........Mark iv. 24; Prov. vi. 27; Isa. viii. 20; Jer. xxii. 29; John xvi. 13.

How we hear.......1 Sam. iii. 9, 10; Ps. cxix. 11; Heb. ii. 1.

To ourselves..........Luke xxi. 34; Phil. ii. 3; Mark vii. 21, 23; 1 Cor. x. 12; 1 Tim. iv. 16.

How we build....1 Cor. iii. 10, 11; 1 Cor. x. 31; Matt. vii. 24.

Lest there be in any of us an evil heart of unbelief....Heb. iii. 12; Rom. xi. 20; 1 Pet. i. 8.

To the sure word of prophecy.......2 Pet. i. 19; 2 Tim. iv. 4; Heb. x. 37; Rev. xxii. 20.

That we endure to the end.......Heb. iv. 1; Rev. ii. 26; Rev. iii. 21; 2 Tim. ii. 3.

THE PEARL OF GREAT PRICE.

"The kingdom of Heaven is like unto a merchantman seeking goodly pearls: who, when he had found one pearl of great price, went and sold all he had, and bought it."—Matt. xiii. 45-46.

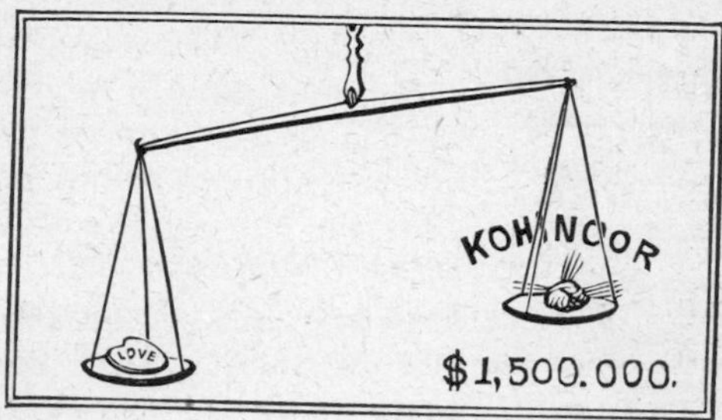

Children, how much gold do you think you could carry? I think each of you could carry about$5,000, (or 18 lbs avoirdupois,) 300 Sunday-school scholars marching singly in procession would make a line a quarter of a mile long, and if each were loaded with gold, they all together would carry $1,500,000. This is the value of the great Kohinoor diamond, among the crown jewels of Queen Victoria, and for some time thought to be the largest diamond in the world. A million and a half dollars! What an amount of money that is! It would build one hundred handsome churches, or 3,000 homes for the poor.

I have no idea, children, that any of you will ever have that much money or own such a valuable diamond. But there is another jewel of immensely more value, that each of you can have, if you want it. Can you tell what is this pearl of greatest price? *It is the love of Jesus in our hearts.* If we have this we are rich, though we have not a single penny besides. But if we have enough money to buy the Kohinoor diamond, and have not this love in our hearts, we are *poor.* *The happiest people in the world are those who love Jesus most.* The merchantman sold all that he had to buy this one pearl, and so we must be willing to give up everything that stands in the way of our giving our hearts to Jesus. J. R. J.

INTEMPERANCE.—Object Lesson.

Prov. xxiiii. 29-35.

Draw the wine glass, (in red chalk if practicable,) and around it the serpent (in white chalk) twining as in the diagram. Have this prepared in advance, and show it to the school. Then in answer to questions, place in order, beginning at the foot of the glass, the different results of intemperance.

From verse 29 bring out the various "woes:" Poverty, Prov. xxiii. 21; Prov. xx. 1. Sorrow, 1 Sam. xxv. 36-37; Isa. v. 22. Contentions, Prov. 20, 1; 2 Sam. xiii. 28; 1 Kings xx. 16-20. Error, Isa. xxviii. 7-8, Bloodshot Eyes, Gen. xlix. 12. Destruction, Nahum i. 10; Matt. xxiv. 49-51; Luke xii. 45, 46.

Verse 33: Lustful Passion, Gen. xix. 32; Perverse Speech, Prov. xxxi. 5; Ps. lxix. 12; Dan. v. 4; Hos. vii. 5.

Verse 34: Dizzy Head, 1 Sam. xxv. 36-38; 1 Sam. xxx. 16-17; 2 Sam. xiii. 28; 1 Kings xvi. 9; 1 Kings xx. 16; Joel i. 5; Matt. xxiv. 38; Luke xvii. 27-29; Luke xxi. 34.

Verse 35: Stupefied Feelings, Prov. xxvii. 22; Jer. v. 3; Jer. xxxi. 18; Prov. xxvi. 9; Eph. iv. 19. Sinful Resolution, Prov. xxvi. 11; Deut. xxix. 19; Isa. xxii. 13; Isa. lvi. 12; 1 Cor. xv. 32-34; 2 Pet. ii. 22.

A few anecdotes and illustrations on the several points will serve to make this a very effective temperance address.

PRACTICAL LESSON.

Verse 31: "Look not," Ps. cxix. 37; Mark ix. 47; 1 John ii. 16.

Verse 32: "Bites," "Stings," "Kills," "At Last,," Ec. x. 8; Jer. 8 17; Amos v. 19; Amos ix. 3; Prov. vi. 11; Isa. xxviii. 3-7-8; Jer. v. 31; Ez. vii. 5, vi. 12; Luke xvi. 25-26; Rom. vi. 21.

BIBLE READING.

THE LIFE OF CHRIST FROM PROPHECY AND HISTORY.

1. HIS GENEALOGY.—Gen. iii. 15; Matt. i. 1-25; Luke iii.
2. HIS BIRTH.—Gen. iii. 15, Gal. iv. 4; Gen. xvii. 7; Gen. xxii. 18, Gal. iii. 16; Gen. xxi. 12, Heb. xi. 17-19; Gen. xlix. 10, Luke ii. 7; Isa. vii. 14, Mal. i. 18; Micah v. 2, Matt. ii. 1.
3. HIS CHARACTER.—Isa. liii. 2 and Luke ix. 58; Isa. xlii. 2, Matt. xii. 15-19; Isa. xl. 11 and Heb. iv. 15; Isa. liii. 9, 1 Peter ii. 22; Psalm lxix. 9; John ii. 17.
4. HIS MINISTRY.—Isa. ix. 1, 2 Matt. iv. 12-16, 23; Isa. liii. 2 Luke iv. 16-21-43; Zech. ix. 9, Matt. xxi. 1-5; Haggai ii. 7-9; Mal. iii. 1, Matt. xxi. 12; John ii. 13-16.
5. HIS SUFFERING.—Psalm xxii. 14-15; Luke xxii. 42-44; Isa. liii. 3, Heb. iv. 15; Isa. l. 6, and Mark xiv. 65; Isa. liii. 7, Matt. xxvi. 63; Isa. liii. 4-6-12, Matt. xx. 28; Ps. xxii. 16, John xix. 18; Ps. xxii. 1, Matt. xxvii. 46; Ps. xxii. 7-8; Matt. xxvii. 39-44; Ps. lxix. 21, Matt. xxvii. 34; Ps. xxii. 18, Matt. xxvii. 35; Ex. xii. 46, John xix. 33-36.
6. HIS DEATH.—Isaiah liii. 9 and Matt. xxvii. 57-60; Psalm xvi. 10 and Acts ii. 31; Psalm lxviii. 18 and Acts i. 9; Psalm cx. 1 and Heb. i. 3; Dan. vii. 14 and Phil. ii. 9-11.
7. HIS RESURRECTION.—Ps. xvi. 10; Matt. xii. 10; Acts ii. 27-31; Rom i. 4; Heb. xiii. 20; 2 John xix. 10-18; Matt. xxvii. 63; Matt. xxviii. 7; Luke xxiv. 44-26; John xx. 20; John xx. 27; Acts i. 3; Acts v. 32; 1 Cor. xv. 20-23.
8. HIS ASCENSION.—Psalm xxiv. 7-10.; Ps. lxviii. 17-18; John xvi. 5-7; John iii. 13; Acts i. 11. Heb. ix. 24; Mark xvi. 19; Acts vii. 55.
9. HIS SECOND COMING.—Acts i. 11; Acts xxv. 31-32; Acts xvii. 31; 2 Cor. v. 10; Matt. xxiv. 36; Matt. xxiv. 3; John v. 22-26-27; Rev. i. 7; 2 Thess. i. 7-9. 1 Thess. iv. 16; Rev. xx. 12; Matt. xiii. 41-43; Matt. xxv. 34-41. 2 Pet. iii. 10; 2 Pet. iii. 11-13.
10. HIS EVERLASTING REIGN.—Psalm xlv. 6-7; Matt. xxviii. 1; Phil. ii. 5-11; Dan. ii. 44. 1 Cor. xv. 24-26-28.

JOSEPH A TYPE OF CHRIST;

OR THE LIKENESS BETWEEN THEM.

Joseph was a shepherd. Gen. xxxvii. 2.

Christ was the Good Shepherd. John x. 11.

Joseph was sent by his father to seek his brethren. Gen. xxxvii. 13-14-16.

Christ was sent by His Father to seek and save His people. John iii. 16, 17.

When Joseph's brethren saw him coming they sought to slay him. Gen. xxxvii. 20.

When Christ came on earth, the Jews, His people, sought to kill Him. Matt. ii. 20.

Joseph was put in a pit and raised from it. Gen. xxxvii. 28.

Christ was put in a tomb and raised from it. Matt. xxvii. 59-60.

Joseph was sold for twenty pieces of silver—the price of a slave under age. Gen. xxxvii. 28.

Christ was sold for thirty pieces of silver—the price of a slave of full age. Matt. xxvi. 15.

Joseph was carried down into Egypt. Gen. xxxix. 1.

Christ was carried down into Egypt. Matt. ii. 13-14.

Joseph was tempted by Potiphar's wife. Gen. xxxix. 7.

Christ was tempted by Satan in the Wilderness. Mark i. 13.

Joseph was condemned by a false witness and put in prison. Gen. xxxix. 19-20.

Christ was condemned by false witnesses and put to death. Matt. xxvi. 59-60.

Joseph was put in prison with two prisoners; one is saved, the other hanged. Gen. xl. 2-3; xli. 22.

Christ was crucified with two prisoners; one He saved, the other was hanged. Luke xxiii. 39-43.

Joseph became Governor, Ruler and Saviour of his people in Egypt. Gen. xlii. 6; xli. 43.

Christ was Governor, Ruler and Saviour of his people on earth. Matt. ii. 6.

Joseph was thirty years old when he began his public ministry. Gen. xli. 46.

Christ was thirty years old when He began His public ministry. Luke ii. 23.

Joseph was blessed with a spirit of wisdom, and the Lord made all that he did to prosper. Gen. xli. 38-39; xxxix. 23.

Christ was blessed with a spirit of wisdom, and the pleasure of the Lord prospered in His hand. Luke ii. 40; Isa. liii. 10.

Joseph went about doing good, laying up food for the famine. Gen. xli. 46-49.

Christ went about doing good, and healing the sick. Matt. iv. 23-24.

Joseph's people had to come to him for their temporal food. Gen. xlii. 3-10.

Christ's peopie all have to come to Him for their spiritual food. John vi. 48-51.

Joseph knew his brethren; they did not know him. Gen. 42. 8.

Christ knew His disciples; they did not know Him. Luke 16-24.

Joseph gave to his people freely, without money or price. Gen. xlii. 25.

Christ gives to His people freely, without money and without price. Isa lv. 1.

Joseph's brethren all had to bow down to him. Gen xlii. 6.

Christ's people all have to bow to Him. Phil. ii. 10.

Joseph was one of twelve brethren, the Patriarchs. Gen. 42.

Christ had His twelve disciples, the Apostles. Matt. x. ii.

Joseph made himself known to his brethren after they supposed him dead. Gen. xlv. 1.

Christ made Himself known to his disciples after they had seen Him laid in the tomb. Luke xxiv. 36-40.

Joseph said to them, "I am Joseph your brother, whom ye sold into Egypt." Gen. xlv. 4.

Christ said to His disciples, "It is I, myself; handle me and see." Luke xxiv. 39.

Joseph forgave his brother their trespasses. Gen. xlv. 3-8.

Christ forgave His people their sins. Matt. ix. 2-6.

Joseph had a beloved brother, Benjamin. Gen. xliii. 29-30.

Christ had a beloved disciple, John. John xiii. 23.

Joseph wept over his brethren. Gen. xlv. 15.

Christ wept over His people. Luke xix. 31.

Joseph dined with his twelve brethren, he the twelfth. Gen. 43-16.

Christ supped with his twelve Apostles. John xiii. 14.

Joseph loved his father and nourished him. John xlvii. 11-12.

Christ loved His Father and obeyed Him. John xv. 10.

Joseph was blest by his father. Gen. xlix. 22-26.

Christ was blest by His Father. John iii. 35.

Joseph's father received his son as from the dead. Gen. xlvi. 30.

Christ's Father received His Son from the dead. Matt. xvi. 19.

Joseph had been a man of sorrow in the pit. Gen. xlii. 21.

Christ was a man of sorrow in the garden. Isa. liii. 3 ; Luke xxii. 44.

Joseph's garments had been stained with blood. Gen. xxxvii. 31.

Christ's garments were stained with blood. John xix. 33.

Joseph's life seems to be without blemish. Gen. xxxix. 2-6.

Christ's life was without blemish. 1 Pet. ii. 22.

Joseph was clothed in fine linen. Gen. xli. 42.

Christ was wrapted in fine linen. Matt. xxvii. 59.

Joseph's bones were raised from the grave and carried up to the earthly Canaan. Gen. l. 25.

Christ arose from the grave, and was carried up to the heavenly Canaan. Luke xxiv 51.

Joseph was raised from the prison to a post of honor and power. Gen. xli. 40-43.

Christ was raised from the grave and crowned with glory and honor. Heb. ii. 9.

Christ's earthly or reputed father's name was Joseph. Matt i. 18.

The man who begged the body of Christ and laid it in his own tomb was named Joseph. Matt. xxvii. 57-60.

When Simeon saw the young child, Jesus, he said, "Now let me die. or depart in peace." Luke ii. 29.

When old Jacob saw his son Joseph, he said, "Now let me die, since thou art yet alive." Gen. xlvi. 30.

J. E. C. *in Watchman and Reflector*.

WHAT CHRIST IS TO US.

Our Advocate. 1 John ii. 1.
" Brother. Mark iii. 35.
" Captain. Heb. ii. 10.
" Daysman. Job ix. 33.
" Eternal life. 1 John v. 20.
" Father. Isa. ix. 6.
" God. 1 John v. 20.
" Helper. Heb. xiii. 6.
" Intercessor. Heb. vii. 25.
" Judge. Acts xvii. 31.
" Keeper. John xvii. 12.
" Light. John i. 4.
" Mediator. 1 Tim. ii. 5.
" Name. Acts xv. 17.
" Offering. Eph. v. 2.

Our Peace. Eph. ii. 14.
" Quickener. Rom. vii. 11.
" Ransom. Mark x. 45.
" Saviour. 2 Pet. iii. 18.
" Teacher. John iii. 2.
" Unspeakable gift. 2 Cor. 9.
" Vine. John xv. 5.
" Wisdom. 1 Cor. i. 30.
" 'Xample. John xiii. 15.
" Yoke-fellow. Matt. ii. 29.
" Zeal. Ps. 69, 9; John ii. 17.
" Alpha and Omega. Rev. i. 8.
" First and last. Rev. i. 11.

CHRIST IS OUR ALL IN ALL.—Col. iii. 11.

BIBLE PROOFS.

The difference between Christians and the world.

Servants of sin—Rom. vi. 16-23.
Entangled—Gal. v. 1.
Sinners—Rom. iii. 23.
Children of devil—John 8, 44.
Prodigal away from home—Luke xv. 13-14.
Sold under sin—Rom. vii. 14.
Led by the devil—2 Tim. ii. 26.
Wicked flee—Prov. xxxviii. 1.
Shall perish—Luke xiii. 3.
Jesus "knows not"—Matt. xxv. 12.
Depart—left hand—Matt. xxv. 41-46.

Serv'ts of God—1 Peter, ii. 15.
Free—Rom. vi. 22.
Saints—1 Cor. i. 2.
Children of God, Gal. iv. 3-7.
Child in his fathers house—Luke xv. 20-25.
Bought—1 Cor. vi. 20.
Led by the Spirit—Rom viii. 14.
Righteous bold—Prov. xxviii. 1
Shall never perish—John x. 25.
Jesus knows His sheep—John x. 27
Come—right hand—Matt. xxv. 31-34.

GEO. A. HALL.

THE DARK SIDE AND THE BRIGHT SIDE OF A CHISTIAN LIFE.

Text Psalm xxx. 5.

"Weeping may endure for a night but joy cometh in the morning." If we were true believers in Christ, sins will make us weep as they did David, Peter and others. But let us not cast away our confidence, if we have fallen, and felt the bitterness of sin; but rather take comfort that "He will not always chide; neither will He keep his anger forever." For it says, "Joy cometh in the morning."

Let us look into the Psalms and we will see the bright side of the believer's life when he is in communion with God, and the dark side when out of communion with God, because of sin.

The Dark Side.	*The Bright Side.*
I. SIN.	I. SIN REMOVED AND COVERED.
"My sin is ever before me, neither is there rest in my bones because of my sin." Ps. xxxviii. 3; li. 3.	"Blessed is he whose transgression is forgiven, whose sin is covered. Ps xxxii. 1, 2; ciii. 12; cxxx. 3, 4.
II. DARKNESS.	II. LIGHT.
"He hath made me to dwell in darkness. Ps. lxxxviii. 6; cxliii. 3.	"The Lord is my light. "In thy light shall we see light." Ps. xxxvi. 9; xxvii. 1; cxix. 130.
III. TROUBLE.	III. PEACE.
"For my soul is full of troubles." Ps. lxxxviii. 3; l. 15.	"I will lay me down in peace and sleep." Ps. iv. 8; lxxxv. 8-10; cxix. 165.
IV. SORROW.	IV. JOY AND GLADNESS.
"Having sorrow in my heart daily." Ps. xiii. 2; cii. 9-11.	"Thou hast put off my sackcloth and girded me with gladness. Ps. v. 11, 12; xxx. 11.

V. MOURNING.

"I go mourning all the day long." Ps. vi. 6; xxxviii. 6.

V. PRAISING.

"My tongue shall speak of thy righteousness and of thy praise all the day long." Ps. xxxiv. 1; xxxv. 28.

VI. DISEASE.

"Filled with a loathsome disease." Ps. vi. 2, 3; xxxviii. 7.

VI. HEALED.

"Who healeth all thy diseases." Ps. ciii. 3; cxlvii. 3.

VII. DISSATISFIED.

"My soul thirsteth for God, for the living God." Ps. xlii. 1, 2; lxiii. 1.

VII. SATISFIED.

"Who satifieth the mouth with good things. (*present.*) Ps. ciii. 5; xxxvi. 8; lxiii. 5. I shall be satisfied, (*future.*) Ps. xvii. 15.

VIII. IN FEAR OF ENEMIES.

"They also that seek after my life lay snares for me." Ps. xxxviii. 12, 19-22; xlvi. 4-9; cxl. 1-5.

VIII. NOT AFRAID OF ENEMIES.

"Thou hast smitten all mine enemies on the cheek bone; whom shall I fear." Ps. iii. 7; xxvii. 1, 2.

IX. BONDAGE.

"Bring my soul out of prison." Ps. lxxix. 11; cxlii. 7; cxlvi. 7.

IX. DELIVERANCE.

"For thou hast delivered my soul from death." Ps. lvi. 13; cxvi. 8; cxxiv. 7.

X. DEATH.

"He hath made me to dwell in darkness as those that have been long dead." Ps. lxxxviii. 10; cxliii. 3.

X. LIFE.

"The Lord shall count when He writeth up the people that this man was born there. Ps. lxxxvii. 6; xvi. 11; xxxvi. 9.

Willful sin after conversion brings darkness, trouble, sorrow, mourning, disease, dissatisfaction, fear, bondage and finally death, which means out of communion or fellowship with God. Let the joyful one obey, Rom. xv. 1-3; Gal. vi. 1. And the mournful one obey, James iv. 8-10, and all will be right.

JOHN CURRIE.

FROM BONDAGE TO CANAAN.

THE CHRISTIAN'S PILGRIMAGE.

OLD TESTAMENT.	NEW TESTAMENT.
1. Egyptian Bondage. Ex. i. 14.	Sin of Soul. Rom. vii. 21.
2. The ten Plagues. Gen. vii. 11.	Conviction. Rom. vii. 24.
3. Passover. Ex. xii. 5, 7.	Christ's Sacrifice. 1 Cor. v. 7.
4. Departure from Egypt. Ex. xii. 40, 42.	Repentance. Acts xxiv. 20.
5. Crossing the Red Sea. Ex. xiv.	Conversion. 2 Cor. v. 17.
6. Waters of Marah. Ex. xv. 23.	Temptation. Heb. ii. 18.
7. Manna. Ex. xvi. 4.	Daily Grace. 2 Cor. xii. 8.
8. The Stayed Hands. Ex. xvii. 11.	Prayer. James v. 16.
9. Law. Ex. xx. 17.	Duty. John xiv. 15.
10. Tabernacle Building. Ex. xxxv. 1, 9.	Church Erection. 1 Cor. xvi. 1.
11. The Golden Calf. Ex. xxxii. 1.	Idolatry. 1 John v. 21.
12. Profane Fire. Lev. x. 1, 2.	Irreverent Thoughts. Matt. xii. 36.
13. Fearing the Giants. Num. xiv. 33.	Unbelief. Heb. iii. 19.
14. Wanderings. Num. xv. 33.	Discipline. 2 Tim. ii. 3.
15. Serpents. Num. xxi. 6.	Sins. 1 Cor. x. 9.
16. The Promised Land. Deut. iii. 27.	Heaven. Rev. xxi. 22.

Concert Exercise.

WANTED FOR THE LORD'S SERVICE.

1. Men like Daniel, who dare to do right.....Dan. vi. 10-16.
2. Men like Shadrach, ready to suffer. Ex. xx. 4, 5; Dan. iii. 4-7.
3. Men in authority, with Nehemiah's faith....Neh. xiii. 4-9.
4. Men like Isaiah, full of eloquence and fervor..Isa. lv. 1-13.
5. Men of courage like Joshua...Num. xiv. 6-9; Josh. vi. 16.
6. Men like Elijah, bold to proclaim the truth..1 Kings xvii. 1.
7. Men like Paul, taught of the Spirit..........1 Cor. xii. 3.
8. Men like Timothy, zealous for the Lord....2 Cor. xvi. 10.
9. Men like the Bereans, gifted with wisdom..Acts xvii. 10, 12.
10. Young men, like Jabez, who fear God.....1 Chron. iv. 10.
11. Young women, like gracious Ruth.........Ruth i. 16, 17.
12. Matrons, like the pious Shunamite......2 Kings iv. 8, 13.
13. Fathers, like Abraham............Gen. xxii.; Prov. x. 21.
14. Brethren, like Aaron and Hur ....Ex. xvii. 9-12.
15. Sisters, who, like Mary, sit at Jesus' feet....Luke x. 38, 39.
16. Heads of families, like Caleb.....Acts x. 2; Num. xiv. 24.
17. Wives, models in their lives............Prov. xxxi. 10-31.
18. Mothers, like Hannah, consecrating their children...1 Sam. i. 10.
19. Maidens, taught of God..2 Kings v. 1-4, 15; Prov. xv. 23.
20. Servants of Christ, like Barnabas. Acts xi. 22-26; Acts ix. 27.

SOWING AND REAPING—Gal. vi. 7.

SEED.	HARVEST.
Idleness	Poverty.
Unkindness	Unkindness.
Tippling	Drunkard's grave.
Profanity	God's curse.
Sinful life	Wretched death.
Rejection of Jesus	Eternal death.

What are you sowing?

M. T. B.

S. S. CONCERT EXERCISE.

THE HEART.

Conductor.—What does the Bible mean by the word *Heart?*

A class, rising.—The "inner man," embracing the seat of the affections and passions, of the conscience, of the mind and of the will.

Conductor.—How many kinds of hearts are spoken of in the Bible?

A Class.—Two; the converted and the unconverted.

Conductor.—What great reason is given why the heart must be kept with diligence?

A Class.—Because out of it are the issues of life. (Repeat Prov. ix. 23).

Conductor.—What did the Saviour say proceeded from the the heart?

A Class.—Evil thoughts, murders, etc. Matt. xv. 19.

Conductor.—Now let the girls give the characteristics of a *converted* heart, and the boys give the Bible *proofs*, as I call the numbers.

(Conductor.)	(Girls.)	(Boys.)
No. 1.	It is set on seeking God.	1 Chron. xi. 16.
" 2.	It is fixed on God.	Psalm cxii. 7.
" 3.	It seeks to be perfect.	Psalm ci. 1-3.
" 4.	It is upright.	Psalm xcvii. 11.
" 5.	It is a clean heart.	Psalm lxxiii. 1.
" 6.	It is a pure heart.	Matt. v. 3.
" 7.	It is true, and free from an evil conscience.	Heb. x. 22.
" 8.	It is honest and good.	Luke viii. 15.
" 9.	It is broken and contrite.	Psalm xxxiv. 18.
" 10.	It is obedient.	Rom. vi. 17.
" 11.	It finds delight in the word of God.	Psalm cxix. 111.
" 12.	It is set free from fear.	Psalm xxvii. 3.
" 13.	It loves to praise God.	Psalm ix. 1.
" 14.	It is a treasury of good things.	Matt. xii. 35.
" 15.	It shows its faith by its works.	James ii. 14-21.

Conductor.—Now give the characteristics of the *unconverted* heart and the *proofs.*

(Conductor.)		(Boys.)	(Girls.)
No.	16.	It is full of evil, and morally insane.	Eccl. ix. 3.
"	17.	It is fully set to do evil.	Eccl. viii. 11.
"	18.	It is deceitful and wicked.	Jer. xvii. 9.
"	19.	It is a treasury of evil things.	Mark vii. 21-22.
"	20.	It is prone to error.	Psalm xcv. 7.
"	21.	It is impenitent.	Rom. ii. 5.
"	22.	It is unbelieving.	Heb. iii. 12
"	23.	It is morally blind.	Eph. iv. 18.
"	24.	It is a deceived heart.	Isa. xliv. 20.
"	25.	It is exposed to the influence of the devil.	John xiii. 2.
"	26.	It is a carnal heart.	Rom. viii. 7.
"	27.	It is full of idols.	Ez. xiv. 3.
"	28.	It is full of pride.	1 Tim. iii. 2.
"	29.	It is full of rebellion,	Jer. v. 23.
"	30.	It is hard as a stone.	Zech. vii. 12.

Conductor.—Is it possible for such hearts to be changed?

A Class, rising.—It is. (Repeat.) Ex. xxxvi. 26.

BY THE GREAT EXCHANGE.

Conductor.—How may this great blessing be obtained?

By the whole school.

(Answered by the following blackboard exercise.)

Give me thy I will give a new

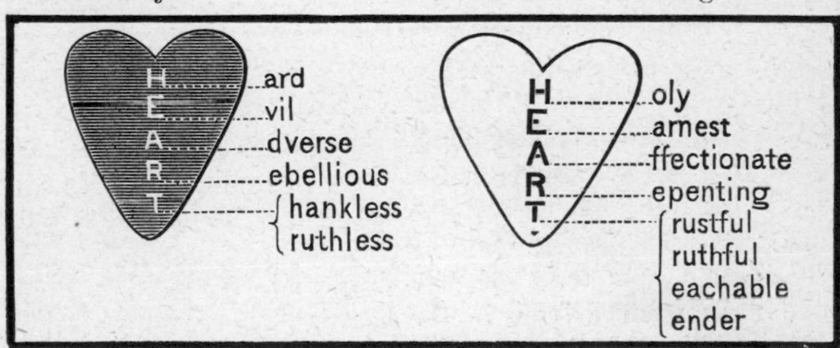

SIN LEAVES ITS MARK.

BLACKBOARD OR OBJECT LESSON.

Philip Jones was a bad boy. His mother had much trouble with him in his father's absence; which took away much of the pleasure and enjoyment of the other children upon the long-looked for return of "Pa," because he had to reprove or punish Philip. How true it is "one sinner destroyeth much good." One bad child will destroy the happiness of a family.

One Monday morning as Philip's father was about starting away, as usual, to his work, he said to Philip, "My boy, go and bring me the hammer and six large nails. Now, Mother, I'm going away to be gone all the week. You have had a great deal of trouble with Philip. *This week* is to decide whether Philip is going to grow up a bad boy. If Philip is bad to-day, when evening comes, you drive one of these nails through this board. For each day that he is bad, drive a nail in the board. But if, after a nail is driven, he should the next day be good, instead of driving a nail that day, you may *draw out one.* Keep the board and show it to me on Saturday night after prayer. This will be Philip's week of trial.

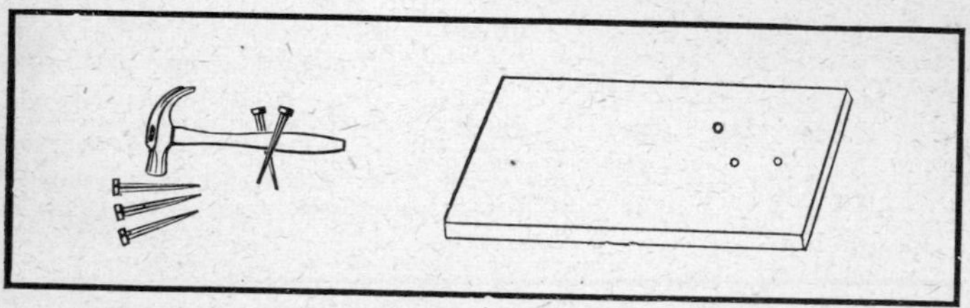

Monday evening came, and with it the usual regrets about Philip's conduct through the day. His mother reminded him of what his father had requested her to do, and Philip admitted that she was compelled to drive the nail. Thus Philip went to his bed with the unpleasant reflection that one nail stood against him.

The same was true of Tuesday and Wednesday thus three nails were driven in the board. The mother said, "Now, Philip, half the week is gone, and it bears a sad record against you. But there are three days yet of which account is to be kept. If you are a good boy the three days left, I will draw out a nail each day, and when father comes home, *there will be no nails* in the board!"

Philip caught the idea with evident pleasure. And it was with great satisfaction his mother, each evening, drew out a nail with kind words of commendation to Philip. Saturday night came, and with it the return of the father. But instead of continuing his caresses with Philip, as with others, he said, Philip will come to me after prayer.

Philip well knew what it meant. *That board and those nails* were to be examined! After prayer the father called for the singular record, and Philip brought them with a mingled look of pleasure and of shame. The father took the board and, seeing no nails in it, drew his boy affectionately to him, and gave him a warm kiss. All the family were pleased, and it was one of the happiest of Saturday nights. Philip, though happier than usual, still *hung his head*, his father inquired what made him look so sad. Philip mastering his feeling, told the whole story, by saying:—"Why, pa, THERE ARE THREE HOLES IN THE BOARD!" Mr. Jones then gave to Philip and to the other children a lesson which they never forgot, upon the truth that "*Sin leaves its mark*," assuring them that God does not thus keep a record of sins committed, but a record that he can *wipe out* and obliterate by the blood of Jesus, so that to the penitent, forgiven soul, there are no marks to cause painful remembrance, as the HOLES IN THE BOARD did to Philip. He assured Philip of his forgiveness of all the past, and entreated him to be a good boy for time to come. He then told him to go to his room and ask Jesus to forgive him and help him to be good, and, above all, to give him a new heart.

[NOTE.—This story never fails to make a good impression. Let it be illustrated on the blackboard, or by an object lesson with a board and nails in hand. Three gimlet holes in the board will enable the speaker to put in and draw out the nails easily. Put in a nail for Monday, another for Tuesday and Wednesday,—then draw out one for Thursday, Friday and Saturday, as you proceed with the story, and you will have the board as it appeared when Philip's father came home,—with THREE HOLES IN IT!"]—REV. W. D. S.

Concert Exercise.

THE LIFE AND TIMES OF ST. PAUL.

What do the Scriptures tell us of his *childhood, education,* and early religious *belief?*.....1. Acts xxii. 3; 2. Acts xxvi. 4, 5; 3. Phil. iii. 5.

What of his persecuting zeal?.....4. Acts xxii. 20; 5. Acts viii. 3; 6. Acts ix. 12; 7. Acts xxii. 4, 5; 8. Acts xxvi. 9, 10, 11.

What of his conversion to Christianity?....9. Acts ix. 3–9. (If desired, two other accounts.)

What of his baptism?.... ....10. Acts xxii. 12–16.

What of his promptness and zeal in preaching Christ?..11. Acts ix. 20–22; 12. Acts xvii. 1–3; 13. Acts xxviii. 23.

What of his commission to preach the gospel?....14. Gal. i. 1; 15. Gal. i. 11, 12.

What of his doctrine, addresses, and epistles?......16. 1 Cor. i. 23, 24; 17. 1 Cor. xv. 3, 4; 18. Rom. iii. 23, 24.

What of his address to the Athenians?........19. Acts xix. 31.

What of the miracles he wrought?....20. Acts xvi. 16–18; 21. Acts xiv. 8–10.

What of his miracles not recorded?........22. Acts xix. 11, 12.

What of the treatment he received from his countrymen?....23. Acts ix. 23, 24; 24. Acts xxiii. 12–15.

What of his own narrations of perils and sufferings?......25. 2 Cor. xi. 24–28.

What of the success that attended his labors?..26. Acts ix. 31; 27. Acts xiv. 1, 3; 28. Acts xvii. 4; 29. Acts xviii. 8; 30. Acts xix. 20.

What of his miraculous deliverance from prison?......31. Acts xvi. 25–30.

What of the viper that fastened on his hand?...32. Acts xxviii. 3–5.

What of the closing record found in the Acts of Apostles?..33. Acts xxviii. 16, 30, 31.

—*S. S. Times.*

Concert Exercise.

THE LORD'S PRAYER—BIBLE PROOFS.

"Our Father"............................Isa. lxiii. 16.
1. By right of creation..........................Mal. ii. 10.
2. By bountiful providence.........................Ps. cxlv. 16.
3. By gracious adoption...........................Eph. i. 5.
"Which art in heaven"..................1 Kings viii. 43.
4. The throne of Thy glory......................Isa. lxiii. 15.
5. The portion of Thy children......................1 Pet. i. 4.
"Hallowed be Thy name."
6. By the thoughts of our hearts..............Ps. lxxxvi. 11.
7. By the words of our lips..........................Ps. li. 15.
8. By the works of our hands..................1 Cor. x. 31.
"Thy kingdom come"...........................Ps. cx. 2.
9. Of providence, to defend us......................Ps. xvii. 8.
10. Of grace, to sanctify us....................1 Thess. v. 23.
11. Of glory, to crown us..........................Col. iii. 4.
"Thy will be done on earth, as it is in heaven".......Acts xxi. 14.
12. Toward us, without resistance..............2 Sam. iii. 18.
13. By us, without compulsion...................Ps. cxix. 36.
14. Universally, without exception.....................Luke i. 6.
15. Eternally, without declension................Ps. cxix. 93.
"Give us this day our daily bread."
16. Of necessity, for our bodies................Prov. xxx. 8.
17. Of eternal life, for our souls................John vi. 34.
"And forgive us our trespasses".............Ps. xxv. 11.
18. Against Thy commands......................1 John iii. 4.
19. Against the grace of Thy gospel.............1 Tim. i. 16.
"As we forgive them that trespass against"...Matt. vi. 15.
20. By defaming our character....................Matt. v. 11.
21. By embezzling our property.....................Heb. x. 34.
22. By abusing our persons........................Acts. vii. 60.
"And lead us not into temptation, but deliver us from evil."
23. Of overwhelming affliction....................Ps. cxxx. 1.

24. Of worldly enticements.................... ....1 John ii. 15.
25. Of Satan's devices...................... ...1 Tim. iii. 7.
26. Of sinful affections...........................Rom. i. 26.
"For thine is the kingdom, and the power, and the glory, for ever."
27. Thy kingdom governs all.......................Ps. ciii. 19.
28. Thy power subdues all.....................2 Chron. xx. 6.
29. Thy glory is above all......................Ps. cxlviii. 13.
"Amen." ....Eph. i. 11.
30. As it is in Thy purposes........................Isa. xiv. 27.
31. So it is in Thy promises.......................2 Cor. i. 20.
32. So be it in our prayers ....Rev. xxii. 20.
33. So shall it be to Thy praise....................Rev. xix. 4.

Concert Exercise.

NINE ATTRIBUTES OF GOD.

As taught in the 145th Psalm. Each person should read or recite in concert the appropriate passage, followed by explanations and illustrations by the leader.

1. Omnipresence.......(v. 18), The Lord is nigh unto all, etc. [present everywhere].
2. Omniscience....... (v. 15), The eyes of all, etc. [knowing all things].
3. Omnipotence.......(v. 10, having all power), All Thy works shall praise Thee.
4. Eternity........(v. 13) endureth throughout all generations [living always].
5. Benevolence.........(v. 9), The Lord is good to all [perfect goodness and kindness].
6. Holiness.....(v. 17), Holy in all His works [perfect holiness].
7. Mercy.........(v. 9), Tender mercies are over all His works [perfect mercy].
8. Justice......(v. 17), Righteous in all His ways [always just].
9. Truth ......(v. 18), Nigh to all that call upon Him in truth.

Concert Exercise.

THE BLOOD OF CHRIST.

Atones for the soul............................Lev. xvii. 11.
Brings us into the covenant of grace...........Matt. xxvi. 28.
Cleanses us from all sin.........................1 John i. 7.
Delivers God's people from judgment.............Ex. xii. 13
Everlasting in its value.........................Heb. xiii. 20.
Furnishes the only ground of peace with God.......Col. i. 20.
Gives us access into His presence...............Heb. x. 19-21.
Has already obtained for us redemption.............Eph. i. 7.
Imparts eternal life...............................John vi. 54.
Justifies us in the sight of God...................Rom. v. 9.
Keeps us in the holy of holies.................Heb. ix. 22-26.
Links us to God's electing purpose...............1 Peter i. 2.
Makes us nigh to Him...............................Eph. ii. 13.
Never needs to be offered again..................Heb. ix. 12.
Overcomes the power of Satan.....................Rev. xii. 11.
Purchases us ....Acts xx. 28
Quenches the righteous wrath of God............Rom. iii. 25.
Redeems us from our state of ruin...........1 Peter i. 18, 19.
Speaks to God and to us of salvation....... ....Heb. xii. 24.
Tunes the voices of the saints in holy song..........Rev. v. 9.
Unites us in Christian communion...............1 Cor. x. 16.
Victorious over tribulation.......................Rev. vii. 14.
Washes us from every stain..........................Rev. i. 6.
X-ian's hope, is the..............................1 Tim. i. 1
Yields the price that bought the church..........Acts xx. 28.
Zealous of good works, makes us.................Titus ii. 14

THE PRECIOUS PROMISES.

I will *help* thee..................................Isa. xli. 10.
I will *hold* thee..................................Isa. xlii. 6
I will *hear* thee...............................Isa. lxv. 24.
I will *heal* thee........ ....Isa. lvii. 17.

THE ASCENDING LORD.

From	Heaven	He came	John iii. 13; 1 Cor. xv. 47.
Of	"	" spake	Matt. v. 12.
To	"	" pointed	Matt. iv. 17; John xvii. 24.
To	"	" ascended	Heb. x. 12; Acts ii. 33.
To	"	" invites us	Matt. vi. 19–21; Rev. iii. 21.
In	"	" intercedes for us	Rom. viii. 34; Heb. vii. 25.
In	"	" prepares a place for us	John xiv. 2
From	"	" will come again.	Lesson.

How to witness for JESUS. W AIT / W ORK for / W ALK with HIM.

Ready When He Comes!

Seed Thought: "Lamps trimmed and burning."

Some will be { Sorry.................... Rev. i. 7.
Glad.................... 1 Thess. ii. 19.

How Will I Be?

The teacher's unconscious influence, like "bread cast upon the waters to return after many days," is beautifully set forth in the above exercise, as put upon the blackboard by Richard P. Clark, teacher of the Young Ladies' Bible Class, Puritan Church, Brooklyn, N. Y. The lesson for the day—Easter Sunday—was, the Resurrection, outlined as above, with comments full of tenderness and pathos, contrasting the glories and miseries of that eventful day, with the direct appeal, Is your lamp trimmed and burning? The truths of the lesson left their convicting and converting influence upon at least one member of the class, who was taken sick during the week and died in the glorious triumphs of a risen Saviour. Before her death she sent word to her teacher thanking him for the faithful presentation of that lesson, and assuring him that it, through him, had been instrumental in bringing peace and comfort to her heart, and that her lamp was trimmed and burning.

Mr. Clark was then sick: that Easter Sunday was his last appearance before the class, his last diagram upon the blackboard, the last lesson he taught. He died with the blessed satisfaction of knowing that his Sabbath-school efforts had not been in vain, and passed to his reward.

"*He that reapeth receiveth wages, and gathereth fruit unto life eternal, that both he that soweth and he that reapeth may rejoice together.*" John iv. 36.

May this lesson, so eminently suggestive, prove an incentive to Sunday-school workers everywhere.

WHAT JESUS SAYS.

"Behold I stand at the door and knock. If any man hear my voice and open the door, I will come in to him and sup with him and he with ME. Rev. iii. 20; John xiv. 20."

This is a representation of what Christ is actually doing at the door of every human heart. We cannot doubt it, for He Himself declares it to be a fact. Besides this we all feel at times that His hand does gently touch our hearts. How *near* He comes. "*At the door.*" How *patient* He is. We have refused to open the door, and yet He lingers and waits. How *earnest* He is. He does not stand in *silence*, but "*knocks*," pleads, begs for admission. He comes to our hearts. Open *now*. Receive this heavenly guest, and the "feast shall be everlasting love."

THE WORLD FOR JESUS.

More than eighteen hundred years ago, Jesus said to His Apostles: "Go ye into all the world and preach the gospel to every creature." He thus taught that His gospel is to be the heritage of the *whole* world. It is a gospel for the *entire* race, and is to be proclaimed everywhere. The picture shows the *effect* of the

gospel where it has been preached. It has carried *light* to the people, and will yet banish darkness from the pagan world. It is to spread from clime to clime in its conquering sweep, until

> "Jesus shall reign where'er the sun
> Does his successive journeys run."

The day will *surely* come when the "earth shall be *filled* with the knowledge of God as the waters cover the great deep."

The field is *vast*, the work is *great*, and the difficulties *formidable*, but victory is assured. "Ask of me and I shall give thee the heathen for thine inheritance, and the uttermost parts of the earth for thy possession." Ps. ii. 8.

"The Duke of Wellington once met a young clergyman, who, being aware of his former residence in the East, and of his familiarity with the ignorance and obstinacy of the Hindoos in support of their false religion, proposed the following question: "Does not your grace think it almost useless and extravagant to preach the gospel to the Hindoos?" The Duke immediately replied: "Look, sir, to your marching orders. 'Preach the gospel to every creature.'"—*Foster*. [tory.

Obedience to these "*marching orders*" will lead to final vic-

But this conquest will be achieved only by the prayers, sacrifices, and toil of God's people. The old and the young are to join in the work. Some may become missionaries. Some may be called to *teach* and others to *preach* the word. Some may obtain *wealth*, and that is to be consecrated to God. "The church must fling down her gold at the feet of Jesus."—*Dr. Eddy.* "God loveth a cheerful giver." The missionary cause waits for the gifts of the people. There is room here for all *workers.* There is a demand for *all* talents. Be ready to take your place when the call comes. If God asks your best *personal* service, give it. If He asks your time, talent, or wealth, lay it *all* upon the altar in the Master's name. He is saying to you, "*Go.*" Go then, in *some* way, and *minister* to the *spiritual wants* of the world.

H. H. B.

HE LEADETH US.

To living fountains of water....................Rev. vii. 17.
Beside still waters...........................Ps. xxiii. 2.
In green pastures.............................Ps. xxiii. 2.
Through the depths.............................Ps. cvi. 9.
Safely.....................................Ps. lxxviii. 53.
Through the wilderness.....................Ps. cxxxvi. 16.
Through the deep...........................Isa. lxiii. 13.
In the right way.................Gen. xxiv. 48; Ps. cvii. 7.
In a plain path.............................Ps. xxvii. 11.
To the rock that is higher......................Ps. lxi. 2.
Being in the way, the Lord led me... ....Gen. xxiv. 27.

A WORLD OF TEARS.

1. Jacob wept.................................Gen. xxxiii. 4.
2. Joseph wept.................................Gen. xliii. 30.
3. Moses wept.................................Ex. ii. 6.
4. Naomi and Ruth wept.........................Ruth i. 9.
5. Jonathan wept.................................1 Sam. xx. 41.
6. David wept.................................2 Sam. iii. 32.
7. Elisha wept.................................2 Kings viii. 11.
8. Hezekiah wept.................................Isaiah xxviii. 3.
9. Peter wept.................................Matt. xxvi. 75.
10. John wept.................................Rev. v. 4.
11. The disciples wept.........................Mark xvi. 10.
12. Mary wept.................................John xx. 11.
13. Paul's friends wept.........................Acts xx. 37.
14. Even Jesus wept.............................John x. 35.

BUT THE BLESSED PROMISES ARE.

1. Though weeping may endure for a night, yet joy cometh in the (resurrection) morning. Ps. xxx. 5.

2. Then there shall be no more crying. Rev. xxi. 4.

3. For God shall wipe away all tears from our eyes. Rev. vii. 17.

4. Then the voice of weeping shall be no more heard. Isa. lxv. 19.

5. For the Lord God will wipe away tears from off all faces. Isa. xxv. 8.

6. Therefore they that sow in tears shall reap in joy. Ps. cxxvi. 5.—*H. B. W.*

Beyond the smiling and the weeping,
  I shall be soon, I shall be soon;
Beyond the waking and the sleeping,
  Beyond the sowing and the reaping.
I shall be soon, I shall be soon.

HORATIO BONAR.

PART II.

KEY OR ANSWERS

TO

TEST QUESTIONS

[PAGES 25 TO 226]

FOUNDED UPON AND ANSWERED IN THE

BIBLE.

WEEKLY BIBLE READINGS.

HOW TO READ THE ENTIRE SCRIPTURES IN ONE YEAR.

THE GROUPING OF EVENTS AND PERSONS CHRONOLOGICALLY,

ARRANGED BY

REV. A. H. TUTTLE, D.D.

1st Week.—B. C. 4004. Gen. i-xi, 9; Job i-xvi.
2nd.—Job. xvii-xlii.
3d.—1996. Gen, xi, 10-xxxvi.
4th.—1840. Gen. xxxvii-Ex.; ii; Ps. lxxxviii; Ex. iii-ix.
5th.—1491. Ex. x-xxxiv.
6th.—1491. Ex. xxxv-xl; Lev. 1-1x; Num. vii; Lev. x-xvii.
7th.—1490. Lev. xviii-xxvii; Heb. i-xiii; Num. i-vi.
8th.—1490. Num. viii-xiv, 39; Ps. xc; Num. xiv, 40-xxxvi.
9th.—1451. Deut. i-xxvi.
10th.—1451.—Deut xxvii-xxxiv; Josh i-xvi.
11th.—1444. Josh xvii-xxiv; Judg. i-iii, 7; Judg. xvii-xxi; Judg. iii, 8-vi, 6; Ruth i-iv; Judg. vi, 7-viii.
12th.—1235. Judg. ix-xiii: 1 Sam. i-iii; Judg. xiv-xvi; 1 Sam. iv-xviii, 4; Ps. ix.
13th.—1063. 1 Sam. xviii, 5-xix, 3: Psa. xi; 1 Sam. xix, 4-17; Psa. lix; 1 Sam. xix, 18-xxi; Ps. lvi, xxxiv; 1 Sam xxii, 1-2; Ps. cxlii; 1 Chr. xi, 15-19; 1 Sam. xxii, 3-19; Ps. xvii, xxxv, lxiv, lii, cix, cxl; 1 Sam. xxii, 20-xxiii, 12; Ps. xxxi; 1 Sam. xxii, 13-23; Ps. liv; 1 Sam. xxiii. 24-xxiv; Ps. lvii, lviii, lxiii; 1 Sam. xxv-xxvi, Ps. cxli.
14th.—1060. 1 Sam. xxvii-xxxi; 1 Chr. x; 2 Sam. i-v, 10; Ps. cxxxix; 1 Chr. xi, 1-14; 2 Sam. xxiii, 8-39. 1 Chr. xi, 20-xii; 2 Sam v, 11-25; 1 Chr. xiv; 2 Sam. vi, 1-11.
15th.—1045. 1 Chr. xiii; 2 Sam. vi, 12-23: Ps. lxvii; 1 Chr. xv-xvi, Ps. xxiii, xxiv, xcvi, cv, cvi; 2 Sam. vii; 1 Chr. xvii; Ps. ii, xvi, xxii, xlv, cx, cxviii, 2 Sam. viii; 1 Chr, xviii; Ps. cviii, 2 Sam. ix-x; 1 Chr. xix; Ps. xx, xxi.
16th.—1035. 2 Sam. xi; 1 Chr. xx, 1-3, Ps. li, xxxii, xxxiii, ciii; 2 Sam. xii-xv; Psa. iii, lx; 2 Sam, xvi, 1-14; Ps. vii; 2 Sam. xvi, 15-xvii; Ps. iv, v, xlii, xliii, lv, lxi, lxii, lxx, lxxi, cxliii, cxliv; 2 Sam. xviii-xxi.
17th.—1018. 1 Chr. xx, 4-8· Ps. xviii; 2 Sam. xxii; 2 Sam. xxiv; 1 Chr. xxi, 1-13; 1 Chr. i-ix; 1 Chr. xxi, 14-30: Ps. xxx, 1 Chr. xxii-xxvii; 1 Kings i; Ps. xii; 1 Chr. xxviii-xxix. 25.
18th.—1015. Ps. vi, viii, x, xix, xxviii, xxix, xxxviii, xxxix, xl, xli, lxv, lxix, lxxii, lxxxvi, xci, xcv, ci, civ, cxx, cxxi, cxxii, cxxiv, cxxxi, cxxxiii, cxlv; 1 K. ii. 1-11; 2 Sam. xxiii, 1-7; 1 Chr. xxix, 26-30.
19th.—1016. 1 K. ii, 12-ix, 24; 2 Chr. i-vii, 11; Ps. xlvii, xcvii, xcviii, xcix, c, cxxxv, cxxxvi; 2 Chr. vii, 12-viii, 11; Song of Sol.
20th.—992. 2 Chr. viii. 12-ix, 22; Prov. i-xxv.
21st.—Prov. xxvi-xxxi; 1 K. ix, 25-xi; 2 Chr. ix, 23-31; Eccles. i-xii.
22d.—976. 1 K. xii-xiv; 2 Chr. x-xii; 1 K. xv, 1-8; 2 Chr. xiii; 1 K. xv, 9-24; 2 Chr. xiv-xvi; 1 K. xv, 25; 2 K. ii; 2 Chr. xvii-xx; Ps. xlvi, lxxviii, lxxxii, cxv.
23d.—891. 2 K. iii-viii; 2 Chr. xxi; 2 K. ix-x; 2 Chr. xxii, 1-9; 2 K. xi-xii, 2 Chr. xxii, 10-xxiv; Jonah i-iv; 2 K. xiii-xiv, 22; 2 Chr. xxv; 2 K. xiv, 23-xv, 7; 2 Chr. xxvi.
24th.—785. Hos. i-vi, 11; Amos i-ix; Joel i-iii, Isa. i-vi.
25th.—771. 2 K. xv, 8-xvii; 2 Chr. xxvii xxviii; Mic. i-ii; Isa. vii-x, 4; Obad. i; Hos. vi, 12-xiv, 2 K. xviii-xx; 2 Chr. xxix-xxxii; Ps. lxxiii, lxxiv. lxxv, lxxvi, xliv, xcii.
26th.—738, Isa. x, 5-xxxvii.
27th.—Isa. xxxviii-lx.
28th.—Isa. lxi-lxvi; Mic iii-vii; Nah. i-iii; 2 K. xxi, 1-18, 2 Chr. xxxiii, 1-20; 2 K, xxi, 19-26; 2 Chr. xxxiii, 21-24; 2 K. xxii-xxiii, 30; 2 Chr.xxxiii, 25-xxxv.
29th.—629. Jer. i-xxiii.
30th.—Jer. xxiv-xlvii.
31st.—Jer. xlviii-lii; Ps. xciv, lxxix, lxxxiii; Zeph. i-iii: Hab. i-iii; 2 K. xxiii, 31-xxv; 2 Chr. xxxvi Dan. i-vii.
32d.—607. Ps. xiii, xiv, xv, xxv, xxvi, xxvi xxxvi, xxxvii, xlix, l, liii, lxxvii, lxxx lxxxix, xciii, cxxiii, cxxx, cxxxvii: Dan. viii-ix.
33d.—553. Ps. cii; Ezek. i-xxii.
34th.—Ezek. xxiii-xxxvii.
35th.—Ezek. xxxviii-xlviii; Lam. i-v; Ezra i-iii, 7; Ps. lxvi, lxxxv,, lxxxvii. cvii, cxi, cxii, cxiii, cxiv, cxvi, cxvii, cxxv, cxxvi. cxxvii, cxxviii, cxxxviv.
36th.—536. Ezra iii, 8-13; Ps. lxxxiv; Ezra iv-v, 2; Dan. x-xii; Ps. cxxix; Zech. i-xiv; Hag. i.ii.
37th.—536. Ezra v, 3-vi, 13: Ps. cxxxviii, Ezra vi, 14-22; Ps. xlviii, lxxxi. cxlvi, cxlvii, cxlviii, cxlix, cl; Ezra vii-x; Esth i-x; Ps. x
38th.—446. Neh. i-xiii; Ps, cxix, i; Mal. i-iv.
39th.—*Anno Domino.* Matt. i-xix.
40th.—Matt. xx-xxviii; Mark i-x,
41st.—Mark xi-vvi; Luke i-x.
42d.—Luke xi-xxiv.
43d.—John i-xviii.
44th.—John xix-xxi; Acts i-xv.
45th.—Acts xvi-xviii, 18; 1 Thess. i-v; 2 Thess i-iii; Acts xviii, 19-xix, 22.
46th.—1 Cor. i-xvi.
47th.—2 Cor. i-xiii; Gal. i-vi.
48th.—Rom. i-xvi.
49th.—Acts xix, 23-xxviii; Jas. i-v.
50th.—Eph. i-vi; Col. i-iv; Philem i; Philip i-iv; 1 Pet. i-v; 1 Tim. i-vi.
51st.—Tit. i-iii. Jude i; 2 Pet. i-iii; 2 Tim. i-iv; 1 John i-v; 2 John i; 3 John i.
52d.—Rev. i-xxii.

ANSWERS

TO

CURIOSITIES OF THE BIBLE

PERTAINING TO

FIRST THINGS.

1. "Let there be light" ....Gen. i. 3.
2. Be fruitful and multiply, etc................Gen. i. 28.
3. After the creation. By God
   and man................Exod. xxxi. 17.; Gen. ii. 2, 3.
4. Eden.................................Gen. ii. 8.
5. Adam................................Gen. ii. 15.
6. On giving names to the animal creation......Gen. ii. 19.
7. The woman Eve...............Tim. ii. 14; Gen. iii. 1.
8. The coming of Christ......................Gen. iii. 15.
9. God.................................Gen. iii. 21.
10. Adam...............................Gen. iii. 24.
11. Abel...............................Gen. iv. 4.
12. Abel...............................Gen. iv. 8.
13. Cain...............................Gen. iv. 9.
14. Cain...............................Gen. iv. 14.
15. Cain. The city of Enoch...................Gen. iv. 17.
16. Lamech.............................Gen. iv. 18.
17. Adah...............................Gen. iv. 19.
18. Jabal..............................Gen. v. 20.
19. Lamech.............................Gen. iv. 23.
20. Tubal-Cain.........................Gen. iv. 22.
21. In.................................Gen. iv. 26.
22. Adam...............................Gen. v. 5.
23. Gopherwood.........................Gen. vi. 14.

24. Noah. The ark.......................Gen. vi. 14, 22.
25. Ararat..............................Gen. viii. 4.
26. To Noah and his family after the flood........Gen. ix. 3.
27. Nimrod..............................Gen. x. 8, 9.
28. Building the Tower of Babel................Gen. xi. 3.
29. Abram...............................Gen. xii. 1, 6.
30. The men of Sodom.......................Gen. xiii. 13.
31. Lot.................................Gen. xiv. 12, 14.
32. Abram...............................Gen. xiv. 13.
33. Ishmael.............................Gen. xvi. 11.
34. Beerlaharoi.........................Gen. xvi. 14.
35. Abraham.............................Gen. xvii. 18.
36. Veal................................Gen. xviii. 7, 8.
37. Hagar in the wilderness..................Gen. xxi. 16.
38. Abraham.............................Gen. xxi. 24.
39. Abraham.............................Gen. xxii. 3.
40. Sarah...............................Gen. xxiii. 1.
41. Abraham purchased a burying-place for Sarah at Machpelah.................Gen. xxiii. 19.
42. Ephron..............................Gen. xxiii. 13.
43. Abraham......................Gen. xxiii. 3, 4, 16, 18.
44. By Abraham in the purchase of land......Gen. xxiii. 16.
45. For a burying-place....................Gen. xxiii. 20.
46. By putting the hand of the person sworn under the thigh of the person administering..Gen. xxiv. 2.
47. Earrings, bracelets, jewels, etc., ...Gen. xxiv. 22, 30, 53.
48. Rebekah.........................Gen. xxiv. 64, 65.
49. He saw angels ascending and descending on a ladder and God above it........Gen. xxviii. 12, 13.
50. Jacob at Bethel......................Gen. xxviii. 22.
51. Rachel..............................Gen. xxix. 9.
52. Rachel..............................Gen. xxxi. 19.
53. Jacob...............................Gen. xxxii. 9.
54. Jacob at the grave of Rachel............Gen. xxxv. 20.
55. In the wilderness, by Anah.............Gen. xxxvi. 24.
56. Joseph..............................Gen. xxxvii. 28.
57. Tamar...............................Gen. xxxviii. 14.
58. Joseph..............................Gen. xli. 14.

59. Pharaoh .... Gen. xli. 42.
60. By Joseph in exchange for bread .... Gen. xlvii. 17.
61. The embalming of Jacob's body .... Gen. l. 2.
62 At Horeb .... Exod. iii. 2.
63. Water turned into blood .... Ex. vii. 20.
64. Song of Moses .... Ex. xv.
65. The Lord shall reign for ever and ever .... Ex. xv. 18
66. Miriam .... Ex. xv. 20.
67. Moses .... Ex. xviii. 13.
68. In enumeration of offerings to the Lord ..... Ex. xxii. 29.
69. Moses .... Ex. xxiv. 4.
70. Aaron .... Ex. xxviii. 1.
71. The words "Holiness to the Lord" upon Aaron's mitre ...... Ex. xxviii. 36; Ex. xxix. 30.
72. Jewelry .... Ex. xxxii. 2.
73. Moses (?) (materially) .... Ex. xxxii. 19.
74. Moses .... Num. i. 1.
75. The tribe of Judah .... Num. x. 14.
76. At Kibroth Hattavah .... Num. xi. 34.
77. Miriam .... Num. xii. 10.
78. Mahlah, Noah, Hoglah, Milcah, and Tirzah, Num. xxvii. 1, 4.
79. Reuben .... Num. xxxiv. 14.
80. The vengeance of God upon disobedient Israel. Deut. xxxii. 22.
81. Jericho .... Josh. vi. 1.
82. Achan .... Josh. vii. 24.
83. Joshua in dividing the land .... Josh. xviii. 8.
84. When Deborah judged Israel .... Judges iv. 4.
85. To the wife of Manoah .... Judges xiii. 13.
86. At Timnath .... Judges xiv. 5, 6.
87. Dan .... Judges xviii. 30.
88. The defeat of the armies of Israel by the tribe of Benjamin .... Judges xx. 18, 26.
89. God save the king .... 1 Sam. x. 24.
90. By Saul .... 1 Sam. xiv. 52.
91. Saul, by falling on his sword .... 1 Sam. xxxi. 4.
92. Ahithophel, by hanging .... 2 Sam. xvii. 23.

93. By David.............................2 Sam. xi. 14, 15.
94. When the men of Judah crossed the
Jordan at Gilgal to King David.........2 Sam. xix. 18.
95. Solomon's navy.........................1 Kings ix. 26.
96. Rehoboam and Jeroboam..............1 Kings xii. 1, 2.
97. Jehoboam..................................1 King xii.
98. The son of Zarephath's daughter........1 Kings xvii. 21.
99. The house of the rolls, or books, the king's
library.................................Ezra vi. 1.
100. Maaseiah...............................Ezra x. 18.
101. In.....................................Job xix. 24, 25.
102. When the morning stars sang together.....Job xxxviii. 7.
103. The children of the wicked..............Psalms cix. 10.
104. Isaiah ....
105. Swords into plowshares, etc., and learn war
no more.................................Isa. ii. 4.
106. B. C. 607 years. By children of Rechab..Jer. xxxv. 1, 11.
107. Daniel, appointed by King Darius over
a province of Chaldea.......................Dan. vi. 2.
108. Repent....................................Matt. iv. 17.
109. Nazareth...................................Mark vi. 17.
110. To Mary Magdalene.........................Mark xvi. 9.
111. Water turned to wine ....John ii. 1.
112. At Cana of Galilee..........................John ii. 2.
113. St. Peter. By the selection of a particular
passage and the explanation thereof.........Acts ii. 14.
114. The death of Ananias and Sapphira for
coveteousness and lying about it..........Acts v. 5, 10.
115. Ananias.....................................Acts v. 5.
116. Stephen....................................Acts vii. 58.
117. The Eunuch of Ethiopia...............Acts viii. 27, 38.
118. At Damascus...............................Acts ix. 20.
119. Cornelius...................................Acts x. 3.
120. At Antioch by Paul and Barnabas..........Acts xiv. 26.
121. In.......................................Acts ; xv. 23.
122. In his Epistle to the Romans................Rom. i. 1.
123. Phebe....................................Rom. xvi. 1
124. To the Romans............................Rom. xvi. 16.

125. In....................................1 Cor. viii. 1.
126. Of them that sleep........................1 Cor. xv. 20.
127. Of the dead in Christ.....................2 Cor. viii. 5.
128. The Macedonians.........................1 Thess. iv. 16.
129. In....................................1 Tim. ii. 13.
130. A heretic..................................Titus iii. 10.
131. Jesus..................................Heb. vii. 22, 27.
132. The candlestick, table and shew-bread,........Heb. ix. 2.
133. Pure....:..................................James, iii. 17.
134. In....................................1 John iv. 19.
135. They are reserved in everlasting chains under darkness..............................Jude 6.
136. Patmos......................................Rev. i. 6.
137. The church at Ephesus......................Rev. ii. 4.
138. From the sea...............................Rev. xiii. 1.
139. In...Rev. xx. 5.
140. They passed away...........................Rev. xxi. 1.

ANSWERS

TO

CURIOSITIES OF THE BIBLE

PERTAINING TO

OLD TESTAMENT PERSONS.

1. Adam.......................................Gen. ii. 20.
2. God.......................................Gen. iii. 19.
3. Cain.......................................Gen. iv. 8, 9.
4. Cain.......................................Gen. iv. 12, 17.
5. Adah, Zillah and Naamah, the daughters of Zillah.......................................Gen. iv. 19, 22.
6. Jubal.......................................Gen. iv. 21.
7. Adam.......................................Gen. v. 5.
8. Methuselah.......................................Gen. v. 26.
9. Asshur.......................................Gen. x. 11.
10. Eber being 464 years old.....................Gen. xi. 17.
11. Abram.......................................Gen. xii. 2.
12. Abram.......................................Gen. xiii. 8.
13. Bera.......................................Gen. xiv. 2.
14. Birsha.......................................Gen. xiv. 2.
15. Melchizedek.......................................Gen. xiv. 18.
16. To Abraham.......................................Gen. xv. 1.
17. To Abraham.......................................Gen. xv. 5.

18. Ishmael.......................Gen. xvii. 20.Gen. xvi. 15.
19. The promise was made to Abraham about Ishmael..............................Gen. xvii. 20.
20. Ishmael..............................Gen. xvii. 20.
21. Abraham..............................Gen. xviii. 27.
22. Abraham and Lot..........Gen. xviii. 2, 4, Gen. xix. 2.
23. The angels who visited Lot in Sodom........Gen. xix. 2.
24. Lot..............................Gen. xix. 5.
25. Abimelech..............................Gen. xx. 3.
26. Hagar..............................Gen. xxi. 15.
27. Ishmael..............................Gen. xxi. 17.
28. Phichol..............................Gen. xxi. 22.
29. Isaac..............................Gen. xxii. 6.
30. Sarah, 127 years old....................Gen. xxiii. 1.
31. Abraham..............................Gen. xxiii. 2.
32. From Ephron..............................Gen. xxiii. 10.
33. Isaac and Rebecca..............................Gen. xxiv. 59.
34. Rebecca..............................Gen. xxiv. 60.
35. Isaac..............................Gen. xxiv. 63.
36. Keturah..............................Gen. xxv. 1.
37. The Philistines..............................Gen. xxvi. 15.
38. Rebecca..............................Gen. xxvii. 46.
39. To Abraham, Isaac, and Jacob...........Gen. xxviii. 14.
40. Jacob..............................Gen. xxviii. 17.
41. Bilhah..............................Gen. xxix. 29.
42. Reuben..............................Gen. xxix. 32.
43. Laban, Gen. xxx. 27, Potiphar............Gen. xxxix. 5.
44. By Jacob when he was covenanting with Laban..............................Gen. xxxi. 46.
45. Jacob..............................Gen. xxxii. 10.
46. Jacob..............................Gen. xxxii. 24.
47. Dinah..............................Gen. xxxiv. 1.
48. Deborah.............................. Gen. xxxv. 8.
49. Benjamin..............................Gen. xxxv. 18.
50. Anah..............................Gen. xxxvi. 24.
51. Reuben..............................Gen. xxxvii. 21.
52. Judah.......................... .Gen. xxxvii. 26, 27.
53. To Potiphar, an officer of Pharaoh......Gen. xxxvii. 36.

54. Joseph by Pharaoh........................Gen. xxxix. 5.
55. Asenath..............................Gen. xli. 45.
56. Poti-pherah, priest of On and his grandsons were Joseph's sons, Ephraim and Manasseh..Gen. xli. 45.
57. Paph-nath-paaneah...........................Gen. xli. 45.
58. By Pharaoh to Jacob........................Gen. xlvii. 8.
59. By Jacob. Samson was of the tribe of Dan.Gen. xlix. 16.
60. At Jacob's funeral..............................Gen. l. 9.
61. Joseph..Gen. l. 17.
62. The Hebrew midwives—Shiphrah and Puah.....Ex. i. 15.
63. Pharaoh's daughter...............................Ex. ii. 10.
64. Moses, by his brethren.....................Ex. ii. 11, 15.
65. Zipporah.......................................Ex. ii. 21.
66. A priest of Midian...............................Ex. iii. 1.
67. Moses..Ex. iv. 6.
68. Moses..Ex. iv. 10.
69. Moses..Ex. iv. 24.
70. Jochebed.......................................Ex. vi. 20.
71. Elisheba.......................................Ex. vi. 23.
72. Aaron's..Ex. vii. 19.
73. Miriam...Ex. xv. 20.
74. Amalekites.................................... Ex. xvii. 8.
75. The hands of Moses by Aaron and Hur....Ex. xvii. 9, 13.
76. Jethro...Ex. xviii. 5.
77. Moses, Aaron, Nadab, Abihu and 70 elders....Ex. xxiv. 9.
78. Moses and Elijah...........1 Kings xix. 8, Ex. xxiv. 18.
79. Bazaleel.......................................Ex. xxxi. 2.
80. Aaron..Ex. xxxii. 4.
81. Moses..Ex. xxxiv. 33.
82. Bezaleel .... Ex. xxxvii. 1.
83. Nadab and Abihu..............................Lev. x. 1, 2.
84. Aaron..Ler. x. 3.
85. Nadab and Abihu...............................Lev. x. 6.
86. The Son of Shelomith.....................Lev.xxiv. 11, 23.
87. The Nazarites..................................Num. vi. 1.
88. By Moses to Hobab..............................Num. x. 29.
89. Eldad and Medad...............................Num. xi. 27.
90. Joshua...Num. xi. 28.

91. Oshea.................................Num. xiii. 8.
92. Oshea.................................Num. xiii. 16.
93. Shammua, Shaphat, Caleb, Igal, Oshea, Palti, Gaddiel, Gaddi, Amiel, Sethur, Nahbi and Geuel......................Num. xiii. 4, 15
94. Anak, the Canaanite......................Num. xiii. 33
95. Nun and Jephunneh.......................Num. xiv. 6.
96. Caleb and Joshua.........................Num. xiv. 38.
97. Korah.................................Num. xvi. 1, 3.
98. Aaron.................................Num. xvi. 48.
99. Eleazar................................Num. xx. 26.
100. Moses and Eleazar.......................Num. xx. 28.
101. Balaam by his ass.......................Num. xxii. 28.
102. Balaam................................Num. xxiii. 10.
103. Balak.................................Num. xxiv. 10.
104. Korah, Dathan and Abiriam...........Num. xxvi. 9, 10.
105. The daughter of Zolephehad—she had four sisters...............................Num. xxvi. 33.
106. Caleb and Joshua........................Num. xxvi. 51.
107. Jochebed..............................Num. xxvi. 59.
108. The daughters of Zolephehad............Num. xxvii. 1.
109. Joshua, the son of Nun...............Num. xxvii. 18, 22
110. The Israelites.........................Num. xxxi. 6, 8.
111. Moses.................................Num. xxxii. 23.
112. Moses.................................Deut. i. 1, 12.
113. Og, King of Bashan......................Deut. iii. 11.
114. Jeremiah and Moses—"the furnace of Iron".......................Josh. xi. 4, Deut. iv. 20.
115. The Israelites..........................Deut. xiv. 2.
116. The tribe of Levi—because the Lord was their inheritance.........................Deut. xviii. 1, 5.
117. God said them to Moses once and to Joshua three times...........................Deut. xxxi. 7.
118. Simeon................................Deut. xxxiii. 1.
119. Caleb and Moses..........Josh. xiv. 11, Deut. xxxiv. 7.
120. Joshua................................Josh. iv. 4, 7.
121. Joshua in Jordan as a memorial of God's deliverance...............................Josh. iv. 9.

122. Joshua.................................Josh. v. 13.
123. Moses and Joshua.................Ex. iii. 5, Josh. v. 15.
124. Hiel, the Bethelite...1 Kings xvi. 34.
See prophecy in...........................Josh. vi. 26.
125. Achan..................................Josh. vii. 21.
126. Achan..................................Josh. vii. 25.
127. Joshua................................Josh. viii. 3, 4.
128. Joshua................................Josh. viii. 30.
129. The Gibeonites..........................Josh. ix. 23.
130. Adoni-Zedek, Hoham, Piram, Japhia and
Debir......................................Josh. x. 3.
131. Joshua..................................Josh. x. 11.
132. The sons of Anak.........................Josh. xv. 14.
133. Joshua.................................Josh. xix. 50.
134. The two kings of the Amorites............Josh. xxiv. 12.
135. Joshua................................Josh. xxiv. 15.
136. Joshua................................Josh. xxiv. 22.
137. Adoni-bezek............................Judges i. 6.
138. Ehud..................................Judges iii. 15.
139. Ehud..............................Judges iii. 27, 28.
140. Shamgar..............................Judges iii. 31.
141. Deborah...............................Judges iv. 4.
142. Barak, with the prophetess Deborah........Judges iv. 8.
143. The song of Deborah...................Judges v. 1, 31.
144. The mother of Sisera....................Judges v. 28.
145. Gideon................................Judges vi. 15.
146. By Gideon when the three hundred were
chosen..............................Judges vii. 5, 6.
147. Gideon and Phurah..................Judges vii. 7, 10.
148. The Midianites and Amalekites............Judges vii. 12.
149. Gideon..............................Judges viii. 16.
150. Jether..............................Judges viii. 20.
151. The Midianites.......................Judges viii. 26.
152. Gideon..............................Judges viii. 24.
153. Abimelech..............................Judges ix. 5.
154. The men of Shechem.....................Judges ix. 25.
155. Abimelech.............................Judges ix. 45.
156. Abimelech at Mount Zalmon..............Judges ix. 48.

157. Abimelech............................Judges ix. 53
158. Abimelech at Thebez....................Judges ix. 54.
159. Jair, a Gileadite........................Judges x. 3, 4.
160. Ibzan...................................Judges xii. 8.
161. Samson..................................Judges xiii. 3.
162. Samson..................................Judges xiii. 5.
163. Manoah.................................Judges xiii. 20.
164. Manoah.................................Judges xiii. 21.
165. Samson................................Judges xiv. 5, 6.
166. Samson..................................Judges xiv. 14.
167. Samson................................Judges xvi. 5, 6.
168. Micah stole 1100 Shekels.............Judges xvii. 2, 3.
169. Micah...................................Judges xvii. 10.
170. The old man of Ephraim.................Judges xix. 20.
171. Seven hundred men of Benjamin.........Judges xx. 16.
172. Elimelech, his wife Naomi and their two sons...Ruth i. 2.
173. Mahlon and Chilion, the sons of Naomi......Ruth i. 4, 5.
174. Ruth to Naomi............................Ruth i. 16.
175. Ruth said these words to Naomi............Ruth i. 16.
176. Naomi....................................Ruth i. 20.
177. Boaz.....................................Ruth ii. 4.
178. Ruth...................................Ruth iv. 10, 14.
179. Obed....................................Ruth iv. 17.
180. Obed, the son of Boaz and Ruth............Ruth iv. 17.
181. Elkanah.................................1 Sam. i. 8.
182. Hannah, the mother of Samuel.............1 Sam. i. 11.
183. Eli.....................................1 Sam. i. 12.
184. Hannah.................................1 Sam. ii. 19.
185. Eli....................................1 Sam. iii. 18.
186. The child Ichabod...................1 Sam. iv. 17, 22.
187. Samuel. He called the monument Ebenezer.1 Sam. vii. 12.
188. Samuel...........................1 Sam. vii. 15, 16.
189. Joel and Abiah.........................1 Sam. viii. 2.
190. Saul...................................1 Sam. ix. 2.
191. The people of the land of Zuph..........1 Sam. ix. 5, 13.
192. Samuel.................................1 Sam. ix. 25.
193. Nahash.................................1 Sam. xi. 2.
194. Samuel.................................1 Sam. xii. 2.

195. Jonathan......................1 Sam. xiv. 24, 27, 43, 45.
196. Saul..................................1 Sam. xiv. 52.
197. Samuel................................1 Sam. xv. 22.
198. Agag, King of the Amalekites, by Samuel..1 Sam. xv 33.
199. Samuel................................1 Sam. xvi. 2.
200. Samuel................................1 Sam. xvi. 7.
201. David...............................1 Sam. xvi. 11, 13.
202. David when he slew Goliath.........1 Sam. xvii. 17, 49.
203. That of Jonathan and David.............1 Sam. xviii. 1.
204. Michael...............................1 Sam. xix. 13.
205. David..................................1 Sam. xx. 3.
206. David..............................1 Sam. xxi. 12, 13.
207. Gad..2. Samuel xxiv. 11; Chron. xxix. 22; 1 Sam. xxii. 5.
208. The prophet Gad........................... 1 Sam. xxii.
209. Doeg, by command of Saul..............1 Sam. xxii. 18.
210. Doeg, the Edomite ....1 Sam. xxii. 19.
211. Abiathar..............................1 Sam. xxii. 20.
212. Abagail and David.....................1 Sam. xxv. 42.
213. Saul slew himself.....................1 Sam. xxxi. 4.
214. The body of King Saul.................1 Sam. xxxi. 10.
215. The inhabitants of Jabesh Gilead... 1. Sam. xxxi. 11, 13.
216. Saul, by falling on his spear.................1 Sam. i. 6.
217. The Amalekite in telling of Saul's death to David..................................2 Sam. i. 15.
218. David..................................2 Sam. i. 19.
219. Of Saul................................2 Sam. i. 25.
220. Asahel...............................2 Sam. ii. 18, 23.
221. By Abner smiting him under the fifth rib..2 Sam. ii. 22, 23.
222. Michal, the daughter of Saul, by David's bravery................................2 Sam. iii. 14.
223. Abner was slain by Joab in Hebron........2 Sam. iii. 27.
224. Abner................................2. Sam. iii. 33.
225. Saul..................................2 Sam. iv. 4.
226. Ishbosheth, the son of Saul..............2 Sam. iv. 5, 6.
227. Michal, the daughter of Saul...........2 Sam. vi. 20, 23.
228. Hadadezer, captured by David............2 Sam. viii. 4.
229. Mephibosheth............................2 Sam. ix. 8.
230. Joab..................................2 Sam. x. 7, 9.

231. David.................................2 Sam. xii. 23.
232. He was called by his mother Lamuel, Prov. xxxi., and by Nathan the prophet, he was called Jedikiah........................2 Sam. xii. 25.
233. From the head of the king of the Ammonites................................2 Sam. xii. 30.
234. Ammonites...........................2. Sam. xii. 31.
235. By his brother Absalom..............2 Sam. xiii. 28, 29.
236. Absalom..............................2 Sam. xiv. 25.
237. Joab...................................2 Sam. xiv. 30.
238. Ahithophel...........................2 Sam. xv. 12.
239. David by Shimel........................2 Sam. xvi. 5.
240. Jonathan and Ahimaaz................2 Sam. xvii. 18.
241. A woman hid them in a well and covered it. 2 Sam. xvii. 19.
242. Ahithophel...........................2 Sam. xvii. 23.
243. David.................................2 Sam. xviii. 3.
244. Absalom..............................2 Sam. xviii. 9.
245. Absalom..............................2 Sam. xviii. 18.
246. Barzillai..............................2 Sam. xix. 37.
247. Asahel................................2 Sam. ii. 23.
Abner.................................2 Sam. iii. 27.
Mephibosheth..........................2 Sam. iv. 6.
Amasa.................................2 Sam. xx. 10.
248. The head of Sheba......................2 Sam. xx. 21.
249. The Seven Sons of Saul................2 Sam. xxi. 8, 9.
250. A man of Gath..........................2 Sam. xxi. 20.
251. Jonathan...............................2 Sam. xxi. 21.
252. Adino..................................2 Sam. xxiii. 8.
253. Eleazar...............................2 Sam. xxiii. 10.
254. Abishai...............................2 Sam. xxiii. 18.
255. Benaiah...............................2 Sam. xxiii. 20.
256. David.................................2 Sam. xxiv. 1.
257. David.................................2 Sam. xxiv. 13.
258. David.................................2 Sam. xxiv. 14.
259. Araunah...............................2 Sam. xxiv. 23.
260. Abishag...............................1 Kings. i. 3, 4.
261. Adonijah...............................1 Kings i. 50.
262. David.................................1 Kings ii. 1, 2.

263. Solomon....................................1 Kings ii. 24.
264. Shimei......................................1 Kings ii. 36.
265. The daughter of Pharaoh, King of Egypt...1 Kings iii. 1.
266. Solomon's decision regarding the two children..............................1 Kings iii. 16, 27.
267. Solomon his son............................1 Kings v. 1.
268. Tyrians......................................1 Kings v. 6.
269. Solomon....................................1 Kings ix. 18.
270. Solomon....................................I Kings x. 22.
271. In the reign of Solomon..................1 Kings x. 27.
272. Jeroboam...................................1 Kings xi. 29.
273. Ahijah......................................1 Kings xi. 30, 31.
274. Ahijah, the Shilonite......................1 Kings xi. 31.
275. Jeroboam...................................1 Kings xii. 8, 9.
276. Jeroboam, king of Israel.................1 Kings xii. 28.
277. Jeroboam, king of Israel.................1 Kings xiii. 1.
278. Jeroboam. He had his arm withered.....1 Kings xiii. 4.
279. Ahijah......................................1 Kings xiv. 1, 13.
280. Ahijah, Jeroboam's wife..................1 Kings xiv. 4.
281. Ahijah, said to be the wife of Jeroboam....1 Kings xiv. 6.
282. Jeroboam...................................1 Kings xiv. 11.
Baasha......................................1 Kings xvi. 4.
Ahab..1 Kings xxii. 38.
283. Ahijah......................................1 Kings xiv. 13.
284. Shishak, king of Egypt...................1 Kings xiv. 25, 26.
285. Asa, because she made an idol in a grove..............................1 Kings xv. 11, 13.
286. Maachah....................................1 Kings xv. 13.
287. Elah...1 Kings xvi. 9.
288. Zimri..1 Kings xvi. 18.
289. Hiel...1 Kingsx vii. 34.
290. The prophecy of Joshua....Josh. vi. 26 ; 1 Kings xvi. 34.
291. Abiram and Segub..........Josh. vi. 26, 1 Kings xvi. 34.
292. The widow's son...........................1 Kings xvii. 17, 24.
293. Elijah's..................1 Kings xvii. 1, 1 Kings xviii. 1.
294. Obidiah.....................................1 Kings xviii. 4.
295. Elijah on Carmel...........................1 Kings xviii. 21.
296. Elijah.......................................1 Kings xix. 4.

297. Moses and Elijah..........Ex. xxiv. 8, 1 Kings xix. 8, 9.
298. Elijah..............................1 Kings xix. 5, 8, 9.
299. Elisha..............................1 Kings xix. 19.
300. Shaphat..............................1 Kings xix. 19.
301. Elisha..............................1 Kings xix. 20.
302. Ahab appropriated the vineyard of Naboth.1 Kings xxi. 7.
303. Jezebel used Ahab's name...............1 Kings xxi. 8.
304. Elijah..............................1 Kings xxi. 19.
305. Ahab..............................1 Kings xxi. 25.
306. Ahab..............................1 Kings xxi. 29.
307. Ahab..............................1 Kings xxii. 30.
308. Ahab..............................1 Kings xxii. 38.
309. Azubah..............................1 Kings xxii. 42.
310. Moabites..............................2 Kings i. 1.
311. King Ahaziah..............................2 Kings i. 2.
312. To Elijah..............................2 Kings i. 9, 18.
313. To Elijah..............................2 Kings ii. 12.
314. Elisha..............................2 Kings ii. 21.
315. Mesha..............................2 Kings iii. 45.
316. Elisha..............................2 Kings iii. 15.
317. Mesha, the King of Moab..............2 Kings iii. 4, 27.
318. Elisha, the Shunammite widow, and her two sons..............................2 Kings iv. 1.
319. Shunammite's son by Elisha.............2 Kings iv. 19.
320. Elisha..............................2 Kings iv. 18, 34.
321. Naaman, Commander of the Syrian Army..............................2 Kings v. 10, 14.
322. Gehazi, the servant of Elisha.............2 Kings v. 27.
323. Elisha to Ahab's son..................2 Kings vi. 32.
324. Elisha..............................2 Kings vii. 1.
325. The lord on whose hand the King leaned....2 Kings vii. 1.
326. Shunammite..........................2 Kings viii. 1, 6.
327. Benhadad, king of Syria.............2 Kings viii. 9, 15.
328. To one of the children of the prophets, by Jehu the king....................2 Kings ix. 1, 11.
329. Jehu..............................2 Kings ix. 20.
330. Jezebel..............................2 Kings ix. 30.
331. Jehu ; the blood of Jezebel...........2 Kings ix. 30, 33.

368. Benaiah..............................1 Chron. xi. 23.
369. The mighty men who came to David at Ziglag..............................1 Chron. xii. 1, 2.
370. The Gadites..............................1 Chron. xii. 8.
371. Issachar..............................1 Chron. xii. 32.
372. Zebulun..............................1 Chron. xii. 33.
373. Uzza..............................I Chron. xiii. 10.
374. The house of Obed-Edom, where it remained three months..............................1 Chron. xiii. 13.
375. Heman, Asaph and Ethan..............................1 Chron. xv. 19.
376. Obed-Edom and Jehiah..............................1 Chron. xv. 24.
377. Gad, 2 Sam. xxiv. 11, 19 ; Nathan, 2 Sam. xii. ....1 Chron. xxi. 11.
378. Oran and his four sons..............................1 Chron. xxi. 20.
379. Solomon..............................1 Chron. xxii. 9.
380. Jonathan, his uncle..............................1 Chron. xxvii. 32.
381. Ahithophel and Hushai..............................1 Chron. xxvii. 33.
382. Joab, of David's Army..............................1 Chron. xxvii. 34.
383. David, King of Israel..............................1 Chron. xxix. 28.
384. Solomon..............................2 Chron. vi. 12, 42.
385. Solomon..............................2 Chron. vii. 12.
386. Rehoboam..............................2 Chron. xi. 21.
387. Nabal and Jeroboam, 1 Sam. xxv. 38....2 Chron. xiii. 20.
388. Zerah..............................2 Chron. xiv. 9.
389. Asa..............................2 Chron. xiv. 11.
390. Asa..............................2 Chron. xvi. 12.
391. Jehoshaphat, King of Judah........2 Chron. xvii. 7, 11.
392. To Jehu, 1 Kings xvi. 7..............................2 Chron. xix. 2.
393. Jehoshaphat, by the prophet Jahaziel. 2 Chron. xx. 16, 17.
394. Jehoram (according to Elijah's prophecy) 2 Chron. xxi. 19.
395. Jehoram..............................2 Chron. xxi. 20.
396. Athaliah..............................2 Chron. xxii. 10.
397. Jehoshabeath hid Joash..............................2 Chron. xxii. 11.
398. Joash, 2 Chron. xxiv. 1..............................2 Chron. xxiii. 11.
399. Athaliah..............................2 Chron. xxiv. 11.
400. Zechariah because he reproved King Joash ....2 Chron. xxiv. 21.
401. Zechariah in the house of the Lord....2 Chron. xxiv. 21.

402. Jehoiada.............................2 Chron. xxiv. 22.
403. Amaziah............................2 Chron. xxv. 6.
404. Amaziah............................2 Chron. xxv. 12.
405. Uzziah..............................2 Chron. xxvi. 10.
406. Uzziah, because he attempted to burn incense. ....2 Chron. xxvi. 19.
407. Ahaz................................2 Chron. xxviii. 3.
408. Oded................................2 Chron. xxviii. 9.
409. Ahaz...............................2 Chron. xxviii. 24.
410. Manasseh.......................2 Chron. xxxiii. 11, 13.
411. Josiah.........................2 Chron. xxxiv. 1.; i. 8.
412. Huldah, the prophetess.............2 Chron. xxxiv. 22.
413. Of Josiah...........................2 Chron. xxxv. 25.
414. Jehoiachin.........................2 Chron. xxxvi. 9.
415. Jehoiachin.........................2 Chron. xxxvi. 9.
416. Cyrus, Isa. xliv. 28...........................Ezra i. 1.
417. Cyrus...Ezra i. 7.
418. To the masons and carpenters.................Ezra iii. 7.
419. By Zerubbabel 52 years after the destruction of the first temple.............................Ezra v. 2.
420. Tatnai...Ezra v. 6.
421. Ezra...Ezra vii. 6.
422. Ezra...Ezra viii. 22.
423. Ezra..Ezra ix. 3, 12.
424. Ezra..Ezra x. 10.
425. Maaseiah...Ezar x. 18.
426. Nehemiah...Neh. i. ii.
427. Nehemiah..Neh. i. 11.
428. Nehemiah.......................................Neh. ii. 5, 18.
429. The daughters of Shallum....................Neh. iii. 12.
430. The Jews..Neh. v. 3.
431. Nehemiah..Neh. v. 11, 18.
432. Nehemiah by Sanballat........................Neh. vi. 5.
433. Nehemiah.......................................Neh. vi. 10, 13.
434. Noadiah...Neh.vi. 14.
435. Ezra, the Scribe....................................Neh. viii. 4.
436. Akkub aud Talmon................................Neh. xi. 19.

437. Tobiah, because he was a Gentile............Neh. xiii. 8.
438. One of the sons of Joiada, because he had married a heathen..........................Neh. xiii. 28.
439. Vashti..............................Esther i. 10, 12.
440. Mordecai..............................Esther ii. 7.
441. Esther..............................Esther ii. 17.
442. Bigthan and Teresh........................Esther ii. 21.
443. Ahasuerus. The good service of Mordecai...Esther vi. 3.
444. Ahasuerus ....Esther viii. 10.
445. Mordecai..............................Esther ix. 4.
446. Hamans'..............................Esther ix. 14.
447. Job....................................Job i. 1.
448. Job....................................Job i. 25.
449. Satan..................................Job ii. 4.
450. Job's wife..............................Job ii. 9.
451. Eliphaz. Bildad. Zophar...................Job ii. 11.
452. Job....................................Job iii. 17.
453. Eliphaz................................Job iv. 15.
454. Job....................................Job vii. 16.
455. Zophar, the Naamathite.....................Job xi. 7.
456. Job....................................Job xiii. 15.
457. Zophar, Bildad, Eliphaz, by Job.............Job xiii. 26.
458. Job....................................Job xiv. 14.
459. Eliphaz, the Temanite......................Job xv. 4.
460. Zophar, Bildad and Eliphaz.................Job xvi. 2.
461. Job....................................Job xvi. 11.
462. Job....................................Job xix. 25.
463. Job....................................Job xxx. 23.
464. Job....................................Job xlii. 11.
465. Jemima, Kezia, Kerenhappuck...............Job xlii. 14.
466. David..................................Psalms i. 4.
467. The fool...............................Psalms xiv. 1.
468. David..................................Psalms xvi. 6.
469. David..................................Psalms xvii. 15.
470. David..................................Psalms xxx. 5.
471. David..................................Psalms lviii. 4.
472. David..................................Psalms lxxi. 18.
473. David..................................Psalms lxxvii. 13.

474. David....................................Psalms cii. 24.
475. David....................................Psalms cxvi. 11.
476. David....................................Psalms cxix. 105
477. Solomon..................................Prov. xvi. 32.
478. Solomon..................................Prov. xviii. 24.
479. He that covereth his sins..............Prov. xxviii. 13.
480. Agur......................................Prov. xxx. 8.
481. Lemuel....................................Prov. xxxi. 1.
482. Solomon..................................Ec. viii. 8.
483. The prophet Isaiah......................Isaiah vi. 5, 7.
484. Ahaz......................................Isaiah vii. 14.
485. Six: Miriam, Ex. xv. 20; Deborah, Judges iv. 4; Huldah, 2 Kings xxii. 14; 2 Chron. xxxiv. 22; Noadiah, Neh. vi. 14; Jezebel..Isaiah viii. 3.
486. Moabites..................................Isaiah xv. 2.
487. Shebna....................................Isaiah xxii. 15, 18.
488. Isaiah.....................................Isaiah xxvi. 19.
489. Israelites.................................Isaiah xxxi. 1.
490. Isaiah, God's command...................Isaiah xxxiv. 4.
491. Hezekiah..................................Isaiah xxxviii. 1.
492. Hezekiah..................................Isaiah xxxviii. 2.
493. Isaiah.....................................Isaiah xxxviii. 21.
494. Hezekiah to Merodach-Baladan messengers..Isa. xxxix. 2.
495. The Jews..................................Jer. viii. 20.
496. Moses and Jeremiah.............Deut. iv. 20, Jer. xi. 4.
497. Jeremiah..................................Jer. xiii. 4.
498. Jeremiah..................................Jer. xiii. 23.
499. Jeremiah..................................Jer. xix. 9.
500. Jeremiah..................................Jer. xx. 2.
501. Pashur changed to Magor-Missabib...........Jer. xx. 3.
502. Melchiah..................................Jer. xxi. 1.
503. Jehoiakim.................................Jer. xxii. 18, 19.
504. Jeremiah..................................Jer. xxiv. 1, 3.
505. Jeremiah, because the Lord commanded him......................................Jer. xxvii. 2.
506. Hananaiah.................................Jer. xxviii. 10.
507. Ahab and Zedekian........................Jer. xxix. 21.
508. Children of Rechab.......................Jer. xxxv. 5, 10.

509. Izijah..Jer. xxxvii. 13.
510. Jonathan's house; Jeremiah.............Jer. xxxvii. 15
511. Ebed-Melech...............................Jer. xxxviii. 10.
512. Jeremiah.....................................Jer. xxxviii. 12.
513. Nebuzar-adan...............................Jer. xxxix. 11, 12.
514. Edel-melech..................................Jer. xxxix. 16, 18.
515. Gedaliah.......................................Jer. xli. 2.
516. Ishmael...Jer. xli. 6, 7.
517. Nebuchadnezzar...........................Jer. xliii. 6, 7.
518. Jeremiah.......................................Jer. xliii. 10.
519. Baruch..Jer. xlv. 25.
520. Elamites..Jer. xlix. 36.
521. Zedekiah.......................................Jer. lii. 8.
522. Nebuchadnezzar...........................Jer. lii. 10.
523. Nebuchadnezzar...........................Jer. lii. 11.
524. Samuel and Zedekiah.........Judges xvi. 21, Jer. lii. 11.
525. Evil-merodech...............................Jer. lii. 31.
526. Ezekiel..Ez. i. 3.
527. Ezekiel..Ez. i. 4, 28.
528. Ezekiel..Ez. iii. 2.
529. Ezekiel..Ez. viii. 3.
530. The man clothed with linen in Ezekiel's vision..Ez. x. 12.
531. Ezekiel, Noah, Daniel, Job...................Ez. xiv. 14.
532. Ezekiel, at the death of his wife..........Ez. xxiv. 16, 17.
533. Ezekiel..Ex. xxxvii.
534. Ezekiel..Ez. xlvii. 12.
535. Daniel, Shadrach, Meshach and Abednego...Dan. i. 6, 11.
536. Daniel...Dan. i. 17.
537. Nebuchadnezzar...........................Dan. iii. 1.
538. Shadrach, Meshach and Abednego........Dan. iii. 19, 20.
539. Nebuchadnezzar...........................Dan. iv. 24, 36.
540. Nebuchadnezzar...........................Dan. iv. 30.
541. Nebuchadnezzar...........................Dan. iv. 33.
542. Nebuchadnezzar...........................Dan. iv. 33.
543. Nebuchadnezzar...........................Dan. iv. 37.
544. Belshazzar....................................Dan. v. 7.
545. Daniel...Dan. v. 24, 29.
546. Darius...Dan. v. 31.

547. Daniel..Dan. vi. 2.
548. Daniel..Dan. vi. 10.
549. Daniel..Dan. ix. 21.
550. Daniel..Dan. x. 15.
551. The wise......................................Dan. xii. 3.
552. Hosea...Hosea iv. 6.
553. The prophet Hosea.............................Hosea iv. 17.
554. Joel..Joel i. 20.
555. Amos..Amos i. 1.
556. Amos..Amos v. 25.
557. Amaziah.......................................Amos vii. 14.
558. Amos..Amos vii. 14.
559. Jonah when he tried to run away from the Lord..............Jonah i. and ii. 3.
560. Jonah...Jonah i. 2, 5.
561. Jonah...Jonah i. 8.
562. Jonah...Jonah ii. 1
563. Jonah...Jonah iii. 4, 5.
564. Jonah before Nineveh..........................Jonah iv. 8.
565. The prophet Nahum.............................Nahum iii.
566. The prophet Habakkuk..........................Hab. ii. 14.
567. Habakkuk......................................Hab. iii. 2.
568. Haggai..Hag. i. 6.
569. Haggai..Hag. ii. 9.
570. Zechariah.....................................Zech. viii. 5.
571. Amos and Zechariah..........Amos vii. 14 ; Zech. xiii. 5.
572. Zechariah.....................................Zech. xiv. 7.
573. Malachi.......................................Mal. iii. 1.
574. Malachi.......................................Mal. iii. 8.
575. They that fear the Lord.......................Mal. iii. 16.

ANSWERS

TO

CURIOSITIES OF THE BIBLE

PERTAINING TO

NEW TESTAMENT PERSONS.

1. Archelaus....................................Matt. ii. 22.
2. John the Baptist..........................Matt. iii. 5, 6.
3. John the Baptist.............................Matt. iii. 7.
4. Angels...Matt. iv. 11.
5. Simon Peter and Andrew..................Matt. iv. 18.
6. Simon Peter and Andrew..................Matt. iv. 19.
7. Peter, Andrew, James and John........Matt. iv. 18, 22.
8. Herod's..Matt. xiv. 6.
9. A woman of Canaan.......................Matt. xv. 22.
10. Salome, mother of James and John.....Matt. xx. 20, 21.
11. Jesus.....................................Matt. xxii. 32.
12. The Scribes and Pharisees...........Matt. xxiii. 23, 24.
13. Zachariah stoned to death...........Matt. xxiii. 35, 37.
14. Roman soldiers (the eagle was their symbol). Matt. xxiv. 28.
15. Christ's.................................Matt. xxiv. 35.
16. Simon, the Leper........................Matt. xxvi. 6.
17. Pontius Pilate...........................Matt. xxvii. 2.
18. Barabbas.................................Matt. xxvii. 16.
19. The wife of Pontius Pilate ; this noble act was deemed worthy of a record in the Bible and should ever be remembered to the honor of womanhood..............Matt. xxvii. 19.
20. "The Saints that slept arose"...........Matt. xxvii. 52.

21. Jesus after the Resurrection............Matt. xxviii. 19.
22. John the forerunner..........................Matt. i. 6.
23. Matthew.....................................Mark ii. 14.
24. Pharisees and Herodians......................Mark iii. 6.
25. The unclean spirit...........................Mark v. 9.
26. Jairus......................................Mark v. 22.
27. Jesus.......................................Mark vi. 3.
28. The deaf and dumb man...............Mark vii. 31, 35.
29. Christ to Peter..........................Mark viii. 33.
30. Moses by Peter, James and John..........Mark ix. 2, 5.
31. Peter to Jesus..............................Mark ix. 5.
32. His disciples...............................Mark x. 14.
33. Jesus to His disciples......................Mark x. 27.
34. The woman who poured the ointment on the Saviour's head..........................Mark xiv. 3, 8.
35. Peter, James and John................Mark xiv. 33, 37.
36. Simon a Cyrenian...........................Mark xv. 21.
37. To three women by an angel.............Mark xvi. 1, 6.
38. Mary Magdalene.............................Mark xvi. 9.
39. His disciples..............................Mark xvi. 15.
40. The angel to Zacharias.... ....Luke i. 19.
41. Zacharias...................................Luke i. 20.
42. John and Christ.....................Luke i. 13 and 31.
43. Zacharias and Mary.......................Luke i. 13, 31.
44. Mary and Elizabeth.......................Luke i. 34, 36.
45. Virgin Mary. "My Saviour"...................Luke i. 47.
46. Augustus Caesar..............................Luke ii. 1.
47. Simeon......................................Luke ii. 25.
48. Simeon..................................Luke ii. 25, 30.
49. Anna, the prophetess....................Luke ii. 36, 37.
50. Anna, the prophetess....................Luke ii. 36. 37.
51. Christ's....................................Luke ii. 49.
52. Scribes and Pharisees........................Luke v. 21.
53. Christ to Scribes and Pharisees..............Luke v. 31.
54. Christ to His disciples.....................Luke vi. 26.
55. The son of the widow of Nain..........Luke vii. 12, 15.
56. His disciples.........................Luke viii. 22, 24.
57. James and John.... ....Luke ix. 54.

58. A Priest and Levite......................Luke x. 30, 31.
59. Samaritan..............................Luke x. 35.
60. The rich fool........................Luke xii. 16, 19.
61. King Herod..........................Luke xiii. 31, 32.
62. Lazarus..............................Luke xvi. 20.
63. Jesus................................Luke xix. 41.
64. Jesus................................Luke xxii. 43.
65. Peter................................Luke xxii. 57.
66. Pilate...............................Luke xxiii. 3.
67. The daughters of Jerusalem...............Luke xxiii. 28.
68. Cleopas..............................Luke xxiv. 18.
69. Christ...............................Luke xxiv. 44.
70. John the Baptist.........................John i. 15.
71. Nathaniel................................John i. 46.
72. Philip...................................John i. 46.
73. "Nathaniel an Israelite, indeed"............John i. 47.
74. The Mother of Jesus.......................John ii. 5.
75. Nicodemus..............................John iii. 1, 2.
76. Jesus....................................John v. 8.
77. John the Baptist.........................John v. 35.
78. Our Saviour..............................John v. 39.
79. Christ...................................John v. 41.
80. Christ.................................John viii. 12.
81. Jairus' daughter........................Matt. ix. 25.
Widow's son of Nain......................Luke vii. 15.
Lazarus..................................John xi. 44.
82. Lazarus..............................John xi. 43, 44.
83. Lazarus..............................John xii. 1, 2.
84. Mary....................................John xii. 3.
85. Christ.................................John xiii. 35
86. Peter..................................John xiii. 37.
87. Peter..................................John xiii. 38.
88. Malchus, the servant...................John xviii. 10.
89. Jesus..................................John xix. 23.
90. Nicodemus..................John iii. 1, viii. 50, xix. 39.
91. Christ...............................John xxi. 18, 19.
92. Peter................................John xxi. 21, 22.

94. John....................................John xxi. 25.
95. His disciples..............................Acts i. 2, 3.
96. David's....................................Acts i. 16.
97. Judas....................................Acts i. 16, 18.
98. Matthias...............................Acts i. 23, 26.
99. Peter, on the day of Pentecost...............Acts ii. 41.
100. Barnabas (who ought not to have possessed land).................Deut. xviii. 20, Acts iv. 36, 37.
101. Ananias and Sapphira.....................Acts v. 1, 10.
102. Judas..Acts i. 18.
Ananias and Sapphira.....................Acts v. 1, 10.
103. Peter. That they might be healed...........Acts v. 15.
104. Gamaliel......................................Acts v. 34.
105. Stephen, Philip, Prochorus, Nicanor. Timon Parmenas and Nicolas.......................Acts vi. 5.
106. Stephen's.....................................Acts vi. 15.
107. Saul, afterward Paul.......................Acts vii. 58.
108. Stephen.................................Acts vii. 54, 60.
109. Stephen.......................................Acts vii. 60.
110. Simon...................................Acts viii. 9, 24.
111. Simon..Acts viii. 24.
112. Candace......................................Acts viii. 27.
113. The Ethiopian eunuch................Acts viii. 27, 38.
114. The eunuch...................................Acts viii. 30.
115. Paul..Acts ix. 3, 4.
116. Paul's..Acts ix. 6.
117. Paul..Acts ix. 8, 9.
118. Ananias.....................................Acts ix. 17, 18.
119. Paul at Damascus............................Acts ix. 25.
120. Dorcas..Acts ix. 39.
121. Peter..Acts ix. 40.
122. Simon...Acts ix. 43.
123. Cornelius....................................Acts x. 1, 2.
124. Simon Peter..................................Acts x. 9.
125. Simon Peter..................................Acts x. 34.
126. Simon Peter..................................Acts x. 38.
127. Agabus.......................................Acts xi. 28.

93. Peter's .... John xxi. 21, 23.
128. King Herod .... Acts xii. 1, 2.
129. Simon Peter .... Acts xii. 8.
130. Herod's .... Acts xii. 21, 22.
131. King Herod .... Acts xii. 23.
132. Elymas, the socerer .... Acts xiii. 8, 10.
133. Elymas .... Acts xiii. 11.
134. Paul and Barnabas .... Acts xiv. 12.
135. Mercurius .... Acts xiv. 12.
136. Jupiter .... Acts xiv. 12.
137. Paul and Barnabas .... Acts xv. 37, 38.
138. Paul and Barnabas .... Acts xv. 36, 40.
139. Lydia at Thyatira .... Acts xvi. 14.
140. Peter and John ; Paul and Silas ...... Acts iv. 3, xvi. 23.
141. Bereans .... Acts xvii. 11.
142. Paul's .... Acts xvii. 28.
143. Dionysius .... Acts xvii. 34.
144. Damaris .... Acts xvii. 34
145. Claudius .... Acts xviii. 2.
146. Paul .... Acts xviii. 3.
147. Aquila .... Acts xviii. 2, 3.
148. Paul at Corinth .... Acts xviii. 6.
149. Apollos .... Acts xviii. 24.
150. Aquilla and Priscila .... Acts xviii. 26.
151. Apollos .... Acts xviii. 27, 28.
152. Chief of Priests, and seven sons of Sceva. Acts xix. 13, 14.
153. Demetrius .... Acts xix. 24.
154. Paul at Troas .... Acts xx. 7.
155. Eutychus .... Acts xx. 9.
156. Paul .... Acts xx. 10.
157. Five ; Anna and Philip's four daughters .... Luke ii. 36.
.... Acts xxi. 9.
158. Agabus .... Acts xxi. 10, 11.
159. Agabus .... Acts xxi. 10, 11.
160 Mnason, an old disciple .... Acts xxi. 16.
161. Paul .... Acts xxi. 26.
162. Trophimus .... Acts xxi. 29.
163. Paul .... Acts xxi. 40.

164. Gamaliel....................................Acts xxii. 3.
165. Paul..Acts xxii. 20.
166. Paul..Acts xxii. 28.
167. Ananias.....................................Acts xxiii. 2.
168. Sadducees...................................Acts xxiii. 8.
169. Paul's......................................Acts xxiii. 12, 13.
170. For St. Paul................................Acts xxiii. 12, 13.
171. Tertullus...................................Acts xxiv. 1.
172. Paul..Acts xxiv. 5.
173. Drusilla, the Jewess........................Acts xxiv. 24.
174. Felix.......................................Acts xxiv. 25.
175. Jesus.......................................John x. 20.
176. Julius......................................Acts xxvii. 1.
Paul..Acts xxvi. 24.
177. Julius......................................Acts xxvii. 1.
178. Paul..Acts xxviii. 1.
179. Paul..Acts xxviii. 3, 6.
180. Publius.....................................Acts xxviii. 7.
181. Paul and 275 companions.....................Acts xxvii. 37,
182. Paul..Acts xxviii. 30.
183. The Jews....................................Rom. x. 2.
184. St. Paul....................................Rom. x. 19.
185. St. Paul....................................Rom. xv. 24, 28.
186. Tryphena Tryphosa...........................Rom. xvi. 12.
187. Persis who labored for the Lord.............Rom. xvi. 12.
188. Lucius, Jason and Sosipater.................Rom. xvi. 21.
189. Quartus.....................................Rom. xvi. 23.
190. Gaius.......................................Rom. xvi. 23.
191. Phebe.......................................Rom. xvi. 27.
192. Crispus, Gaius and Stephanas' household..1 Cor. i. 14, 16.
193. The Jews....................................1 Cor. i. 23.
194. The Greeks..................................1 Cor. i. 23.
195. Corinthians.................................1 Cor. ix. 2.
196. Paul..1 Cor. x. 30.
197. Paul..1 Cor. xv. 9.
198. The house of Stephanas......................1 Cor. xvi. 15.
199. Felix.......................................Acts xxiii 24.
Festus......................................Acts xxiv. 27.

Fortunatus..............................1 Cor. xvi. 17.
200. Jesus Christ..............................2 Cor. v. 21.
201. Aretas..............................2 Cor. xi. 32.
202. James, Cephas and John..............................Gal. ii. 9.
203. "They which are of faith" and "If ye be Christs"..............................Gal. iii. 7 and 29.
204. Tychicus..............................Eph. vi. 21, 22.
205. Paul to the Philippians..............................Phil. ii. 10.
206. Epaphroditus whom Paul sent as a messenger to the Philippians..............................Phil. ii. 25, 27.
207. Paul..............................Phil. iii. 8.
208. Epaphroditus..............................Phil. iv. 18, 23.
209. Onesimus..............................Col. iv. 9.
210. See..............................Acts xiii. 6, Heb. v. 8, Col. iv. 11.
211. Luke..............................Col. iv. 14
212. Paul..............................1 Thes. ii. 18.
213. Paul..............................Thes. v. 21.
214. Paul..............................Gal. vi. 9, 2 Thes. iii. 13.
215. Onesiphorus..............................2 Tim. i. 16.
216. Philetus and Hymeneus..............................2 Tim. ii. 17, 18.
217. Timothy..............................2 Tim. iii. 15.
218. Demas..............................2 Tim. iv. 10.
219. Alexander..............................2 Tim. iv. 14.
220. Aratus..............................Acts xvii. 28.
Menander..............................1 Cor. xv. 33.
Epimendes..............................Titus i. 12.
221. Paul..............................Titus i. 15.
222. John and Paul..............................2 John i. 10, Titus iii. 10.
223. Zenas..............................Titus iii. 13.
224. Archippus..............................Philem. i. 2.
225. Philemon..............................Philem. i. 22.
226. Angels..............................Heb. i. 14.
227. Jesus..............................Heb. iii. 3.
228. Melchisedec..............................Heb. v. 6.
229. Rahab..............................Heb. xi. 31.
230. Paul..............................Heb. xii. 21.
231. James..............................James i. 17.
232. James..............................James ii. 19.

233. James....................................James iv. 14.
234. Peter....................................1 Peter ii. 25.
235. Paul....................Rom. v. 3, 2 Cor. xii. 9, 10.
James....................................James i. 2.
Peter....................................1 Peter iv. 13.
236. Peter....................................1 Peter v. 8.
237. Peter....................................2 Peter i. 19.
238. Peter....................................2 Peter ii. 5.
239. Diotrephes..............................3 John 5.
240. John....................................Rev. i. 9.
241. Satan....................................Rev. ii. 12, 13.
242. The Laodiceans by the Lord.............Rev. iii. 14, 16.
243. Those who have washed their robes and made them white.....................Rev. vii. 13, 17.
244. Gabriel.......................Dan. ix. 21, Luke i. 19.
Michael.........................Jude i. 9, Rev. xii. 7.
245. Satan's..................................Rev. xii. 12.

ANSWERS

TO

CURIOSITIES OF THE BIBLE

PERTAINING TO

OLD TESTAMENT PLACES.

1. In the creation. See........................Gen. i. 2.
2. In the garden of Eden........................Gen. iii. 8.
3. In the land of Nod........................Gen. iv. 16.
4. From the river of Egypt to the Euphrates....Gen. xv. 18.
5. At Beer-lahairoi to in the wilderness to Hagar.Gen. xvi. 14.
6. Sodom and Gomorrah....................Gen. xix. 24.
7. Zoar................................Gen. xix. 30.
8. At Beer-sheba, by Abraham...............Gen. xxi. 33.
9. Jehovah-Jireh........................Gen. xxii. 14.
10. Luz..................................Gen. xxviii. 19.
11. At Peniel..........................Gen. xxxii. 24, 30.
12. Bethlehem..........................Gen. xxxv. 19.
13. Ephrath or Bethlehem................Gen. xxxv. 20.
14. Bethlehem...........................Gen. xlviii. 7.
15. In a cave in the field of Machpelah .... Gen. xlix. 30, 31, and l. 13.
16. Mt. Horeb to Moses........................Ex. iii. 2.
17. At Elim................................Ex. xv. 27.
18. Mount Sinai..........................Ex. xix. 18, 24.
19. At the foot of Mount Sinai..............Ex. xxxii. 1, 4.
20. From Heaven..........................Lev. ix. 24.
21. At Kibroth-hattaavah....................Num. xi. 34.
22. The wilderness of Paran..................Num. xii. 16.
23. The plains of Moab....................Nnm. xxvi. 3, 4.

24. All the territory that Caleb passed over when he spied the land........................Deut. i. 36.
25. At Mosera..Deut. x. 6.
26. Upon the door-posts of the house and upon the gates..Deut. xi. 20.
27. Mt. Gerizim................................Deut. xxvii. 12.
28. Mt. Ebal................................Deut. xxvii. 13.
29. Mt. Nebo................................Deut. xxxii. 49.
30. In the land of Moab......................Deut. xxxiv. 6.
31. Gilgal..Josh. v. 9, 12.
32. Gilgal..Josh. v. 10, 12.
33. The city of Jericho..............................Josh. vi. 20.
34. In the valley of Achor......................Josh. vii. 24, 26.
35. Ai..Josh. viii. 5. 25.
36. King of Ai................................Josh. viii. 23, 29.
37. Gibeon..Josh. ix. 3, 15.
38. Gibeon, Chephirah, Beeroth, Kirjath-Jearim..Josh. ix. 17.
39. The cave at Makkedah..........................Josh. x. 17.
40. Kedesh, Shechem, Hebron, Bezer, Romoth-Gilead and Golan..........................Josh. xx. 7, 8.
41. At Shechem, in the ground bought by Jacob..Josh. xxiv. 32.
42. Bezek, where the thumbs and great toes of 70 kings were cut off..........................Judges i. 5, 7.
43. In Bezek..Judges i. 5, 7.
44. On Mount Tabor..........................Judges iv. 12, 15.
45. At Jehovah-Shalom......................Judges vi. 21, 24.
46. In the valley of Moreh by Israelites........Judges vii. 1.
47. Shechem................................Judges ix. 39, 45.
48. From Mount Zalmon......................Judges ix. 48, 49.
49. Thebez................................Judges ix. 50, 53.
50. The cities of Havoth-Jair......................Judges x. iv.
51. Zorah................................Judges xiii. 2, 24.
52. Gaza..Judges xvi. 1, 3.
53. Ashdod..1 Sam. v. 3.
54. Between Mizpeh and Shem......................1 Sam. vii. 12.
55. At Bezek. Israel 300,000, Judah 30,000.....1 Sam. xi. 8.
56. At Gilgal..1 Sam. xv. 33.

57. At Gath.......................................1 Sam. xvii. 4.
58. Nob..1 Sam. xxi. 1, 6.
59. To Endor...........................1 Sam. xxviii. 7, 8.
60. Mount Gilboa.....................................2 Sam. 1, 6.
61. At Hebron.......................................2 Sam. ii. 3, 4
62. Jerusalem, the city of David..............2 Sam. v. 7, 9.
63. At Rabbah..........................2 Sam. xii. 29, 31.
64. Mount Olivet..............Mark xiv. 26 ; 2 Sam. xv. 30.
65. In Gibeon......................................1 Kings iii. 5.
66. At Jerusalem.........................1 Kings iii. 15, 28.
67. At Ezion-Geber on the Red Sea...........1 Kings ix. 26.
68. At Bethel.................................1 Kings xiii. 4.
69. At Bethel and Dau.........................1 Kings xii. 29.
70. Hill of Samaria...........................1 Kings xvi. 24.
71. Mount Carmel.............................1 Kings xviii. 20.
72. Mount Horeb threatened by Jezebel.....1 Kings xix. 8, 9.
73. On the top of a hill near Samaria.......2 King iii. 10, 12.
74. Kir-haraseth...................................2 Kings iii. 25.
75. Damascus, King Benhadad...........2 Kings viii. 7, 15.
76. Jerusalem..............................2 Kings xii. 6, 12.
77. Jerusalem................................2 Kings xxi. 13.
78. At Megiddo.............................2 Kings xxiii. 29.
79. At Jabesh in Zelah.......2 Sam. xxi. 14 ; 1 Chron. x. 12.
80. In Jerusalem during Solomon's reign .....2 Chron. i. 15.
81. On Mount Moriah..........................2 Chron. iii. 1.
82. Solomon's temple, being built on the same spot where Abraham attempted to offer up Isaac.....................Gen. xxii. 2 ; 2 Chron. iii. 1.
83. At Mareshah.......................2 Chron. xiv. 8, 10.
84. Joash was hid six years in the house of God.........................2 Chron. xxii. 11, 12.
85 Jerusalem, by building towers and gates and repairing the wall.....................2 Chron. xxvi. 9.
86. Jericho.................................2 Chron. xxviii. 15.
87. Jerusalem, under Hazekiah..........2 Chron. xxx. 13-26.
88. Jerusalem...Ezra x. 9.
89. Shushan....................................Esther ix. 16.
90. Babylon.......................................Isa. xiii. 19.

91. Babylon....................................Isa. xiii 20.
92. Jerusalem, because he prophesied unfavorably..............................Jer. xvxvii. 12, 16.
93. At Ribbah, by the order of Nebuchadnezzar..............................Jer. xxxix. 5, 7.
94. At Taphanhes in Egypt.....................Jer. xliii. 9.
95. Jerusalem..................................Jer. lii. 4, 6.
96. Jerusalem..................................Lam. ii. 10.
97. Near Babylon.............................Dan. iii. 1, 20.
98. Bethel.......................................Amos v. 5.
99. The belly of a fish........................Jonah ii. 1.
100. Nineveh....................................Nahum iii. 6.
101. Destruction of Nineveh..................Nahum iii. 10.

ANSWERS

TO

CURIOSITIES OF THE BIBLE

PERTAINING TO

NEW TESTAMENT PLACES.

1. Capernaum.................................Matt. xi. 23.
2. At Bethany where Martha and Mary lived..Matt. xxi. 17.
3. Near Bethany........................Matt. xxi. 17, 19.
4. At Jerusalem..........................Matt. xxvii. 29.
5. On a mountain............................Mark iii. 13.
6. Rome...Luke ii. 1.
7. At the lake of Gennesaret....................Luke v. 1.
8. Transfiguration Mount—to Jesus...........Luke ix. 33.
9. Calvary..................................Luke xxiii. 33.
10. Nazareth....................................John i. 46.
11. Cana of Galilee..........................John ii. 1, 9.
12. At Enon....................................John iii. 23.
13. Mount of Olives..............Luke xxi. 37, John viii. 1.
14. In a cave...................................John ii. 38.
15. Bethany.........Matt. xxvi. 6, Mark xiv. 3, John xii. 1.
16. Cana of Galilee................John i. 47, John xxi. 2.
17. Mount Olivet.................................Acts i. 12.
18. In the upper room at Jerusalem...........Acts i. 12, 14.
19. At Damascus.........................Acts ix. 19, 20.
20. Joppa..................................Acts ix. 36, 43.
21. Caeserea.....................................Acts x. 1.
22. Antioch....................................Acts xi. 26.
23. Paphos in Cyprus......................Acts xiii. 6, 11.
24. Antioch in Pisidia......................Acts xiii. 14, 51.
25. At Lystra...............................Acts xiv. 8, 19.

26. At Antioch..............................Acts xiv. 26.
27. At Thessalonica ; of the disciples..........Acts xvii. 1, 6.
28. People of Berea........................Acts xvii. 10, 11.
29. At Athens..............................Acts xvii. 23.
30. At Ephesus............................Acts xx. 17, 31.
31. Tarsus.................................Acts xxii. 3.
32. Melita.................................Acts xxvii. 41.
33. Melita...............................Acts xxviii. 1, 6.
34. Laodicea...............................Col. ii. 1.
35. On the Isle of Patmos......................Rev. i. 9.
36. At Ephesus, Smyrna, Pergamos, Thyatira, Sardis,
Philadelphia and Laodicea...................Rev. i. 11.
37. Babylon...............................Rev. xviii. 21.
38. New Jerusalem.........................Rev. xxi. 12, 14.

ANSWERS

TO

CURIOSITIES OF THE BIBLE

PERTAINING TO

OLD TESTAMENT THINGS.

1. Light..Gen. i. 3, 5.
2. He divided the waters under the firmament from the waters above, and called the firmament heaven..................................Gen. i. 7, 8.
3. He gathered the waters and called the dry land earth..................................Gen. i. 10, 11.
4. He made the sun, moon and stars..........Gen. i. 16, 19.
5. The fowl of the air and every living thing in the waters..................................Gen. i. 20-23.
6. All living creatures on the earth, with man. Gen. i. 24-31.
7. On the sixth day, Friday, man, and subsequently redeemed............Luke xxiii. 54; Gen. i. 31.
8. He rested and appointed the Sabbath day....Gen. ii. 2, 3.
9. Seven. At the creation..........................Gen. ii. 2.
   In the wilderness on the giving of manna...Ex. xvi. 25.
   In the fourth commandment...............Ex, xx. 10.
   In the Sabbath of the seven years.........Lev. xxv. 4.
   In the jubilee seven times seven years......Lev. xxv. 9.
   The Sabbath of the land in the 70 years captivity..........................2 Chron. xxxvi. 21.
   The prophetic Sabbath of the world.........Heb. iv. 9.
10. See..Gen. ii. 7.
11. On the occasion of giving names to the animal creation..................................Gen. ii. 19.

12. The fall of the first, the agony and the burial of the second Adam; Luke xxii. 44; John xviii. 1; John xix. 41, 42; 1 Corinthians xv. 45........Gen. iii. 3-7.
13. Sewing fig leaves........Gen. iii. 7.
14. The serpent........Gen. iii. 14.
15. To go on his belly and eat dust........Gen. iii. 14.
16. A cherubim and a flaming sword........Gen. iii. 24.
17. If thou dost not well, sin lieth at the door.....Gen. iv. 7.
18. See........Gen. iv. 11, 12.
19. Gopher-wood........Gen. vi. 14.
20. Three hundred cubits (547 ft.)........Gen. vi. 15.
21. That water had abated from the face of the earth........Gen. viii. 8.
22. A dove........Gen. viii. 12.
23. The confusion of tongues........Gen. xi. 6, 9.
24. In........Gen. xiii. 14.
25. The battle of the four kings........Gen. xiv. 1, 2.
26. Abram's expedition against the four kings. Gen. xiv. 13, 22.
27. See........Gen. xv. 18; Gen. xvii. 8.
28. ....Gen. xii. 3; Gen. xvii. 8 and Gen. xvii. 16.
29. Because they sought to abuse angels......Gen. xix. 4, 11.
30. He rained upon them fire and brimstone....Gen. xix. 24.
31. Because she disobeyed God in looking behind her........Gen. xix. 26.
32. Seven ewe lambs........Gen. xxi. 30.
33. Jewels of gold and silver, and raiment.....Gen. xxiv. 53.
34. Then Isaac sowed in that land (Gerar) and received in the same year an hundred-fold..Gen. xxvi. 12.
35. A name given by Laban to the monument erected by Jacob, signifying "the Lord watch between me and thee when we are absent one from another."........Gen. xxxi. 49.
36. See........Gen. xxxv. 5.
37. The oak under which Deborah was buried was called Allon-bachuth, or the oak of weeping........Gen. xxxv. 8.
38. Dukes........Gen. xxxvi. 15.

39. Because he was the son of his old age.....Gen. xxxvii. 3.
40. A coat of many colors from Jacob to Joseph..................................Gen. xxxvii. 3.
41. Acts xxvii. 23; Gen. vii. 1; Gen. xix. 12; Gen. xxx. 17; Gen. xxxix. 5.
42. Balm, honey, spices, myrrh, nuts and almonds..................................Gen. xliii. 11.
43. Seventy souls, Jacob and his family........Gen. xlvi. 27.
44. And Joseph bought all the land of Egypt for Pharaoh, for the Egyptians sold every man his field because the famine prevailed over them: so the land became Pharoah's.....Gen. xlvii. 20.
45. Because of their cruelty to the Shechemites..Gen. xlix. 7.
46. Forty days..Gen. l. 3.
47. Jacob, Gen. l. 2; Joseph......................Gen. l. 26.
48. Abraham, Isaac and Jacob; Christ said, "God is not the God of the dead but of the living,"....................Matt. xxii. 32, Ex. iii. 6, 15.
49. It became leprous as snow....................Ex. iv. 6.
50. It became blood...................................Ex. iv. 9.
51. To perform wonders.............................Ex. iv. 21.
52. It became a serpent.............................Ex. vii. 9.
53. It swallowed them................................Ex. vii. 12.
54. Water turned into blood; it lasted seven days..Ex. vii. 19. 25.
55. 1. Water turned into blood; 2. Frogs; 3. Lice; 4. Flies; 5. Murrain; 6. Boils; 7. Thunder, hail and fire; 8. Locusts; 9. Darkness; 10. Death of the first-born...Ex. vii. viii. ix.
56. The plague of darkness....................Ex. x. 22, 23.
57. Death of the first-born.........................Ex. xi. 5.
58. A lamb or a kid...................................Ex. xii. 5.
59. By a bunch of hyssop dipped in blood and applied to the lintel and side posts of the door..Ex. xii. 22.
60. The Hebrews of the Egyptians...............Ex. xii. 35.
61. Six hundred thousand..........................Ex. xii. 37.
62. Pillar of cloud by day, pillar of fire by night..Ex. xiii. 21

63. For the Israelites the way through the Red Sea was a way of life, and to the Egyptians it was a way of death........................Ex. xiv.
64. Six hundred................................Ex. xiv. 7.
65. The stretching of his hand over the sea......Ex. xiv. 27.
66. The waters of Marah into which Moses threw a tree................................Ex. xv. 25.
67. It was white like coriander seed and tasted like honey................................Ex. xvi. 31.
68. Bread in the morning and quail in the evening................................Ex. xvi. 12, 13.
69. Forty years................................Ex. xvi. 35
70. The nation of Israel..........Ex. xxxi. 13 ; Lev. xxii. 9.
The first-born..........................Num. viii. 17.
Aaron and his family...................Ex. xxix. 44.
The tribe of Levi..........Num. viii. 14 ; Ex. xviii. 25.
The tabernacle..........................Ex. xxix. 43.
The temple...........................2 Chron. vii. 16.
71. Six years................................Ex. xxi. 2.
72. The boring of the ear with an awl to the door..Ex. xxi. 6.
73. Three times a year......................Ex. xxiii. 17.
74. Moses, Aaron, Nadab, Abihu and seventy elders................................Ex. xxiv. 9, 10.
75. Six days................................Ex. xxiv. 16.
76. Forty days and forty nights................Ex. xxiv. 18.
77. Shittim wood............................Ex. xxv. 10.
78. 3 feet 9 in. long, 2 feet 3 in. wide and high..Ex. xxv. 10, 22.
79. Boards of shittim wood overlaid with gold.Ex. xxvi. 15, 30.
80. Four. 1st, twined linen ; 2d, goat's hair ; 3d, ram's skins ; 4th, skin of an unknown (badger) animal........................Ex. xxxvi. 1-14.
81. See......................Num. xiv. 12 and Ex. xxxii. 10.
82. On both sides...........................Ex. xxxii. 15.
83. Because he was angry with Aaron and the people for making a golden calf for worship.Ex. xxxii. 19.
84. He burned it in the fire, ground it to powder, strewed it upon the water and made the people drink it..........................Ex. xxxii. 20.

85. When Aaron made the golden calf Moses said, "Who," etc.......................Ex. xxxii. 26.
86. About three thousand men...............Ex. xxxii. 28.
87. Because they had given of their ornaments to make the golden calf..Ex. xxxii. 2, 3 and Ex. xxxiii. 5.
88. He put the veil off when he spoke to the Lord and took it on when he spoke to the people............................Ex. xxxiv. 30, 35.
89. A box made of shittim wood; it contained the two tables of stone, Aaron's rod, and the golden pot that had manna....Heb. ix. 4; Ex. xxxvii.
90. 3 feet 9 in. long, 2 feet 3 in. wide..........Ex. xxxvii. 6.
91. Polished brass.............................Ex. xxxviii. 8.
92. Ark of the Covenant.....................Ex. xl. 20, 21.
Inside of the ark was the "testimony," or the two tables of stone, on which were engraved the "ten commandments........1 Kings viii. 9.
Before the ark was laid a pot containing an omer of manna........................Ex. xvi. 32, 34.
Aaron's rod that budded.................Num. xvii. 10.
By the side of the ark was a copy of the book of the law.......................Deut. xxxi. 26.
Paul says the pot of manna and Aaron's rod were inside the ark.......................Heb. ix. 4.
93. Turtle-dove and pigeon.....................Lev. v. 7.
94. Samuel ordered that portion for Saul, which was a mark of highest respect, the shoulder being the priest's portion, Num. vi. 20; 1 Sam. ix. 24...........................Lev. vii. 32.
95. Moses took the blood of a ram that had been offered up and put it on the tip of their right ears, upon the thumb of their right hands, and upon the great toes of their right feet.............................Lev. viii. 23. 24.
96. It descended from heaven..................Lev. ix. 24.
97. Nadab and Abihu.........................Lev. x. 1, 2.
98. By scraping and plastering with new mortar. Lev. xiv. 42.
99. They were not to mar the corners of the beard. Lev. xix. 27.

100. To love them as themselves..............Lev. xix. 33, 34.
101. The high-priest..............................Lev. xxi. 14.
102. For a free-will offering a blemished animal might be used..............................Lev. xxii. 23.
103. Death..............................Lev. xxiv. 16.
104. The fiftieth year..............................Lev. xxv. 9.
105. Because the land was God's and they were only strangers and sojourners there.......Lev. xxv. 23.
106. Consumption and burning ague...........Lev. xxvi. 16.
107. See..............................Lev. xxvi. 16.
108. Those that did not keep the commandments.Lev. xxvi. 16.
109. From 20 years old and upward, all able to go forth to war..............................Num. i. 3.
110. The tribe of Judah, 74,600....................Num. i. 27.
111. Because they had to serve at the tabernacle...Num. i. 47.
112. That they might not be destroyed as the first-born of Egypt were....................Num. iii. 40, 43.
113. The tribe of Levi, 22,273....................Num. iii. 43.
114. See..............................Num. iii. 43-49.
115. The principal and the fifth part thereof.......Num. v. 7.
116. See..............................Num. v. 12-31.
117. See..............................Num. vi. 1, 21.
118. At fifty..............................Num. viii. 25.
119. "Rise up, Lord, and let thine enemies be scattered," and "Let them that hate flee before thee," and "Return, O Lord, to the many thousands of Israel."................Num. x. 35. 36.
120. The dew..............................Num. xi. 9.
121. He ordered him to appoint seventy elders as assistants..............................Num. xi. 16.
122. They lay three feet thick over the ground...Num. xi. 31.
123. In meekness..............................Num. xii. 3.
124. For speaking against Moses. By Moses' prayer..............................Num. xii. 1, 13.
125. Twelve—one man from each tribe............Num. xiii. 2.
126. A branch with a cluster of grapes borne between them on a staff..................Num. xiii. 23.
127. Forty days..............................Num. xiii. 25.

128. The giants, the sons of Anak, in whose sight they were as grasshoppers................Num. xiii. 33.
129. Because they believed evil reports and cowardly refused to enter the promised land..Num. xiv. 33.
130. They were deprived of entering the land of Canaan..............................Num. xiv. 26-35.
131. They were smitten by a plague and died..Num. xiv. 26, 39.
132. Stoned to death........................Num. xv. 32, 36.
133. "Speak unto the children of Israel and bid them that they make fringe on the borders of their garments, and that they put upon the fringe of the border a riband of blue, that ye may look upon and remember all the commandments of the Lord and do them."................................Num. xv. 38.
134. By standing between between the living and the dead with a pot of incense in his hand...............................Num. xvi. 46, 48.
135. Fourteen thousand and seven hundred.....Num. xvi. 49.
136. Almond..................................Num. xvii. 8.
137. As a token against the rebels and as a proof that Aaron had been especially chosen by God...................................Num. xvii. 10.
138. See....................................Num. xviii. 20.
139. Of the ashes of a red heifer.............Num. xix. 1-11.
140. Thirty days.............................Num. xx. 29.
141. With fiery serpents which bit them.......Num. xxi. 4, 6.
142. By looking to a serpent of brass raised on a pole...................................Num. xxi. 8, 9.
143. The song at the well...................Num. xxi. 17, 18.
144. It crushed his foot and spoke words unto him...............................Num. xxii. 25, 28.
145. Balaam's ass.........................Num. xxii. 28, 30.
146. In....................................Num. xxiii. 7, 18.
147. No. Balaam blessed Israel instead of cursing him...................................Num. xxiv. 10.
148. For a house full of silver and gold.......Num. xxiv. 13.
149. Twenty-four thousand....................Num. xxv. 9.

150. 601,730 .... Num. xxvi. 51.
151. Only two—Caleb and Joshua .... Num. xxvi. 65.
152. Referring to their father, said, "He died in his own sin." .... Num. xxvii. 1, 3.
153. In .... Num. xxvii. 8, 11.
154. In .... Num. xxx. 3, 5.
155. One thousand .... Num. xxxi. 4.
156. Gold, silver, brass, iron, tin and lead .... Num. xxxi. 22.
157. Forty-three .... Num. xxxiii. 1-50.
158. Six .... Num. xxxv. 6, 15.
   1. Bezer .... Deut. iv. 43.
   2. Ramoth-Gilead .... Deut. iv. 43.
   3. Golan .... Deut. iv. 43.
   4. Hebron .... Josh. 21, 13.
   5. Shechem .... Josh. xxi. 21.
   6. Kedesh .... 1 Chron. vi. 76.
159. That they should marry in their own tribe .... Num. xxxvi. 6.
160. In .... Deut. ii. 6.
161. The Emims .... Deut. ii. 11.
162. By Og, King of Bashan .... Deut. iii. 11.
163. That he might be permitted to see the land of Canaan .... Deut. iii. 25, 27.
164. See (and other passages) .... Deut. iv. 28.
165. In .... Ex. xx. and Deut. v.
166. "Because he loved them," and "Because he kept his word." .... Deut. vii. 8.
167. Their clothes waxed not old .... Deut. viii. 4.
168. That they might know that man did not live by bread alone, but by every word that precedeth out of the mouth of God .... Deut. viii. 4.
169. They were not to disfigure themselves .... Deut. xiv. 1, 2.
170. In .... Deut. xvi. 17.
171. Because God said, "Ye shall henceforth return no more that way" .... Deut. xvii. 16.
172. See .... Deut. xviii. 15, 19.
173. Two or three .... Deut. xix. 15.
174. Trees used for meat. They are man's life .... Deut. xx. 20.

175. Birthright, priesthood and blessing........Deut. xxi. 15.
176. He was to be stoned to death............Deut. xxi. 18, 21.
177. The woman shall not wear that which pertaineth unto a man, neither shall a man put on a woman's garment..................Deut. xxii. 5.
178. "Thou shalt not put any in thy vessel."...Deut. xxiii. 24.
179. One year..............................Deut. xxiv. 5.
180. That all raiment of the poor should be returned at sunset, and that a widow's raiment was never to be taken in pledge at all.....Deut. xxiv. 10.
181. The widow............................Deut. xxiv. 17.
182. He must not be muzzled. He may eat if he wish..................................Deut. xxv. 4.
183. Unjust weight........................Deut. xxv. 14, 15.
184. The blessing from Mount Gerizim, upon which stood the elders of the tribe of Simeon, Levi, Judah, Issachar, Joseph, and Benjamin. The cursing from Mount Ebal, upon which stood the elders of Reuben, Gad, Asher, Zebulum, Dan, and Naphtali..Deut. xxvii. 12, 13.
185. In..................................Deut. xxviii. 1, 4.
186. "Blessed shall be thy basket and thy store". Deut. xxviii. 5.
187. Eagles indicated Romans...........Dent. xxviii. 49, 50.
188. In..............................Deut. xxviii. 15, 68.
189. See.................................Deut. xxviii. 37.
190. In the morning thou shalt say, "Would God it were even," and at even thou shalt say, "Would God it were morning."........Deut. xxviii. 67.
191. Admah and Zeboim.....................Deut. xxix. 23.
192. "With thy holy one."..................Deut. xxxiii. 8.
193. In.................................Deut. xxxiii. 6-25.
194. Thirty days..........................Deut. xxxiv. 8.
195. By covering them with stalks of flax and afterward letting them down from a window by a cord...........................Josh. ii. 6, 15.
196. A line of scarlet thread in the window........Josh. ii. 18.
197. 1. At the deliveration of the Israelites from Egypt...................................Josh. iii. 14.

2. By Elijah............................2 Kings ii. 8.
3. By Elisha............................2. Kings ii. 14.

198. Moses' deliverance of Israel, Ex. iii. 11 ; Josh. vi. 20 ; Judges vii. 7, 22 ; 1 Sam. xvii. 4 ; 2 Chron. xiv. 12, 13 ; 2 Chron. xvi. 8.
199. Cursed............................Josh. vi. 26.
200. He and all he had were stoned and burned to death............................Josh. vii. 24-26.
201. See............................Josh. viii. 3-28.
202. Hewers of wood and drawers of water......Josh. ix. 23.
203. By hail-stones and casting down upon them great stones from heaven................Josh. x. 1, 11.
204. The sun and the moon....................Josh. x. 12.
205. When Joshua commanded it to stand still. Josh. x. 12, 13. When Hezekiah prayed that it should be turned back ten degrees as a sign.......2 Kings xx. 11.
206. About a whole day............................Josh. x. 13.
207. Five kings on five trees................Josh. x. 26, 27.
208. Forty-eight............................Josh. xxi. 41.
209. The stone which Joshua set up as a memorial and witness of a covenant with the tribes of Shechem............................Josh. xxiv. 26, 27.
210. Seventy kings............................Judges i. 7.
211. Caleb gave him his daughter Achsah for a wife............................Judges i. 12, 14.
212. Because he showed the besiegers the entrance to the city............................Judges i. 25, 26.
213. It had two edges and was 18 inches long...Judges iii. 16.
214. See............................Judges iii. 20.
215. He slew six hundred Philistines with it....Judges iii. 31.
216. Nine hundred chariots of iron..............Judges iv. 3.
217. Her wise ladies............................Judges v. 29.
218. For doing evil............................Judges vi. 1, 6.
219. By trying how each man would drink at a brook............................Judges vii. 1, 7.
220. The tribe of Ephraim....................Judges viii. 1.
221. Men of Succoth to Gideon's army........Judges viii. 4, 6.
222. Gideon had seventy sons................Judges viii. 30.

223. A woman threw a piece of millstone on his head.................................Judges ix. 53.
224. That it might not be said a woman slew him. Judges ix. 54.
225. Because of her faithfulness to her father...Judges xi. 40.
225. Forty-two thousand......................Judges xii. 6.
227. By not being able to pronounce the "h" in the word "Shibboleth"..................Judges xii. 6.
228. Forty years.............................Judges xiii. 1.
229. Two. Isaac, Gen. xviii. 10; Samson......Judges xiii. 3.
230. From Manoah's altar....................Judges xiii. 20.
231. Out of the eater came forth meat, and out of the strong came forth sweetness; the conditions were thirty sheets and thirty changes of raiment...........................Judges xiv. 13, 14.
232. Thirty men of the Philistines...........Judges xiv. 19.
233. By tying 300 foxes tail to tail and putting a fire brand between each pair............Judges xv. 1, 5.
234. One thousand...........................Judges xv. 15.
235. The jaw-bone used by Samson..........Judges xv. 15, 19.
236. By having his seven locks of hair shaven while he was asleep..................Judges xvi. 19, 20.
237. They put out his eyes and made him grind in the prison-house.......................Judges xvi. 21.
238 He pulled down the house where the Philistines were assembled................Judges xvi. 22, 30.
239. Three thousand.......................Judges xvi. 27.
240. Samson slew more at his death than during his life.................................Judges xvi. 30.
241. Seven hundred..........................Judges xx. 16.
342. When there was no king in Israel........Judges xxi. 25.
343. Four times..............................1 Sam. iii. 3.10.
344. Thirty thousand.........................1 Sam. iv. 10.
345. The glory is departed. By Phineas' wife to her son whom she named Ichabod...........1 Sam. iv. 21.
246. Drawn on a new cart by two cows..........1 Sam. vi. 7.
247. By thunder..........................1 Sam. vii. 9, 10.
248. Because of the bad government of Samuel's sons...............................1 Sam. viii. 1, 5.

249. The daughters of the Israelites...........1 Sam. viii. 13.
250. See.................................1 Sam. ix. 9.
251. By his meeting three men, one carrying three kids, another three loaves, and another a bottle of wine.........................1 Sam. x. 3, 4.
252. That he might thrust out their right eyes....1 Sam. xi. 2.
253. Two. 1st, Elijah, 1 Kings xviii. 42; James v. 17, 18; 2d, Samuel................1 Sam. xii. 16, 18.
254. By thunder and rain.....................1 Sam. xii. 17.
255. In the days of the prophet Samuel........1 Sam. xii. 18.
256. Lest the Hebrews make them swords and spears..............................1 Sam. xiii. 19.
257. With a file...........................1 Sam. xiii. 21.
258. Samuel prophecying concerning Saul..1 Sam. xv. 26, 28.
259. And Jesse took an ass laden with bread and a bottle of wine and a kid, and sent them by David his son unto Saul................1 Sam. xvi. 20.
260. Six cubits and a span (11 fet 8 in.).. ....1 Sam. xvii. 4.
261. Josh. x. 16; Judges vi. 2; 1 Sam. xiii. 6....1 Sam. xxii. 1.
262. David at Keilah........................1 Sam. xxiii. 11.
263. Cutting off the skirt of his robe...........1 Sam. xxiv. 4.
264. Adam, Gen. ii. 21; Abraham, Gen. x. 2; Saul and his army.....................1 Sam. xxvi. 12.
265. One year and four months................1 Sam. xxvii. 7.
266. Seven years and six months...............2 Sam. ii. 11.
267. David was thirty years old when he began to reign and he reigned forty years...........2 Sam. v. 4.
268. When they heard the sound of a goig in the tops of the mulberry trees................2 Sam. v. 24.
269. Three months...........................2 Sam. vi. 11.
270. See...................................2 Sam. vii. 24.
271. Forty thousand.........................2 Sam. x. 18.
272. "Set ye Uriah in the fore front of the hottest battle and retire ye from him, that he may be smitten and die."....................2 Sam. xi. 15.
273. King David to Joab......................2 Sam. xi. 15.
274. At a sheep shearing among all the king's sons...............................2 Sam. xiii. 23, 29.

275. Two hundred shekels weight (six pounds)..2 Sam. xiv. 26.
276. See..................................2 Sam. xix. 18.
277. By hanging seven of Saul's sons........2 Sam. xxi. 1, 9.
278. Moses, Ex. xv.; Num. xxi. 17; Deut. xxxii.; Deborah and Barak, Judges v.; Hannah and David's, 1 Sam. iii..................2 Sam. xxii. 1.
279. In......................................2 Sam. xxiii.
280. In..................................2 Sam. xxiii. 8, 39.
281. By forcing Joab to number the people ....2 Sam. xxiv. 1, 4.
282. For three days......................2 Sam. xxiv. 10, 13.
283. A three days' pestilence; 70,000 died.....2 Sam. xxiv. 15.
284. By repentance......................2 Sam. xxiv. 15, 16.
285. During all the days of Solomon...........1 Kings iv. 25.
286. Twelve thousand........................1 Kings iv. 26.
287. The Sidonians..........................1 Kings v. 6.
288. By sea on floats, 2 Chron. ii. 16............1 Kings v. 9.
289. Because every stone was chiselled, every beam sawn, every hole drilled, and every bolt fitted before being brought to the city.....1 Kings vi. 7.
290. Seven years, in the 4th year of Solomon's reign..................................1 Kings vi. 38.
291. Thirteen years..........................1 Kings vii. 1.
292. Jachin and Boaz.......................1 Kings vii. 21.
293. Fire came from heaven and consumed the sacrifice, and the Glory of the Lord filled the house, 2 Chron. vii. 1.............1 Kings viii. 10-2.
294. Twice...................................1 Kings ix. 2.
295. "Israel shall be a proverb and a bye-word among all people."......................1 Kings. ix. 7.
296. The Gentiles were his bondsmen and the Israelites were his honorable servants..1 Kings ix. 21. 22.
297. Queen of Sheba had heard of the fame and wisdom of Solomom ....1 Kings x. 1, 7.
298. Six hundred and sixty-six talents, valued at $56,900 each, or a total of $37,895,400....1 Kings x. 14.
299. By the navies of Hiram and Tarshish......1 Kings x. 22.

300. A chariot cost 600 shekels and a horse 150 shekels............ ....1 Kings x. 29.
301. When the prophet Elijah tore King Jeroboam's cloak in twelve pieces........1 Kings xi. 29, 31.
302. Rehoboam's threat to make his little finger thicker than his father's loins and to chastise them with scorpions instead of whips. ....1 Kings xii. 10, 11.
303. A lion slew him in the way..............1 Kings xiii. 24.
304. Cracknels..............................1 Kings xiv. 3.
305. By Elijah or Elias, James v. 17, 18.......1 Kings xvii. 1.
306. The ravens that fed Elijah...............1 Kings xvii. 6.
307. Four hundred and fifty.............1 Kings xviii. 19, 22.
308. Three; Jesus in the wilderness, Moses on Horeb, and Elijah near Horeb, Matt. iv. 2; Ex. xx. 28........................... 1 Kings xix. 8.
309. One hundred thousand were slain........1 Kings xx. 20.
310. In the battle of Israel with Syria, 100,000 of the latter were slain.................1 Kings xx. 23, 29.
311. Syrians against Israel; 100,000 Syrians slain................................1 Kings xx. 29.
312. 1st. A lion killed the disobedient prophet, 1 Kings xiii. 24; 2d. A lion killed the man that disobeyed the prophet, 1 Kings xx. 35. 36; 3d. Lions killed Daniel's enemies, Dan. vi. 24; 4th. Bears killed Elisha's mockers..2 Kings ii. 24.
313. Elijah, with ashes upon his face..........1 Kings xx. 38.
314. Naboth, by Jezebel's wicked plot.......1 Kings xxi. 6, 14
315. His mantle.............................2 Kings ii. 13.
316. When the prophetic disciples searched for the body of Elijah.........................2 Kings ii. 16.
317. Mesha, King of Moab, was a sheepmaster, and rendered unto the king of Israel an hundred thousand lambs and an hundred thousand rams, with the wool.... ....2 Kings iii. 4.
318. When the Moabites looked at the water and the sun shining.........................2 Kings iii. 22

319. By means of the prophet Elisha; he multiplied the widow's oil....................2 Kings iv. 4, 7.
320. See..............................2 Kings iv. 18, 20.
321. By Elisha in restoring the poisoned pottage at Gilgal.............................2 Kings iv. 41.
322. Two talents of silver and two changes of garment..................................2 Kings v. 23.
323. By Elisha when he caused iron to swim....2 Kings vi. 6.
324. See..................................2 Kings vi. 13.
325. The Syrian army at Dotham..............2 Kings vi. 18.
326. Eighty pieces of silver ($45)..............2 Kings vi. 25.
327. At the seige of Samaria.................2 Kings vi. 28.
328. Four..................................2 Kings vii. 3.
329. Assyrian army..........................2 Kings vii. 3-9.
330. Jehu he drove furiously..................2 Kings ix. 20.
331. Four. 1st. The person who spoke to the witch of Endor, 1 Sam. xxviii. 8, 14; 2d. The dead man by Elijah, 1 Kings xvii. 17, 24; 3d. The Shunammite's son by Elisha, 2 Kings iv. 33, 36; 4th. The man who touched the bones of Elisha................2 Kings xiii. 20, 21.
332. See..............................2 Kings xiii. 20, 2i.
333. Nehushtan.........................2 Kings xviii. 4.
334. The brazen serpent that Moses had made was broken in pieces by Hezekiah...........2 Kings xviii. 4.
335. The brazen serpent......................2 Kings xviii. 4.
336. Sennacherib, king of Assyria.........2 Kings xix. 36-37.
337. Mount of Corruption..................2 Kings xxiii. 13.
338. Eber, Peleg, Rew.........................1 Chron. i. 25.
339. Shushan had a servant, an Egyptian, named Jarha, and gave his daughter to wife.1 Chron. i. 34, 35.
340. They were men of might and swift as roes..................................1 Chron. xxii. 8.
341. The Ark was brought from the house of Obed-edom to Jerusalem................1 Chron. xvi. 7, 36.
342. It was a talent of gold and had precious stones in it............................1 Chron. xx. 2.

343. Three. 1st. Sennacherib's army, 2 Kings xix. 35; 2d. The first-born in Egypt, Ex. xii. 29; 3d. Israelites .... 1 Chron. xxi. 14, 15.
344. The Lord made him to understand by writing by His hand .... 1 Chron. xxviii. 19.
345. One hundred and fifty shekels (at 33c.) about $50 .... 2 Chron. i. 17.
346. On floats by sea to Joppa .... 2 Chron. ii. 16.
347. One hundred and fifty-three thousand and six hundred .... 2 Chron. ii. 17.
348. The flowers, lamps and tongs .... 2 Chron. iv. 21.
349. The tables of stone .... 2 Chron. v. 10.
350. When the voice of united praise was heard. 2 Chron. v. 13.
351. He kneeled down on his knees .... 2 Chron. vi. 13.
352. At the dedication of the temple .... 2 Chron. vi. 36.
353. By sending fire from heaven .... 2 Chron. vii. 1, 3.
354. "A proverb and a bye-word among all nations." .... 2 Chron. vii. 20.
355. Gold, silver, ivory, apes, and peacocks .... 2 Chron. ix. 21.
356. Four thousand .... 2 Chron. ix. 25.
357. "To our tents, O Israel." .... 2 Chron. x. 16.
358. "Lord, it is nothing to thee whether it be few or many." .... 2 Chron. xiv. 11.
359. The Lord is with you while you be with him and if ye seek him he will be found of you, but if ye forsake him he will forsake you. 2 Chron. xv. 2.
360. Horns of iron .... 2 Chron. xviii. 10.
361. A certain man drew a bow at a venture and smote the king of Israel between the joints of the harness .... 2 Chron. xviii. 33. By chance there came down a priest that way and passed on the other side, Luke x. 31.
362. After the battle against the Moabites and Ammorites .... 2 Chron. xx. 25.
363. Because a band of men who came with the Arabians had slain the elder sons .... 2 Chron. xii. 1.
364. To repair the temple .... 2 Chron. xxiv. 9.
365. To repair the house of the Lord .... 2 Chron. xxiv. 10, 13.

366. Seven, viz.: Stephen, Acts vii. 58, 60; a blasphemer, Lev. xxiv. 23; a gatherer of sticks on the Sabbath, Num. xv. 32, 63; Achan, Josh. vii. 25; Adoram, 1 Kings xii. 18; Naboth, 1 Kings xxi. 13, and Zachariah..............................2 Chron. xxiv. 21.
367. He opened the doors of the house of the Lord and repaired them...............2 Chron. xxix. 3.
368. See..............................2 Chron. xxx. 10.
369. He stopped the upper water course of Gihon and brought it straight down to the west side of the city of David............2 Chron. xxxii. 30.
370. Manasseh, king of Judah............2 Chron. xxxiii. 11.
371. He was returned to his home and kingdom..............................2 Chron. xxxiii. 13.
372. King Jehoiachin was only eight years old and was said to have done evil in the sight of the Lord..........................2 Chron. xxxvi. 9.
373. Rehum and Shimshai to Artazerxes..........Ezra iv. 9.
Tatnai and others to Darius.................Ezra v. 6.
374. See....................................Ezra vii. 21.
375. Confiscation of goods......................Ezra vii. 26.
376. "Yet now there is hope."..................Ezra x. 2.
377. In self-defence at there building of the wall of Jerusalem.......................Neh. iv. 13. 18.
378. After the captivity—at Jerusalem..........Neh. viii. 17.
379. During the forty years' march through the wilderness............................Neh. ix. 21.
380. The third of a shekel......................Neh. x. 32.
381. By lots, one out of ten....................Neh. xi. 1, 2.
382. Ten thousand talents of silver..............Esther iii. 9.
383. See....................................Esther viii. 9.
384. By post on horseback....................Esther viii. 10.
385. The attempt made by Haman to destroy Jews all in the kingdom of Ahasuerus......... Esther ix. 21.
386. Because they saw that his grief was very great..Job ii. 13.
387. "By the breath of his nostrils they are consumed."..............................Job iv. 9.

388. "The sparks that fly upward." .... Job v. 7.
389. "A shock of corn in its season." .... Job v. 26.
390. "The white of an egg." .... Job vi. 6.
391. "To the weaver's shuttle." .... Job vii. 6.
392. "As of few days and full of trouble." .... Job xiv. 1.
393. "Acquaint thyself with God." .... Job xxii. 21.
394. "Some remove the land-marks." .... Job xxiv. 2.
395. See .... Job xxxviii.
396. "The stars sang together." .... Job xxxviii. 7.
397. Because they rejoiced at God's creation .... Job xxxviii. 7.
398. See .... Job xxxix. 13, 14.
399. Yes, God gave him twice as much .... Job xlii. 10, 12.
400. Psalms .... Psalms.
401. In the first psalm .... Psalm. i.
402. See .... Psalms ix. 17.
403. At God's right hand .... Psalms xvi. 11.
404. See .... Psalms xviii.
405. "My God, my God, why hast thou forsaken me?" .... Psalms xxii. 1.
406. "I shall not want." .... Psalms xxiii. 1.
407. "Then the Lord will take me up." ...... Psalms xxvii. 10.
408. "In the beauty of holiness." .... Psalms xxix. 2.
409. See .... Psalms xxix. 3, 10.
410. "The righteous forsaken or his seed begging bread .... Psalms xxxvii. 25.
411. "A stranger" and "a sojourner." ...... Psalms xxxix. 12.
412. "Like a green olive tree." .... Psalms lii. 8.
413. Into his bottle .... Psalms lvi. 8.
414. Angels .... Psalms lxxviii. 25.
415. A doorkeeper in the house of God ..... Psalms lxxxiv. 10.
416. The 14th Psalm and .... Psalm liii.
417. The 117th psalm .... Psalms cxvii.
418. The 119th psalm .... Psalms cxix.
419. "Teach me thy statutes." .... Psalms cxix. 33.
420. "A lost sheep." .... Psalms cxix. 176.
421. "They shall reap in joy." .... Psalms cxxvi. 5.
422. "He shall doubtless come again rejoicing bringing his sheaves with him .... Psalms cxxvi. 6.

423. "While I live."........................Psalms cxlvi. 2.
424. See..Prov. i. 5, 6.
425. See..........................Prov. i. 10 ; i. 15 ; i. 14, 15.
426. See...........Heb. xii. 6 ; Rev. iii. 19 ; Prov. iii. 11, 12.
427. Wisdom's ways.............................Prov. iii. 17.
428. "Thy fathers commandment and the law of thy mother."..........................Prov. vi. 20, 22.
429. To have his clothes burned.................Prov. vi. 27.
430. The blessing of the Lord....................Prov. x. 22.
431. "Righteousness.".......Psalms xxxiii. 12 ; Prov. xiv. 34.
432. Ruling one's spirit..........................Prov. xvi. 32.
433. "He that ruleth his spirit."................Prov. xvi. 32.
434. "An offended brother.".....................Prov. xviii. 19.
435. "In the way he should go."...............Prov. xxii. 6.
436. "He shall stand before kings and not before mean men..Prov. xxii. 29.
437. See..Prov. xxv. 19.
438. "Cold water to a thirsty soul."............Prov. xxv. 25.
439. "Hell" and "Destruction."...............Prov. xxvii. 20.
440. The wicked flee when no man pursueth, the righteous as brave as a lion...............Prov. xxviii. 1.
441. See..........1 John i. 9 ; Lev. v. 5, and Prov. xxviii. 13.
442. Ants, conies, locusts and spiders.......Prov. xxx. 24. 28.
443. See..Prov. xxx. 33.
444. "All is vanity."..............................Ecclesiastes.
445. See..Ec. i. 7.
446. A good name.....................................Ec. vii. 1.
447. Crackling of thorns under a pot..............Ec. vii. 6.
448. In the war with death..........................Ec. viii. 8.
449. "Fear God and keep his commandments."....Ec. xii. 13.
450. Esther and Solomon's Songs.
451. "Strong as death."....................Sol.'s Songs viii. 6.
452. "Love."..................................Sol.'s Songs viii. 7.
453. Bulls, Psalms xxii. 12 ; fatlings, Ezek. xxxix. 18 ; trees..Isa. ii. 13.
454. Suits of apparel, rings, etc................Isa. iii. 18, 23
455. See...Isa. iii. 18, 23.
456. Maher-shalal-hash-baz............................Isa. viii. 1.

457. See.......................................Isa. viii. 6.
458. See.......................................Isa. viii. 13.
459. Isaiah; "And there shall be a highway for the remnant of his people..................Isa. xi. 15, 16.
460. Pride.......................................Isa. xvi. 6.
461. See.......................................Isa. xviii. 2.
462. Let us eat and drink, for to-morrow we die..Isa. xxii. 13.
463. Till ye be left as a beacon on the mountain's top. Isa. xxx. 17.
464. The Lord is our judge, lawgiver and king. Isa. xxxiii. 22.
465. See.......................................Isa. xxxiv. 13.
466. 2 Kings xix. and..........................Isa. xxxvii.
467. Figs. Prescribed by the prophet Isaiah for King Hezekiah.....................Isa. xxxviii. 21.
468. "A drop in a bucket."......................Isa. xl. 15.
469. "They shall renew their strength."............Isa. xl. 31.
470. Abraham...................2 Chron. xx. 7; Isa. xli. 8.
471. See.....................Isa. xxiv. 16; Isa. xli. 17, 18.
472. See.....................Luke v. 21; Isa. xliii. 25.
473. "To the wicked."..........................Isa. xlviii. 22
474. "In going astray."..........................Isa. liii. 6.
475. Yes. See..................Ez. xviii. 21, 22; Isa. lv. 7.
476. In fading.......................................Isa. lxiv. 6.
477. See.......................................Isa. lxv. 20.
478. Stork, turtle, crane and swallow..............Jer. viii. 7.
479. A linen girdle. On the banks of Euphrates..Jer. xvii. 4.
480. Pen of iron and point of diamonds ....Jer. xiii. 1.
481. The sin of Judah...........................Jer. xvii. 1.
482. See........Psalms xxxii. 16; Isa. xxx. 1; Jer. xvii. 5, 6.
483. Deceitful above all things and desperately wicked.......................................Jer. xvii. 9.
484. King Uzziah is called Azariah, 2 Kings xv. 1; Jehoahaza is quoted Shallum, 2 Kings xxiii. 31, 1 Chron. xv. 3; Solomon is called by his mother Lemuel, Prov. xxxi. 1; Jehoichin is mentioned as Coniah..2 Kings xxiv. 8, and Jer. xxii. 24.
485. To illustrate God's dealings with those of the house of Judah who had gone into captivity and with those who were left in Jerusalem. Jer. xxiv. 1, 3.

486. Four. Pharoah to be relieved of the plague, Ex. viii. 8 ; Israel to be relieved of serpents, Num. xxi. 7; Jereboam when his hand withered, 1 Kings xiii. 6; Zedekiah for deliverance..............................Jer. xxxvii. 3.
487. "Take great stones in thy hand and hide them in the clay in the brick kiln...........Jer. xliii. 9.
488. To show where Nebuchadnezzer would set up his throne in his conquest with Egypt which the prophet then foretold..................Jer. xliii. 9.
489. See...................Isa. xiii. 1, 22 ; Isa. xiv. 2 ; Jer. l.
490. See......................................Lam. iii. 27.
491. Lamentations...........................Lam. i. ii. iv. v.
492. See......................................Ezek. vii. 13.
493. See......................................Ezek. xx. 38.
494. At the death of prophet Ezekiel's wife. Ezek. xxiv. 15, 18.
495. Because the Prince of Tyre had set himself up as God and lifted up his heart in pride. Ezek. xxviii. 2.
496. Sardius, topaz, diamond, beryl, sapphire, emerald, carbuncle...................Ezek. xxviii. 13.
497. The prophet Ezekiel..................Ezek. xxxvii. 17.
498. A prophetic name of Jerusalem..........Ezek. xlviii. 35.
499. Isaiah, Jeremiah, Ezekiel and Daniel.
500. Samuel, 1 Sam. ii. 18, 26 ; Abijah, 1 Kings xiv. 1, 13 ; Obadiah, 1 Kings xviii. 12 ; Josiah, 2 Kings xxii. 1, 2 ; Solomon, David, Shadrach, Meshach and Abednego.........Dan. i. 6, 17.
501. At the dedication of the image, as representations of authority..........................Dan. iii. 2.
502. One thousand............................Dan. v. 1.
503. MENE ; God hath numbered thy kingdom and finished it. TEKEL ; weighed in the balance and found wanting. PERES ; thy kingdom is divided................................Dan. v. 26, 28.
504. Two.....................Gen. xlix. 10 ; Dan. ix. 24, 27.
505. In.......................In Jude i. 9 ; Dan. x. 13, 21.
506. And I heard but understood not.............Dan. xii. 8.
507. "They shall say to the mountains, 'Cover us,'

and to the hills, 'Fall on us.'" .... Hos. x. 8.

508. Before the great and terrible day when the Lord shall come .... Joel ii. 31.

509. See .... Amos v. 8.

510. Two. See .... Luke viii. 24 ; Jonah i. 5.

511. Six, viz.: 1st. A lot by soldiers for Christ's garment, Matt. xxvii. 35 ; 2d. A lot to select an apostle, Acts i. 26 ; 3d. A lot to find who stole the Babylonish garment, Josh. vii. 17, 25 ; 4th. A lot for the partition of the land of Canaan, Josh. xviii. 10 ; 5th. A lot between Saul and Jonathan, 1 Sam. xiv. 42, 45 ; 6th. A lot for the cause of the storm ... Jonah i. 7.

512. "Forty days and Nineveh shall be overthrown. Jonah iii. 4.

513. See. 1 Sam. xv. 35 ; Jer. xviii. 10; Amos vii. 3. Jonah iii. 10.

514. Jonah's gourd .... Jonah iv. 10.

515. In .... Micah iv. 3.

516. In .... Micah iv. 3.

517. "They shall sit every man under his vine and none shall make them afraid." .... Micah iv. 3, 7.

518. In Habakkuk .... Hab. ii. 4.

519. See .... Hab. ii. 14.

520. See .... Zech. iii. 4.

521. In .... Zech. iv. 6.

522. Twice. In .... Joel iii. 3 ; Zech. viii. 5.

523. See .... Zech. xii. 10.

524. See .... Jer. vi. 26 ; Amos viii. 10 ; Zech. xii. 10.

525. Hosea, Joel, Amos, Obadiah, Jonah, Micah, Nahum, Habukkuk, Zephaniah, Haggai, Zachariah and Malachi.

526. Isaiah the first and the last is Malachi.

527. When they gathered into the store-house ..... Mal. iii. 10.

528. 1st. The destruction of Jerusalem under the emblem of a burning oven, Mal. iv. 1 ; 2d. The manifestation of Christ under the emblem of the Son of Righteousness, Mal. iv. 2 ; 3d. The coming of John the Baptist in the spirit and power of Elijah .... Mal. iv. 5.

ANSWERS

TO

CURIOSITIES OF THE BIBLE

PERTAINING TO

NEW TESTAMENT THINGS.

1. Emmanuel (God with us)........................Matt. i. 23.
2. Birth-place of Christ..........................Matt. ii. 1.
3. Herod's death. To Joseph....................Matt. ii. 19.
4. Eternal life in Heaven.......................Matt. v. 12.
5. See..Matt. v. 35.
6. See.....................................Matt. vi. 25, 34.
7. See..Matt. x. 30.
8. "A bruised reed shall he not break and a smoking flax shall he not quench"..............Matt. xii. 20.
9. Sin against the Holy Ghost.................Matt. xii. 31.
10. Gather all nations and sever the wicked from the just.................................Matt. xiii. 41, 49.
11. Wisdom...............Job xxviii. 18; Matt. xiii. 45, 46.
12. See........................Gen. xl. 20; Matt. xiv. 6.
13. Turning water into wine...................John ii. 7, 10.
    Feeding multitudes on two occasions.
    ....Matt. xiv. 15, 21, xv. 34, 38.
14. Man's soul...............................Matt. xvi. 26.
15. Twice at the beginning of his ministry..John ii. 15, and near the close..................Matt. xxi. 12.
16. See......................................Matt. xxi. 16.
17. "Thou shalt love the Lord thy God with all thy heart, with all thy soul, and with all thy mind"..................................Matt. xxii. 37.
18. "Thou shalt love thy neighbor as thyself" .Matt. xxii. 39.

19. "All the law and the prophets" .... Matt. xxii. 40.
20. In .... Matt. xxv. 31, 46.
21. Three hours .... Matt. xxvii. 45.
22. "I am with you always" .... Matt. xxviii. 20.
23. To heal sickness and to cast out devils .... Mark iii. 15.
24. The raising of Jairus' daughter .... Mark v. 41.
25. The deaf and dumb man "Ephphatha" ..... Mark. vii. 34.
26. When rebuked for healing on the Sabbath .... Mark iii. 5.
and when blessing little children .... Mark x. 14.
27. He first appeared unto her .... Mark xvi. 9.
28. Go ye into all the world and preach the gospel unto every creature" .... Mark xvi. 15.
29. "They shall take up serpents" .... Mark xvi. 18.
30. First chapter of Luke .... Luke i.
31. To Daniel in his visions .... Dan. viii. 15.
To Zacharias .... Luke i. 12, 13.
To Mary, mother of Jesus .... Luke i. 28.
32. "My Saviour' .... Luke i. 47.
33. He asked for a writing-table .... Luke i. 63.
34. The birth of Christ .... Luke ii. 17.
35. Lead him to the top of a hill to cast him down. Luke iv. 29.
36. "I know thee who thou art, the Holy one of God" .... Luke iv. 33, 34.
37. See .... Matt. viii. 29, Mark iii. 11, Luke iv. 33, 41.
38. Earnestness, determination and patience .... Luke viii. 15.
39. Forgive us our debts .... Matt. xi. 12.
Forgive us our sins .... Luke xi. 4.
40. See .... Matt. vi. 6, Luke xi. 11.
41. In the case of Zaccheus .... Luke xix. 2.
At this point the children of Israel first entered the promised land .... Josh. v. 12, 13.
42. It was the first city taken from the Canaanites and that by a mere ceremony .... Josh. vi. 10, 20.
Here Zaccheus met Jesus and was converted. Luke xix. 1, 8.
43. See .... Matt. iv. 11, Luke xxii. 43.
44. Being in "agony" .... Luke xxii. 44.
45. On his way to Calvary. "Weep for yourselves" .... Luke xxiii. 28.

46. The crucifixion of Christ.................Luke xxiii. 33.
47. "This is Jesus, the king of the Jews" in Hebrew, Greek and Latin..................Luke xxiii. 38.
48. Law of Moses. Prophets and Psalms......Luke xxiv. 44.
49. "Darkness" comprehended it not.............John i. 5.
50. See.......................................John i. 15.
51. Cana of Galilee...........................John ii. 11.
52. "For God so loved the world that He gave," etc.......................................John iii. 16.
53. "It is located west of the Jordan." Here John baptised because by Christ there was plenty of water.....................................John iii. 23.
54. See.........................Isaiah xii. 3, John iv. 14.
55. See..John v. 7.
56. See.......................................John v. 19.
57. "Passed from death unto life"..............John v. 24.
58. See.......................................John v. 24.
59. Death.....................................John v. 24.
60. "Search the Scriptures"...................John v. 39.
61. He never compelled His followers to obey His invitation to become disciples.............John vi. 67.
62. If any man do his will....................John vii. 17.
63. See....................Matt. xxii. 46, John viii. 1, 11.
64. A sinner is the servant (slave) of sin........John viii. 34.
65. "Eternal life"............................John x. 28.
66. "I am the resurrection and the life, he that believeth on though he were dead, yet shall he live. Whosoever liveth and believeth on me shall never die"........................John ii. 25, 26.
67. Jesus wept................................John xi. 35.
68. Four. 1. The raising of Jairus' daughter...Mark v. 35, 42.
2. The son of the widow of Nain.........Luke vii. 11, 14.
3. Lazarus..............................John xi. 43, 44.
4. Christ...............................Matt. xxviii. 6.
69. See.........................John i. 45, John xii. 20, 22.
70. "If ye have, love one another"............John xiii. 35.
71. See.......................................John xvii. 3.
72. See.......................................John xvii. 15.

73. See....................................John xviii. 3, 8.
74. Three. 1st. Before Caiphas................Matt. xxvi. 57.
2d. Before the council......................Luke xxiii. 3.
3d. Before Annas..........................John xviii. 13.
75. "If I have spoken evil bear witness of the evil, but if well, why smitest thou me"....John xviii. 23.
76. David and Jesus........Psalms xxii. 18, John xix. 23, 24.
77. Eight. 1st. Eloi, Eloi, Lama. Sebachthani...Mark xv. 34.
2. "Father forgive them for they know not what they do"..........................Luke xxiii. 34.
3. "To-day thou shalt be with me in Paradise"..................................Luke xxiii. 43.
4. "Father into Thy hands I commend my spirit"..................................Luke xxiii. 46.
5. "Woman, behold thy son"..............John xix. 46.
6. "Behold thy mother"..................John xix. 27.
7. "I thirst"............................John xix. 28.
8. "It is finished"......................John xix. 30.
78. See...............John iii. 1, John vii. 50, John xix. 39.
79. Water into wine......John ii. 3, draught of fishes...................................John xxi. 6.
80. When Peter wished to know what would happen to John......................John xxi. 21, 23.
81. Because they were the witnesses of His resurrection, and a full conception of this fact was necessary for the future ages.........Acts i. 2.
82. His body unconfined by the laws of nature, he appeared, the doors being shut, and vanished from the sight of the two disciples of Emmaus, Luke xxiv. 31; John xv. 19; finally unrestrained by the laws of gravitation, rose materially into a cloud that received Him out of their sight..................................Acts i. 9.
83. On the day of Pentecost.......................Acts ii. 2.
84. On the day of Pentecost......................Acts ii. 13.
85. The death of Ananias and Sapphira for covetousness and lying..........................Acts v. 5, 10.

86. A blasphemer..........................Acts vi. 11, 15.
87. The testimony of Stephen....................Acts vii. 55.
88. Twelve as seated, Mark xiv. 62. Once as standing..................................Acts vii. 56.
89. At the stoning of Stephen....................Acts vii. 58.
90. Street which is called "Straight"............Acts ix. 11.
91. On the coast of Palestine, a seaport visited by Jonah ; the presence of the Lord, Jonah also ; the home of Dorcas and Simon, the Tanner..................................Acts ix. 36, 43.
92. Intending after Easter to bring him (Peter) forth for execution..........................Acts xii. 4.
93. 1st. The angel announcing the birth of Christ..Luke ii. 9.
2d. At St. Paul's conversion..................Acts ix. 3.
3d. Peter's deliverance from prison..........Acts xii. 7.
94. "Thou art my son, this day have I begotten thee" in the second Psalm................Acts xiii. 33.
95. When some apostles were sent to Antioch. Acts xv. 22, 23.
96. Barnabas wanted to take John with them, Paul didn't..........................Acts xv. 37, 38.
97. "Believe on the Lord Jesus Christ".........Acts xvi. 31.
98. "Thou shalt be saved"......................Acts xvi. 31.
99. St. Paul. "To the unknown God".........Acts xvii. 23.
100. "Because that Claudius Ceasar had commanded all Jews to depart from Rome........Acts xviii. 1, 2.
101. The labors of St. Paul. Here the temple of Diana, the fourth wonder of the world, was located..............................Acts xix. 17, 41.
102. "Repentance toward God"..................Acts xx. 21.
103. In his address at Jerusalem.............Acts xxii. 1, 22.
104. "I was free born"........................Acts xxii. 28.
105. "The Sadducees say there is no resurrection, neither angel nor spirit ; but the Pharisees confess both...........................Acts xxiii. 8.
106. "They would neither eat nor drink till they had killed Paul..........................Acts xxiii. 12.
107. In the case of Felix......................Acts xxiv. 25.
108. Pharisee...................................Acts xxvi. 5.

109. See....................................Acts xxvi. 18.
110. "That I may make (or ordain) thee a minister"..............................Acts xxvi. 16, 18.
111. Paul and his companions shipwrecked.....Acts xxvii. 37.
112. Melita.................................Acts xxviii. 3, 9.
113. Two years ....Acts xxviii. 30.
114. "Maketh not ashamed".....................Rom. v. 5.
115. "Love to them that love God"............Rom. viii. 28.
116. See....................................Rom. ix. 16-17.
117. Retaliation by forgiveness..................Rom. xii. 20.
118. Love....................................Rom. xiii. 10.
119. "All things"..............................1 Cor iii. 21.
120. "The best gifts"..........................1 Cor. xii. 31.
121. "Faith, Hope and Charity"...............1 Cor. xiii. 13.
122. He was seen by 500 brethren at once........1 Cor. xv. 6.
123. Ten times, namely:
   1st. The women and many others.......Matt. xxviii. 1, 9.
   2d. To Mary Magdalene.................John xx. 16, 18.
   3d. To Peter..........................Luke xxiv. 18, 34.
   4th. To the disciples on the road to Emmaus...............................Luke xxiv. 13, 18.
   5th. To the apostles without Thomas.........John xx. 24.
   6th. To the eleven......................John xx. 26, 27.
   7th. To seven of the disciples.............John xxi. 1, 2.
   8th. To the five hundred...................1 Cor. xv. 6.
   9th. To James...............................1 Cor. xv. 7.
   10th. To all the apostles at His Ascension..Mark xvi. 19, Luke xxiv. 50, Acts i. 3–12.
124. Saints, believers, disciples and brethren......1 Cor. xv. 6.
125. A moment in a twinkle of an eye...........1 Cor. xv. 52.
126. See....................................1 Cor. xv. 2.
127. Because in its pages we see the glory of God.2 Cor. iii. 18.
128. "He knew no sin"........................2 Cor. v. 21.
129. See........................1 Cor. ix. 14; Gal. vi. 6.
130. Light......................................Eph. v. 8.
131. Macedonia...............2 Cor. viii. 1, 5; Phil. iv. 15, 18.
132. Laodicea...................................Col. ii. 1.
133. He cannot sin, nor repent nor deny himself..2 Tim. ii. 13.
134. All Scripture was given by inspiration of God.......................2 Peter i. 21, 2 Tim. iii. 16.
135. See...........................John iii. 16, Titus iii. 5.

136. Ministering spirits to the heirs of salvation.....Heb. i. 14.
137. It is a discerner of the thoughts of the heart..Heb. iv. 12.
138. Over Jerusalem..........................Luke xix. 41.
At the grave of Lazarus....................John xi. 35.
In the garden at Gethsemane................Heb. v. 7.
139. The golden pot, Aaron's rod and tables of the covenant..............................Heb. ix. 4.
140. Soul, John xii. 27, Spirit, John xiii. 21, and body...................................Heb. x. 5.
141. In......................................James i. 23.
142. "Golden rule"..........................James ii. 8.
143. Read....................................James ii. 17.
144. See.....................................James iii. 7.
145. See...............1 Cor. iii. 2 ; Heb. v. 12, 1 Peter ii. 2.
146. A meek and quiet spirit...................1 Peter iii. 4.
147. "The holy commandment"...............2 Peter ii. 11.
148. See.....................................2 Peter iii. 8.
149. Second Epistle of John....................3 John i. 14.
150. Five, Obediah, Philemon 1st and 2nd John and Jude.
151. "The faith of the saints"....................Jude i. 3.
152. Which is, which was, which is to come—the Almighty....................................Rev. i. 8.
153. Pergamos where Satan dwelleth.............Rev. ii. 13.
154. That which is good.......................1 Thes. v. 21.
The form of sound words...................2 Tim. i. 13.
Our confidence............................Heb. iii. 14.
Our profession............................Heb. iv. 14.
That which we have already................Rev. ii. 25.
155. See.....................................Rev. iii. 1.
156. Sinner's repentance......................Luke xv. 10.
Satan's overthrow.........................Rev. xii. 12
157. Mary's...................................Luke i. 46
Zacharias.................................Luke i. 68, 80.
Heavenly hosts at the birth of Christ......Luke ii. 13, 14.
Song of the Lamb..........................Rev. xiv.
158. Heaven...................................Rev. xix. 9.
159. See.....................................Rev. xx. 4.
160. See.....................................Rev. xxii. 9.
161. Come....................................Rev. xxii. 17.

162. See....................................Rev. xxii. 21

163. From Evidences within itself.—All Scripture is given by inspiration of God, ...2 Tim. iii. 16 For the prophecy came not in old time by the will of man, but holy men of God spoke as they were moved by the Holy Ghost.....2 Peter i. 21.

From traditionary evidence.—It claims to be, and establishes the claim beyond all reasonable dispute.

The Jews preserved it as such; the Church has held it as such; and its own teachings, and especially its predictions, so clearly fulfilled, prove it to be the word of God.

From presumptive evidence.—It being admitted that there is a Creator, then creation implies government—and government implies *law*—man created a moral agent, it is presumed his Creator would give him a revelation, or some law or rule of action.

From positive evidence—*External.*—The antiquity of the Scriptures, as proven by the persons, who were the immediate instruments of these revelations, being contemporaneous with the events of which they wrote, also the concurring dates of the books containing the doctrines. The testimony of ancient authors (Strabo, Justin, Pliny, Tacitus, Josephus, etc.) The uncorrupted preservation of the book of Scripture as proven by the Septuagint and Josephus the Jewish historian. The credibility of the testimony of the sacred writers; they were in circumstances to know the truth and had no interest in making a good story; their interest lay in another direction.

From miracles, as those of Moses in the passage in the Red Sea, etc., and those of Christ, the greatest of which was His resurrection. From prophecies and their fulfillment, such as the prediction to Adam of the serpent and the seed of woman ; the apostacies, punishments and restoration of the Jewish nation, and upward of 100 distinct predictions concerning the birth, life, sufferings, death and resurrection of Christ. The unity that pervades the different books of the Bible, though written by different men of different ages and in different languages.

Internal.—The character and attributes of God. The divine government. The moral and beneficial tendency of the Scriptures. The style and manner of the sacred writers. The influence of the Holy Spirit. The gospel plan of salvation. The faithful promises of God as exemplified in the life and character of believers.

From collatteral evidence.—The marvellous diffusion of Christianity, especially during the first three centuries of the Christian era, when it became the established religion of the Roman Empire. The actual effort produced upon mankind.

From corroborative evidence.—Modern discoveries among the ruins of ancient Nineveh and other cities of Bible antiquity.

CURIOSITIES OF THE BIBLE.

PERTAINING TO

OLD TESTAMENT.

TIME, QUANTITY AND NUMBER.

1. Seventh day....................................Gen. ii. 2
2. One hundred and twenty.....................Gen. vi. 3
3. Three hundred cubits × 19 inches 547 feet...Gen. vi. 15.
4. Seven days..................................Gen. vii. 1, 4.
5. About one hundred years..............Gen. v. 32, vii. 6.
6. By twos..Gen. vii. 9.
7. Three hundred and seventy-four days.Gen. viii. 11, viii. 14.
8. Seven times.......................... .Gen. xviii. 23, 33.
9. Seven years for each..................Gen. xxix. 20, 28.
10. Seventeen.................................Gen. xxxvii. 2.
11. Seven years of plenty....................Gen. xli. 2, 53.
12. Seven years..................................Gen. xli. 53.
13. Seventeen years..........................Gen. xlvii. 28.
14. Forty days.......................................Gen. l. 3.
15. Three months....................................Ex. ii. 2.
16. Six sisters.....................................Ex. ii. 16.
17. Eighty years old...............................Ex. vii. 7.
18. Seven days................................Ex. vii. 19, 25.
19. Fourteenth day of the first month............Ex. xii. 6.
20. Seven days....................................Ex. xii. 15.
21. Eight in all. Passover, etc..................Ex. xii. 10.

22. Four hundred and thirty years..............Ex. xii. 40.
23. Six hundred..............................Ex. xiv. 7.
24. Three days...............................Ex. xv. 22.
25. 94,466 bushels every day, making in forty years 1,370,002,600 bnshels...................Ex. xvi. 15, 16.
26. Forty years..............................Ex. xvi. 35.
27. Six years................................Ex. xxi. 2.
28. Seven days...............................Ex. xxii. 30.
29. Six days.................................Ex. xxiv. 16.
30. Seven days...............................Ex. xxiv. 16.
31. Forty days and nights....................Ex. xxiv. 18.
32. Seven days...............................Ex. xxix. 30.
33. Three thousand...........................Ex. xxxii. 28.
34. Eighty days and nights......Ex. xxiv. 18, Ex. xxxiv. 28.
35. Seven times..............................Lev. xiv. 7.
36. Five years...............................Lev. xix. 25.
37. On the first day of the seventh month......Lev. xxiii. 24.
38. Seven days...............................Lev. xxiii. 34.
39. Seven days...............................Lev. xxiii. 36.
40. Every fiftieth year......................Lev. xxv. 10.
41. They ate of the superabundance of the sixth year..............................Lev. xxv. 20, 22.
42. At fifty years of age....................Num. viii. 25.
43. Seventy..................................Num. xi 16.
44. Three feet deep..........................Nnm. xi. 31.
45. Seven years..............................Num. xiii. 22.
46. Forty days...............................Num. xiii. 25.
47. Two hundred and fifty men................Num. xvi. 35.
48. Seven days...............................Num. xix. 11.
49. Seven of each........................Num. xxiii. 29, 30.
50. Twenty-four thousand.....................Num. xxv. 9.
51. One thousand.............................Num. xxxi. 4.
52. Seven nations............................Deut. vii. 1.
53. Twice.............Ex. xxiv. 18, xxxiv. 28, Deut. ix. 18.
54. From the time they began to put the sickle to the corn.................................Deut. xvi. 9.
55. After they had gathered in the corn and the wine.....................................Deut. xvi. 13.

56. Two or three.............................Deut. xix. 15.
57. One year.................................Deut. xxiv. 5.
58. Seven ways.............................Deut. xxviii. 7.
59. Thirty days.............................Deut. xxxiv. 8.
60. Forty.........................Ex. xvi. 35, Josh. v. 6.
61. Seven.....................................Josh. vi. 4.
62. Thirteen..................................Josh. vi. 18.
63. About a whole day........................Josh. x. 13.
64. Five. Kings of Hebron, Jarmeath, Jerusalem,
Sachist and Eglon.........................Josh. x. 23.
65. Thirty-one..............................Josh. xii. 1, 24.
66. Three men..............................Josh. xviii. 2, 4.
67. Six.......................................Josh. xx. 7, 8.
68. Forty-eight...............................Josh. xxi. 41.
69. Eighteen years..........................Judges iii. 14.
70. Nine hundred chariots of iron..............Judges iv. 13.
71. Seven years...............................Judges vi. 1.
72. Eighteen years.............................Judges x. 8.
73. Forty-two thousand........................Judges xii. 6.
74. Seven years...............................Judges xii. 9.
75. Forty years...............................Judges xiii. 1.
76. Seven days..............................Judges xiv. 12.
77. One thousand............................Judges xv. 15.
78. Seven....................................Judges xvi. 8.
79. Three thousand..........................Judges xvi. 27.
80. Seven hundred...........................Judges xx. 16.
81. Thirty thousand.........................1 Sam. iv. 10.
82. Ninety-eight...........................1 Sam. iv. 15, 18.
83. Seven months..............................1 Sam. vi. 1.
84. Two oxen on a new cart....................1 Sam. vi. 7.
85. One year and four months...............1 Sam. xxvii. 7.
86. Seven and six months.....................2 Sam. ii. 11.
87. Seventy years old..........................2 Sam. v. 4.
88. Three months.............................2 Sam. vi. 11.
89. Seven hundred............................2 Sam. viii. 4.
90. Forty thousand............................2 Sam. x. 18
91. On the seventh day.......................2 Sam. xii. 18.
92. Two hundred shekels weight...............2 Sam. xiv. 26.

93. Three days..............................2 Sam. xxiv. 13.
94. Twelve thousand.........................1 Kings iv. 26.
95. Seven years.............................1 Kings vi. 38.
96. Thirteen years..........................1 Kings vii. 1.
97. Seven days and seven days more..........1 Kings viii. 65.
98. Six hundred and sixty-six talents valued at $56,000 each...........................1 Kings x. 14.
99. A cloud about the size of a man's hand..1 Kings xviii. 44.
100. One hundred thousand footmen..........I Kings xx. 29.
101. Twenty-seven thousand men.............1 Kings xx. 30.
102. One hundred thousand lambs and rams with the wool.............................2 Kings iii. 4.
103. Seven days............................2 Kings iii. 9.
104. Seven times...........................2 Kings iv. 35.
105. Seven times...........................2 Kings v. 10.
106. Two talents of silver and two changes of garments...............................2 Kings v. 23.
107. Eighty pieces of silver ($45)..........2 Kings vi. 25.
108. Four..................................2 Kings vii. 3.
109. Seven years...........................2 Kings xi. 21.
110. Two....................Judges ix. 8, 15 ; 2 Kings xiv. 9.
111. Fifteen years.........................2 Kings xx. 6.
112. Ten degrees...........................2 Kings xx. 11
113. Three day's pestilence in which seventy thousand died........2 Sam. xxiv. 15, 1 Chron. xxi. 14.
114. Six hundred shekels of gold...........1 Chron. xxi. 25.
115. One hundred thousand talents of gold and one hundred thousand talents of silver..1 Chron. xxii. 14.
116. Four thousand.........................1 Chron. xxiii. 5.
117. Three thousand six hundred............2 Chron. ii. 2.
118. One hundred and fifty-three thousand six hundred..............................2 Chron. ii. 17.
119. Seven days and the feast seven days......2 Chron. vii. 9.
120. Four thousand.........................2 Chron. ix. 25.
121. Five hundred thousand men.............2 Chron. xiii. 17.
122. Seven hundred oxen, seven thousand sheep.................................2 Chron. xv. 11.

123. Seven thousand seven hundred rams and the same number of he-goats.........2 Chron. xvii. 11.
124. Six years (Joash)......................2 Chron. xxii. 12.
125. Seven of each.........................2 Chron. xxix. 21.
126. Seven thousand........................2 Chron. xxx. 24.
127. Seven days...................................Ez. vi. 22.
128. Fifty-two....................................Neh. vi. 15.
129. Seven days.............................Neh. viii. 17, 18.
130. Half a shekel before Ex. xxx. 13 ; a third of a shekel afterward......................Neh. x. 32.
131. At King Ahasuerus royal feast lasting seven days...Esth. i. 5.
132. Seven maidens..............................Esth. ii. 9.
133. Ten thousand talents of silver...............Esth. iii. 9.
134. Ten sons....................................Esth. ix. 14.
135. Three thousand camels..........................Job. i. 3.
136. Ten children ....Job i. 2, 18.
137. Seven days and nights.......................Job ii. 13.
138. One hundred and forty years..............Job. xlii. 16.
139. Pure as silver tried seven times in a furnace....Ps. xii. 6.
140. Seven times a day........................Ps. cxix. 164.
141. Six things............................Prov. vi. 16, 19.
142. Seven times as much.......................Prov. vi. 31.
143. Seven pillars................................Prov. ix. 1.
144. As seven men who can render a reason...Prov. xxvi. 16.
145. Seven or eight...............................Ec. xi. 2.
146. The moon shall be as light as the sun, and the light of the sun shall be seven-fold the light of seven days..............................Isa. xxx. 26.
147. Seventy years..............................Jer. xxv. 11.
148. He would punish him and make his country a perpetual desolation.......................Jer. xxv. 12.
149. For seven days...............................Ez. iii. 15.
150. They went up into it by seven steps...........Ez. xl. 22.
151. It was seven cubits broad......................Ez. xli. 3.
152. Seven years............................Dan. iv. 16, 32.
153. One thousand.................................Dan. v. 1.
154. For thirty days..............................Dan. vi. 7.

155. Seventy weeks.................................Dan. ix. 24.
156. Two....................Gen. xlix. 10, Dan. ix. 24, 27.
157. Forty days....................................Jon. iii. 4.
158. One hundred and twenty thousand...........Jon. iv. 11.
159. Three times............Isa. ii. 4, Joel iii. 10, Micah iv. 3.
160. Seven lamps and seven pipes.................Zech. iv. 2.
161. Fourteen Books are mentioned in the Bible but not included in it, namely :

1. The Book of the Wars of the Lord.......Num. xxi. 14.
2. " " " Jaster........................Josh. x. 13.
3. " " " Samuel, the Seer......1 Chron. xxix. 29.
4. " " " Nathan, the Prophet..." " xxix. 29.
5. " " " Gad, the Seer..........." " xxix. 29.
6. " " " Abijah, the Shilomite......2 " ix. 28.
7. " " " the visions of Iddo, the Seer" " ix. 29.
8. " " " the kings of Judah and Israel " xii. 15.
9. " " " Shemaiah, the Prophet........" xii. 15.
10. " " " Iddo, the Seer, concerning genealogies........................" xii. 15.
11. " " story of the prophet and Iddo...." xiii. 22.
12. " " Jehu, son of Hanini............." xx. 34.
13. " " the Acts of Uzziah, written by Isaiah, the Prophet..............2 Chron. xxvi. 22.
14. " " the visions of Isaiah, the Prophet................2 Chron. xxxii. 32.

162. Each of the following Eight Verses contain all of the letters of the Alphabet but one.

1. Joshua vii. 24..............................all except Q
2. 1 Kings i. 9............................ " " Q
3. 2 Kings xvi. 15.......................... " " X
4. 1 Chron. xii. 40......................... " " Q
5. Ezra vii. 21............................. " " J
6. Ezekiel xxviii. 13....................... " " Q
7. Daniel iv. 37............................ " " Q
8. Gal. i. 14............................... " " K

ANSWERS

TO

CURIOSITIES OF THE BIBLE.

PERTAINING TO

NEW TESTAMENT.

TIME, QUANTITY AND NUMBER.

1. Six petitions..............................Matt. vi. 9, 13.
2. Seven baskets..............................Matt. xv. 37.
3. Seven times..............................Matt. xviii. 21.
4. Seventy times seven (490)..............Matt. xviii. 22.
5. At the judgment. See................Matt. xxv. 31, 32.
6. Three hours..............................Matt. xxvii. 45.
7. Two thousand..............................Mark v. 13.
8. Six hours..............................Mark xv. 25, 34.
9. Seven years..............................Luke ii. 36.
10. Three years and six months..............Luke iv. 25.
11. A certain king drew a bow at a venture. 11 Chron. xviii. 33.
    By chance there came a priest that way and
    passed by on the other side..............Luke x. 31.
12. Thirty-one..............................Luke xv. 3.
13. Three, viz: Annas, John xviii. 13; Caiaphas,
    Matt. xxvi. 57; Pilate..............Luke xxiii. 3.
14. Forty-six years..............................John ii. 20.
15. Twelve baskets..............................John vi. 13.
16. Two persons..............................John viii. 17.
17. Nine, viz:
    1. Dorcas by Peter..............................Acts ix. 37–41
    2. Eutychus by Paul ....Acts xx. 9–12

3. The widow's son by Elijah.........1 Kings xvii. 17, 24.
4. The Shunammite's son by Elisha.....2 Kings iv. 33, 36.
5. The man who touched the bones of Elisha. 2 Kings xiii. 21.
6. Christ's resurrection..................Matt. xxviii. 7.
7. Jairus' daughter.......................Mark v. 35, 42.
8. The son of the widow of Nain........ Luke vii. 11, 14.
9. Lazarus...........................John xi. 43, 44.

18. Five: each hand, and foot and side.........John xix. 34.
19. Four: Man's fall, Christ's agony, burial and resurrection...............................John. xix. 41.
20. One hundred and fifty-three...............John xxi. 11.
21. Forty days.....................................Acts i. 3.
22. One hundred and twenty....................Acts i. 15.
23. Three thousand...............................Acts ii. 41.
24. Five thousand ....Acts iv. 4.
25. Above forty years old........................Acts iv. 22.
26. Seven..Acts vi. 5.
27. Forty years old...............................Acts vii. 23,
28. Forty years old...........................Acts vii. 29, 30.
29. He is represented as seated thirteen times. See Mark xiv. 62. Once as standing...........Acts vii. 56.
30. Seven, viz:
    1. A blasphemer,..........................Lev. xxiv. 23.
    2. A man gathering sticks..............Num. xv. 32, 36.
    3. Achan........ ....Joshua vii. 25.
    4. Adoram.............................1 Kings xii. 18.
    5. Naboth.................................1 Kings xxi. 13.
    6. Zechariah...........................2 Chron. xxiv. 21.
    7. Stephen...........................Acts vii. 58, 60.
31. Three days...................................Acts ix. 9.
32. Peter, three times...........................Acts x. 16.
33. Four hundred and fifty years...............Acts xiii. 20.
34. Nine, viz:
    1. Joseph, butler and baker......................Gen. lx
    2. Samson..............................Judges xvi. 21.
    3. Jeremiah............................Jer. xxxix. 15.
    4. Zedekiah................................Jer. lii. 11.
    5. Jehoiachin...............................Jer. lii. 31.

6. John the Baptist.. ....Luke iii. 20.
7. The apostles.......... ....Acts v. 18.
8. Peter...Acts xii. 6.
9. Paul and Silas............................Acts xvi. 24.

35. Fifty thousand pieces of silver ....Acts xix. 19.
36. Seven days.................................Acts xx. 6.
37. Four thousand.............................Acts xxi. 38.
38. Forty..Acts xxiii. 13.
39. Four hundred and seventy men............Acts xxiii. 23.
40. Paul and his 276 companions..........Acts xxvii. 34, 40.
41. Seven days..................................Acts xxviii. 14.
42. Two whole years............... ....Acts xxviii. 30.
43. Eleven times, viz. :

1. To the Marys.........................Matt. xxviii. 1, 9.
2. To Mary Magdalene......................John xx. 16.
3. To Simon.................................Luke xxiv. 34.
4. To two disciples going to Emmaus.......Luke xxiv. 13.
5. To the disciples, Thomas absent...........John xx. 19.
6. To the disciples with Thomas present......John xx. 26.
7. To seven disciples at Sea of Tiberias......John xxi. 1, 2.
8. To the Eleven and probably to five hundred.......... ....Matt. xxviii. 16, 1 Cor. xv. 6.
9. To James.................................1 Cor. xv. 7.
10. To the apostles at Jerusalem..................Acts i. 4.
11. To Paul on his way to Damascus............Acts ix. 4.

44. A moment.....................................1 Cor. xv. 52.
45. Five times, 195 stripes....................11 Cor. xi. 24.
46. Arabia three years............................Gal. i. 18.
47. Seven times, viz. :

1. At the creation............................ ..Gen. ii. 2.
2. In the wilderness..........................Ex. xvi. 29.
3. In the fourth commandment................Ex. xx. 10.
4. In the Sabbath of the seven years........Lev. xxv. 4.
5. In the year of Jubilee.................Lev. xxiv. 8, 15.
6. In the land of captivity............2 Chron. xxxvi. 21.
7. The prophetic sabbath of the world, Psalms xcv. 11.............................Heb. iv. 9.

48. Seven seals.. ....Rev. v. 1, 9.

49. Half an hour. When the seventh seal was opened............................... ...Rev. viii. 1.
50. Seven thousand men..........................Rev. xi. 13.
51. One hundred and forty four thousand........Rev. xiv. 3.
52. A talent......................................Rev. xvi. 21.
53. One hour................................Rev. xviii, 19.
54. For one thousand years......................Rev. xx .2.
55. Twelve gates, the names of the twelve tribes of Israel........................... ....Rev. xxi. 12.
56. Twelve thousand furlongs..................Rev. xxi. 16.
57. 1930 years....... ... .Bible chronology.

ANSWERS

TO

CURIOSITIES OF THE BIBLE.

PERTAINING TO

OCCUPATIONS.

1. Tubal Cain, Gen. iv. 22 ; Bezaleel, Ex. xxxi. 2;
   Hiram.............................1 Kings vii. 13.
2. Agur, Prov. xxx. 1 ; Lemuel.............Prov. xxxi. 1.
3. Lazarus..............................Luke xvi. 20.
4. Clement..............................Phil. iv. 3.
5. Noah.................................Gen. vi. 14.
6. Cain.................................Gen. iv. 17.
7. Phichol, Gen. xxi. 22 ; Nahshon, Num. i. 7 ;
   Johanan..............................Jer. xli. 11, 16.
8. Joseph, Matt. xiii. 55 ; Jesus... ....Mark vi. 3.
9. Cornelius............................Acts x. 1.
10. Bigthan, Esther ii. 21 ; Blastus, Acts xii. 20 ;
    Erastus.............................Rom. xvi. 23.
11. Crispus.............................Acts xviii. 8.
12. Ahijah ....1 Kings iv. 3.
13. Benaiah............................2 Sam. viii. 18.
14. Alexander..........................2 Tim. iv. 14.
15. Ahithophel, 2 Sam. xv. 12 ; Zechariah...2 Chron. xxvi. 5.
16. Rab-shakeh, 2 Kings xviii. 17 ; Nehemiah....Neh. i. 111.
17. Prochorus, Acts vi. 5 ; Philip, vi. 5 ; Nicanor...Acts vi. 5.
18. Ehud, Judges iii. 15 ; Barak...............Judges iv. 6.
19. Jeduthun...........................1 Chron. xvi. 41.
20. Gamaliel...........................Acts v. 34, 40.
21. Joseph.............................Gen. xliv. 5.
22. Augustus Cæsar, Luke ii. 1 ; Claudius Cæsar..Acts xviii. 2.

23. Matthew, Matt. x. 3 ; .... Luke, Col. iv. 14.
24. Balaam .... Num. xxii. 5.
25. Zebedee and others .... Mark i. 19.
26. Ishmael .... Gen. xxi. 18.
27. Gideon, Judges viii ; Sisera, Judges iv. 7 ;
Amasai .... 1 Chron. xii. 18.
28. Harhaiah .... Neh. iii. 8.
29. Zebul, Jud. ix. 28; Gedaliah, 2 K. 25, 22 ; Pilate. Luke 23, 6.
30. Lot, Gen. xii. 5 ; Nabal, 1 Sam. xxv. 23 ;
Shaphat .... 1 Chron. xxvii. 29.
31. Philetus .... 2 Tim. ii. 17.
32. Nimrod .... Gen. x. 8.
33. Jubal .... Gen. iv. 21.
34. Shamgar .... Judges iii. 31 ; Jephthah, Judges xi. 12.
35. Zenas .... Titus iii. 13.
36. Joshua .... Num. xiv. 6.
37. Barak .... Judges iv. 6.
38. Asaph .... 1 Chron. xvi. 5 ; David, 1 Sam. xvi. 23.
39. Ethan .... 1 Chron. vi. 44.
40. Jambres, Jannes .... 2 Tim. iii. 8.
41. Lucius .... Rom. xvi. 21 ; Manaen, Acts xiii. 1.
42. Shammah .... 2 Sam. xxiii. 11.
43. Potiphar.... Gen. xxxvii. 36 ; Joash, 1 Kings xxii. 26.
44. Tertullus .... Acts xxiv. 1.
45. Luke .... Col. iv. 14.
46. Daniel .... Dan. vi. 2.
47. Caleb .... Num. xxxiv. 19.
48. Huldah .... 2 Kings xxii. 14 ; Anna, Luke ii. 36.
49. Gallio .... Acts xviii. 12.
50. Asaph .... 2 Kings xviii. 18.
51. Barabbas .... Matt. xxvii. 16.
52. Hananiah .... Jer. xxviii. 10 ; NicodemusJohn iii. 1.
53. Lydia .... Acts xvi. 14.
54. Jehoshaphat .... 2 Sam. viii. 16.
55. Gad. .... 1 Sam. xxii. 5 ; Iddo, 2 Chron. ix. 29.
56. Gehazi .... 2 Kings v. 20.
57. Shaphan .... 2 Kings xxii. 12 ; Ezra, Ezra. vii. 6.
58. Abel, Gen. iv. 2 ; David .... 1 Sam. xvi. 19.

59. Heman................................1 Chron. vi. 33.
60. Onesimus..............................Philem i. 10.
61. Asahel.................................2 Sam. ii. 18.
62. Simon...................................Acts viii. 9.
63. Ziba, 2 Sam. ix. 2 ; Shebna.................Isa. xxii. 15.
64. Simon...................................Acts. ix. 43.
65. Zaccheus, Luke xix. 2 ; Matthew.............Matt. x. 3.
66. Judas..................Acts v. 37 ; Syntyche Phil. iv. 2.
67. Aquila, Acts xviii. 3 ; Paul.................Acts xviii. 3.
68. Archelaus...............Matt. ii. 22 ; Herod, Matt. ii. 22.
69. Cain.....................................Gen. iv. 2.
70. Adonijah.................................1 Kings i. 5.
71. Gad..............................1 Chron. xxix. 29.
72. Simon Magnus........Acts viii. 9, Bar Jesus, Acts xiii. 6.

ANSWERS TO BIBLE MATHEMATICS.

1. *Addition.*—Add to your faith, virtue; and to virtue, knowledge; and to knowledge, temperance; and to temperance, patience; and to patience, godliness; and to godliness, brotherly kindness; and to brotherly kindness, love.—2 Peter i. 5, 8.

If these things be in you and abound, they will make you neither barren nor unfruitful in the knowledge of our Lord Jesus Christ.—2 Pet. i. 8.

2. *Subtraction.*—He that lacketh these things is blind, and cannot see afar off, and hath forgotten that he was purged from his old sins.—2 Peter. i. 9.

3. *Multiplication.*—Grace and peace be multiplied unto you through the knowledge of God and of Jesus our Lord.–2 Peter i.2

He that ministereth seed to the sower both minister bread for your own food, and multiply your seed sown and increase the fruits of your righteousness.—2 Cor. ix. 10.

4. *Division.*—Come out from among them and be ye separate, saith the Lord, and touch not the unclean thing; and I will receive you, and will be a father unto you, and ye shall be my sons and daughters, saith the Lord Almighty.—2 Cor. vi. 17, 18.

ANSWERS

TO

CURIOSITIES OF THE BIBLE

INVOLVING ARITHMETICAL CALCULATIONS IN THEIR SOLUTION.

1. **12** sons Jacob had × .... Gen. xxxv. 22
7 times the Israelites compassed Jericho + ... Josh. vi. 42.
6 measures of barley Boaz gave Ruth ÷ ...... Ruth iii. 15.
10 sons Haman had — .... Esther ix. 10.
2 of each kind unclean beasts entered the ark × . Gen. vii. 9.
50 men went to seek Elijah — .... 2 Kings ii. 16.
30 years old Joseph before Pharoah ÷ ... . Gen. xli. 46.
5 stones David selected to meet Goliath — .. 1 Sam. xvii. 40.
15 furlongs distant Bethany was × .... John xi. 18.
4 anchors they cast out — .... Acts xxvii. 29.
8 persons were saved in the ark .. Gen. viii. 18 ; 2 Pet. ii. 5.
The number of scholars, 188.

2. **3000** camels Job had ÷ .... Job i. 3.
30 men were sent to take Jeremiah + ... Jer. xxxviii. 10.
1000 lords Belshazzar entertained — .... Dan. vii. 1.
10 righteous not found in Sodom × .... Gen. xviii. 32.
30 years of age David began to reign at ÷ ...... 2 Sam. v. 4.
300 in Gideon's band + ... Judges vii. 8.
1000 Philistines Samson slew with a jaw-bone—. Judges xv. 16.
1005 Solomon's songs numbered × .... 1 Kings iv. 32.
7 days Job's friends tarried in silence — .... Job ii. 13.
153 in the miraculous draft of fishes .... John xxi. 2.
The number of sheep, 575.

3. 666 talents of gold presented to Solomon ÷ ...1 Kings x. 14.
3 shekels,—(the temple tax)—9 times × ....Neh. x. 32.
30 pieces of silver Christ was betrayed with —. Matt. xxvi. 15.
4000 singers were in the temple jubilee + ...1 Chron. xxiii. v.
100 prophets were hid in a cave × ....1 Kings xviii. 4.
70 years Israel was in captivity..............Jer. xxv. 12.
Total cost $96,600. ÷
300 cubits long was Noah's Ark — ....Gen. vi. 15.
88 children Rehoboam had + ...2 Chron. ix. 21.
276 persons suffered shipwreck with Paul ÷ ..Acts xxvii. 37.
6 1-4 fingers and toes × ....2 Sam. xxi. 20.
7 years in building Solomon's temple + ...1 Kings vi. 38.
30 feet high was Solomon's Temple..........1 Kings vi. 2.
The height of spire 138 feet.

4. 70 years, "three score and ten" ÷...............Ps. xc. 10.
7 withs that bound Samson × ....Judges xvi. 7.
6 cubits the height of Goliath + ...1 Sam. xvii. 4.
1000 oxen that Job had + ...Job. xii. 12.
3000 men that bound Samson + ...Judges xv. 11.
430 years Israel was in Egypt — ....Ex. xii. 40.
18 letters, Maher-shalal-hash-baz — ....Isa. viii. 1.
70 years Tyre should be forgotten + ...Isa. xxiii. 15.
4000 murderers in the wilderness — ....Acts xxi. 38.
7000 talents of silver overlaid the walls ÷ ...1 Chron. xxix. 4.
2 disciples "two by two" — ....Mark vi. 7.
490 times, forgiven "seventy times seven" + ..Mark xviii. 2.
5 bleeding wounds ÷..........Ps. xxii. 16, John xix. 34.
4 lepers at the gates.....................2 Kings vii. 3. =
His age, 54 years; 27 years in the ministry.

ANSWERS

TO

CURIOSITIES OF THE BIBLE.

PERTAINING TO

QUOTATIONS.

1. God to Noah........................Gen. vi. 5 ; viii. 21.
2. God to Noah and his sons..................Gen. ix. 6.
3. Abraham to God..........Deut. xxxii. 4 ; Gen. xviii. 25.
4. Moses to God..............................Ex. xv. 11.
5. By Moses.................................Ex. xxi. 24.
6. Moses to the Israelites..................Ex. xxiii. 2.
7. God to Moses.........................Lev. xix. 18, 34.
8. God to the Hebrews......................Lev. xix. 32.
9. Balaam to Balak........................Num. xxiii. 10.
10. Moses to the Reubenites and Gadites.....Num. xxxii. 23.
11. Moses to the Israelites....................Dent. x. 12.
12. God to Zion, Zech. ii. 8 ; Moses to Hebrews, Deut. xxxii. 10.
13. Moses to Asher.......................Deut. xxxiii. 25.
14. God......................................1 Sam. ii. 30.
15. Samuel to Saul.........................1 Sam. xiii. 14.
16. The Lord to Samuel......................1 Sam. xvi. 7.
17. David's Soliloquy.........................2 Sam. i. 23.
18. Nathan to David...........................2 Sam. xii. 7.
19. Queen of Sheba to Solomon..............1 Kings x. 7.
20. The sons of the Prophets to Elisha.........2 Kings iv. 40.
21. Job to his wife................................Job ii. 10.

22. Job to his friends.............................Job. v. 7.
23. Bildad to Job.............................Job viii. 9.
24. Job to Zophar.............................Job xii. 2.
25. Job to his friends.........................Job. xiii. 15.
26. Job.............................Job. xvii. 9.
27. David to God.............................Ps. xxiii. 1.
28. Job.............................Job xix. 20.
29. David.............................Ps. xxxiii. 17.
30. David.............................Ps. xxxvii. 35.
31. David.............................Ps. lv. 6.
32. David.............................Ps. ciii. 12.
33. David.............................Ps. cvi. 48.
34. David.............................Ps. cxxxvii. 2.
35. Solomon.............................Prov. xii. 10.
36. Solomon.............................Prov. xiii. 15.
37. Solomon.............................Prov. xiv. 10.
38. Solomon.............................Prov. xv. 1.
39. Solomon.............................Prov. xv. 13.
40. Solomon.............................Prov. xvi. 31.
41. Solomon.............................Prov. xvi. 32.
42. Solomon.............................Prov. xvii. 24.
43. Solomon.............................Prov. xvii. 28.
44. Solomon.............................Prov. xix. 14.
45. Solomon.............................Prov. xxi. 14.
46. Solomon.............................Prov. xxii. 1.
47. Solomon.............................Prov. xxii. 7.
48. Solomon.............................Prov. xxii. 29.
49. Solomon.............................Prov. xxiii. 2.
50. Solomon.............................Prov. xxiii. 5.
51. Solomon.............................Prov. xxv. 22.
52. Solomon.............................Prov. xxvi. 4.
53. Solomon.............................Prov. xxvii. 2.
54. Solomon.............................Prov. xxvii. 6.
55. Solomon.............................Prov. xxvii. 6.
56. Solomon.............................Prov. xxviii. 13.
57. Solomon.............................Prov. xxix. 1.
58. Solomon.............................Prov. xxix. 25.
59. Agur.............................Prov. xxx. 8.

60. Solomon.................................Eccl. i. 9.
61. Solomon.................................Eccl. iii. 1.
62. Solomon.................................Eccl. v. 5.
63. Solomon.................................Eccl. xii. 12.
64. Isaiah.................................Isa. xxii. 13.
65. Isaiah.................................Isa. xxix. 21.
66. Isaiah.................................Isa. xxx. 7, 15.
67. Isaiah to the Jews.................................Isa. li. 20.
68. Jeremiah to the Jews .... Jer. viii. 11.
69. God to Jeremiah.................................Jer. xiii. 23.
70. Jeremiah to the Israelites.................................Jer. xvii. 5.
71. Jeremiah.................................Jer. xvii. 9.
72. Jeremiah.................................Jer. xxiii. 10.
73. God to Hosea.................................Hosea iv. 17.
74. God to Amos.................................Amos iii. 3.
75. Angel to Zerubbabel.................................Zech. iv. 6.
76. Jesus to the multitude.................................Matt. vi. 29.
77. Jesus to his disciples.................................Matt. vii. 6.
78. Jesus to Peter.................................Matt. xvi. 23.
79. Jesus.................................Acts xx. 35.
80. Paul to Corinthians.................................1 Cor. i. 21.
81. Paul to Corinthians.................................1 Cor. xv. 33.
82. Paul to Ephesians.................................Eph. iv. 26
83. Paul to Thessalonians.................................1 Thes. v. 21
84. Paul to Timothy.................................1 Tim. vi. 6.
85. James.................................James ii. 18.
86. James.................................James iii. 5.
87. Peter.................................1 Peter iv. 8,
88. Peter.................................2 Peter iii. 11.
89. John.................................1 John iv. 18
90. Jude.................................Jude i. 14
91. Spirit to John.................................Rev. ii. 10,
92. John to the Elder.................................Rev. vii. 17.
93. Spirit and Bride to John.................................Rev. xxii. 17.

ANSWERS

TO

BIBLE SCENES

FROM THE BOOK OF RUTH.

1. Moab.......... ....Ruth i. 1.
2. Elimelech and his family......................Ruth i. 2.
3. Bethlehem.....................................Ruth i. 2.
4. Elimelech—Naomi...............................Ruth i. 3.
5. Orpah and Ruth................................Ruth i. 4.
6. Naomi, Orpah and Ruth....... ....Ruth i. 6.
7. Naomi and Ruth—Orpah.....................Ruth i. 16.
8. Ruth................................ ....Ruth i. 22.
9. Ruth...Ruth ii. 3.
10. Fields of Boaz...............................Ruth ii. 4.
11. Boaz and Ruth.......................... Ruth iv. 10.
12. Obed... ....Ruth iv. 16.
13. David and Christ..........................Ruth iv. 22.

THE TEN COMMANDMENTS IN RHYME.

I. Adore one God—none else can reign ;
II. And take not thou his name in vain.
III. Keep holy thou the Sabbath day,
IV. Thy parents honor and obey.
V. Thou shall not kill or angry be.
VI. Commit not thou adultery.
VII. To steal no neighbor's goods take care,
VIII. Against him no false witness bear.
IX. Covet not thy neighbor's wife
X. Or goods—and thou shalt enter life......Ex. xx. 3, 17.

THE NEW COMMANDMENT.

A New Commandment I Give Unto You, that Ye Love One Another, as I have loved you. —*John xiii.* 34.

ANSWERS

TO

CURIOSITIES OF THE BIBLE

PERTAINING TO

METAPHORS OF GOD'S WORD.

A.

1. Adder. Because (1st) it is often *deaf*, Ps. lviii. 4. (2nd) It is *poisonous*, Ps. cxl. 3. (3rd) It *stings*, Prov. xxiii. 32. Note—It stings our concience, Rom. ii. 15 ; and it stings to death, Jas. i. 15; 1 Cor. xv. 56. (4th) It is to be *trodden under foot*, Ps. xci. 13. Hence Gen. iii. 15 ; Rom. xvi. 20.
2. Advocate. 1 John ii. 1 ; because he is a mediator between the judge and the prisoner, 1 Tim. ii. 5.
3. Anchor. This is made an emblem of hope, because (1st) *It fastens itself on something out of sight*, Heb. vi. 19 ; and (2nd) *It stays the ship in u storm*, Acts 27, 29.
4. Ants. Used metaphorically of *industry*, in Prov. vi. 6 ; of *forethought*, in Prov. xxx. 25 ; and of *individual responsibility*, in Prov. vi. 7, 8.
5. Ashes. Metaphorical of *frailty* Gen. xviii. 27 ; because worthless, and the remains of something better ; of *humiliation*, in Esther iv. 1 ; Isa. lxi. 3 ; of *sin* in xliv. 20. because unsatisfying, and miserable to the taste.
6. Awaking. Used of *repentance* Rom. xiii. 11 ; Eph. v. 14 of *resurrection* Job. xiv. 12 ; John ; xi. 11 ; Dan. xii. 2

B.

7. Babes. 1 Pet. ii. 2. (1st) They are *free from pride and malice*, Mark x. 14, 15. (2nd) They *partake of the nature of their father*, John iii. 6. (3rd) *They grow as they advance in years*, 2 Pet. iii. 18.

8. Blindness. 2 Cor. iv. 4; Eph. iv. 18.
9. Bulls. In Ps. xxii. 12, 13; Isa. xxxiv. 7. Bears, in Prov. xxviii. 15; Boars, in Ps. lxxx. 13; Bees, in Ps. cxviii. 12; Birds, in Rev. xviii. 2.
10. Beam, in contrast with *Mote*, Matt. vii. 3, 4.
11. Bridegroom, Matt. xxv. 5, 6. Bishop. 1 Pet. ii. 25. Bread. John vi. 48.
12. Brooks. Used metaphorically of *wisdom* Prov. xviii. 4; *prosperity*, Job xx. 17: *consolation* Ps. xlii. 1, cx. 7.
13. Balances. Dan. v. 27.

C.

14. Crown. Used for *immortal life* in Jas. i. 12; Rev. ii. 10: for *eternal glory* in 1 Pet. v. 4: and for *heavenly purity* in 2 Tim. iv. 8.
15. Candle. Signifies the *soul of man*, Prov. xx. 27: the *favor of God*, Job xxix. 3: and *spiritual gifts*, Matt. v. 15.
16. Cover. (*verb*). Used for *protecting* in Ps. xci. 4; and for *pardoning* in Ps. xxxii. 1.
17. Cord. Is associated with *death* in Eccles. xii. 6; *ruin* in Jer. x. 20: *strength* in Eccles. iv. 12; *enlargement* in Isa. liv. 2; *love* in Hos. xi. 4; *affliction* in Job. xxx. 11. and xxxvi. 8; *sin* in Prov. v. 22 and Isa. v. 18.
18. Cedar. It denotes a *king*. 2 Kings xiv. 9; an *empire* Ezek. xxxi. 3: the *faithful people of God*, Ps. xcii. 12.
19. Chaff. Used of *false doctrine*, Jer. xxiii. 28; and of the *destruction of the wicked* in Ps. i. 4.; Isa. v 24.

D.

20. Dogs. Ps. xxii, 16; Matt. xv. 26. This methaphor possesses its forces from the contempt in which dogs are held in Eastern towns:—(1) Dogs *snarl and gnash with their teeth.* So the wicked, Ps. xxxvii. 12. (2) Dogs have to be *shut out of doors.* So the wicked from heaven, Rev. xxii. 15. (3) Dogs are *greedy* and *dissatisfied.* So are the wicked, Isa. lvi. 11. (4) Dogs are *foolish*, Prov. xxvi. 11. (5) Dogs are *to be avoided*, Phil. iii. 2.
21. Dew. Ps. cx. 3; Hos. vi. 4. Distil. Deut. xxxii. 2. Draw. Isa. xii. 3. Drown. 1. Tim. vi. 9. Drop. Ps. lxv.

11 ; Ezek. xx. 46 ; Prov. xix. 13. DRINK. Job xv. 16. DROUGHT. Isa. lviii. 11. DITCH. Job ix. 31. DEEP. Ps. xlii. 7 ; or DEPTHS. Mic. vii. 19.

22. DARKNESS. Used for *sorrow*, Joel ii. 2 ; *death*, Job x. 21, 22 ; *secrecy*, Matt. x. 27 ; *sin*, John i. 5 ; *hell*, Matt. viii. 12 ; 2 Pet. ii. 4.

23. The word DOOR is used (1) of *Christ*, in John x. 9, because he is the only way into heaven for sinners ; (2nd) of *faith*, in Acts xiv. 27, because faith opened salvation to the Gentiles ; (3rd) of *opportunity for preaching*, in 1 Cor. xvi. 9 Col. iv. 3, because, by utterance of the mouth, preaching enters into the heart ; (4th) of the *heart* in Rev. iii. 20, as giving entrance to truth ; (5th) of the *lips*, as sending forth the voice, Ps. cxli. 3 ; (6th) of *heaven*, Matt. xxv. 10 ; (7th) of *sloth*, Prov. xxvi. 14.

24. DEN. Applied to Jerusalem, Jer. ix. 11 ; to Temple, Matt. xxi. 13.

E.

25. END. Prov. xxiii. 18, and 1 Pet. i. 9.

26. EYE-SALVE. Rev. iii. 18.

F.

27. FOUNDATION. Isa. xxviii. 16 ; 1 Cor. iii. 11. FOUNTAIN. Zech. xiii. 1. FORERUNNER. Heb. vi. 20. FIRSTFRUITS. 1 Cor. xv. 20.

28. FLOWER. Job xiv. 2.

29. FOWLER. Prov. vi. 5.

30. FAN. Jer. xv. 7, and Matt. iii. 12.

31. FOX. Used of *false prophets*, Ezek. xiii. 4 ; of a *wicked ruler*, Luke xiii. 32.

G.

32. GREY HAIRS. Hosea vii. 9. GOLD TARNISHED. Lam. iv. 1. GRASS WITHERED. 2 Kings xix. 26.

33. GRASSHOPPERS, Judges vi.

34. GOATS. Matt. xxv. 32. GRASS. Ps. xcii. 7 ; xxxvii. 2.

35. GIRDLE. Eph. vi. 14. It is meant to show that we are held up when weak by the power of truth (Isa. xxii. 21.)

H.

36. HOUSE. *The Grave*, Job xxx. 23. *The body*, Job iv. 19, 2 Cor. v. 1. *The Church*, 1 Tim. iii. 15. *Heaven*, John xiv. 2.
37. HAMMER. Jer. xxiii. 29. HONEY. Ps. cxix. 103.
38. HEN GATHERING HER CHICKENS UNDER HER WINGS. Matt. xxiii. 37.

I.

39. ISLES. Isa. xlix. 1.
40. INCENSE. Used of *prayer*, Ps. cxli. 2 ; and of the *merits of Christ*, Rev. viii. 3.

J.

41. JEWELS. Mal. iii. 17.

K.

42. KISS. Used in connection with *love*, Song of S., i. 2 ; *reverence*, Exod. xviii. 7, and 1 Sam. x. 1 ; *submission*, Ps. ii. 12 ; and *deceit*, Matt. xxvi. 49.
43. KINGS. Rev. i. 5, 6, compared with Rev. xxii. 5.

L.

44. LEAVES. Used of *prosperity* Ps. i. 3 ; *eternal life*, Rev. xxii. 2 ; *mortality*, Isa. lxiv. 6 ; *timidity*, Lev. xxvi. 36.
45. LILY. Used of *Christ*, Song of S., ii. 1 : *believers*, Hos. xiv. 5. LAMB. Used *Christ*, John i. 29 ; *believers*, Isa. xl. 11.
46. LION. Used for *Christ*, Rev. v. 5 : for *believers*, Prov. xxviii. 1 ; for *Satan*, 1 Peter v. 8 ; for *wicked men*, 2 Tim. iv. 17, Ezek. xxii. 25.
47. LEAVEN. Used of *sin*, Matt. xvi. 6, 1 Cor. v. 6, 7 ; of *grace*, Matt. xiii. 33.
48. LIGHT. Of *God's word*, Ps. cxix. 105 : of *happiness*, Isa. lviii. 8 ; of a *good king*, 2 Sam. xxi. 17.
49. LEPROSY. Like *sin* ; (1) *defiling*, Lev. xiii. 44, 45 : (2) *spreading*, Lev. xiii. 22, 1 Cor. v. 6 ; (3) *separating*, Numb. v. 2, Rev. xxi. 27 ; (4) *sometimes incurable*, 2 Kings v. 7, with Jer. xiii. 23.
50. LEANNESS. Put for *temporal calamity*, Isa. x. 16 ; for *spiritual weakness*, Isa. xxiv. 16, Ps. cxi. 15.

M.

51. MILK. Isa. lv. 1 ; MARROW, Ps. lxiii. 5 ; MEAT, John iv. 32, 34 ; MANNA, Rev. ii. 17.
52. MORNING. Put for *swiftness*, Ps. cxxxix. 9 ; *divine truth*, Isa. viii. 20 (margin) ; and *resurrection*, Ps. xlix. 14.
53. MEMBERS, in Eph. v. 30 ; MAN, in Eph. iv. 13 ; MERCHANTMAN, Matt. xiiii. 45.
54. MIRE. Used for *sin* 2 Peter ii. 22 ; *contempt*, 2 Sam.xxii. 43.

N

55. NIGHT. Put for *death*, in John ix. 4 ; for *time of ignorance*, in Rom. xiii. 12 ; and for *affliction*, in Isa. xxi. 12.
56. NOON. Amos viii. 9.
57. NEST. Hab. ii. 9.
58. NURSE. Used of *Christian kings*, in Isa. xlix. 23 ; and of *Christian ministers*, in 1 Thess. ii. 7.

O.

59. OINTMENT. Descriptive of *Christ's name*, Song of S., i. 3 ; and of *brotherly unity*, in Ps. cxxxiii. 2.
60. ORPHANS. Lam. v. 3 ; John xiv. 18 (marg.) and OUTCASTS, in Jer. xxx. 17.
61. OAK. In Isa. vi. 13 ; Amos ii. 9.

P.

62. PILLARS. Gal. ii. 9, and Jer. i. 18.
63. PALACE. Applied to *temple of Jerusalem*, 1 Chron. xxix. 1 ; to *church of God*, Ps. lxxviii. 69, xlviii. 13.
64. PRISON. Of *sin*, Isa. xlii. 7 ; and of *the grave*, Isa. liii. 8.
65. PRINCE. Isa. ix. 6.
66. PIT. *Snare*, Ps. vii. 15 ; *sorrow*, Ps. xl. 2 ; *grave*, Isa. xxxviii. 17.
67. POISON. Rom. iii. 13 ; James iii. 8.

Q.

68. QUENCH. *Love*, Song of S., viii. 7 ; *life*, Isa. xliii. 17 ; 2 Sam. xiv. 7 ; xxi. 17 ; *temptation*, Eph. vi. 16 ; *Holy Spirit*, 1 Thes. v. 19 ; *Divine wrath*, Isa. i. 31 ; 2 xxii. 17.

R.

69. RAZOR. See Ps. lii. 2 ; Isa. vii. 20.

70. REED. Used for *instability*, Luke vii. 24 ; *despondency*, Isa. xlii. 3 ; and *disappointing hope*, Isa. xxxvi. 6 ; 2 Kings xviii. 21.
71. REAPING. See John iv. 36, 38 ; Matt. iii. 39.
72. RACE. 1 Cor. ix. 24 ; Heb. xii. 1.

S.

73. SALT. Matt. v. 13. STEWARDS, 1 Pet. iv. 10. SHOWERS, Mic. v. 7. SHEEP, John x. 27. SOLDIERS, 2 Tim. ii. 3. STONES, 1 Pet. ii. 5. STRANGERS, 1 Pet. ii. 11.
74. SHADOW. Used in connection with *death*, Ps. xxiii. 4, *divine care*, Ps. xci. 1 ; and *law of Moses*, Heb. x. 1.

T.

75. TRAPS. Josh. xxiii. 13. THORNS, 2 Sam. xxiii. 6, THIEVES, John x. 8.
76. TOWER. Ps. lxi. 3.
77. TENT. Used of the *heavens*, Isa. xl. 22 ; the *church*, Isa. liv. 2. TEMPLE. The *heavens*, Ps. xi. 4 ; the *church*, Eph. ii. 21.

V.

78. VIRGINS. Matt. xxv. 1, etc. VESSELS, 2 Tim. ii. 20.
79. VIPERS. Matt. iii. 7.
80. VAPOR. James iv. 13, 14.

W.

81. WATER. John vii. 38, 39. WIND. John iii. 8.
82. WOLVES. Matt. vii. 15. WANES. Jude 13. WELLS WITHOUT WATER. 2 Pet. ii. 17.

Y.

83. YOKE. Describes the *service of Christ*, Matt. xi. 29 : *cruel oppression*, 1xii. 4 ; *spiritual bondage*, Acts xv. 10.

ANSWERS

TO

BIBLE STUDIES.

PERTAINING TO

SCRIPTURE CHARACTERS.

KEY TO BIBLE CHARACTERS, NO. 1.—AHASUERUS.—Esther viii. 1.

1. A-bigail............................1 Sam. xxv. 3, 39.
2. H-or............................Numb. xx. 27, 28.
3. A-bner............................1 Sam. xiv. 50.
4. S-anballat............................Neh. iv. 7.
5. U-zza............................1 Chron. xiii. 10.
6. E-liezer............................Gen. xv. 2.
7. R-amoth............................Josh. xx. 8.
8. U-r............................Gen. xi. 31.
9. S-hiloh............................Gen. xlix. 10.

KEY TO BIBLE CHARACTERS, NO. 2.—ISHMAEL, ABRAHAM.—Genesis xxi. 16 ; xvi. 16.

1. I-r-a............................2 Sam. xx. 26.
2. S-egu-b............................1 Kings xvi. 34.
3. H-amo-r............................Gen. xxxiii. 19.
4. M-ar-a............................Ruth i. 20.
5. A-rauna-h............................2 Sam. xxiv. 22.
6. E-thiopi-a............................Acts viii. 27.
7. L-ukewar-m............................Rev. iii. 16.

KEY TO BIBLE CHARACTERS, NO. 3.—ADULLAM.—

1. A-bed-nego..........................Dan. iii, 27, 28.
2. D-othan.............Gen. xxxvii. 17 ; 2 Kings vi. 13, 20.
3. U-zziah..........................2 Chron. xxvi. 19, 20.
4. L-aban..............................Gen. xxvii. 43.
5. L-uz................................Gen. xxviii. 19.
6. A-chan.............................Josh. vii. 24, 25.
7. M-anoah.............................Judges xiii. 2.

KEY TO BIBLE CHARACTERS, NO. 4.—PHILADELPHIA.—
Rev. i. 11.

1. P-hilemon............................Philemon 1, 1.
2. H-erodion..............................Rom. xvi. 11.
3. I-turæ.....................................Luke iii. 1.
4. L-ystra...................................Acts xiv. 21.
5. A-pollos.................................Acts xviii. 24.
6. D-amascus..............................2 Cor. xi. 32, 33.
7. E-penetus..................................Rom. xvi. 5.
8. L-ebbeus.....................................Matt. x. 3.
9. P-hebe..................................Rom. xvi. 1, 2.
10. H-erodians.............................Matt. xxii. 16.
11. I-talian Band................................Acts x. 1.
12. A-gabus...................................Acts xxi. 10.

KEY TO BIBLE CHARACTERS, NO. 5.—ELIMELECH.—Ruth i. 2.

1. E-liab..................................1 Sam. xvi. 6, 7.
2. L-aish...............................Judges xviii. 29.
3. I-ssachar.............................Gen. xlix. 14.
4. M-achpelah............................Gen. xxiii. 17.
5. E-bed-melech.......................Jer. xxxviii. 7, 15.
6. L-ebanon.................................Deut. iii. 25.
7. E-zion-geber.........................1 Kings xxii. 48.
8. C-yrus.....................................Isa. xliv. 28.
9. H-iel...................................1 Kings xvi. 34.

KEY TO CHARACTERS, NO. 6.—AHITHOPHEL.—2 Samuel
xvii. 1, 23.

1. A-bijah..................................1 Kings xiv. 1.
2. H-uldah...............................2 Chron. xxxiv. 22.

3. I-shmael..............................Gen. xvi. 12.
4. T-imnath-heres..........................Judges ii. 9.
5. H-aman........................Esther vi. 6 ; vii. 10.
6. O-rnan..............1 Chron. xxi. 23 ; 2 Sam. xxiv. 23.
7. P-i-Hahiroth........................Exod. xiv. 9, 28.
8. H-ebron...............................2 Sam. iii. 2, 3.
9. E-ben-ezer............................1 Sam. vii. 10.
10. L-amech..................................Gen. v. 28.

KEY TO BIBLE CHARACTERS, NO. 7.—OBADIAH.—1 Kings xviii. 3.

1. O-rpah..................................Ruth i. 14, 15.
2. B-aalah, or Kirjath-jearim..1 Sam. vii. 2 ; 1 Chron. xiii. 6.
3. A-mos..........................Amos. i. 1 ; vii. 14, 15.
4. D-aniel..............................Daniel vi. 3 ; v. 29.
5. I-shbi-benob.........................2 Sam. xxi. 16, 17.
6. A-chsah...............................Judges i. 12, 13.
7. H-iel.......................Josh. vi. 26, 1 Kings xvi. 34.

KEY TO BIBLE CHARACTERS, NO. 8.—REBEKAH.—Genesis xxvii. 6, 46.

1. R-ehoboam..........................1 Kings xii. 13, 19.
2. E-leazar................................Numb. iv. 16.
3. B-alaam...............................Numb. xxxi. 8.
4. E-lijah.....................1 Kings xviii. 22 ; xix. 2, 3.
5. K-eilah............................1 Sam. xxiii. v. 12.
6. A-i..Josh. vii. 5.
7. H-iram................................1 Kings ix. 27, 28.

KEY TO BIBLE CHARACTERS, NO. 9.—BARZILLAI.— II Sam. xvii. 27, 29.

1. B-eersheba..........................Gen. xxvi. 26, 33.
2. A-bsalom...............................2 Sam. xv. 10.
3. R-echabites.........................Jer. xxxv. 18, 19.
4. Z-elophehad...........................Numb. xxvii. 7.
5. I-chabod................................1 Sam. xiv. 3.
6. L-achish.............................2 Kings xiv. 19.
7. L-evites.................................Deut. xviii. 1.
8. A-bner...............................2 Sam. iii. 30, 38.
9. I-saac..................................Gen. xxii. 7, 8.

KEY TO BIBLE CHARACTERS, NO. 10.—JEROBOAM.—
1 Kings xii. 26, 33.

1. J-esse............................1 Sam. xvii. 58.
2. E-uphrates............ ....Josh. i. 4.
3. R-amah..........................1 Sam. vii. 15, 17.
4. O-thniel..........................Judges iii. 9, 10.
5. B-athsheba..............................1 Kings ii. 13.
6. O-g..............................Numb. xxi. 33, 35.
7. A-hio..................................2 Sam. vi. 3.
8. M-ordecai..............................Esther ix. 4.

KEY TO BIBLE CHARACTERS, NO. 11.—GEHAZI.—
2 Kings v. 25, 27.

1. G-ilgal.............................. Josh. iv. 20.
2. E-ndor..........................1 Sam. xxviii. 7, 9.
3. H-ur..................................Exod. xvii. 12.
4. A-biathar..........................1 Sam. xxii. 20.
5. Z-arephath. ....1 Kings xvii. 9, 15, 16.
6. I-ndia............ ....Esther i. 1.

KEY TO BIBLE CHARACTERS, NO. 12.—CORNELIUS.—
Acts x. 1, 2.

1. C-laudius Lysias.......... ....Acts xxiii. 26.
2. O-nesiphorus........................2 Tim. i. 16, 17.
3. R-ome................................Acts xviii. 2.
4. N-ain............................Luke vii. 11, 15.
5. E-uroclydon........................Acts xxvii. 14.
6. L-aodiceans........................Rev. iii. 14, 19.
7. I-llyricum..............................Rom. xv. 19.
8. U-rbane...............................Rom. xvi. 9.
9. S-usanna..............................Luke viii. 3.

KEY TO BIBLE CHARACTERS, NO. 13.—EVIL-MERODACH.—
2 Kings xxv. 27.

1. E-xorcists..............................Acts xix. 13.
2. V-eil.....................................Ruth iii. 15.
3. I-mage.................................1 Sam. xix. 13.
4. L-oaves........... ....Lev. xxiii. 17.

5. M-urrain..............................Exod. ix. 3.
6. E-gypt....................Gen. xxxvii. 28; Matt. ii. 13.
7. R-ue..............................Luke xi. 42.
8. O-nion..............................Numb. xi. 5.
9. D-oeg..............................1 Sam. xxii. 9.
10. A-rgument..............................Job. xxiii. 4.
11. C-oat..............................Gen. xxxvii. 33.
12. H-usband..............................Prov. xii. 4.

KEY TO BIBLE CHARACTERS, NO. 14.—GAMALIEL,—Acts v. 34.

1. G-alilee..............................Acts ii. 7.
2. A-nna..............................Luke ii. 36.
3. M-nason..............................Acts xxi. 16.
4. A-nanias..............................Acts v. 5.
5. L-uke..............................2 Tim. iv. 11.
6. I-conium..............................Acts xiv. 19.
7. E-mmaus..............................Luke xxiv. 13.
8. L-ydda..............................Acts ix. 32.

KEY TO BIBLE CHARACTERS, NO. 15.

The earliest, the deepest, and the most lasting impressions the mind receives are those which the mother imparts. The piety of **Isaac** may in some degree be traced to the faith and prayerfulness of *Sarah* (Heb. xi. 11; Gen. xvii. 15, 16; Gen. xxi. 6). The eminence of Jacob was possibly to some extent to be ascribed to the home influence and special affection of *Rebekah.* While Esau was much engaged in the chase, Jacob was under the tuition of his mother. (Gen. xxv. 27, 28). **Moses** and **Aaron** were examples of the holy influence the eminent piety of their mother *Jochebed* had upon them (Exod. vi. 20; Heb. xi. 23). Though **Samson** is an affecting illustration of backsliding from the ways of the Lord, yet his early devotedness to the service of God was doubtlessly owing to the influence of his mother, the prayerful and believing *wife of Manoah* (Judges xiii). **Samuel** was born in the atmosphere of *Hannah's* devotion, and his childhood spent under her pious care (1 Sam. i. 27, 28). Other Old Testament worthies might be selected to show the beneficial influence the maternal relation directly or indirectly exerts. The most remarkable proof in the New Testament of the salutary influence of maternal piety is that of *Eunice* and *Lois* on the mind, character and usefulness of **Timothy** (2 Tim. i. 5).

Maternal influence, so often used for good, possesses also great power for mischief to the interests of those on whom it is exercised. "As is the mother, so is the daughter." (Ezek. xvi. 44). The wickedness of **Ahaziah** is accounted for on this principle: "His mother *Athaliah* was his counsellor to do wickedly" (2 Chron. xxii. 3). The inspired historian does not leave on record the fact of a YOUNG WOMAN committing such an atrocious deed as to ask that a good and faithful man should be beheaded, without telling the reader she was instructed of *Herodias*, her mother to do this thing (Matt. xiv. 6, 8).

KEY TO BIBLE CHARACTERS, NO. 16.

Samson, though the strongest man, was so weak when trusting in himself that he was twice ensnared by Philistine women. His strength was not in his hair, but in the Lord; and while his locks were unshorn he retained the outward sign of his devotedness to the Lord. When he parted with his locks he resigned the last sign of his being a Nazarite, his apostasy was complete, and he was the easy victim of his enemies (Judges xvi. 17, 20).

Goliath of Gath, the mighty Philistine giant, trusted in the height of his form and the strength of his arm; but he fell before the sling and stone of the shepherd youth who assailed him in the strength of the Lord, and not relying on his own skill, strength or weapons (1 Sam. xvii. 40, 45).

Hazael, the king of Syria, relying upon his own moral strength, shrunk from the scenes of infamy which Elisha, the prophet predicted he would enact. His self-confidence induced him to exclaim, "But what, is thy servant a dog, that he should do this great thing?" (2 Kings viii. 13). His subsequent history shows that he exceeded in his doings the wickedness which in his words he deprecated and deemed impossible.

Nebuchadnezzar, trusting in himself and in his vast resources, in the spirit of self-vaunting, walked in his palace, and said: "Is not this great Babylon, that I have built for the house of the kingdom by the might of my power, and for the honor of my majesty?" (Dan. iv. 30). While he was yet boastfully speaking, even in the same hour, he is deprived of his reason, and sent to herd with the beasts of the field. And afterwards he acknowledges his sin, adores the righteousness of God, and leaves on record his testimony, "I, Nebuchadnezzar, praise and extol and honor the King of heaven, all whose works are truth, and his ways judgment: and those that walk in pride he is able to abase" (Dan. iv. 37). The original document containing this testimony Sir Henry Rawlinson has discovered and brought to England.

Peter the apostle trusted to himself when he said to his Lord, "Though all should be offended, yet will not I" (Mark xiv. 29): and, "Lord, I am ready to go with thee both into prison and to death" (Luke xxii. 33). He failed, and he denied the Heavenly Master to whom he had expressed the strongest attachment.

KEY TO BIBLE CHARACTERS, NO. 17.

Nadab and **Abihu,** the sons of Aaron, recklessly entered on the service of the Lord, and "offered strange fire before the Lord, which he commanded them not. And there went out fire from the Lord and devoured them, and they died before the Lord" (Lev. x. 1, 2).

Miriam treated her brother Moses irreverently, and spake against him, and she was smitten with leprosy, and she was shut out of the camp seven days (Num. xii. 1, 8; 10, 14, 15).

Korah, Dathan and **Abiram** formed a conspiracy, and treated Moses with irreverence, and attempted to take upon themselves to offer incense. The earth swallowed up some, and "fire from the Lord consumed the two hundred and fifty men that offered incense" (Numb. xvi. 31, 35).

Uzzah irreverently put forth his hand and touched the Ark when the oxen shook it. And the anger of the Lord was kindled against Uzzah; and God smote him there for his error, and there he died by the Ark of God (2 Sam. vi. 6).

Eutychus, a young man attending the preaching of Paul, fell into a deep sleep. He sunk down with sleep, and "fell down from the third loft, and was taken up dead" (Acts xx. 9).

These are some of the solemn warnings against indifference and irreverence towards holy things and persons; and there are others which may be searched out.

KEY TO BIBLE CHARACTERS, NO. 18.

Enoch walked with God in the exercises of devotion, and he had the testimony that he pleased God, and was translated, that he should not see death (Gen. v. 24; Heb. xi. 5).

Isaac was eminent for his solitary meditation and devotional spirit, and God blessed him, and gave him the desire of his heart (Gen. xxiv. 63, 67).

Jacob lived in the habit of prayer, so that his very dreams were of heaven and God; see the account of the vision of Bethel. But the highest honor on his devotion was reserved for the more extraordinary scene at Peniel, when his name was changed from Jacob to that of Israel, as a memorial that he had power with God (Gen. xxxii. 28).

God put honor on the devotion of **Elijah,** when he stayed the clouds that they rained not upon the earth for the space of six months, and when he miraculously fed him during that period. Again, in answer to the prayer of Elijah, God caused rain to fall and abundance to appear on the earth (James v. 17, 18).

Hezekiah in his trouble prayed unto the Lord, and the Lord honored him by granting his request, and saying unto him, "I have heard thy prayer, I have seen thy tears: behold I will add unto thy days fifteen years" (Isa. xxxviii. 5).

Daniel maintained his habit of devotion, though death was the sentence which he incurred by calling upon his God. The Lord honored him by shutting the mouths of the lions, to which he had been cast to be devoured (Dan. vi. 27).

The disciples in the upper room at Jerusalem, continuing in devotion for ten days, were honored with the gifts and graces of the Holy Spirit, and endowed with miraculous power (Acts i. 14 ; ii. 4).

KEY TO BIBLE CHARACTERS, NO. 19.

We might answer this question by quoting the greater part of the eleventh chapter of the Epistle to the Hebrews. In addition to the worthies there named, we may notice—**the shepherds,** who showed their faith in the message of the angel by immediately leaving their flocks and going to Bethlehem to see the young child. **Simeon** and **Anna**, watching in the temple, by faith waited for "the consolation of Israel." **The Syrophenician woman**, whose faith sustained her importunity amidst discouragements, until the boon she sought for her daughter was granted. **The woman** who touched the hem of Christ's garment and was healed. Many others of this class may be cited ; but the most striking illustration of the power of faith is **the dying thief,** who adddressed Christ as "Lord," though in the depth of his humiliation ; whose faith saw him entering "paradise," though dying in the greatest ignominy ; and who begged an interest in his remembrance as the richest blessing, though he appeared in the extreme of destitution. He realized a living Saviour, though that Saviour was in the agonies of death.

KEY TO BIBLE CHARACTERS, NO. 20.

Isaac is the most remarkable instance of early consecration to God in his voluntary concurrence with the purpose of his father who bound him on the altar to offer him up as a living sacrifice. He was abundantly blessed in his wife Rebekah, in the renewal of the Abrahamic covenant, and in his prosperity in the land of Gerar.

Moses was a child of faith and prayer, and displayed remarkable decision in his youthful days; so that while he was educated by Egyptian tutors in every department of science, he resisted the idolatrous influences, and adhered most firmly to the religion of his pious mother. He was honored of God by being chosen to lead the tribes of Israel, and was favored with more intimate communion with God than any other of the Lord's servants.

Samuel was born in an atmosphere of piety, and when but a child was called of God to the prophetic office. He was blessed and honored of God to the end of his days on earth. He anointed Saul and David, the first and second kings of Israel, and was the medium of communication between God and his people.

David "was but a youth" when he gave himself to the Lord, and he was raised to the throne of Israel.

Josiah, though only a child of eight years when he ascended the throne, yet continued during thirty-one years to reign and to do that which was right in the sight of the Lord (2 Kings xxii. 1, 2).

Jeremiah, though we have no definite data by which we can tell his age when called to be a prophet, yet he must have been very young to justify him in saying, "Ah, Lord God! behold I cannot speak, for I am a child." He was for many years favored with Divine manifestations, and blessed with holy courage in the performance of his arduous work.

Timothy, from his childhood, was a possessor of eminent piety, and was honored of God as a faithful preacher of the gospel and a recipient of two epistles, which have been documents of reference to the church of Christ in general, and to young ministers in particular.

These and many others illustrate the truth recorded by Samuel, "Them that honor me I will honor; and they that despise me shall be lightly esteemed" (1 Sam. ii. 30).

ANSWERS

TO

BIBLE STUDIES.

PERTAINING TO

History, Biography and Geography.

KEY TO BIBLE STUDY, No. 1—PARADISE.

1. P-hilip.......................................Acts vi. 5.
2. A-raunah.............................2 Sam. xxiv. 22.
3. R-echabites.....................................Jer. xxxv.
4. A-chash..............Josh. xv. 16, etc ; Judges i. 12, etc.
5. D-an...Rev. vii.
6. I-mlah.................................1 Kings xxii. 9.
7. S-tephanas............................1 Cor. xvi. 15.
8. E-zekiel........................

KEY TO BIBLE STUDY, NO. 2.—DO GOOD

1. D-eborah.................................Judges iv. 9.
2. O-badiah..............................1 Kings xviii. 13.
3. G-ehazi..................................2 Kings v. 20, 22
4. O-bededem..............................2 Sam. vi. 19.
5. O-rpha...Ruth i. 4.
6. D-avid..............................2 Sam. xviii. 24, 23.

KEY TO BIBLE STUDY NO. 3.—MOSES—AARON.

1. M-ammo-*n* ....Luke xvi. 9, 14.
2. O-n-*o*..................................Neh. vi. 2 ; xi. 35.
3. S-hina-*r*......................................Gen. xi. 1, 9.
4. E-phphath-*a*................................Mark vii. 34.
5. S-heb-*a*....1 Kings xl. 2, 10 ; Jer. vi. 20 ; Ezek. xxvii. 22

KEY TO BIBLE STUDY NO. 4.—THE BRANCH, Zec. iii. 8. vi. 12.

1. T-eman.............................Gen. xxxvi. 15.
2. H-or.............................Num. xx. 22, 28.
3. E-lisheba.............................Exodus vi. 23.
4. B-arnabas.............................Acts xiv, 12.
5. R-ephidim.............................Ex. xvii. 1, 3.
6. A-mram.............................Ex. vi. 20.
7. N-icodemus.............................John iii. 1, 3.
8. C-ephas.............................John i. 42.
9. H-anani.............................2 Chron. xvi. 7.

KEY TO BIBLE STUDY NO. 5.—"GOD HATH MADE MAN UPRIGHT."

Eccles. vii. 29.

1. G-ad.............................2 Sam. xxiv. 11, etc.
2. O-badiah.............................1 Kings xviii. 3.
3. D-ecapolis.....................Matt. viii. 28 ; Mark v. 20
4. H-aman.............................Esther iii. 6.
5. A-biathar.............................1 Sam. xxii. 20.
6. T-abor.............................Judges iv. 6.
7. H-anani.............................2 Chron. xvi. 7.
8. M-ahanaim.............................Gen. xxxii. 2.
9. A-bner.............................2 Sam. iii. 37, 38.
10. D-arius.............................Ezra vi. 6, 15.
11. E-lisheba.............................Exodus vi. 23.
12. M-ephibosheth.............................2 Sam. ix. 6, 7.
13. A-gag.............................1 Sam. xv. 9, 33.
14. N-ob.............................1 Sam. xxii. 19
15. U-rijah.............................Jer. xxvi. 23.
16. P-hilip.............................Luke iii. 1.
17. R-ephidim.............................Exodus xvii. 8.
18. I-shmael.............................Jer. xli. 2.
19. G-abbatha.............................John xix. 13.
20. H-aran.............................Genesis xi. 27.
21. T-arshish.............................2 Chron. xx. 36

KEY TO BIBLE STUDY, NO. 6.—ELIMELECH.—BETHLEHEM.—
Ruth i. 2.

1. E-lia-*b*.............................Num. xxvi. 8, 9.
2. L-uk-*e*.............................Col. iv. 14.
3. I-scario-*t*.............................Matt. x. 4.
4. M-eriba-*h*.............................Num. xx. 13.
5. E-ba-*l*.............................Deut. xi. 29.
6. L-ak-*e*.............................Luke viii. 33.
7. E-la-*h*.............................1 Sam. xvii. 2.
8. C-oloss-*e*.............................Col. i. 2.
9. H-ela-*m*.............................2 Sam. x. 16.

KEY TO BIBLE STUDY, NO. 7.—GENESIS.—NUMBERS.

1. G-ideo-*n*.............................Judges vii. 20.
2. E-sa-*u*.............................Gen. xxv. 27.
3. N-ahu-*m*.............................Nahum i. 1.
4. E-lia-*b*.............................1 Sam. xvi. 6.
5. S-alom-*e*.............................Mark xv. 40.
6. I-zha-*r*.............................1 Chron. vi. 2.
7. S-osthene-*s*.............................Acts xviii. 17.

KEY TO BIBLE STUDY, NO. 8.—"THE DAY SPRING."—
Luke i. 78.

1. T-urtle-doves.............................Luke ii. 20.
2. H-erod.............................Matt. ii.
3. E-gypt.............................Matt. ii. 13.
4. D-ream.............................Gen. xxviii. 12.
5. A-ser.............................Luke ii. 36.
6. Y-oke.............................Matt. xi. 30
7. S-tar.............................Matt. ii. 2
8. P-assover.............................Ex. xii. 11.
9. R-achel.............................Jer. xxxi. 15.
10. I-mmanuel.............................Isa. vii. 14.
11. N-azareth.............................Luke ii. 51.
12. G-ethsemane.............................Matt. xxvi. 36.

KEY TO BIBLE STUDY NO. 9.—ISAIAH—DANIEL.

1. I-chabo-*d*........................1 Sam. iv. 21; xiv. 3.
2. S-amari-*a*............................1 Kings xvi. 24.
3. A-hima-*n* ....Num. xiii. 22.
4. I-su-*i*.......... ....Gen. xlvi. 17; Num. xxvi. 44.
5. A-nis-*e*..............................Matt. xxiii. 23.
6. H-ie-*l*..............................1 Kings xv. 34.

KEY TO BIBLE STUDY, NO. 10. "LORD SAVE US, WE PERISH."—Matt. viii. 25.

1. L-ot....................................Gen. xiii. 11.
2. O-thniel.......... ... .Judges iii. 9.
3. R-achel..............................Gen. xxix. 17.
4. D-eborah..............................Judges v. 7.
5. S-hishak.. ....1 Kings xiv. 25.
6. A-hab...............................1 Kings xviii. 17.
7. V-ashti.... ....Esther i. 9.
8. E-sther..............................Esther viii. 3.
9. U-r.......................................Gen. xv. 7.
10. S-myrna...................................Rev. i. 11.
11. W.......................................
12. E-den.....................................Gen. ii. 8.
13. P-hilistines............................1 Sam. xix. 8.
14. E-gyptians...........................Isaiah xx. 4.
15. R-hegium..........................Acts xxviii. 11.
16. I-conium............................Acts xiii. 51.
17. S-eir..Deut. ii. 4.
18. H-oreb.....................................Deut. i. 6.

KEY TO BIBLE STUDY, NO. 11.—"INCREASE OUR FAITH."—Luke xvii. 5.

1. I-sh-bosheth...........................2 Sam. iv. 5.
2. N-ethaneel......................2 Chron. xvii. 7, 9.
3. C-apernaum..............................Matt. xi. 23.
4. R-immon. ....2 Kings v. 18.
5. E-lymas.......... ....Acts xiii. 8, 12.

6. A-rk....................Gen. vii. 11, 13; viii. 13, 116.
7. S-amuel........................1 Sam. iii; xii. 2, 23
8. E-unice........................2 Tim. i. 5; iii. 15.

9. O-g..............................Num. xxi. 33.
10. U-pharsin..........................Dan. v. 25.
11. R-ehoboam........................1 Kings xii. 13.

12. F-ire.............. ....Jer. xxiii. 29.
13. A-ngels............. ....Heb. i. 14.
14. I-shmael............................Jer. xli. 2.
15. T-itus...........................2 Cor. vii. 5, 7.
16. H-orn...............................Luke i. 69.

KEY TO BIBLE STUDY, NO. 12, "EVEN CHRIST PLEASED NOT HIMSELF."—Rom. xv. 3.

1. E-sther..............,.................Es. vii. 3.
2. V-ashni.................. ....1 Chron. vi. 28.
3. E-li............................1 Sam. iv. 10, 11.
4. N-ebuchadnezzar... ....2 Chron. xxxvi. 10.

5. C-esar...............................Luke ii. 1.
6. H-ezekiah........................2 Kings xx. 1, 7.
7. R-abshakeh.......................2 Kings xviii. 19.
8. I-saiah..........................2 Kings xix. 5, 6
9. S-himei............................2 Sam. xvi. 5.
10. T-homas... ....John xx. 24.

11. P-aul..................... ....Acts ix. 8, 16
12. L-aban.........................Gen. xxxi. 24
13. E-ve.....................................Gen. iii
14. A-sabel...........................2 Sam ii. 18
15. S-amson............................Judges xvi.
16. E-sau..........................Gen. xxv. 27, 34
17. D-avid..........................1 Sam. xvii. 49.

18. N-abal..........................1 Sam. xxv. 10.
19. O-badiah.......................1 Kings xviii. 1.
20. T-arshish.... ....2 Chron. ix. 21

21. H-ushai........ ....2 Sam. xv. 32.
22. I-saac........................ ....Gen. xxvi. 7.
23. M-ary..................................Mark xvi. 9.
24. S-imeon................................Gen. xlii. 24.
25. E-liezer.............................Gen. xv. 2; xxiv.
26. L-ebanon..............................2 Chron. ii. 8.
27. F-elix..................................Acts xxiv. 27.

KEY TO BIBLE STUDY, NO. 13.—DAVID.

1. D-evil......................................1 Pet. v. 8.
2. A-quila...............................Acts xviii. 2, 3.
3. V-eil.....................................Ruth iii. 15.
4. I-dolatry..............................Ezek. xx. 16.
5. D-aniel...................................Dan. vi. 22.

KEY TO BIBLE STUDIES, NO. 14.—GOD IS LOVE.

1. G-oliath........................ ..1 Sam. xvii. 4, 10.
2. O-badiah..........................1 Kings xviii. 4.
3. D-avid..................................... Psalms.
4. I-shmael...............................Gen. xxi. 13.
5. S-aul......................................1 Sam. xv.
6. L-ydia.................................Acts xvi. 14.
7. O-mri..........................1 Kings xvi. 23, 24.
8. V-ashti............ ....Es. i. 11, 12.
9. E-lijah........... ....2 Kings ii. 19

KEY TO BIBLE STUDY, NO. 15.—"TAKE FAST HOLD OF INSTRUCTION."—Proverbs iv. 13.

1. T-arshish..................................Jonah i. 3.
2. A-braham..........................Gen. xviii. 7, 8.
3. K-idron............................2 Sam. xv. 23.
4. E-zra.................... ....Ezra vii. 6.
5. F-elix.............................Acts xxiv. 22, 26.
6. A-aron......... .... Exod. xxxii. 22, 24.
7. S-himei.......... ....2 Sam. xvi. 5, 6.
8. T-imothy.............. ....2 Tim. iv. 13.

9. H-iram..........................1 Kings v. 9, 10.
10. O-phir..........................1 Kings ix. 28.
11. L-azarus..........................John xi. 43, 44.
12. D-emas..........................2 Tim. iv. 10.
13. O-nesimus..........................Philermon 10.
14. F-elix..........................Acts xxiii. 23, 24, 31.
15. I-saac..........................Gen. xxii. 9.
16. N-aboth..........................1 Kings xxi. 1, 4.
17. S-hiboleth..........................Judges xii. 5, 6.
18. T-rogyllium..........................Acts xx. 15.
19. R-amah..........................1 Sam. ii. 11.
20. U-zzah..........................2 Sam. vi. 6, 7.
21. C-ain..........................Gen. iv. 5, 8.
22. T-imothy..........................2 Tim. iii. 15.
23. I-shbosheth..........................2 Sam. iv. 5, 6.
24. O-nesiphorus..........................2 Tim. i. 16.
25. N-icodemus..........................John iii. 1, 2.

KEY TO BIBLE STUDY, NO. 16.—"WAIT ON THE LORD."—
Psalm xxvii. 14.

1. W-idow of Nain..........................Luke vii. 12.
2. A-braham..........................Gen. xii. 12, 13.
3. I-shmael..........................Gen. xxi. 18.
4. T-imothy..........................2 Tim. i. 5, iii. 15.
5. O-nesimus..........................Philermon 10.
6. N-ehemiah..........................Neh. i. 3, 4.
7. T-abitha..........................Acts ix. 39, 40.
8. H-aggai..........................Hag. i. 3, 4.
9. E-lijah..........................1 Kings xviii.
10. L-ot..........................Gen. xiv. 14.
11. O-badiah..........................1 Kings xviii. 7, 9.
12. R-amah..........................1 Sam. xxv. 1.
13. D-avid..........................1 Sam. xiii. 14.

KEY TO BIBLE STUDY, NO. 17.—"NOT SLOTHFUL IN BUSINESS."
Romans xii. 11.

1. N-athaniel..........................John i. 47.

2. O-g....................................Num. xxi. 33.
3. T-abeel.............................Ezra iv. 7.
4. S-olomon.............................1 Kings x. 1.
5. L-amech..............................Gen. iv. 23.
6. O-nesiphorus.........................2 Tim. i. 16.
7. T-erah...............................Gen. xi. 31.
8. H-erod...............................Matt. ii. 3.
9. F-elix...............................Acts xxiv. 1, 22.
10. U-riah..............................2 Sam. xi. 14, 17.
11. L-amentations.......................Lam. iii.
12. I-shmael............................2 Kings xxv. 25.
13. N-aboth.............................1 Kings xxi. 16.
14. B-artimæus..........................Mark x. 46, 49.
15. U-z.................................Job i. 1.
16. S-isera.............................Judges iv. 22.
17. I-mmanuel...........................Isa. vii. 14,
18. N-ahash.............................1 Sam. xi. 2.
19. E-liezer............................Gen. xv. 2; xxiv. 12
20. S-hadrach...........................Dan. iii. 13.
21. S-imeon.............................Luke ii. 34, 35.

KEY TO BIBLE STUDY NO. 18.—"GOD IS LOVE."—1 John iv. 8.

1. G-aza's strong gates Samson bore quite away.—Judg. xvi. 2, 3.
2. O-nesimus' debt Paul said he would pay. Philem. 19.
3. D-gon before the ark fell flatly down. 1 Sam. v. 3, 38.
4. I-chabod's father died beneath God's frown. 1 Sam. iv. 21.
5. S-anballat's servant bore a letter forth. Neh. vi. 5, 6.
6. L-aban's large flocks were bless'd for Jacob's worth. Gen. xxx. 30
7. O-thniel by brav'ry won his cousin's hand. Jud. i. 13.
8. V-ashti refused t'obey her lord's command. Esth. i. 12.
9. E-gypt for many years the Hebrews fed. (Gen. xlvii. 27.)

Till forth from thence they were by Moses led.
That *God is Love* should cheer each anxious heart.
And from that love nought can his children part.

KEY TO BIBLE STUDY NO. 19.—"CEASE TO DO EVIL."—Isa. i. 16.

1. C-rispus.......................1 Cor. i. 14 ; Acts xviii. 8.
2. E-lisha.......................2 Kings ii. 11, 12.
3. A-bimelech.......................Judges ix. 48, 49.
4. S-olomon.......................1 Kings iv. 33.
5. E-hud.......................Judges iii. 15.
6. T-harshish.......................1 Kings x. 22.
7. O-rnan's.......................2 Chron. iii. 1.
8. D-avid's.......................2 Sam. xxi. 17.
9. O-thniel.......................Judges iii. 9, 11.
10. E-glon.......................Judges iii. 14.
11. V-ashti.......................Esther i. 9.
12. I-shbosheth.......................2 Sam. iii. 15, 16.
13. L-ot.......................Gen. xiii. 10, 11.

KEY TO BIBLE STUDY, NO. 20.—"PRAY WITHOUT CEASING."—
1 Thessalonians v. 17.

1. P-hilip.......................Acts viii. 31, 35.
2. R-ebekah.......................Gen. xxiv. 63, 64.
3. A-chan.......................Josh. vii. 24, 25.
4. Y-oung pigeon.......................Lev. xii. 6.
5. W-indow.......................2 Kings ix. 32, 33.
6. I-shmael.......................Gen. xxv. 12, 16.
7. T-ekoah.......................2 Sam. xiv. 1, 20.
8. H-annah.......................1 Sam. ii. 1.
9. O-mri.......................1 Kings xvi. 23, 24.
10. U-zziah.......................2 Chron. xxvi. 9, 10.
11. T-aberah.......................Numb. x. 2, 3.
12. C-aleb.......................Josh. xv. 14, (See Numb. xiii. 33).
13. E-sau.......................Gen. xxv. 27, 28.
14. A-maziah.......................2 Chron. xxv. 6, 11.
15. S-aul.......................1 Sam. xxxi. 4.
16. I-saac.......................Gen. xxiv. 2, 3.
17. N-athaniel.......................John i. 47.
18. G-ibeon.......................Josh. x. 12.

KEY TO BIBLE STUDY, NO. 21.—MIZPAH.—Genesis xxxi. 48, 49.

1. M-nason (Calmet)........................Acts xxi. 16.
2. I-chabod........... ....1 Sam. iv. 21.
3. Z-iklag..........................1 Sam. xxvii. 6.
4. P-aul..................................Acts ix. 15.
5. A-gag............................1 Sam. xv. 33.
6. H-aman............................Esther vii. 10.

KEY TO BIBLE STUDY, NO. 22.—"PRINCE OF PEACE,"—
Isaiah ix. 6.

1. P-isgah..............................Num. xxiii. 14.
2. R-ebekah.........................Gen. xxvii. 41, 46.
3. I-conium...............................Acts xiv. 1, 6.
4. N-athaniel..................................John i. 48.
5. C-ushi...........................2 Sam. xviii. 31, 32.
6. E-lhanan................................2 Sam. xxi. 19.
7. O-thniel...............................Judges i. 12, 13.
8. F-elix...................... ....Acts xxiv. 25.
9. P-haraoh...........................Gen. xii. 18, 20.
10. E-zra......................................Ezra vii. 6.
11. A-haziah..............................2 Kings ix. 27.
12. C-apernaum..........................Matt. iv. 13.
13. E-noch....................................Gen. v. 24.

KEY TO BIBLE STUDY, NO. 23.—"SEARCH THE SCRIPTURES."—
John v. 39.

1. S-hibboleth..........................Judges xii. 5, 6.
2. E-vening....................................Gen. i. 5.
3. A-lmighty... ....Job xxxvii. 23 ; Jer. xxxii. 17.
4. R-od (Aaron's)........................Numb. xvii. 8.
5. C-ountless...................................Rev. vii. 9.
6. H-o, every one that thirsteth............. ....Isa. lv. 1.
7. T-urn ye, turn ye......................Ezek. xxxiii. 11.
8. H-ead.......................................Eph. v. 23.
9. E-ternity...............................Isa. lvii. 15.

10. S-pirit............ ....John iv. 23, 24.
11. C-ome..................................Rev. xxii. 17.
12. R-eady... ....Matt. xxiv. 44.
13. I-mage....................................Gen. i. 26.
14. P-eace.....................................John xx. 26.
15. T-oil................................Matt. vi. 28, 29.
16. U-rim..............................Numb. xxvii. 21.
17. R-eed.....................................Matt. xi. 7.
18. E-mpty....................................Luke i. 53.
19. S-aved...............................

KEY TO BIBLE STUDY, NO. 24.—"CONSIDER THE LILIES."—
Matt. vi. 28.

1. C-hedorlaomer........................... Gen. xiv. 17.
2. O-mri.............................1 Kings xvi. 28.
3. N-ebuchadnezzar........................Dan. iv. 33.
4. S-aul...............................1 Sam. xxviii 8.
5. I-shobosheth ....2 Sam. iv.
6. D-avid..2 Sam. i.
7. E-vil-merodach.............................Jer. lii. 31.
8. R-ehoboam..........................1 Kings xii. 8.

9. T-iglath-pileser........ ....2 Kings xvi. 7.
10. H-ezekiah.....................2 Kings xix. 15, 21.
11. E-glon.............................Judges iii. 21, 17.

12. L-emuel...............................Prov. xxxi. 1.
13. I-nner court. ....Esther v. 1.
14. L-achish... ....2 Chron. xi. 9, xxv. 27.
15. I-saiah.............................2 Kings xx. 5, 7.
16. E-sarhaddon... ....2 Kings xix. 37.
17. S-olomon.... ....2 Chron. i. 12.

KEY TO BIBLE STUDY, NO. 25.—"BE COURTEOUS."—1 Peter iii. 8.

1. B-arzillai.........................2 Sam. xvii. 27, 29.
2. E-li..................................1 Sam. iv. 17, 18.

3. C-ain................................Gen. iv. 9, 10.
4. O-bed................................2 Chron. xxii. 1.
5. U-riah................................2 Sam. xi. 15.
6. R-euben................................Gen. xxxvii. 22.
7. T-obiah................................Neh. iv. 3.
8. E-hud................................Judges iv. 16, 15.
9. O-bed................................Ruth iv. 14, 17.
10. U-zzah................................2 Sam. vi. 6, 7.
11. S-amson................................Judges xvi. 30.

KEY TO BIBLE STUDY, NO. 26. "THE LORD IS MY LIGHT."—Psalms xxvii. 1.

1. T-homas................................John xx. 24.
2. H-aman................................Esther v. 11.
3. E.zra................................Ezra vii.6.
4. L-emuel................................Prov. xxxi. 1.
5. O-thniel................................Judges iii. 9.
6. R-ehoboam................................1 Kings xii. 1.
7. D-arius................................Dan. vi. 25.
8, I-shbosheth................................2 Sam. iv. 5–8.
9. S-anballat................................Neh. vi. 1.
10. M-anoah................................Judges xiii. 15, 16.
11. Y-oke................................Matt. xi. 30.
12. L-ot................................Gen. xiii. 10.
13. I-shmael................................2 Kings xxv. 25.
14. G-ehazi................................2 Kings v. 20, 27.
15. H-eber the Kenite................................Judges v. 24.
16. T-iglath-pileser................................2 Kings xv. 29.

KEY TO BIBLE STUDY, NO. 27. JONATHAN—2 Sam. xv. 36. ABIATHAR.—2 Sam. xv.35.

1, J-oshu-*a*................................Exodus xvii. 9.
2. O-re-*b*................................Judges vii. 25.
3. N-imsh-*i*................................1 Kings xix. 16.

4. A-mas-*a*..............................2 Sam. xvii. 25,
5. T-rumpe-*t*.... ....Josh. vi.4, ·5.
6. H-ulda-*h*......................2 Kings xxii. 14, 16.
7. A-rmeni-*a*.........................2 Kings xix. 37.
8. N-ebuchadnezza-*r*....................Dan. iv. 8, 25, 35.

KEY TO BIBLE STUDY, NO. 28.—"COME UNTO ME."—Matt. xi. 28.

1. C-aleb..............................Numbers xiv. 24.
2. O-badiah....... ....1 Kings xviii. 3.
3. M-ary Magdalene..........................Mark xvi. 9.
4. E-lizabeth....................................Luke i. 5.
6. U-r..Neh.-ix.7.
6. N-ain.......................................Luke vii. 11.
7. T-admor..................................2Chron, viii. 4.
8. O-phir......................................1 Kings ix. 28.
9. M-icah.......................................Micah. i. 1.
10. E-lijah....................................1 Kings xvii, 1.

KEY TO BIBLE STUDY, NO. 29.—"PRINCE OF PEACE." Isa. ix.6.

1. P-riest...Heb. v. 6.
2, R-oot...Rev. v.5.
3. I-mage of God............................2 Cor. iv. 4.
4. N-azarene....................................Matt. ii. 23.
5. C-ounsellor.......................... ....Isa. ix. 6.
6· E-verlasting Father........ ....Isa. ix. 6.
7. O-ffspring of David........................Rev. xxii. 16.
8. F-ountain......................................Zech. xiii. 1.
9. Prophet......................................Deut. xviii. 18.
10. E-mmanuel....................................Matt. i. 23.
11. A-lpha...Rev. i. 8.
12. C-hief Corner Stone.........................1 Peter ii. 6.
13. E-ternal Life................................1 John v. 20.

KEY TO BIBLE STUDY, NO.30. "THE LORD BLESS THEE, AND KEEP THEE." NUMBERS vi. 24.

1. T-imothy.......................................1 Tim. i.2.
2. H-iram...................................1 Kings. v 10. 11.

3. F-lijah..Luke ix. 30. 33.

4. L-eah...Gen. xxix. 16.
5. O-bed...Ruth iv. 16.
6. R-euben......................................Gen. xxxv. 23.
7. D-avid.......................................1 Sam. xvii. 14.

8. B-arnabas.....................................Acts xiii. 1.
9. L-ysias.......................................Acts xxiii. 26.
10. E-lhanan....................................2 Sam. xxi. 19.
11. S-hebna.....................................Isa. xxxvii. 2.
12. S-harezer...................................2 Kings xix. 37.

13. T-ola...Judges x. 1.
14. H-ezekiah...................................2 Chron. xxxii. 33.
15. E-srom......................................Luke iii. 33.
16. E-liphaz....................................Job ii. 11.

17. A-rba.......................................Joshua xxi. 11.
18. N-athan.....................................2 Sam. xii. 1.
19. D-eborah....................................Judges iv. 4.

20. K-ish..1 Sam. x. 21.
21. E-liezer....................................Gen. xv. ii.
22. E-unice.....................................2 Tim. i. 5.
23. P-hilip.....................................John i. 43.

24. T-ertullus..................................Acts xxiv. 1, 2.
25. H-erod......................................Luke iii. 19.
26. E-lymas.....................................Acts xiii. 6, 8.
27. E-zekiel....................................Ezek. i. 3.

KEY TO BIBLE STUDY, NO. 31.—ZERUIAH—ABIGAIL—SISTERS OF DAVID.—1 Chron. ii. 16, 17.

1. Z-ib-*a*.......................................2 Samuel xix. 24, 29.
2. E-liashi-*b*...................................Nehemiah iii.1 ; xiii. 4, 9.
3. R-abb-*i*......................................Matthew xxiii. 8.
4. U-nbelievin-*g*................................Revelation xxi. 8.
5. I-turæ-*a*.....................................Luke iii. 1.
6. A-bisha-*i*....................................1 Samuel xxvi. 6.
7. H-anamee-*l*...................................Jeremiah xxxii. 7, 15.

Zeruiah was mother of Joab, Abishai, and Asahel, who are spoken of as sons of Zeruiah.

KEY TO BIBLE STUDY, NO. 32.—JERICHO.—JOSH. vi, 25—SAMARIA—1 KINGS xvi. 24, 28.

1. J-uda-*s*....................John xii. 4; Matt. xxvi. 15.
2. E-zr-*a*..............................Ezra vii. 10.
3. R-amathaim Zophi-*m*.....................1 Sam. i 1.
5. I-ndi-*a*..............................Esther i. 1.
5. C-hedorlaom-*r*....................Gen. xiv, 9, 12.
6. H-agga-*i*..........................Ezra v. 1, etc.
7. O-she-*a*............................Num. xiii. 8.

KEY TO BIBLE STUDY, NO. 33.—"COUNSELLOR."—Isaiah ix. 6.

1. C-edar..............................1 Kings vi. 15.
2. O-ak..............................Genesis xxxv. 4.
3. U-rijah..........................Jeremiah xxvi. 23.
4. N-o.......Jer. xlvi. 25; Ezek. xxx. 14-46, Nahum iii. 8.
5. S-ycamore...............................Luke xix. 4.
6. E-schol..............................Num. xiii. 23.
7. L-uke..................................Col. iv. 14.
8. L-ydia................................Acts xvi. 14.
9. O-bed....................................Matt. i. 5.
10. R-ebekah........................Genesis xxvii. 6, 7

KEY TO BIBLE STUDY, NO. 34.—"ASK AND YE SHALL RECEIVE." John xvi. 24.

1. A-thaliah..................................2 Kings xi.
2. S-hebna..........................Isaiah xxii. 15, 19.
3. K-irjath-arba..........................Joshua xx. 7.
4. A-bed-nego............................Daniel iii. 14.
5. N-ehushtan..........Num. xxi. 8, 9; 11 Kings xviii, 4.
6. D-iana....................................Acts xix. 35.
7. Y-oke..........................Matthew xi. 29, 30.
8. E-lhanan..............................1 Chron. xx. 5.

9. S-un....... ....Malachi iv. 2.
10. H-ur..........................Exodus xvii. 10, 12.
11. A-dah's........................Genesis iv. 20, 21.
12. L-uz..........................Genesis xxviii. 19.
13. L-evi..................................Luke v. 29.
14. Rome....................................Luke ii. 1.
15. E-bed-melech.....................Jeremiah xxxix. 16.
16. C-anaan.................Gen. xii. 5, 7 ; Heb. xi. 13, 16.
17. E-d..................................Joshua xxii. 34.
18. I-ddo.....................................Zech. i. 1.
19. V-eil of the Temple.......Matt. xxvii. 51 ; Heb. x. 19, 20.
20. E-leazar.....................Joshua iii. 13 ; Deut. x. 6.

KEY TO BIBLE STUDY, NO. 35.—SIN IS THE TRANSGRESSION OF THE LAW.—1 John iii. 4-

1. S-alem....... ....Heb. vii. 2.
2. I-chabod..............................1 Sam. iv. 21.
3. N-azareth...............................John i. 46.
4. I-shbosheth............................2 Sam. ii. 10.
5. S-almon.......... ....Ruth iv. 21.
6. T-ertullus ....Acts xxiv. 1.
7. H-azael...... ....1 Kings xix. 15.
8. E-liab.............................1 Sam. xvii. 28.
9. T-ahpenes..........................1 Kings xi. 19.
10. R-amah............................1 Sam. vii. 17.
11. A-thenians..........................Acts xvii. 22, 23.
12. N-aaman..............Luke iv. 27 ; 2 Kings iii.; ix. 24.
13. S amson............................Judges xvi. 30.
14. G-ilead..............................1 Kings xvii. 1.
15. R-uth.................................Matt. i. 3, 5.
16. E-bed-melech............ ....Jer. xxxviii. 16.
17. S-eir......................................Deut. ii. 5.
18. S-ardis....................................Rev. iii. 1.
19. I-ssachar ....Gen. xxx. 17, 18.
20. O-thniel... ....Judges iii. 9, 10.
21. N-ehemiah........................Neh. ii. 6 ; v- 14.

22. O-nesimus ....Phil. 10, 15.
23. F-orty ....Acts vii. 23.
24. T-amar ....2 Sam. xiv. 27.
25. H-agar .... Gen. xvi. 1; xxi. 18.
26. E-liam ....2 Sam. xi. 3.
27. L-ahai-roi ....Gen. xxv. 11.
28. A-sher ....Deut. xxxiii. 24, 25.
29. W-atch ....Mark xiii. 37.

KEY TO BIBLE STUDY, NO. 36.—"LOVE NOT THE WORLD."—1 John ii. 15.

1. L-evi ....Num. xvi. 1.
2. O-bed ....Ruth iv. 17.
3. V-oice ....John x. 4.
4. E-liab ....1 Sam. xvii. 28.
5. N-athanael ....John i. 45, 46.
6. O-mri ....1 Kings xvi. 28.
7. T-arsus ....Acts xxi. 39.
8. T-heudas ....Acts v. 36.
9. H-ebron ....Josh. xiv. 13.
10. E-lijah ....1 Kings xix. 4.
11. W-ages ....Exodus ii. 9.
12. O-bed-edom ....2 Sam. vi. 11, 12.
13. R-amah ....1 Sam. ii. 11.
14. L-entiles ....Gen. xxv. 34.
15. D-aniel ....Dan. x. 11.

KEY TO BIBLE STUDY, NO. 37.—"BE NOT FAITHLESS."—John xx. 27.

1. B-alaam ....2 Peter ii. 15.
2. E-gypt ....Gen. xxi. 21.
3. N-aboth ....1 Kings xxi. 3.
4. O-mer ....Exodus xvi. 36.
5. T-arsus ....Acts xi. 25.

6. F-orty.................................. Acts vii. 23.
7. A-bel.......................................Heb. xi. 4.
8. I-nterpreter ....Gen. xlii. 23.
9. T-imothy.....................................1 Tim. i. 2.
10. H-ezekiah...............................11 Kings xx. 21.
11. L-aban.................................Gen. xxiv. 29, 67.
12. E-lisha...................................2 Kings xiii. 14.
13. S-amaria...............................1 Kings xvi. 28.
14. S-himei..................................2 Sam. xvi. 5.

KEY TO BIBLE STUDY, NO. 38.—HAMAN.—Esther vi. 11.

1. H-adassa-*h*.................................Esther ii. 7.
2. A-s-*a*...............................2 Chron. xiv. 9, 15.
3. M-iria-*m*..Num. xii.
4. A-mas-*a*.................................2 Sam. xx. 10.
5. N-aama-*n*.......................................2 Kings v.

KEY TO BIBLE STUDY, NO. 39.—Jesus.

1. J-oseph.......................Ps. cv. 17-22, Luke i. 68-77.
2. E-sau.................Gen. xxv. 29-34 ; Heb. xii. 16, 17.
3. S-aul...............1 Sam. x. 1-16 ; Acts viii. I ; ix. 15.
4. U-zzah...................................2 Sam. vi. 6, 7.
5. S-ardis..Rev. iii. 1-7.

"No voice can sing, no heart can frame,
Nor can the memory find
A sweeter sound than Jesus' name,
The Saviour of mankind.

KEY TO BIBLE STUDY NO. 40.—LOVE.

1. L-ois...2 Tim. 1-5.
2. O-badiah.............................1 Kings xviii. 4.
3. V-ashti..................................Esther i. 10-19.
4. E-li...1 Sam. iii. 13.

1 Cor. xiii. 13.—"And now abideth faith, hope, charity these three ; but the greatest of these is charity."

1 John iv. 11.—"Beloved, if God so loved us, we ought also to love one another."

KEY TO BIBLE STUDY, NO 41.—LOVE AS BRETHREN.—1 Peter iii. 8.

1. L-amech. ....Gen. iv. 19, 22.
2. O-badiah...........................1 Kings xviii. 7, 12.
3. V-anity.... ....Eccles. i. 1, 14.
4. E-lah....................................1 Sam. xxi. 9.
5. A-bijam.................................1 Kings xiv. 31.
6. S-abeans.. ....Job i. 14, 15.
7. B-lastus... ....Acts xii. 20.
8. R-amoth Gilead.........................2 Kings ix. 1, 2.
9. E-lam......................................Gen. xiv. 1.
10. T-ertius.................................Rom. xvi. 22.
11. H-aggith.................................1 King i. 5.
12. R-uth.... ....Ruth iv. 10.
13. E-d...Josh. xxii. 34.
14. N-aphtali................................Gen. xxx. 8.

KEY TO BIBLE STUDY, NO. 42.—ANAMMELECH.—2 Kings xvii. 31.

1. Heman......................................1 Kings iv. 31.
2. Camel..Lev. xi. 4.

KEY TO BIBLE STUDY, —NO. 43. —WAIT ON THE LORD.—
Psalm xxvii. 14. [Answered in Part.]

1. W-ell................................2 Sam. xvii. 17, 19.
2. A-mos........... ....Amos i. 11
3. I-rad...Gen. iv. 17, 18.
4. T-ola..Judges x. 1.

KEY TO BIBLE STUDY, NO. 44.—EVE—Gen. iii. 20.

1. E-lijah ....1 Kings xix. 1–4.
2. V-ine ....John xv. 1.
3. E-sther ....Esther ii. 7.

KEY TO BIBLE STUDY, NO. 45.—" SARGON—TARTAN.'—Isa. xx.1.

1. S-anballa-*t*...................................Neh. iv. 1.
2. A-ban-*a*....................................2 Kings v. 12.
3. R-ide-*r* ....Exodus xv. 1.

4. G-rea-*t*............................Psa. cxxxvi. 4.
5. O-she-*a*............................Num. xiii. 8.
6. N-u-*n*............................Num. xiii. 8

KEY TO BIBLE STUDY, NO. 46.—SAMUEL.—HANNAH.—
1. Sam. i. 20.

1. S-eraiah............................Jer. li. 59.
2. A-bana............................2 Kings v. 12.
3. M-attan............................2 Kings xi. 18.
4. U-pharsin............................Dan. v. 25.
5. E-liada............................2 Chron. xvii. 17.
6. L-ibnah............................Joshua xxi. 13.

KEY TO BIBLE STUDY, NO. 47.—THE GOOD SHEPHERD.—
John x. 11.

1. T-abitha............................Acts ix. 36—39.
2. H-agar............................Gen. xxi. 14.
3. E-zekiel............................Ezekiel i. 1.
4. G-ehazi............................2 Kings v. 25.
5. O-reb............................Judges vii. 25.
6. O-badiah............................1 Kings xviii. 5.
7. D-aniel............................Daniel vi. 23.
8. S-amson............................Judges xv. 16.
9. H-ezekiah............................2 Kings xx. 5.
10. E-lah............................1 Sam. xvii. 2.
11. P-eter............................Luke xxii. 61, 62.
12. H-oreb............................Exodus iii. 1.
13. E-sau............................Gen. xxvii. 41.
14. R-ahab............................Heb. xi. 31.
15. D-avid............................1 Sam. xix. 1, 2.

KEY TO BIBLE STUDY, NO. 48.—"HOW MANIFOLD ARE THY WORKS"—Psa. civ. 24.

1. H-yssop............................1 Kings iv. 33.
2. O-aks of Bashan............................Isa. ii. 13.
3. W-illow trees............................Psa. cxxxvii. 2.

4. M-yrtle tree....................................Isa. lv. 13.
5. A-lmond tree ....Eccles. xii. 5.
6. N-uts ....Gen. xliii. 2.
7. I-sraelites...................................Exod. xv. 27.
8. F-ig tree ....Matt. xxiv. 32.
9. O-il tree.......................................Isa. lxi. 19.
10. L-ign aloes ....Num. xxiv. 5, 6.
11. D-ry tree....................................Ezek. xvii. 24.
12. A-lmug tree...........................1 Kings x. 11, 12.
13. R-ose ....Isa. xxxv. 1.
14. Eden..Gen. ii. 9.
15. T-ree of life...................................Rev. xxii. 2.
16. H-eath ....Jer. xvii. 5, 6.
17. Y-ear by year ....Deut. xiv. 22.
18. W-heat..Exod. ix. 32.
19. O-live tree...............................Judges ix. 8, 9.
20. R-od...Num. xvii. 8.
21. K-ernels ....Num. vi. 4.
22. S-ycamore tree...............................Luke xix. 45.

KEY TO BIBLE STUDY, NO. 49,—"LOVE YOUR ENEMIES."—Matt. v. 44.

1. L-uke............................ 2 Tim. iv. 11 ; Col. iv. 14.
2. O-phir...................................1 Kings ix. 28 ; x. 11.
3. V-ine..John xv. 1.
4. E-shcol.....................................Numbers xiii. 23.
5. Y-early ....Heb. ix. 7, etc.
6. O-bed-Edom.....................................2 Sam. vi. 11.
7. U-zzah ....2 Sam. vi. 6, 7.
8. R-ehoboam ....1 Kings xii. 8.
9. E-lijah ....2 Kings ii. 11.
10. N-icodemus...John iii. 1.
11. E-lah......................................1 Kings xvi. 8–10.
12. M-anasseh (55 years).....................2 Chron. xxxiii. 1.
13. I-saac..Gen. xxvii. 1.
14. E-zekiel ....Ezek. iii. 26 ; xxiv. 27
15. S-heba..2 Sam. xx.

KEY TO BIBLE STUDY, NO. 50.—REFUGE—Heb. vi. 18 ; vii. 21.

1. R-izpah................................2 Sam. xxi. 8--10.
2. E-sther..................................Esther ii. 17.
3. F-elix..............................Acts. xxiv. 24, 25.
4. U-nicorn ....Numbers xxiii. 22.
5. G-ourd...............................Jonah iv. 5, 6,
6. E-uroclydon.........................Acts xxvii. 14.

KEY TO BIBLE STUDY, NO. 51.—GOD BE WITH YOU.—
Gen. xlviii. 21.

1. G-ood...............................Matt. xix. 16, 17.
2. O-nesimus...................................Phil. x. 10.
3. D-orcas..................................Acts ix. 36—41.
4. B-oaz...Ruth iv. 13.
5. E-aster ....Acts xii. 4.
6. W-hite..................................Rev. vii. 13, 14.
7. I-saac......................................Gen. xxi. 4, 6.
8. T-imothy.......................................2 Tim. i. 2.
9. H-ushai ....2 Sam xvii. 5–14.
10. Y-esterday.....................................Ps. xc. 4.
11. O-mega ....Rev. xxii. 13.
12. U-rim.......................................Ex. xxviii. 30.

KEY TO BIBLE STUDY, NO. 52—PEACE—John xiv. 27.

1. P-hicol ....Gen. xxi. 22.
2. E-bedmelech........................Jer. xxxviii. 7, etc.
3. A-bram...Gen. xiv. 13.
4. C-ephas...John i. 42.
5. E-lim..Exodus xv. 27.

KEY TO BIBLE STUDY, NO. 53.—OMNISCIENCE.—Psa. 147, 5.

1. O-mri ....1 Kings xvi. 23, 24.
2. M-icaiah..............................1 Kings xxii. 26.
3. N-amaan.....................................2 Kings v. 1.
4. I-shbosheth.....................2 Sam. iii. 13 ; iv. 5, 6.
5. S-himei...................2 Sam xvi. 5 ; xix. 16, 21.
6. C-hilion.......................................Ruth i. 2.

7. I-conium............................Acts xiii. 51.
8. E-mmaus............................Luke xxiv. 13.
9. N-azarite ....Numbers vi., 1.
10. C-leopas.................. ....Luke xxiv. 18.
11. E-lias..... ....Matt. xi. 14.

KEY TO BIBLE STUDY, NO. 54.—"SEEK YE THE KINGDOM OF GOD."—Luke xii. 31.

1. S-imeon..................................Acts xiii. 1.
2. E-lias....................................James v. 17.
3. E-lymas..................................Acts xiii. 8.
4. K-ish ....1 Sam. ix. 1.
5. Y-outh....................................Lam. iii. 27.
6. E-penetus..............................Rom. xvi. 5.
7. T-ertius............................ ..Rom. xvi. 22.
8. H-achilah ....1 Sam. xxvi. 1.
9. E-thiopia................................Esther i. 1.
10. K-ezia..................................Job xlii. 14, 15.
11. I-saiah...................................Isaiah i. 1.
12. N-aomi............... ....Ruth i. 20.
13. G-ideon................ ....Judges vi. 11.
14. D-arius............... ....Dan. ix. 1.
15. O-rpah...................................Ruth i. 2, 4.
16. M-iriam................................Exodus xv. 20.
17. O-badiah..............................Obadiah i. 1.
18. F-elix........................... Acts xxiii. 26, 33.
19. G-ath................ ....1 Sam. vi. 17.
20. O-both..... ....Num. xxxiii. 43.
21. D-rusilla ....Acts xxiv. 24.

KEY TO BIBLE STUDY, NO. 55.—"WATCH AND PRAY."—Matt. xxvi. 41.

1. W-ater............................. .John iv. 14.
2. A-rimathea..........................John xix. 38.
3. T-abitha...............................Acts ix. 40.
4. C-armi...............................Joshua vii. 1.
5. H-iddekel............................Daniel x. 4.

6. Amos .... Amos i. 1.
7. N-oadiah.................................Neh. vi. 14.
8. D-emitrius.................................Acts xix. 24.
9. P-hinehas................................ Num. xxv. 11.
10. R-ezin ....2 Kings xvi. 6.
11. A-bel....................................2 Sam. xx. 18.
12. Y-oke.....................................Lam. iii. 27.

KEY TO BIBLE STUDY, NO. 56.—HAGAR—Genesis xvi. 6-10.

1. H-azael......................2 Kings viii. 12 ; xiii. 22.
2. A-chan.................................Joshua vii. 24.
3. G-ideon..............................Judges vii. 24, 25.
4. A-bimelech ....Judges ix. 53, 54.
5. R-abbah.................................2 Sam. xi. 1.

KEY TO BIBLE STUDY, NO. 57.—FAITH.—1 Peter i. 5 ; 1 John v. 4.

1. F-ire.................................Jeremiah xxiii. 29.
2. A-rk.......................................Gen. vii. 1.
3. I-conium...................................Acts xiv. 1-6.
4. T-hyatira..................................Acts xvi. 14.
5. H-eaven...............................Hebrews xi. 16.

KEY TO BIBLE STUDY, NO. 58.—"GOD IS LOVE."—1 John 4. 8.

1. G-old (tried in the fire).........Zec. xiii. 9 ; 1 Peter 1. 7.
2. O-ath................................Heb. vi. 16, 17.
3. D-eath ....Rom. vi. 23.
4. I-dle soul................................Prov. xix. 15.
5. S-alt ....Matt. v. 13.
6. L-amb ....Rev. v. 6.
7. O-x...Isaiah i. 3.
8. V-eil...................................Matt. xxvii. 51.
9. E-agle....................................2 Sam. i. 23.

KEY TO BIBLE STUDY, NO. 59.—HEZEKIAH.—Isaiah xxxvii. 15. —ZEDEKIAH.—2 Kings xxv. 7.

1. H-u-*z*....................................Gen. xxii. 21.
2. E-v-*e* ....Gen. iii. 20.

3. Z-elopheha-*d*............................Num. xxvii. 7.
4. E-unic-*e*..............................2 Tim. i. 5.
5. K-insfol-*k*.... ....Job xix. 14.
6. I-tta-*i* ....2 Sam. xv. 19.
7. A-s-*a*...... ....1 Kings xv. 13.
8. H-anania-*h*.................... ....Daniel i. 7.

KEY TO BIBLE STUDY, NO. 60.—"LIVE PEACEABLY."—
Rom. xii. 18.

1. L-uke...................................Col. iv. 14.
2. I-srael...................... :........Gen. xxxii. 28.
3. V-ine...................................John xv. 5.
4. E-lam ....Exodus xv. 27.
5. P-hilippi...... ....Phil. iv. 15, 16.
6. E-zra.................... ....Ezra vii. 6.
7. A-mos..............................Acts xv. 16, 17.
8. C-ilicia.......... ....Acts xxi. 39.
9. E-liakim.........................2 Kings xxiii. 34.
10. A-bner....................................2 Sam. ii. 8.
11. B-athsheba ....1 Kings i. 11.
12 L-evi...............................2 Chron. xi. 14.
13. Y-outh ....Lam. iii. 27.

KEY TO BIBLE STUDY, NO. 61.—"YET THERE IS ROOM,"—
Luke xiv. 22.

1. Y-outh...........................1 Sam. xvii. 33.
2. E-liam...................................2 Sam. xi. 3.
3. T-hessalonica ....2 Tim. iv. 10.
4. T-irzah..............................1 Kings xvi. 9.
5. H-aran........ ....Gen. xi. 29.
6. E-thiopia..........................Jer. xxxviii. 7.
7. R-ahab....................................James ii. 25.
8. E-glah..................................2 Sam. iii. 5
9. I-ron..............................Judges iv. 2, 3.
10. S-othenes ....Acts xviii. 17.

11. R-echab .... 2 Kings x. 15, 16.
12. O-mri .... 1 Kings xvi. 21, 22.
13. O-bed .... Ruth iv. 16, 17.
14, M-ene .... Dan. v. 25.

KEY TO BIBLE STUDY, NO. 62.—AMASA.—2 Sam. xvii. 25; xx. 10.—ABNER.—1 Sam. xiv. 50, 51; 2 Sam. iii. 27.

1. A-rabi-*a* .... Gal. i. 17.
2. M-era-*b* .... 1 Sam. xiv. 49.
3. A-bdo-*n* .... Judges xii. 13—15.
4. S-almon-*e* .... Acts xxvii. 7.
5. A-*r* .... Deut. ii. 9.

KEY TO BIBLE STUDY, NO. 63.—"LET THERE BE LIGHT."—Gen. i. 3.

1. L-achish .... 2 Kings xiv. 19.
2. E-gypt .... Gen. xii. 10; xlii. 1, 2.
3. T-ibni .... 1 Kings xvi. 21.
4. T-ekel .... Dan. v. 27.
5. H-aman .... Esther iii. 10.
6. E-lijah .... 1 Kings xxi. 17.
7. R-izpah .... 2 Sam. xxi. 10.
8. E-sarhaddon .... 2 Kings xix. 37.
9. B-enhadad .... 1 Kings xx. 42.
10. E-glon .... Judges iii. 14.
11. L-evi .... Deut. x. 8.
12. I-saiah .... 2 Kings xix. 20.
13. G-ilboa .... 1 Sam. xxxi. 8.
14. H-anani .... 1 Kings xvi. 1.
15. T-iglath-pilnesar .... 2 Chron. xxviii. 20.

KEY TO BIBLE STUDY, NO. 64.—"ALL SEEK THEIR OWN."—Phil. ii. 21.

1. A-bner .... 1 Sam. xvii. 57.
2. L-ebbeus .... Matt. x. 3.
3. L-ystra .... Acts xiv. 8, 13.

4. S-ihon..Deut. i. 4.
5. E-liezer..Gen. xxiv. 33.
6. E-nos..Gen. iv. 26.
7. K-adash-barnea..Num. xxxii. 8.
8. T-amar..2 Sam. xiv. 27.
9. H-annah..1 Sam. i. 23, 28.
10. E-lijah..1 Kings xix. 13, 15.
11. I-talian..Acts x. 1.
12. R-abbah..2 Sam. xii. 27.
13. O-phir..1 Kings xxii. 48.
14. W-ood..1 Sam. xiv. 26, 27.
15. N-azareth..Luke i. 26, 27.

KEY TO BIBLE STUDY, NO 65.—CROSS.—Gal. vi. 14.

1. I-saa-*c*..Gen. xxvi. 18.
2. S-ei-*r*..Gen. xxxvi. 8.
3. S-*o*..2 Kings xvii. 4.
4. S-tephana-*s*..1 Cor. i. 16.
5. M-atthia-*s*..Acts i. 26.

KEY TO BIBLE STUDY, NO. 66.—RUTH—BOAZ.—Matt. i. 5.

1. R-aha-*b*..Heb. xi. 31.
2. U-nt-*o*..Matt. xi. 28.
3. T-ol-*a*..Judges x. 1.
4. H-u-*z*..Gen. xxii. 21.

KEY TO BIBLE STUDY, NO. 67.—KADESH-BARNEA.—Deut. ix. 23.

1. K-esi-*a*..Job xlii. 14.
2. A-ge-*e*..2 Sam. xxiii. 11.
3. D-alpho-*n*..Esther ix. 7.
4. E-lieze-*r*..Gen. xv. 2.
5. S-hime-*a*..1 Chron. iii. 5.
6. H-oba-*b*..Num. v. 29.

KEY TO BIBLE STUDY, NO. 68.—"GOD RESISTETH THE PROUD."
—1 Peter v. 5.

1. G-era..2 Sam. xvi. 5.
2. O-thniel..Judges i. 13
3. D-elilah..Judges xvi. 18.

4. R-hoda .... Acts xii. 13.
5. E-aster .... Acts xii. 4.
6. S-hushan. .... Neh. i. 1.
7. I-conium.. Acts xiii. 51.
8. S-in.. Exodus xvi. 1.
9. T-arsus.. Acts xxi. 39.
10. E-noch .... Jude 14, 15.
11. T-heudas.. Acts v. 36.
12. H-ebron.. Numbers xiii. 22.
13. T-yre.. Isaiah xxiii. 8.
14. H-ezekiah.. 2 Kings xviii. 4.
15. E-phraim.. Numbers xiii. 8.
16. P-halti.. 1 Sam. xxv. 44.
17. R-ebekah.. Gen. xxvii. 6, 17.
18. O-badiah.. 1 Kings xviii. 3.
19. U-zziah.. 2 Chron. xxvi. 19.
20. D-eborah.. Judges v. 7.

KEY TO BIBLE STUDY, NO. 69—"IT SHALL BE WELL WITH THE RIGHTEOUS."—Isa. iii. 10.

1. I-srael .... Num. xi. 10.
2. T-aberah.. Num. xi. 3.
3. S-eer.. 1 Sam. ix. 9.
4. H-obab.. Num. x. 29.
5. A-bsalom.. 2 Sam. xiv. 25.
6. L-ydia.. Acts xvi. 13, 14.
7. L-uke.. 2 Tim. iv. 11.
8. B-ethany.. Luke x. 38 ; John xi. 1.
9. E-lah .... 1 Sam. xvii. 2.
10. W-isdom.. Prov. viii. 11.
11. E-zekiel .... Ezek. i. 1.
12. L-evi.. Gen. xxxv. 23.
13. L-amech.. Gen. v. 28.
14. W-ise-men .... Matt. ii. 1–11.
15. I-shmael.. Gen. xxi. 9–21.
16. T-abor .... Psalm lxxxix. 12.
17. H-oreb.. Deut. v. 1.

18. T-hyathira ....Acts xvi. 14.
19. H-ophni ....1 Sam. ii. 34.
20. E-uphrates...............................Gen. ii. 14.
21. R-achel..... ....Gen. xxix. 9.
22. I-saac.. ....Genesis xxvii. 22 23
23. G-ehazi............................2 Kings v. 20.
24. H-ezekiah...... ....2 Kings xx. 8-11.
25. T-yre.......................... ...... 1 Kings v. 1.
26. E-limelech.......... ....Ruth i. 1, 2.
27. O-badiah..................................Obad. i. 1.
28. U-rim and Thummim................Exodus xxviii. 30.
29. S-alvation.............................Rev. vii. 9-21.

KEY TO BIBLE STUDY, NO. 70. — "HOPE THOU IN GOD."— Psalm xlii. 11.

1. H-ebron...............................1 Sam. ii. 2-4.
2. O-thniel.......... ....Judges i. 11, 33.
3. P-adan-aram ....Gen. xxviii. 5.
4. E-lisha...............................2 Kings iii. 11.
5. T-erah................................Gen. xi. 31, 32.
6. H-azael.............................2 Kings viii. 15.
7. O-livet........... ....2 Sam. xv. 30.
8. U-ri...........................Exodus xxxi. 1, 2.
9. I-sbosheth............................2 Sam. iv. 5, 6.
10. N-achons................................2 Sam. vi. 6.
11. G-ilgal................................Josh. v. 9. 12.
12. O-bed... ....Ruth iv. 17.
13. D-emetrius............................Acts xix. 24.

KEY TO BIBLE STUDY, NO. 71.—HARDEN NOT YOUR HEARTS.— Psalm xcv. 8.

1. H-adad...............................1 Kings xi. 14.
2. A-lexandria..........................Acts xviii. 24.
3. R-ome........................ ....Acts xix. 21.
4. D-ura.......................................Dan. iii. 1.
5. E-lah...................................1 Sam. xxi. 9.
6. N-adab.. ....1 Kings xiv. 20.

7. N-athan......................................1 Kings i. 10.
8. O-ded..................................2 Chron. xxviii. 9.
9. T-ertius..................................Rom. xvi. 22.
10. Y-oke..................................Gen. xxvii. 40.
11. O-zem..................................1 Chron. ii. 15.
12. U-riah..................................2 Sam. xii. 9.
13. R-ephidim..................................Exodus xvii. 8.
14. H-ephzi-bah..................................2 Kings xxi. 1.
15. E-phphatha..................................Mark vii. 34.
16. A-senath..................................Gen. xli. 45.
17. R-ahab........................James ii. 15 ; Heb. xi 31.
18. T-yrannus..................................Acts xix. 9.
19. S-abeans..................................Job. i. 15.

KEY TO BIBLE STUDY, NO. 72.—ADD TO YOUR FAITH, VIRTUE.—
2 Peter i. 5.

1. A-pollos......................................Acts xviii. 24.
2. D-amaris..................................Acts xvii. 34.
3. D-agon..................................1 Sam. v. 2.
4. T-atnai..................................Ezra v. 3.
5. O-rnan..................................1 Chron. xxi. 18,
6. Y-arn..................................1 Kings x. 28.
7. O-badiah..................................Obadiah i.
8. U-z..................................Job i. 1.
9. R-ehoboth..................................Gen. xxvi. 22.
10. F-estus..................................Acts xxiv. 27.
11. A-rchippus..................................Phil. i. 2.
12. I-shbi-benob..................................2 Sam. xxi. 16.
13. T-ebeth..................................Esther ii. 16.
14. H aggith..................................2 Sam. iii. 4.
15. V-ine..................................Isaiah v. 7.
16. I-dumea..................................Ezekiel xxxv. 15.
17. R-aguel..................................Num. x. 29
18. T-oi..................................2 Sam. viii. 10.
19. U-zziah..................................Zec. xiv. 5.
20. E-domites..................................Gen. xxvi. 9.

KEY TO BIBLE STUDY, NO. 73.—"BE GLAD IN THE LORD."— Psa. xciv. 34.

1. B-artimeus.......................................Mark x. 46.
2. E-lymas.......................................Acts. xiii. 8.
3. G-ilgal.......................................Jud. ii. 1.
4. L-ehi.......................................Jud. xv. 19.
5. A-dam.......................................Josh. xiii. 16.
6. D-ura.......................................Dan. iii. 1
7. I-saac.......................................Gen. xxvi. 1.
8. N-athan.......................................2 Sam. xii. 13.
9. T-ilgath-pilneser.......................2 Chron. xxviii. 20.
10. H-iram.......................................1 Kings vii. 45.
11. E-glon.......................................Jud. iii. 14.
12. L-ystra.......................................Acts xiv. 8.
13. O-mri.......................................1 Kings xvi. 16.
14. R-amah.......................................1 Sam. ii. 11.
15. D-othan.......................................2 Kings vi. 13.

KEY TO BIBLE STUDY, NO. 74.—DANIEL.

1. D-orcas.......................................Acts ix. 36.
2. A-bel.......................................Gen. iv. 8.
3. N-athan.......................................2 Sam. xii. 7.
4. I-srael.......................................Gen. xxvii. 41.
5. E-gypt.......................................Ex. xiii. 3.
6. L-emuel.......................................Prov. xxxi. 1.

KEY TO BIBLE STUDY. NO 75.—WASH AND BE CLEAN.— 2 Kings v. 19.

1. W-idow.......................................Luke xxi. 3.
2. A-binadab.......................................1 Sam. xvii. 13.
3. S-hiloh.......................................1 Sam. iii. 21.
4. H-adassah.......................................Esther ii. 7.
5. A-malekites.......................................1 Sam. xxx. 1.
6. N-aamah.......................................Gen. iv. 22.
7. D-amascus.......................................Acts ix. 19, 20.

8. B-enhadad .... 1 Kings xx. 32.
9. E-phesus .... Acts xix. 1—9.
10. C-armel .... 1 Sam. xxv. 2, 3.
11. L-ydia .... Acts xvi. 14, 15.
12. E-gypt .... Gen. xvi. 1.
13. A-bsalom .... 2 Sam. xviii. 18.
14. N-isroch .... 2 Kings xix. 37.

KEY TO BIBLE STUDY, NO 76.—PATIENCE.—Rom. v. 3.

1. P-aul .... 1 Tim. i. 1.
2. A-bel .... Gen. iv. 11.
3. T-imothv .... 2 Tim. iii.. 15.
4. I-sraelites .... Exod. xix. 4, 5.
5. E-sau .... Gen. xxv. 33.
6. N-athaniel .... John i. 45, 49.
7. C-anaan .... Ex. iii. 8.
8. E-phraim .... Gen. xlviii. 20.

KEY TO BIBLE STUDY, NO. 77.—CLEANSE THOU ME FROM SECRET FAULTS.—Psa. xix. 12.

1. C-ain .... Gen. iv. 12.
2. L-amech .... Gen. v. 28.
3. E-ve .... Gen. iii. 20.
4. A-dam .... Gen. iii. 20.
5. N-ehemiah .... Neh. i. 4.
6. S-aul .... 1 Sam. xv. 17-30.
7. E-paphroditus .... Phil. ii. 25.
8. T-ertius .... Rom. xvi. 20.
9. H-achilah .... I Sam. xxiii. 19.
10. O-ded .... 2 Chron. xxviii. 9.
11. U-rijah .... 2 Kings xvi. 11.
12. M-anoah .... Jud. xiii. 17.
13. E-d .... Josh. xxii. 34.
14. F-elix .... Acts xxiv. 27.
15. R-ehoboam .... 2 Chron. x. 13.
16. O-n .... Gen. xli. 45.
17. M-oab .... 2 Kings iii. 27.

18. S-arah............................Gen. xviii. 11.
19. E-sau ....Gen. xxxiii. 19.
20. C-yrus............................Isa. xlv. 1.
21. R-achab............................Jer. xxxv. 6.
22. E-zek............................Gen. xxvi. 21.
23. T-homas............................John xx. 19.
24. F-estus............................Acts xxv. 9-11.
25. A-chan............................Josh. vii. 20.
26. U-zzah............................2 Sam. vi. 6.
27. L-azarus............................John xi. 43.
28. T-ertullus............................Acts xxiv. 2.
29. S-amuel............................1 Sam. xv. 22.

KEY TO BIBLE STUDY, NO 78.—DRAW NIGH TO GOD.—Jas. iv. 8.

1. D-aniel............................1 Chron. iii. 1.
2. R-iblah............................2 Kings xxv 6.
3. A-haziah's............................2 Kings xi. 1.
4. In-a-well............................2 Sam. xvii. 18, 19.
5. N-ob............................1 Sam. xxii. 19.
6. I-shbi-benob............................2 Sam. xxi. 16.
7. G-oliath............................1 Sam. xvi. 23.
8. H-anani............................2 Chron. xvi 7.
9. T-hebez............................Jud. ix. 50-54.
10. O-rpah............................Ruth i. 14.
11. G-adara............................Mark v. 1-9.
12. O-rnan............................1 Chron. xxi. 18.
13. D-othan............................2 Kings xi. 13.

KEY TO BIBLE STUDY, NO. 79.—I WILL COME AGAIN.—
John xiv. 3.

1. I-ssachar............................Gen. lix. 14.
2. W-isdom............................Prov. viii. 30.
3. I-saac............................Gen. xxi. 16.
4. L-evites............................Num. i. 50.
5. L-ehi............................Jud. xv. 9.

6. C-ain..............................Gen. iv. 16.
7. O-badiah..........................1 Kings xviii. 4.
8. M-elchizedec.......................Gen. xiv. 18.
9. E-li...............................1 Sam. iii. 13.

10. A-hithophels.......................2 Sam. xvii. 7.
11. G-omorrah.........................Gen. xix. 28.
12. A-himaaz..........................2 Sam. xvii. 17.
13. I-chabod...........................1 Sam. iv. 22.
14. N-ebo.............................Deut. xxxiv. 1, 5.

KEY TO BIBLE STUDY, NO. 80.—JESUS WEPT.—John xi. 35.

1. J-oppa.............................Acts ix. 39.
2. E-limelech..........................Ruth i. 2.
3. S-hephatiah........................2 Sam. iii. 4.
4. U-zziah...........................2 Chron. xxvi. 1.
5. S-tephanas.........................2 Cor. xv. 25.

6. W-onderful..........................Isa. ix. 6.
7. E-liab.............................1 Sam. xvii. 28.
8. P-adanaram........................Gen. xxviii. 2.
9. T-erah.............................Gen. xi. 31.

KEY TO BIBLE STUDY, NO. 81.—OVERCOME EVIL WITH GOOD.—Rom. xii. 21.

1. O-phir............................2 Chron. viii. 18.
2. V-ine.........................Ps. lxx. 8; Is. v. 1.
3. E-zekiel..........................Ezekiel i. 1.
4. R-echabites.......................Jer. xxxv. 2.
5. C-ain..............................Gen. iv. 8.
6. O-thniel..........................Jud. i. 12, 13.
7. M-ary..................Ex. xv. 20; 1 Chron. iv. 17.
8. E-gypt.............................Ex. xx. 33.
9. E-sau.............................Gen. xxvii. 34.
10. V-ophsi..........................Num. xiii. 14.
11. I-srael...........................Gen. xlii. 30.
12. L-azarus.........................Luke xvi. 20.

13. W-omen of Thebez..................Jud. ix. 50.
14. I-bzan............................Jud. xii. 8, 9.

15. T-yre.............. ....Ezek. xxvii. 28.
16. H-ananiah..................................Dan. i. 7.

17. G-erizim..................................Deut. xi. 29.
18. O-badiah............................1 Kings xviii. 4.
19. O-wl.... ....Isa. xiii. 19.
20. D-aniel....................Ezek. xiv. 14; Dan. vi. 14.

KEY TO BIBLE STUDY, NO. 82.—EZRA.—EZRA X. 6.

1. E-l-beth-el..............................Gen. xxxv. 7.
2. Z-ipporah.................................Ex. xviii. 2.
3. R-uth......................................Ruth. i. 16.
4. A-sahel........... ....2 Sam. ii. 18.

KEY TO BIBLE STUDY, NO. 83.—"LET NOT YOUR HEABT BE TROUBLED."—John xiv. 1.

1. L-aodicean.............................. Rev. iii. 14.
E-phesus...................... ....Rev. ii. 1.
T-hyatira................................Rev. ii. 18, 28.

2. N-icodemus... ....John iii. 1, 21.
3. O-nesiphorus.........................2 Tim. i. 16, 18.
4. T-imothy.................................1 Tim. i. 2.

5. Y-oke..................................... Matt. xi. 29.
6. O-lives, Mount of.........................Acts i. 12.
7. U-nity....... ....Ephes. iv. 3.
8. R-edeemer................. ....Psa. xix. 14.

9. H-annah. ....1 Sam. i. 14.
10. E-li.......................................1 Sam. i. 17.
11. A-saph.............................1 Chron. xxv. 1.
12. R-amoth Gilead..........................Deut. iv. 34.
13. T-iberias, Sea of.........................John xxi. 1.

14. B-ethseda, Pool of........ ....John v. 2.
15. E-utychus... .... Acts xx. 9.

16. T-yre.................................Isaiah xxiii. 8.
17. R-ezin ....2 Kings xv. 37.
18. O-badiah......................... ....1 Kings xviii. 4.
19. U-riah................... ....2 Sam. xi. 15.

20. B-athsheba . . . . 2 Sam. xi. 3.
21. L-odebar . . . . 2 Sam. ix. 4, 5.
22. E-sther . . . . Esther viii. 1.
23. D-avid . . . . Matt. i. 1.

KEY TO BIBLE STUDY, NO. 84.—THE NIGHT COMETH.—
John ix. 4.

1. T-heophilus . . . . Luke i. 3; Acts i. 1.
2. H-azeroth . . . . Num. xii. 15, 16.
3. E-phphatha . . . . Mark vii. 34.
4. N-imrod . . . . Gen. x. 8, 9.
5. I-saac . . . . Gen. xxiv. 63.
6. G-ershom . . . . Exodus ii. 22.
7. H-iddekel . . . . Gen. ii. 14.
8. T-roas . . . . 2 Tim. iv. 13.
9. C-ana . . . . John xxi. 2.
10. O-badiah . . . . 1 Kings xviii. 5, 6.
11. M-anasseh . . . . 2 Kings xx. 21.
12. E-non . . . . John iii. 23.
13. T-imothy . . . . Tim. iv. 12.
14. H-aran . . . . Gen. xi. 27.

KEY TO BIBLE STUDY, NO. 85.—"REST IN THE LORD."—
Psalm xxxvii. 7.

1. R-abbah . . . . 2 Sam. xi. 1.
2. E-kron . . . . 2 Kings i. 2.
3. S-amaria . . . . 1 Kings xvi. 32.
4. T-admor . . . . 1 Kings ix. 18
5. I-shmael . . . . Gen. xvii. 20.
6. N-ahash . . . . 1 Sam. xi. 1.
7. T-arshish . . . . Jonah i. 3.
8. H-iel . . . . 1 Kings xvi. 34.
9. E-bedmelech . . . . Jer. xxxviii. 12, 13.
10. L-emuel . . . . Prov. xxxi. 1.
11. O-livet . . . . 2 Sam. xv. 30.
12. R-ipzah . . . . 2 Sam. xxi. 8.
13. D-amascus . . . . Gen. xv. 2.

KEY TO BIBLE STUDY, NO. 86.—RICHES.—Job xxxvi. 19.

1. R-uby..............................Prov. xxxi. 10.
2. I-dol..............................1 Cor. viii. 4.
3. C-amel.............................Matt. xix. 24.
4. H-eavens...........................Psalm viii. 3.
5. E-nd...............................1 Peter iv. 7.
6. S-pikenard.........................John xii. 3.

KEY TO BIBLE STUDY, NO. 87.—ASA—EVE.—2 Chron. xv. 2, Gen. iii. 20.

1. A-b-*e*-l..............................1 Sam. vi. 18.
2. S-i-*v*-an.............................Esther viii. 9.
3. A-r-*e*-tas............................2 Cor. xi. 32.

KEY TO BIBLE STUDY, NO. 88.—SERPENT.—1 Cor. x. 9.

1. S-ight.............................Luke iv. 18.
2. E-yes..............................John xi. 15.
3. R-est..............................Matt. ix. 28.
4. P-erdition.........................2 Peter iii. 7.
5. E-lements..........................2 Peter iii. 10.
6. N-ails.............................John xx. 25.
7. T-hieves...........................Matt. xxvii. 38.

KEY TO BIBLE STUDY, CHRISTMAS, NO. 89. — IMMANUEL. — *Isaiah* vii. 14.

1. I-saiah.............................. ....Isaiah ix. 6, 7.
2. M-artha..................................Luke x. 40, 41.
3. M-ary.......................................Luke x. 39.
4. A-nna....................................Luke ii. 36-38.
5. N-icodemus ....John xix. 39, 40.
6. U-r...Gen. xi. 28, 31.
7. E-mmaus...........................Luke xxiv. 13-35,
8. L-azarus..............................John xi. 43, 44.

KEY TO BIBLE STUDY.—NEW YEARS, NO. 90.—"LOOKING UNTO JESUS."—*Heb.* xii. 2.

1. L-ydia... ....Acts xvi. 14, 15
2. O-nesiphorus...........................2 Tim. i. 16, 18.
3. O-nesimus.........................Philemon 10, 11.
4. K-orah................. ....Numb. xvi. 32, 33.
5. I-saiah........... ....Isaiah ix. 6.
6. N-icodemus............... ....John iii. 1.
7. G-aius....................................3 John 1.
8. U-zziah..........................2 Chron. xxvi. 19, 20.
9. N-athanael.............................John i. 45, 49.
10. T-ychicus...........................Ephesians vi. 21.
11. O-badiah.........................1 Kings xviii. 3, 4.
12. J-udas........................ ....Matt. xxv. 47.
13. E-lisha............................2 Kings v. 10, 14.
14. S-tephen................................Acts vii. 59, 60.
15. U-r..Genesis xi. 31.
16. S-imon.............................Luke xxii. 31, 34.

KEY TO SCRIPTURE ENIGMAS.

KEY TO ENIGMA, NO 1.—DAVID.

KEY TO ENIGMA, NO. 2.—"EVE."—Gen. iii 20.

KEY TO ENIGMA, NO. 3.—"GOG."—Rev. xx. 8, 9.

KEY TO ENIGMA, NO. 4.—THE RIVER THAT WENT OUT OF EDEN.
—Gen. ii. 10.

KEY TO ENIGMA, NO. 5—THE STONE WHICH SLEW GOLIATH.

KEY TO ENIGMA, NO. 6.—SUNDAY.—SABBATH.—Ex. xx. 10.

KEY TO ENIGMA, NO. 7.—BABEL.

1. B-abel.......................................Gen. xi. 9.
2. A-bel.......................................Gen. iv. 4.
3. B-el or Baal...........................Judges ii. 13, etc.
4. El ....Gen. xxxv. 7.

KEY TO ENIGMA, NO. 8.—SINAI.—Exod. xx.

1. Sin.......................................Rom. vi. 23.
2. Ai.......................................Josh. vii. 2.

KEY TO ENIGNA, NO. 9.

First, Morning.................................Psa. xxx. 5.
Second, Star....................................1 Cor. xv. 41.
Whole, MORNING-STAR ....Rev. xxii. 16.

KEY TO ENIGMA, NO. 10.—VINE.—John xv. 5.

1. V-igilance .... 1 Peter v. 8.
2. I-nheritance .... 1 Peter i. 4.
3. N-egligence .... 2 Peter i. 12.
4. E-vidence .... Heb. xi. 1.

KEY TO ENIGMA, NO. 11.—MANOAH.—Judges xiii.

1. Man. 2. Oh! 3. Ah!

KEY TO ENIGMA, NO. 12.—SUBMISSION.—Matt. xviii. 11; Job. i. 11.

KEY TO ENIGMA, NO. 13. JOSEPH'S COFFIN.—Gen. i. 26; Exod. xiii. 19; Josh. xxiv. 32.

KEY TO ENIGMA, NO. 14.

1. Rain .... Isaiah lv. 10.
2. Bow .... Lam. ii. 4.
3. Rainbow .... Gen. ix. 12, 13.

KEY TO ENIGMA, NO. 15.

1. Fig 2. Tree.

Whole, Fig-tree .... Luke xiii. 6; Mark xi. 13, 14, 20, 21.

KEY TO ENIGMA, NO. 16.—"ABRA."—Mark xiv. 36; Rom. viii. 15; Gal. iv. 6.

KEY TO BIBLE ACROSTICS.

KEY TO ACROSTIC, NO. 1.—THE BREASTPLATE—URIM AND THUMMIM.

1. T-oh-*u*..1 Sam. i. 50.
2. H-adadeze-*r*.............................. 2 Sam. viii. 3.
3. E-l-*i*..................................1 Sam. iv. 18, 19.
4. B-ochi-*m*...Jud. ii. 4, 5.
5. R-eb-*a*..Josh. xiii. 21.
6. E-tha-*n*...Psa. 89—title.
7. A-hilu-*d*.....................................2 Sam. viii. 16.
8. S-anballa-*t*..Neh. ii. 10.
9. T-abera-*h*...Num. xi. 3.
10. P-all-*u*..................................1 Chron. v. x. 2, 3.
11. L-eshe-*m*....................Josh. xix. 47, Gen. xxx. 5.
12. A-krabbi-*m*.......................................Num. xxiv. 4.
13. T-o-*i*..2 Sam. viii. 9, 10.
14. E-liaki-*m*...................................2 Kings xviii. 18.

KEY TO EASTER ACROSTIC, NO. 2.—NOW IS CHRIST RISEN FROM THE DEAD.—1 Cor. xv. 20.

1. N-oah..Gen. ix. 20, 21.
2. O-badiah..Obadiah i.
3. W-orship..Matt. iv. 10.
4. I-bzan..Judges xii. 8.
5. S-alem...Gen. xiv. 18.
6. C-apernaum.......................................Matt. iv. 13.
7. H-aggai...Ezra v. 1.
8. R-echabites.......................................Jer. xxxv. 13.
9. I-ttai ....2 Sam. xv. 19.
10. S-enacherib...................................2 Kings xviii. 3.
11. T-obiah..Nem. iv. 3.

12. R-ephidim......................... Exodus xvii. 8.
13. I-shbosheth........................... 2 Sam. iv.
14. S-amuel.............................. 1 Sam. xii. 18.
15. E-benezer............................ 1 Sam. vii. 12.
16. N-ehemiah............................ Nem. i. 11.
17. F-elix.............................. Acts xxiv. 25.
18. R-amah of Benjamin................. 1 Sam. xxviii. 3.
19. O-mri............................... 1 Kings xvi. 16.
20. M-attan............................. 2 Kings xi. 18.
21. T-ertullus........................... Acts xxiv.
22. H-aman.............................. Esther vii. 10.
23. E-bed-meleh the eunuch............. Jer. xxxviii. 7.
24. D-ungeon........................... Jer. xxxviii. 13.
25. E-l-elohe-Israel................... Gen. xxxiii. 20.
26. A-chan............................ Joshua vii, 1.
27. D-evil.............................. Eph. vi. 11.

KEY TO BIBLE ANAGRAMS.

KEY TO ANAGRAM, NO. 1.

Nos. 6, 5, 1, 2, 3 Haman.......................Esther vii. 10.
" 3, 4, 5, 6, Noah............................Gen. x. 1.
" 6, 2, 1, Ham..............................Gen. x. 6.
" 1, 2, 3, Man..............................Gen. iii. 24.
" 1, 2, 4, 3, Maon.........................Josh. xv. 55.
" 3, 2, 5, 1, Naam.......................1 Chron. iv. 15.
" 3, 4, No.................................Jer. lvi. 25.
" 4, 3, On...............................Gen. xli. 45.

KEY TO ANAGRAM, NO. 2.—NEBUCHADNEZZAR.—Dan. ii. 28.

N-er ....1 Sam. xiv. 50.
E-zra....................................Ezra vii. 11.
B-ezer...................................Deut. iv. 43.
U-z...Job. i. 1.
C-ana.......................................John ii. 1.
H-ur....................................Exod. xvii. 12.
A-bana...................................2 Kings v. 12.
D-an.....................................Gen. xlix. 16.
N-un................................Numbers xxvii. 18.
E-hud..................................Judges iii. 15.
Z-eeb..................................Judges vii. 25.
Z-ebah................................Judges viii. 5.
A-bner.....................................2 Sam. ii. 8.
R-euben...............................Deut. xxxiii. 6.

KEY TO ANAGRAM, NO. 3.—JERUSALEM.—Matt. ii. 1.

J-ael.....................................Judges v. 24.
E-lam.......................................Gen. x. 22.
R-am.....................................1 Chron. ii. 9.
U-r...Gen. xv. 7.
S-amuel...................................1 Sam. vii. 6.
A-r.....................................Numb. xxi. 28.
L-emuel..................................Prov. xxxi. 1.
E-sau...................................Gen. xxxvi. 9.
M-ars Hill...............................Acts xvii. 22.

KEY TO SCRIPTURE ALPHABETS.

KEY TO SCRIPTURE ALPHABET, NO. 1.

A-ugustus.................................Luke ii. 1.
B-artimeus.............................Mark x. 46, 52.
C-ain...................................Genesis iv. 8
D-elilah.......................Judges xvi. 4, 21.
E-sau.............................Genesis xxv. 28.
F-estus..................................Acts xxiv. 27.
G-alilee............................Matthew iii. 13.
H-erod......................................Matt. ii. 16.
I-dumea..............................Isaiah xxxiv. 5.
J-acob.....................................Gen. xxxii. 7.
K-irjath-jearim............................1 Sam. vii. 2.
L-ebanon.........................Jeremiah xviii. 14.
M-elchizedek.........................Genesis xiv. 18.
N-abal..............................1 Samuel xxv. 37.
O-nesiphorus.........................II. Tim. i. 16, 18.
P-haraoh......................Exodus viii. 28, 32.
Q-ueen Esther..............................Esther ii. 15.
R-ab-shakeh..................II. Kings xviii. 19, 25.
S-ennacherib...................II. Kings xix. 35, 37.
T-abitha..................................Acts ix. 36, 41.
U-r......................................Nehemiah ix. 7.
V-ashti......................................Esther i. 12.
W-hale.....................................Genesis i. 21.
Y-outhful.................................II. Tim. ii. 22.
Z-accheus ....Luke xix. 24.

KEY TO SCRIPTURE ALPHABET, NO. 2.

A-bsalom ....2 Sam. xviii. 9.
B-abel... ....Gen. xi. 49.
C-armel............................1 Kings xviii. 42, 43.
D-eborah...................................Gen. xxxv. 8.
E-sau...Heb. xii. 16.
F-elix.............................. ....Acts xxiv. 25.
G-abriel....... ....Dan. ix. 21.
H-annah........... ....1 Sam. i. 27, 28.
I-srael..............................Gen. xxxii. 22, 28.
J-ethro........ .... Exodus iii. 1.
K-adesh-barnea................. ....Deut. i. 19.
L-azarus.............................Luke xvi. 20, 21.
M-olech.....................................Lev. xx. 2, 3.
N-oah...................................Gen. vi. 13, 22.
O-phel ....2 Chron. xxvii. 3.
P-atmos..Rev. i. 9.
Q-uartus.................. ....Rom. xvi. 23.
R-achab.......................................Matt. i. 5.
S-amson...................................Jud. xiv. 5, 6.
T-yre.....................................2 Sam. xxiv. 7.
U-phaz...Jer. x. 9.
V-ashti........ ....Esther i. 9, 19.
Z-oar...Gen. xix. 22.

KEY TO SCRIPTURE ALPHABET, NO. 3.

A-hasuerus....................................Esther i. 1.
B-elshazzar..............................Daniel v. 1, 4.
C-aleb... ....Num. xiii. 30, 33.
D-eborah............... ....Judges iv. 4, 14.
E-ngedi...............................1 Sam. xxiv. 1, 17.
F-estus.................................Acts xxvi. 24.
G-ethsemane...............John xviii. 1, 2. Matt. xxvi. 36.
H-ebron.......................................2 Sam. ii. 11.
I-shmael...........................Gen. xvi. 16, xxi. 9.
J-erusalem..........................Psalm cxxxvii. 6.
K-ish..1 Sam. ix. 1, 2.

L-ucifer..............................Isaiah xiv. 12.
M-arcus..............................Col. iv. 10.
N-inevah..............................Zephaniah ii. 13.
O-nesimus..............................Philemon i. 16.
P-udens..............................2 Timothy iv. 21.
R-hoda..............................Acts xii. 13, 14.
T-roas..............................Acts xx. 6, 7.
U-zzah..............................2 Sam. vi. 6, 7.
V-ashti..............................Esther i. 19.
Z-ion..............................Psalm cxxxv. 21.

KEY TO ALPHABET OF SCRIPTURE GEOGRAPHY NO. 4.

A-rnon..............................Num xxii. 36.
B-erea..............................Acts xvii. 10, 11.
C-armel..............................1 Kings xviii. 20, 38.
D-othan..............................Gen. xxxvii. 17.
E-gypt..............................1 Kings x. 28, 29.
F-air Havens..............................Acts xxvii. 8.
G-ezer..............................1 Kings ix. 16.
H-achilah..............................1 Sam xxiii. 19.
I-conium..............................Acts xvi. 2.
J-abbok..............................Gen. xxxii. 22-32.
K-irjath-arba..............................Gen. xxiii. 2.
L-ebanon..............................1 Kings v. 6-9.
M-arah..............................Exodus xv. 23-25.
N-ain..............................Luke vii. 11.
O-phel..............................Neh. xi. 21.
P-atara..............................Acts xxi. 1.
R-ephidim..............................Exodus xvii. 8.
S-iloam..............................John ix. 7.
Tadmor..............................2 Chron. viii. 4.
U-r..............................Gen. xv. 7.
V-ineyards, Plains of the..............................Judges xi. 33.
W-ilderness..............................Numbers xxxiii. 6, 7.
Z-idon..............................Gen. xlix. 13.

APPENDIX.

COMPRISING

Historical, Statistical

AND

Tabular Information.

THE LOST BOOKS.

The books referred to in and by the sacred writers and not comprised in the Bible and known as the lost books of the Bible are as follows:

THE BOOK OF THE WARS OF THE LORD.—Num. xxi. 14. This was probably what its title indicates, a narrative of the Hebrew wars by an unknown author, and of which or of its writer there remains no trace. This was probably used by Moses when writing the Pentateuch.

BOOK OF JASHER.—Josh. x. 13, II. Sam. 1 18. It was supposed to be a collection of poems on historical and other subjects sang by the people as "Jasher" means "Sang."

ELEVEN ADDITIONAL WORKS are referred to by name in the Bible as having been used in composing the Books of 1 and 2 Chronicles, some of which were also used by the compiler of the books of Kings. These eleven are:—

The book of Samuel, the Seer, 1 Chron. xxix. 29.

The book of Nathan, the prophet, 1 Chron. xxix. 29.

The book of Gad, the Seer, 1 Chron. xxix. 29.

The book of Ahijah, the Shilonite, 2 Chron. 9-29.

The vision of Iddo, the Seer, 2 Chron. ix 29.

The book of the Kings of Israel and Judah, 1 Chron. ix. 1.

The book of Shemaiah, the prophet, 2 Chron. xii. 15.

The book of Iddo, the Seer, about genealogies, 2 Ch. xii. 15.

The Story of the prophet Iddo; 2 Chron. xiii. 22.

The Book of Jehu, the son of Hanani, 2 Chron. xx. 34.

The Prophecy of Enoch, Jude 14.

BOOKS OF THE OLD TESTAMENT.

NAME.	CHAPT'S.	DIVISION.	AUTHOR.
Genesis......	50	Books of the Law.	Moses.
Exodus......	40	"	"
Leviticus	27	"	"
Numbers	36	"	"
Deuteronomy	34	"	"
Joshua... ..	24	Historical.	Joshua.
Judges......	21	"	Samuel.?
Ruth	4	"	Samuel.?
1 Samuel. ...	31	"	Samuel, Gad and
2 Samuel.....	24	"	Nathan.
1 Kings	22	"	Nathan, Gad, Ahijah
2 Kings.. ...	25	"	Iddo, Isaiah and others
1 Chronicles.	29	"	Ezra and
2 Chronicles.	36	"	others.
Ezra.........	10	"	Ezra.
Nehemiah....	13	"	Nehemiah.
Esther	10	"	Ezra.?
Job.........	42	Poetical.	Moses.?
Psalms	150	"	David and others.
Proverbs	31	"	Solomon.
Ecclesiastes..	12	"	"
S'ng of Sol'm'n	8	"	"
Isaiah	66	Major Prophets.	Isaiah.
Jeremiah. ...	52	"	Jeremiah.
Lamentations	5	"	"
Ezekiel......	48	"	Ezekiel.
Daniel.......	12	"	Daniel.
Hosea.......	14	Minor Prophets.	Hosea.
Joel.........	3	"	Joel.
Amos........	9	"	Amos.
Obadiah.....	1	"	Obadiah.
Jonah.......	4	"	Jonah.
Micah........	7	"	Micah.
Nahum......	3	"	Nahum.
Habakkuk ..	3	"	Habakkuk.
Zephaniah ..	3	"	Zephaniah.
Haggai	2	"	Haggai.
Zechariah..	14	"	Zechariah.
Malachi.....	4	"	Malachi.

BOOKS OF THE NEW TESTAMENT.

NAME.	CHAPT'S.	DIVISION.	AUTHOR.
Matthew......	28	Historical	Matthew.
Mark.........	16	"	Mark.
Luke	24	"	Luke.
John.........	21	"	John.
The Acts.....	28	"	Luke.
Romans......	16	The Pauline Epistles.	Paul.
1 Corinthians.	16	"	"
1 Corinthians.	13	"	"
Galatians....	6	"	"
Ephesians....	6	"	"
Philippians...	4	"	"
Colossians....	4	"	"
1 Thessalonians	5	"	"
2 Thessalonians	3	"	"
1 Timothy...	6	"	"
2 Timothy....	4	"	"
Titus.........	3	"	"
Philemon	1	"	"
Hebrews......	13	"	Paul.?
Epistle of James	5	General Epistles.	James.
1 Peter.......	5	"	Peter.
2 Peter.......	3	"	"
1 John.......	5	"	John.
2 John.......	1	"	"
3 John.......	1	"	"
Jude.........	1	"	Jude.
Revelation. ..	22	Prophetical	John.

INTERESTING BIBLE FACTS.

The learned Prince of Grenada, heir to the Spanish throne, imprisoned by order of the Crown for fear he should aspire to the throne, was kept in solitary confinement in the old prison at the Place of Skulls, Madrid. After thirty-three years in this living tomb death came to his release, and the following researches taken from the Bible and marked with an old nail on the rough walls of his cell told how the brain sought employment through the weary years:

In the Old Testament.		New Testament.	Total.
Books,	39	27	66
Chapters,	920	266	1,195
Verses,	23,214	7,959	31,173
Words,	592,493	181,253	773,746
Letters,	2,728,100	838,380	3,566,480

The middle chapter and the shortest in the Bible is Psalm 117.

The middle verse in the Bible is Psalm cxviii. 8.

The word "and" occurs in the Old Testament 10,684 times.

The word "Jehovah" occurs 6,855 times.

In the Bible the word "Lord" is found 1,853 times.

"Reverend" occurs but once and that in Psalm cxi. 9.

The middle book of the Old Testament is Proverbs.

The middle chapter is Job xxix.

The middle verse is II. Chronicles xx. 13.

The shortest verse is I. Chron. i. 25; the longest, Esther viii. 9.

All the letters of the alphabet are in Ezra vii. 21, except *f* and *j*.

II. Kings xix. and Isaiah xxxvii. are alike.

The book of Esther contains 10 chapters, but neither the word "Lord" nor "God," are to be found in it.

The middle book of the New Testament is II. Thessalonians.

The middle chapter is between Romans xiii. and xiv.

The middle verse is Acts xvii. 17.

The shortest verse is John xi. 35.

In Psalm cvii. four verses are alike—the 8-15-21, and 31.

Acts of the Apostles xxvi. is the finest chapter to read.

Psalm xxiii. is regarded as the most beautiful chapter.

The four most inspiring promises in the Bible are John xiv. 2; John vi. 37; St Matthew xi. 28 and Psalm xxxvii. 4.

THE FATE OF THE APOSTLES.

St. Matthew was martyred in a city in Ethiopia.

St. Mark was dragged through the streets of Alexandria, in Egypt, till he expired.

St. Luke was hanged upon an olive tree in Greece.

St. John, after having been put into a caldron of boiling oil at Rome, and receiving no hurt, died a natural death at Ephesus, in Asia.

St. Peter was crucified at Rome, and, according to his request, with his head downward, thinking himself unworthy to die in the posture which his Lord had died.

St. James the Great was beheaded at Jerusalem.

St. James the Less was thrown from a pinnacle of the temple and beaten to death with a fullar's club.

St. Phillip was hanged against a pillar at Hierapolis, a city in Phrygia, till he expired.

St. Thomas was pierced through the body with a lance, at Corarandel, in the East Indies.

St. Bartholomew met his death by being flayed alive.

St. Jude was shot to death with arrows.

St. Simeon, the zealot, was crucified in Persia.

St. Andrew was bored to a cross, from which he preached till he expired.

St. Matthias was first stoned and afterward beheaded.

St. Barnabas was stoned to death by the Jews at Salamais.

St. Paul the great Apostle to the Gentiles, was beheaded at Rome by the tyrant Nero.

Such was the fate of the first preachers of the gospel of peace, according to tradition and the best accounts we have of their end, and truly they were "sent forth as sheep among wolves."

THE SEVEN BIBLES OF THE WORLD.

THE KORAN OF THE MOHAMMEDANS.

The name Koran is derived from an Arabic word *guard*, to "read," and this from the older Shemitic, meaning to "cry aloud," to "pronounce," "utter," "dictate." It is supposed to have obtained its name from the claim made, that it was *dictated* to Mohammed by the angel Gabriel. This Mohammed was born at Mecca about 570 A.D. and died at Medena 632.

In his fifteenth year (610) he claimed that he received a visit from the Angel Gabriel in the wild solitude of Mount Hira near Mecca. He was frightened and attempted to commit suicide, but his wife predicted that he would be the prophet of Arabia. The angel appeared to him again in a vision, saying "I am Gabriel, and thou art Mohammed, the prophet of God. Fear not." His public career as a reformer now began. The revelations of Gabriel, now like the sound of a bell and again like the voice of a man, continued from time to time for more than twenty years and are deposited in the Koran. Mohammed dictated his revelations leaf by leaf as occasion demanded. A year after his death, Zayd, his chief amanuensis collected the scattered fragments "from palm leaves, and tablets of white stone and from the breast of men" but without regard to chronological order.

The Koran has 114 chapters. These vary greatly in their length, from 40 octavo pages to a short paragraph containing a verse or two. Besides this there is an artificial division into sixty-five equal parts, and each of these again subdivided into four equal parts. There are seven principal editions or ancient copies of the Koran, but they all agree in the same total of words which are 77,639 and the same total of letters 323,015.

The Koran admits the Divine authority of the Jewish Scriptures, makes the fear of a personal God the groundwork of its religion. It promulgates the doctrine of Allah's sovereignty, of his immutable throne, of his eternal decrees, and of his continual personal providence. It teaches a great judgment to come, a resurrection-day of final account, "the book" in which each man shall read the true value of the life lived by him in this preparatory world, the meeting with his sins that have gone before him, and a sublime vigorous doctrine of prayer. But it has no reference to the doctrine of the cross or any hint of the mediatorial idea. Besides it has three great positive deformities—the doctrine of polygamy, of slavery and the sensual aspect it gives to the happiness of Paradise. The Koran is the most positive rival of the Bible, but infinitely below it in purity, interest and value. The one is of the earth, earthly; the other is from heaven, heavenly. The Koran is sectional: the Bible is universal.

THE THREE VEDAS OF THE HINDOOS.

The word Vedas is derived from the Sanscrit *Va'dahaz* "to know." The three Vedas are in Sanscrit, in prose and hymns, The hymns, numbering about 1000, and though formerly one work, they are divided into four parts; these are the sacred writings of the Hindoos, of great antiquity, but of uncertain date. They are regarded as containing the true knowledge of God, of His religion and of His worship. These Vedas vary greatly in age, represent many stages of thought and worship, the earliest being the simplest. The Vedas have their origin in the wonder with which early man regarded the universe and the operations going on in it. They consist, therefore, largely of highly figurative addresses to the great powers of nature under seemingly different representations, between whom, however, a great power (OM) is divinely recognized. Graduallv these powers became more and more endowed with personality, and ultimately came to be regarded as real divinities, to whose number more were gradually added.

The hymns of the Vedas embrace the earliest known lyrics of the Aryan settlers of India. Dr. Monier Williams thinks they were probably composed by a succession of poets at different dates, between 1500 and 1000 B. C. The third division of each Veda is not earlier than 600 B.C. and shows the working of the Aryan mind upon religious and philosophic problems. Writers upon this subject mark the beginnings of certain Vedic works with 1200, 1000, 800 and 600 years B. C.

THE ZENDAVESTA OF THE PERSIANS.

Zendavesta, a Persian compound word, meaning (the living word, or commentary and text), is the collective name of the Sacred books of the Parsees containing the doctrines of the ancient Persian religion founded by Zoroaster. It is supposed he was born in Bacria, his father's name being Pournsaspa. This is all that is known of his personal life. The time in which he lived is utterly uncertain, some placing him 500 years before Christ, and others 6000 years before Plato.

The religious system which he developed is a complete dualism, Ormuz being the creator and ruler of all that is good and bright, Ahriman the chief of that which is dark and evil.

To each of these supreme beings belongs a member of subordinate spirits and all that exists is divided between these two realms. Man has to choose and according to his choice he will after death go to Ormuz or to Ahriman. The way to the first is pure thought, pure speech and pure actions. The only object of worship was fire. The priests who maintained and conducted the worship were the Magi.

THE EDDAS OF THE SCANDINAVIANS.

The two Eddas (or Great grandmothers) is a name given to the books by Bishop Svejusson, to indicate that they are the mothers of all Scandinavian poetry, but, they are attributed to Frodi, a priest in Iceland, retiring between 1054 and 1133 A.D. The older one consists of old mythic poems. It contains a system of old Scandinavian mythology with narratives of the exploits of the gods and heroes, and some account of the religious doctrines of the ancient Scandinavians. Saemund, one of the earlier Christian priests in Iceland who was born about the middle of the eleventh century, and died in 1133 A.D., having a fondness for Paganism collected certain old pagan songs of unknown authorship, written at different periods between the sixth and eighth centuries, mostly of a religious character. This collection is called *The Elder* or *Poetic Edda*, and embodies thirty-nine poems. The younger or prose Edda is a collection of prose of a similar character. This is the work of Gnorro Sturleson, educated by Saemund's grandson, and nearly a century after him, put together. He also wrote a kind of prose synopsis of the whole mythology elucidated by new fragments of traditionary verse. This Sturleson was born in Iceland in 1178 and was assassinated there in 1241 on his return from Norway.

THE TRI-PITAKA OF THE BUDDHISTS.

Pitaka (literally basket) is with the Buddhists a term denoting a division of their sacred literature, and occurs in combination with *tri* , "three,"—*Tripitaka* meaning the three great divisions of the canonical works, the *Veiaya* (discipline), abhidharma (metaphysics), and *Sutra* (aphorisms in prose), and collectively therefore the whole Buddhist's code. Gantama Broddha, the alleged founder of Booddhism was born 624 or 556 B.C. in Northern India. The story of his life is a tissue of montrous falls, but after a life of severe asceticism, he began to publish abroad the deep things his meditations had revealed. His doctrines were proclaimed orally but not written. After his death about 543 five hundred of his disciples held a council and each recited what he had heard, then the whole assembly repeated aloud what had been thus gathered up. By a second and third council these teachings were formulated ; but it is not proved that any written statement of them is earlier than B.C. 100–88, although some are of opinion that the Buddhist Canonical Scriptures as they now exist were fixed two and a half centuries before the Christian era. It is yet unsettled whether the original language was Sanscrit or Pali, probably the latter.

THE FIVE KING OF THE CHINESE.

In the five cannonical or classical books called "King" are the sacred writings of the chinese. "King" means "web of cloth" or the warp that keeps the threads in their place. They contain the best sayings of the best sages on the duties of life. These sayings cannot be traced to a period higher than the eleventh century. Confucius collected them from various sources in the sixth century B.C., and in this collection they have been pretty faithfully handed down to us. In these books are the oldest monuments of Chinese poetry, history, philosophy and jurisprudence, some portions of which belong to the most ancient uninspired writings of the human race.

Next to the five King in value are the *Sse-Shee* or the four books. These were written by Confucius and his disciples, and must be regarded as the most trustworthy source of insight into the intellectual and political life of the Chinese.

THE SCRIPTURES OF THE CHRISTIANS.

The Bible (Greek Ta Bablia) "The Books" is the name given by Chrysostom in the fourth century A.D. to that collection of sacred writings recognized by Christians as the documents of their divinely inspired religion. In language and contents they are divided into two parts—the Old and New Testament.

The Old Testament is a collection of thirty-nine books written partly in the Hebrew and partly in the Chaldaic language, and containing all that remains of Hebrew-Chaldaic literature down to the middle of the second century B.C. A period of about four hundred years elapsed between the writing of the last book in the Old Testament and the writing of the first book in the New. The New Testament is a collection of twenty-seven books containing the history and doctrines of Christianity written mostly in the Greek language by eight authors and covering a period of about sixty years.

The books of the Holy Bible were written in different ages from Moses to John (B.C. 1650 to A.D. 90 a period of more than 1700 years) by men specially prepared for the work by direct inspiration from the Divine source of all knowledge.

THE DOUAY BIBLE so-called because it was translated by English Roman Catholic divines connected with the colleges at Rheims and Douay in France. Both Testaments were translated from the Vulgate or Latin which was the version authorized in the Roman Catholic Church. The New was published at Rheims in 1582 and the Old at Douay in 1609-16.

Among the most notable changes are those in the Ten Commandments. The second is omitted and the tenth divided into two.

THE NAME OF GOD

[*In Seventy Languages or Dialects.*]

1. Aeolian............ Ilos.
2. Arabic............Allah.
3. Assyrian...........Ellah.
4. Breton............Doue.
5. Bengali..........Ishuar.
6. Catalan............ Deu.
7. Creolese...........Godt.
8. Chaldiac....... ....Elah.
9. Chinese........... Zung.
10. Croatian...........Bogu.
11. Danish.............Gud.
12. Dalmatian..........Rogt.
13. Doric...............Ilos.
14. Dutch.............Godt.
15. Egyptian.......... Zeut.
16. English.............God.
17. Etruvian...........Chur.
18. Finnish ....Jumala.
19. Flemish...........Goed.
20. Fiji..............Kalou.
21. French............Dieu.
22. Galic............... Dia.
23. German............Gott.
24. Greenland........Gudib.
25. Greek ....Theos.
26. Hawaiian...........Akua.
27. Hebrew.......... Eloah.
28. Hungarian... ..... Isten.
29. Hindostanee........Rain.
30. Icelandic .... Guo.
31. Irish ....Dia.
32. Italian.............Iddio.
33. Japanese..........Kami.
34. Kafir.............Utixo.
35. Latin....... ......Deus.
36. Lapland ....Jubmal.
37. Madagascar. ....Tannan.
38. Magi.................Orsi.
39. Malay...............Alla.
40. Manx (Isle of Man)...Jee.
41. Mohawk........Yehovah.
42. Norwegian.........Gud.
43. Namacqua.........Eloba.
44. Old German.........Diet.
45. Persian.............Syra.
46. Piedmontese......Iddiou.
47. Polacca .... Bung.
48. Polish..............Bog.
49. Portuguese ....Deos.
50. Provencal....... ..Dion.
51. Peruvian............Lian.
52. Russian............Bott.
53. Runnic...............As.
54. Rorotongan ....Atua.
55. Saxon ....God.
56. Spanish. ....Dios.
57. Scandinavian.......Odin.
58. Swedish............Gud.
59. Swiss....... ......Gott.
60. Slavic. ....Buch.
61. Syrian ....Adad.
62. Teutonic............Goth.
63. Tembloan.. ......Fetiyo.
64. Turkish............Alah.
65. Tartar..........Magatal.
66. Tyrrhenian.........Eher.
67. Vandois ....Diou.
68. Wallachian.........Zenc.
69. Welsh..............Duw.
70. Zulu...............Tixo.

WORDS MENTIONED BUT ONCE IN THE BIBLE.

There are 2,300 words that are mentioned only once in the Bible. The following list are among the most notable :

Afterноon ..... Judges xix. 8.
Anna............Luke ii. 36.
Ancestor.......Lev. xxvi. 45.
Ancle.......... Ezek. xlvii. 3.
Anvil..............Isa. xli. 7.
Arches............Ezek. xl. 16.
Aunt............Lev. xviii. 14.
Back-biter.........Rom. i. 30.
Back-slider.....Prov. xiv. 14.
Back-bone.........Lev. iii. 9.
Ball..............Isa. xxii. 18.
Barbers...........Ezek. v. 1.
Beacon..........Isa. xxx. 17.
Bellows...........Jer. vi. 29.
Benches........Ezek. xxvii. 6.
Benefactors.... Luke xxii. 25.
Betrayers........ Acts vii. 52.
Bishopric...........Acts i. 20.
Blaze.............Mark i. 45.
Bosses............Job. xv. 26.
Bowmen..........Jer. iv. 29.
Bribery...........Job. xv. 34.
Bursting........Isa. xxx. 14.
Cab...........2 Kings vi. 25.
Cabins........Jer. xxxvii. 16.
Candles...........Zeph. i. 12.
Cart-rope.... ....Isa. v. 18.
Cart-wheel.....Isa. xxviii. 17.
Castor... .... Acts xxviii. 11.
Cellars.....1 Chon. xxvii. 28.
Chapel......... Amos vii. 13.
Charmed ....Jer. viii. 17.
Chatter ....Isa. xxxviii. 14.
Checker-work.1 Kings vii. 16.
Cheek-bone..... . Psa. iii. 7.
Chickens......Matt. xxiii. 37.
Chimney........Hosea xiii. 3.
Chrysolite..... .. Rev. xxi. 20.
Coffin............ Gen. l. 26.
Colony..........Acts xvi. 12.
Colored..........Rev. xvii. 3.
Confectionaries.1 Sam. viii. 13.
Conquerors......Rev. viii. 37.
Constellations ....Isa. xiii. 10.
Coppersmith....2 Tim. iv. 14.
Cousin............Luke i. 36.
Cracknels. ....1 Kings xiv. 3.
Creditors.............Isa. l. 1.
Cripple. ....Acts xiv. 8.
Crisping-pins......Isa. iii. 22.
Cup-bearer.........Neh. i. 11.
Damnable.........2 Pet. ii. 1.
Dealer....... ....Isa. xxi. 2.
Decently .....1 Cor. xiv. 20.
Defamed........1 Cor. iv. 13.
Delicacies .... ..Rev. xviii. 3.
Detest... ....Deut. vii. 26.
Devilish.... ....James iii. 15.
Discerner........ Heb. iv. 12.
Disgrace........ ...Jer. xiv. 21.
Doctor............Acts v. 34.
Drinks.......... Heb. ix. 10.

Driver.........Job. xxxix 7.
Dropsy..........Luke xiv. 2.
Dry-shod.... .....Isa. xi. 15.
Dues........... Rom. xiii. 7.
Dwarf...........Lev. xxi. 20.
Easter.............Acts xii. 4.
Ebony.........Exk. xxvii. 15.
Embroider.....Ex. xxviii. 39.
Empire...........Esth. i. 20.
Evangelists ......Eph. iv. 11.
Evenings............Jer. v. 6.
Execution........ Esth. ix. 1.
Eye-brows.....,..Lev. xiv. 9.
Farm...........Matt. xxii. 5.
Fashions.......Ezek. xlii. 11.
Fellow-citizens....Eph. ii. 19.
Ferry-boat.. ..2 Sam. xix. 18.
Fish-hooks....... Amos iv. 2.
Flag.............Job. viii. 11.
Forgers...........Job. xiii. 4.
Freckled.........Lev. xiii. 39.
Frozen....... Job xxxviii. 30.
Gardener........John xx. 15.
Gay..............James ii. 3.
Grandmother..... 2 Tim. i. 5.
Grease..........Psa. cxix. 70.
Grey-hound....Prov. xxx. 31.
Gulf ....Luke xvi. 26.
Handkerchiefs...Acts xix. 12.
Hats.............Dan. iii. 21.
Heresy.........Acts xxiv. 14.
Heretic............Titus iii. 10.
Hymn...... ... Matt. xxvi. 30.
Immortal........1 Tim. i. 17.
Influences....Job xxxviii. 31.
Intelligence.......Dan. xi. 30.
Inventors.........Rom. i. 30.
Itch.........Deut. xxviii. 27.

Jailer.......... ....Acts xvi. 23.
Juice... ....Sol. Song viii. 2.
Julia.............Rom. xvi. 15.
Kettle...........1 Sam. ii. 14.
Kicked........Deut xxxii. 15.
Ladder.......Gen. xxviii. 12.
Land-marks......Job. xxiv. 2.
Lanterns........John xviii. 3.
Lioness...........Ezek. xix. 2.
Liquors..........Ex. xxii. 29.
Looking-glass.Job. xxxvii. 18.
Lukewarm. ......Rev. iii. 16.
Magician.........Dan. ii. 10.
Magnificence.....Acts xix. 27.
Malefactor.....John xviii. 30.
Malicious... ....3 John i. 10.
Mansions........John xiv. 2.
Martyrs..........Rev. xvii. 6.
Master-builder...1 Cor. iii. 10.
Meal-time.........Ruth ii. 14.
Meddled.......Prov. xvii. 14.
Melons...........Num. xi. 5.
Mess............2 Sam. xi. 8.
Mile............ Matt. v. 41.
Millions........Gen xxiv. 60.
Minstrel.......2 Kings iii. 15.
Modest.. ....1 Tim. ii. 9.
Moles............. Isa. ii. 20.
Monuments........Isa. lxv. 4.
Mortgaged.........Neh. v. 3.
Mourner.........2 Sam xiv. 2.
Mufflers........... Isa. iii. 19.
Muse...........Psa. cxliii. 5.
Musicians......Rev. xviii. 22.
Nailing............Col. ii. 14.
Native.........Her. xxii. 10.
Necromancer..Deut. xviii. 11.
News........ Prov. xxv. 25.

Novice.......... 1 Tim. iii. 6.
Oar.......... Ezek. xxvii. 29.
Observer..... Deut. xviii. 10.
Onions............Num xi. 5.
Opinions....1 Kings xviii. 21.
Oration..........Acts xii. 21.
Orchard...Song of Sol. iv. 13.
Orphans....... ...Lam v. 3.
Ostrich.........Job xxxix. 13.
Outcast.. ......Jer. xxx. 17.
Outlandish.. ....Neh xiii. 26.
Outrageous....Prov. xxvii. 4.
Ovens... ....Ex. viii. 3.
Overcharged......2 Cor. ii. 5.
Overspread.......Gen. ix. 19.
Overwhelm........Job vi. 27.
Owe.............Rom xiii. 8.
Paddle.........Deut. xxiii. 13.
Painting..........Jer. iv. 20.
Parlors...1 Chron. xxviii. 11.
Parties......... Ex. xxii. 9.
Pastor..........Jer. xvii. 16.
Patterns..........Heb. ix. 23.
Paws............Lev. xi. 27.
Payment......Matt. xviii. 25.
Pedigrees.........Num. i. 18.
Penknife......Jer. xxxvi. 23.
Philosophers....Acts xvii. 18.
Phylacteries....Matt. xxiii. 5.
Pipers..........Rev. xviii. 22.
Planets.... ..2 Kings xxiii. 5.
Plantation.......Ezek. xvii 7.
Plastered........Lev. xiv. 48.
Plough..........Luke ix. 62.
Policy..........Dan. viii. 25.
Polishing.........Lam. iv. 7.
Portray.........Ezek. iv. 1.
Presbytery......1 Tim. iv. 14.
Prices............Acts iv. 44.
Princess........... Lam. i. 1.
Private....... ..2 Pet. .i. 20.
Prognosticators.Isa. xlvii. 13.
Providence......Acts xxiv. 2.
Psalmist......2 Sam. xxiii. 1.
Puffeth up......1 Cor. viii. 1.
Pulpit... ....Neh. viii. 4.
Quantity........Isa. xxii. 24.
Quicksands....Acts xxvii. 17.
Quivered.........Hab. iii. 16.
Ragged........ ...Isa. ii. 21.
Reaper..........Amos ix. 13.
Rebuker...........Hos. v. 2.
Recorded........Neh. xii. 22.
Reformation......Heb. ix. 10.
Remembrances ..Job xiii. 12.
Revengers.....2 Sam. xiv. 11.
Reverend.........Psa. cxi. 9.
Reviving..........Ezra ix. 8.
Rewarder....... . Heb. xi. 6.
Rifled.......... Zec. xiv. 2.
Ringleader......Acts xxiv. 5.
Rip..........2 Kings viii. 12.
Rites....... .... Num. ix. 3.
Roasteth........Prov. xii. 27.
Rovers.......1 Chron. xii. 21.
Rubbing..........Luke vi. 1.
Rude............2 Cor. xi. 6.
Sacrilege ....Rom. ii. 22.
Sadness.... .... Ecclec. vii. 3.
Sailors....... .Rev. xviii. 17.
Sap.............Psa. civ. 16.
Satiate..........Jer. xxxi. 14.
Scaffold......2 Chron. vi. 13.
Scalp... ... ..Psa. lxviii. 21.
Scorch...........Rev. xvi. 8.
Seed-time......Gen. viii. 22.

Senators.... .. ..Psa. cv. 22.
Shearer........ .Acts viii. 32.
Sheep-skins.......Heb. xi. 37.
Shiloh.... .....Gen. xlix. 10.
Shoulderblade...Job xxxi. 22.
Shroud.........Ezek. xxxi. 3.
Screech-owl....Isa. xxxiv. 14.
Sighs ....Lam. i. 22.
Sister-in-law.......Ruth i. 15.
Slave... ....Jer. ii. 14.
Snorting........Jer. viii. 16.
Snout...........Prov. xi. 22.
Spectacle.. ......1 Cor. iv. 9.
Spiced......Songs Sol. viii. 2.
Spite..............Psa. x. 14.
Spitting............ Isa. l. 6.
Spokesman........Ex. iv. 16.
Sprout.......... .Job xiv. 7.
Stacks............Ex. xxii. 6.
Stamping........Jer. xlvii. 3.
Star-gazers... ..Isa. xlvii. 13.
Stoics... ....Acts xvii. 18.
Stomach.........1 Tim. v. 23.
Stripling......1 Sam. xvii. 56.
Sue............. Matt. v. 40.
Sundry.............Heb. i. 1.
Supped.........1 Cor. xi. 25.
Supreme.........1 Pet. ii. 13.
Sureties.......Prov. xxii. 26.
Tattlers.... ......1 Tim. v. 13.
Taverns.......Acts xxviii. 15.
Taxes............Dan. xi. 20.
Temper........Ezek. xlvi. 14.
Traitor... ....Luke vi. 16.
Translate.......2 Sam. iii. 10.
Treachery.....2 Kings ix. 23.
Tutors.......... ..Gal iv. 2.
Unmerciful........Rom. i. 31.
Usurp...........1 Tim. ii. 12.
Vagabonds... .. Psa. cix. 10.
Vomited.........Jonah ii. 10.
Voyage........Acts xxvii. 10.
Wagon.......... Num. vii. 3.
Water-spouts. ...Psa. xlii. 7.
Way-marks.....Jer. xxxi. 21.
Weasel..........Lev. xi. 29.
Wedlock....... Ezek. xvi. 38.
Western......Num. xxxiv. 6.
Wines............Isa. xxv. 6.
Wintered......Acts xxviii. 11.
Wires...........Ex. xxxix. 3.
Wits......... . Psa. cvii. 27.
Worker......1 Kings vii. 14.
Wreath..... 2 Chron. iv. 13.
Yoked..........2 Cor. vi. 14.
Youthful........2 Tim. ii. 22.

BIBLE PROPER NAMES.

And their meanings.

Adam	Red	Gen. ii. 19
Alexander	Defending men	Mark xv. 21
Amasa	Burden	2 Sam. xvii, 25
Amos	Burden	Amos. i. 1
Anak	Long Neck (?)	Num. xiii. 22
Aquila	An eagle	Acts xviii. 2
Aristarchus	Best ruling	Acts xix. 29
Aristobulus	Best counsellor	Rom. xvi. 10
Artaxerxes	Honored king (?)	Ezra iv. 8
Asa	Physician	1 Kings xv. 8
Asaph	Collector	2 Kings xviii, 18
Asher	Fortunate, happy	Gen. xxx. 13
Augustus	Venerable	Luke ii. 1
Belshazzar	Protects	Dan. v. 1
Benjamin	Of the right hand	Gen. xxxv. 18
Beulah	Married	Isa. lxii. 4
Cain	Possession	Gen. iv. 1
Caleb	A dog	Num. xxvi. 65
Christ	The anointed	Matt. i. 1
Cyrus	The Sun	2 Chron. xxxvi. 22.
Daniel	God's judge	Dan. i. 6
Deborah	Bee	Judges iv. 4
Dinah	Vindicated	Gen. xxx. 21
Dorcas	Gazelle	Acts ix. 36
Ebenezer	Stone of help	1 Sam. iv. 1
Eli	My God	Matt. xxvii. 46
Elijah	My God is Jehovah.	1 Kings xvii. 1
Elisha	God is salvation	1 Kings xix. 16
Elishaphat	Whom God judges.	2 Chron. xxiii. 1
Elizur	God is a rock	Num. i. 5
Emmanuel	God with us	Matt. i. 23
Enoch	Experienced (?)	Gen. iv. 17
Epaphroditus	Handsome	Phil. ii. 25
Erastus	Beloved	Acts xix. 22

Esau..............	Hairy............	Gen. xxv. 25......
Esther............	Star..............	Esther ii. 7........
Eutychus.........	Fortunate.........	Acts xx. 9.........
Eve...	Life...............	Gen. iii. 20........
Ezekiel............	Whom God will	strengthen. Ezek. i. 3
Ezra..............	Help..	Ezra vii. 1........
Felix.............	Happy.	Acts xxiii. 24......
Festus............	Joyful.......	Acts xxiv. 27......
Fortunatus........	Prosperous........	1 Cor. xvi. 17......
Gabriel...........	Man of God.......	Dan. viii. 16: .....
Gamaliel..........	Benefit of God.....	Num. i. 10.........
Gideon............	One who cuts down.	Judges vi. 11......
Hagar	Flight.	Gen. xvi. 3.......
Hannah..........	Gracious..........	1 Sam. i. 2.... ....
Heman...........	Faithful..'........	1 Kings iv. 31......
Hermon..........	Lofty.............	Deut. iii. 8......
Hezekiah.........	The might of Jeh-	ovah 2 Kings xviii. 1
Hiram............	Noble (?)..........	2 Sam. v. 11.......
Hobab............	Beloved...........	Num. x. 29........
Hosea............	Salvation.........	Hosea i. 1.........
Huldah......... ..	Weasel...........	2 King xxii. 14.....
Ichabod	Inglorious........	1 Sam. iv. 21......
Ira.............	Watchful..........	2 Sam. xx. 26 .....
Ishaiah....... ...	Whom Jehovah	lends. 1 Chron. vii. 3
Ishmael...........	Whom God hears..	Gen. xvi. 15. .....
Israel............	Soldier of God.....	Gen. xxxii. 28 .....
Jacob.............	Supplanter........	Gen. xxv. 26......
Jarius............	God enlightens....	Mark v. 22 ......
Japheth..........	Extension	Gen. v. 32.........
Japho.......... .	Beauty...........	Josh. xix. 46.......
Jared.............	Descent..........	Gen. v. 15.........
Jedaiah...........	Jehovah knoweth..	1 Chron. xxiv. 7...
Jehoshaphat	Whom Jehovah ju	dgeth. 1 Kings xv. 24
Jehovah..........	The Eternal One...	Ex. vi. 3.........
Jemima..........	Dove.............	Job. xlii. 14. .....
Jeremiah.........	Whom Jehovah has	appointed..Jer. i. 1
Jerusha..........	Possession........	2 Kings xv. 33.....
Jesus.............	Saviour...........	Matt. i. 21........

Name	Meaning	Reference
Job	A desert	Gen. xlvi. 13
Joel	Jehovah is might	Joel i. 1
Jonah	Dove	2 Kings xiv. 25
Jonathan	Whom Jehovah	gave..1 Sam. xiii. 2
Joseph	He shall add	Gen. xxx. 24
Joshua	Jehovah is salvation	Num. xiv. 6
Josiah	Whom Jehovah h	eals. 2 Kings xxi. 24
Jotham	Jehovah is upright.	Judges ix. 5
Katurah	Incense	Gen. xxv. 1
Laban	White	Gen. xxiv. 29
Leah	Languid	Gen. xxix. 16
Lemuel	(devoted) To God	Prov. xxxi 1
Levi	Associate (?)	Gen. xxix. 34
Lot	Veil	Gen. xi. 27
Lucius	A noble	Acts xiii. 1
Malachi	Messenger of Je	hovah..... Mal. i. 1
Manasseh	To forget	Gen. xli. 51
Manoah	Rest	Judges xiii. 2
Martha	Lady	Luke x. 38
Mary	Rebellion (?)	Matt. i. 16
Matthew	Gift of Jehovah	Matt. ix. 9
Michael	Who (is) like unto	God (?)..Dan. x. 13
Moses	Saved from the	water ....Ex. ii. 10
Naaman	Pleasantness	2 Kings v. 1
Naham	Consolation	1 Chron. iv. 19
Naomi	Pleasant	Ruth i. 2
Narcissus	Benumbing	Rom. xvi. 11
Nathan	Gift	2 Sam. vii. 2
Nathanael	Gift of God	John i. 45
Nebat	Aspect	1 King xi. 26
Nehemiah	Jehovah, comforts.	Neh. i. 1
Noah	(1) Rest, (2) wander	ing......Gen. v. 29
Obadiah	Worshipper of	Jehovah.... Obad i
Ozias	Might of Jehovah	Matt. i. 8
Paul	Little	Acts xiii. 9
Peter	A stone	Matt. xvi. 18
Phebe	Moon	Rom. xvi. 1
Philip	Lover of horses	Matt. x. 3

Phinehas	Serpent's mouth	Num. xxv. 7
Priscilla	Ancient	Acts xviii. 2
Rachel	Ewe	Gen. xxix. 6
Rebecca	A noose	Romans ix. 10
Rhoda	Rose	Acts xii. 13
Rizpah	Hot coal	2 Sam. iii. 7
Salome	Perfect	Mark xv. 40
Samson	Like the sun	Judges xiii. 24
Samuel	Heard of God	1 Sam. i. 20
Sarah	Princess	Gen. xvii. 15
Satan	Adversary	1 Chron. xxi. 1
Selah	Forte (?)	Psa. iii. 2
Sheba	An oath	2 Sam. xx. 1
Shimeon	A harkening	Ezra x. 31
Silas	The forest	Acts xv. 22
Solomon	Peaceable	2 Sam. v. 14
Stephanas	A crown	1 Cor. i. 16
Susanna	Lily	Luke viii. 3
Thaddaeus	Praise	Matt. x. 3
Theophilus	Loved of God	Luke i. 3
Thomas	A twin	Matt. x. 3
Titus	Protected	2 Cor. ii. 13
Timothy	Honoring God	2 Cor. i. 1
Tryphena	Delicate	Rom. xvi. 12
Tychicus	Fortuitous	Acts xx. 4
Tyrannus	Tyrant	Acts xix. 9
Uriah	Light of Jehovah	2 Sam. xi. 3
Vashni	Strong	1 Chron. vi. 28
Vashti	Beautiful	Esther i. 9
Vophsi	Expansion	Num. xiii. 14
Zaccheus	Pure	Luke xix. 2
Zachariah	Whom Jehovah Re	members 2 K. xiv 29
Zadok	Just	2 Sam. viii. 17
Zedekiah	Justice of Jehovah	1 Kings xxii. 11
Zophar	Chatterer	Job. ii. 11

HISTORY OF THE LATE REVISION OF THE BIBLE.

It originated in the mother-church of Anglo-Saxon Christendon in May, 1870, and enlisted the services of one hundred and one biblical scholars from the Episcopal Church and all the leading Protestant denominations of England and the United States. Of these scholars, sixty-seven were English and Scotch; thirty-seven belonging to the Old Testament Company, thirty to the New Testament Company. Thirty were Americans. There never was such a force employed on any other version. The Latin **Vulgate** of Jerome, the English version of Wiclif, the German Version of Luther, and nearly all other ancient and modern versions, are the work of individuals. The authorized English Version, the most accurate of all, is the work of forty-seven scholars, appointed by royal authority, (King James), and engaged for seven years (1604-1611); but they all belonged to one and the same Church of England before it divided into a number of separate ecclesiastical organizations, and before the American nation was born. In the new revision, all branches of English-speaking Christendom using King James' Bible had a share, the revisers being appointed in the first instance by the Convocation of Canterbury, May 6, 1870, and then by the committee itself, which was at the outset clothed with authority to enlarge its numbers from the ranks of recognized biblical scholars, "to whatever nation or religious body they may belong."

In accordance with the authority given the English Committee they invited the appointment of a similar American Committee to be associated with them, with the same principles and objects and to be in constant correspondence with them, that both together might issue one and the same revisions for all English-speaking people.

The first meeting of the American companies was held in New York, October 4, 1872. A division was made, the Greek scholars taking the New Testament and the Hebrew scholars the Old Testament. The meetings of the two American companies were held every month from September to May, inclusive, in each year at rooms Nos. 42 and 44 Bible House, New

York. A summer meeting was held in the month of July, usually at New Haven, Andover, or Princeton. The summer meetings continued for a week; the other meetings for two days. The members sat around a common table, and freely and fully discussed such passages or chapters as had been previously assigned for the particular meeting. Dr. Philip Schaff was president of the American committees.

The attitude of the English Committee toward the suggestions of the American revisers was always that of readiness to give them most respectful consideration. A large proportion of the suggestions of the American Committee was incorporated in the revised edition. In cases where they were not incorporated, note was made in an appendix of the American Committee's reading, and the appendix was printed in the Revised Bible as issued.

The Revision was completed July 10, 1884, in eighty-five sessions, occupying seven hundred and ninety-two days, generally of six hours each. Every proposed change of the Authorized Version was decided finally by a vote of a majority of two-thirds, the decision in the first revision being by a majority only.

It should be noted as a matter of wonder and congratulation that the English and American Committees, divided by the ocean, and representing two independent and high-minded nations sensitive of their honor, should, after several years of unbroken and conscientious labor, have arrived at such a substantial harmony in the translation of their most sacred book, which is recognized by both as their infallible guide in all matters of faith and duty.

This Anglo-American Revision of the Bible is the noblest monument of Christian Union and Co-operation in the nineteenth century.

The finger of God is manifest in the work and the glory of God is the assured result. Seventy millions of English-speaking people scattered over the globe can now read in their own language the most faithful translation of the original Scriptures that has yet been given to man.

OLD TESTAMENT WORDS CONTRASTED.

AUTHORIZED VERSION.	REVISED VERSION.
Ancient, Isa. xlvii. 6	Elder or aged.
Artillery, 1 Sam. xx. 40	Missile weapons.
Assay, Deut. iv. 34	Attempt, try
Apothecary, Exod. xxx. 25	Perfumer.
Avenging, Judges v. 2	Leaders.
Besom, Isa. xiv. 23	Broom.
Bewray, Isa. xvi. 3	Betray.
Bittern, Isa. xiv. 23	Porcupine.
Bonnet, Ex. xxviii. 40	Mitre.
Bosses, Job xv. 26	Knob.
Botch, Deut. xxviii. 27	Boil.
Bravery, Isa. iii. 18	Splendor, finery.
Borrow, Exod. xi. 2	Ask.
Breaches, Judges v. 17	Creeks or harbors.
Brigandine, Jer. xlvi. 4	Scale armor.
Bunches, Isa. xxx. 6	Humps (of oarsels).
Cabins, Jer. xxxvii. 16	Cellars, vaults.
Candle, Job xviii. 6	Lamp.
Cankerworm, Joel. i. 4	Caterpillar.
Caldron, Jer. lii. 18	Pot.
Carriage, Judges xviii. 21	Baggage.
Champaign, Deut. xi. 30	Plain.
Chapiters, Exod. xxxvi. 38	Capital.
Chapmen, 2 Chron. ix. 14	Traders.
Charger, Num. vii. 13	Platter.
College, 2 Kings xxii. 14	Second ward.
Coast, Jer. xxv. 32	Uttermost part.
Comely, Psa. xxxiii. 1	Becoming.
Cracknel, 1 Kings xiv. 3	Cake.
Crooked, Job xxvi. 13	Fleet or fleeing
Conversation, Psa. xxxvii. 14	Manner of life.
Cunning, Gen. xxv. 27	Knowing, skillful, (not artifice).
Daysman, Job ix. 33	Umpire or arbiter.
Dead things, Job xxvi. 5	The shades.
Despite, Ezek. xxv. 6	Reproachful contempt.

Discipline, Job xxxvi. 10 .... Instruction.
Discover, Psa. xxix. 9 .... Uncover, or lay bare.
Diet, Jer. lii. 34 .... Allowance.
Dragons, Psa. lxxiv. 13 .... Monsters.
Dregs, Isa. li. 17 .... Bowl.
Eschew, Job i. 1-8 .... Flee from, avoid.
Fats, Joel ii. 24 .... Vats.
Fenced, Num. xxxii. 17 .... Fortified, defended.
Fine, Job xxviii. 1 .... Refine.
Fires, Isa. xxiv. 15 .... The east.
Flag, Exod. ii. 5 .... Reed-grass.
Flagons of wine, Hosea iii. 1 .... Pressed grapes.
Flood, Joshua xxiv. 14 .... The river.
Foxes, Judges xv. 4 .... Jackals.
Fray, Deut. xxviii. 26 .... Frighten.
Fretting, Lev. xiv. 44 .... Devouring, corroding.
Gallant, Isa. xxxiii. 21 .... Splendor, stately.
Galleries, Cant. vii. 5 .... Curls of hair.
Goodman, Prov. vii. 19 .... Master of the house.
Gracious, Prov. xi. 16 .... Filled with grace.
Groves, Exod. xxxiv. 13 .... Pillars.
Grow up, Mal. iv. 2 .... Leap.
Habergeon, Exod. 28. 32 .. Coat of mail for head and shoulders.
Harness, 1 Kings xxii. 34 .... Armor.
Hats, Dan. iii. 21 .... Mantles.
Handywork, Psa. xix. 1 .... Workmanship.
Hearth, Jer. xxxvi. 22 .... Brazier.
Hell, Psa. xvi. 10 .... Sheol, Hades, the underworld.
House of God, Judges xx. 18 .... Bethel.
Hypocrite, Job. viii. 13 .... Ungodly.
Images, Lev. xxvi. 30 .... Sun images.
Images, Gen. xxxi. 19 .... Teraphim, household goods.
Jasher, 2 Sam. i. 18 .... The upright.
Knop, Exod. xxv. 31 .... Bud of bud-shaped protuberance.
Kerchief, Ezek. xiii. 18, 21 .... Covering for the head.
Kid of the goats, Gen. xxxvii. 31 .... He-goat.
Lace, Exod. xxviii. 28 .... Band.
Lamps, Ezek. i. 13 .... Torches.

Leasing, Psa. iv. 2........................Lying, falsehood.
Linen yarn, 1 Kings x. 28..................Droves of horses.
Lover, Psa. 38. 11. Intimate friend, not necessarily opposite sex.
Manner with the, Num. v. 13....................In the act.
Mean, Isa. ii. 9..................Common, lowly (not base).
Meat, Gen. i. 30.............................Food in general.
Minish, Exod. v. 19.............................Diminish.
Mount, Jer. vi. 6...................................Mound.
Mount Ephraim, Josh. xxiv. 33....Hill country of Ephraim.
Multitude of No., Jer. xlvi. 25.................Amen of No.
Mules, Gen. xxxvi. 24.......................Warm springs.
Nitre, Jer. ii. 22.......................................Lye.
Neesing, Job xi. 18.............................Sneezing.
Nephews, Judges xii. 14.......................Grandchildren.
Occupy, Ezek. xxvii. 16...............Use, trade with trade.
Ointment, Cant. i. 3, ...Unguent, perfume.
Offend, Psa. cxix. 165.....................Make to stumble.
Ouches, Exod. xxviii. 11...Sockets for setting precious stones.
Owl, Lev. xi. 16.................. ....Ostrich.
Paddle, Deut. xxiii. 13........................Small spade.
Painful, Psa. lxxiii. 16..........................Toilsome.
Palestina, Exod. xv. 14.......................... Philistia.
Paper reeds, Isa. xix. 7........ ....Meadows.
Plain of Mamre, Gen. xviii. 1........ ......Oaks of Mamre.
Poll, Num. i. 2................. .... .Head.
Pots, Jer. xxxv. 5..................................Bowls.
Prevent, Psa. xviii. 5.......... ....Meet, anticipate.
Purtenance, Exod. xii. 9...............Intestines or inwards.
Quick, Lev. xiii. 10.......... ....Living.
River of Egypt, Num. xxxiv. 5..Brook of Egypt (not the Nile).
Rereward, 1 Sam. xxix. 2.........................Rearguard.
Reward, Jer. ix. 5...............................Present.
Road, 1 Sam. xxvii. 10................................Rain.
Satyrs, Isa. xiii. 21.................................Goats.
Saving health, Psa. lxvii. 2......................Salvation.
Scall, Lev. xiii. 30..............Eruption of the skin, tetter.
Scape-goat, Lev. xvi. 8...........................Removal.
Scrabble, 1 Sam. xxi. 13.............................Scrawl.

Screech-owl, Isa. xxxiv. 14 .... Night monster.
Scum, Ezek. xxiv. 6 .... Rust.
Scrip, 1 Sam. xvii. 40 .... Wallet or small bag.
Seethe, Exod. xvi. 23 .... Boil.
Several, 2 Kings xv. 5 .... Separate.
Shameful spewing, Hab. ii. 16 .... Ignominy.
Sherd, Isa. xxx. 14 .... Shred or fragment.
Shroud, Ezek. xxxi. 3 .... Cover, shelter
Silverling, Isa. vii. 23 .... Piece of silver.
Slime, Gen. xi. 3 .... Bitumen.
Spider, Prov. xxxviii. 28 .... Lizard.
Spoil, Gen. xxxiv. 27 .... Plunder.
Stay upon, Isa. x. 20 .... Lean upon.
Straitly, Gen. xxiii. 7 .... Strictly.
Sweet influences, Job xxxviii. 31 .... Cluster or chain.
Tabernacle, Num. xxiv. 5 .... Tent.
Table, Isa. xxx. 8 .... Tablet.
Tablet, Exod. xxxv. 22 .... Armlet, locket.
Tablet, Isa. iii. 20 .... Perfume box.
Tache, Exod. xxvi. 6 .... Clasp.
Thought, 1 Sam. ix. 5 .... Anxiety.
Thick clay, Hab. ii. 6 .... Pledges.
Tired, 2 Kings ix. 30 .... Attired.
Torches, Nah. ii. 3 .... Steel.
Troop, Amos ix. 6 .... Vault.
Turtle, Cant. ii. 12 .... Turtle-dove.
Unicorn, Num. xxiii. 22 .... Wild ox.
Vagabond, Gen. iv. 12 .... Wanderer.
Valley, Joshua xi. 16 .... Lowland.
Veil, Ruth iii. 15 .... Mantle.
Vex, Exod. xxii. 21 .... Harass, oppress.
Well, Cant. iv. 15 .... Spring.
Wench, 2 Sam. xvii. 17 .... Maidservant.
Wimple, Isa. iii. 22 .... Neck-covering, shawl.
Witty, Prov. viii. 12 .... Ingenious, clever.
Wounds, Prov. xviii. 8 .... Dainty morsels.

NEW TESTAMENT WORDS CHANGED.

AUTHORIZED VERSION 1611.	REVISED VERSION 1881.
Allow, Luke xi. 48	Consent.
A proper child, Heb. xi. 23	Goodly child.
Begged, Matt. xxvii. 58	Asked.
Brightness, Heb. i. 3	Effulgence.
By and by, Matt. xiii. 21	Straightway.
Candlestick, Matt. v. 15	Stand.
Careful, Luke x. 61	Anxious.
Certain of the chief, Acts xix. 31	Certain of the Presidents.
Children, 1 Cor. xiv. 20	Babes.
Compel, Luke xiv. 23	Constrain.
Condemn, John iii. 17	Judge.
Concupiscence, Rom. vii. 8	Coveting.
Conformed, Rom. xii. 2	Fashioned.
Conversion, Philip iii. 20	Citizenship.
Country, Matt. ix. 31	Land.
Damnation, 1 Cor. xi. 29	Judgment.
Debate, Rom. i. 29	Strife.
Damned, Mark xvi. 16	Condemned.
Defile, 1 Cor. iii. 17	Destroy.
Deputy, Acts xiii. 7	Proconsul.
Devotions, Acts xvii. 23	Objects of your worship.
Doctrine, John vii. 16	Teaching.
Easter, Acts xii. 4	Passover.
Effect, Gal. iv. 17	Seek.
Ensue, 1 Pet. iii. 11	Pursue.
Executioner, Mark vi. 27	A soldier of his guard.
Fetched a compass, Acts xxviii. 13	Made a circuit.
Fold, John x. 16	Flock.
Guilty, Matt. xxvi. 66	Worthy of death.
Have not, James ii. 1	Hold not.
Hell, Acts ii. 27	Hades.

Hid, 2 Cor. iv. 3 .... Veiled.
Honest, Phillip iv. 8 .... Honorable.
In high places, Eph. vi. 12 .... In the heavenly places.
If they shall enter, Heb. iv. 5 .... They shall not enter.
Jesus, Acts vii. 45 ; Heb. iv. 8 .... Joshua.
Kept, John xvii. 12 .... Guarded.
Knowledge, Eph. i. 17 .... Full knowledge.
Lest, Matt. v. 25 .... Lest happily.
Let, Rom. i. 13 .... Hindered.
Lunatic, Matt. iv. 24 .... Epileptic.
Masters, James iii. 1 .... Teachers.
Meat, Matt. iii. 4 .... Food.
Minister, Luke iv. 20 .... Attendant.
Multitude, Luke xxiii. 1 .... Company.
Nephews, 1 Tim. v. 4 .... Grand children.
Occupy, Luke xix. 13 .... Trade.
Order, Matt. xi. 10 .... Prepare.
Prevent, 1 Thess. iv. 15 .... Precede.
Repent, 2 Cor. vii. 8 .... Regret.
Room, Luke xiv. 10 .... Place.
Seats, Rev. iv. 4 .... Thrones.
Strain at, Matt. xxiii. 24 .... Strain out.
Take no thought, Matt. vi. 34 .... Be not anxious.
Teach, Matt. xxviii. 19 .... Make desciples.
The people, John vii. 20 .... The multitude.
The temple, Matt. xxiii. 35 .... The sanctuary.
Took up our carriages, Acts xxi. 15 .... Took up our baggage.
Tribute, Matt. xvii. 24 .... Half shekel.
Usury, Matt. xxv. 27 .... Interest.
Virtue, Mark v. 30 .... Power.
Wavereth, James i. 6 .... Doubteth.
Were all dead, 2 Cor. v. 14 .... All died.
Wealth, 1 Cor. x. 24 .... Good.
Worship, Luke xiv. 10 .... Glory.
Will be rich, 1 Tim. vi. 9 .... Desire to be rich.
Washed, John xiii. 10 .... Bathed.
Writing table, Luke i. 63 .... Writing tablet.

NEW TESTAMENT PHRASES.

	AUTHORIZED VERSION.	REVISED VERSION.
Matt. 3. 14.	John forbad him.	John would have hindered [him.
Matt. 5. 22.	Angry with his brother without a cause.	Angry with his brother.
Matt. 5. 48.	Be ye perfect.	Ye shall be perfect.
Matt. 10. 4.	Simon the Canaanite.	Simon the Cananæan.
Matt. 14. 8.	She being before instructed.	She being put forward.
Matt. 15. 27.	Truth, Lord, yet the dogs eat.	Yea, Lord, for even the dogs [eat.
Matt. 18. 28.	Pay me what thou owest.	Pay what thou owest.
Matt. 26. 15.	They covenanted with him for thirty pieces.	They weighed unto him thirty pieces.
Mark 4. 29.	The fruit is brought forth.	The fruit is ripe.
Mark 6. 20.	He heard him he did many things.	When he heard him, was much perplexed.
Mark 9. 23.	If thou canst believe.	If thou canst!
Luke 3. 23.	Jesus himself began to be about thirty years of age.	Jesus himself, when he began (to teach) was about thirty years of age.
Luke 8. 23.	Were filled with water.	Were filling with water.
Luke 9. 32.	When they were awake.	When they were fully awake.
Luke 16. 9.	That when ye fail they may receive.	That when it shall fail they.

Luke 18. 12.	
I give tithes of all that I possess.	I give tithes of all that I get.
Luke 22. 56.	
A certain maid beheld him as he sat by the fire.	A certain maid seeing him as he sat in the light of the fire.
Luke 24. 25.	
O fools.	O foolish men.
Luke 24. 53.	
Praising and blessing God.	Blessing God.
Luke 24. 17.	
One with another as ye walk and are sad.	One with another as ye walk? And they stood still, looking sad.
John 6. 11.	
When he had given thanks he distributed to the disciples.	And having given thanks, he distributed to them that were set down.
John 9. 17.	
What sayest thou of him that he hath opened thine eyes?	What sayest thou of him, in that he opened thine eyes?
John 10. 14-15.	
I am the good Shepherd and know my sheep and am known of mine. As the Father knoweth me, even so know I the Father.	I am the good Shepherd; and know mine own, and mine own know me, even as the Father knoweth me, and I know the Father.
John 11. 20.	
Mary sat still in the house.	Mary still sat in the house.
Acts 2. 3.	
Cloven tongues.	Tongues parting asunder.
Acts 3. 19.	
When the time of refreshing shall come.	That so there may come seasons of refreshing.
Acts 15. 23.	
The apostles and the elders and the brethren.	The apostles and the elder brethren.
Acts 16. 7.	
The spirit suffered them not.	The spirit of Jesus suffered [them not.
Acts 18. 5.	
Paul was pressed in the spirit.	Paul was constrained by the [word.
Acts 26. 28.	
Almost thou persuadest me to be a Christian.	With but little persuasion thou wouldest fain make me a Christian.

Rom. 3. 25.	
To declare his righteousness for the remission of sins that are past.	To show his righteousness, because of the passing over of the sins done afore time.
Rom. 4. 19.	
He considered not his own body now dead.	He considered his own body now as good as dead.
Rom. 7. 6.	
That being dead wherein we were held.	Having died to that wherein we were holden.
Rom. 11. 7.	
The rest were blinded.	The rest were hardened.
Rom. 16. 5.	
The first fruits of Achaia.	The first fruits of Asia.
1 Cor. 6. 20.	
Glorify God, therefore in your body and in your spirit.	Glorify God, therefore in your body.
1 Cor. 11. 24.	
He brake it and said, Take, eat.	He brake it and said, this is my body.
2 Cor. 2. 14.	
Always causeth us to triumph.	Always leadeth us in triumph.
2 Cor. 5. 10.	
We must all appear.	We must all be made manifest.
2 Cor. 12. 9.	
Think ye that we excuse ourselves unto you.	Ye think all the time that we are excusing ourselves unto you.
Gal. 4. 14.	
And my temptation which was in my flesh.	That which was a temptation to you in my flesh.
Gal. 5. 17.	
So that ye cannot do the things that ye would.	That ye may not do the things that ye would.
Eph. 4. 29.	
But that which is good to the use of edifying.	But that which is good for edifying as the need may be.
Eph. 5. 29.	
We are members of his body, of his flesh and of his bones.	We are members of his body.
Phil. 4. 3.	
Help those women which labored.	Help these women, for they labored.
Phil. 2. 15.	
Among whom ye shine.	Among whom ye are seen.
Col. 2. 8.	
Any man spoil you.	Any one that maketh spoil of [you.

Col. 2. 18.	
Intruding into those which he hath not seen.	Dwelling in the things which he hath seen.
2 Thess. 2. 1.	
By the coming.	Touching the coming.
1 Tim. 1. 4.	
Godly edifying.	A dispensation of God.
1 Tim. 3. 16.	
Manifest in the flesh.	Was manifested in the flesh.
1 Tim. 6. 5.	
Supposing that gain is godliness.	Supposing that godliness is a way of gain.
Philem. 2.	
And to our beloved Apphia.	And to Apphia our sister.
Heb. 6. 7.	
By whom it is dressed.	For whose sake it is also tilled.
Heb. 11. 13.	
Having seen them afar off, and were persuaded of them and embraced them.	Having seen them and greeted them from afar.
1 Pet. 3. 8.	
Be courteous.	Humble minded.
1 Pet. 3. 15.	
Sanctify the Lord God in your hearts.	Sanctify in your hearts. Christ as Lord.
1 Pet. 3. 21.	
The answer of a good concience.	The interrogation of a good conscience.
3 John 12.	
And ye know.	And thou knowest.
Rev. 4. 6.	
Beasts.	Living creatures.
Rev. 22. 11.	
Let him be righteous still.	Let him do righteousness still.
Rev. 22. 14.	
Blessed are they that do his commandments.	Blessed are they that wash their robes.

THE OLD AND NEW VERSIONS CONTRASTED.

THE ACCOUNT OF THE CREATION.—GEN. i. 1-31.

THE AUTHORIZED VERSION.

1. In the beginning God created the heaven and the earth.

2. And the earth was without form, and void ; and darkness *was* upon the face of the deep : and the Spirit of God moved upon the face of the waters.

3. And God said, Let there be light : and there was light.

4. And God saw the light, that *it was* good : and God divided the light from the darkness.

5. And God called the light Day, and the darkness he called Night : and the evening and the morning were the first day.

6. And God said, Let there be a firmament in the midst of the waters : and let it divide the waters from the waters.

7. And God made the firm ament, and divided the waters which *were* under the firmament from the waters which *were* above the firmament : and it was so.

8. And God called the firmament Heaven : and the evening and the morning were the second day.

9. And God said, Let the waters under the heaven be gathered together unto one place, and let the dry *land* appear : and it was so.

10. And God called the dry *land* Earth ; and the gathering together of the waters called he Seas : and God saw that *it was* good.

THE REVISED VERSION.

1 In the beginning God
created the heaven and the
2 earth. And the earth was
waste and void ; and darkness
was upon the face of
the deep : and the spirit
of God moved upon the
3 face of the waters. And
God said, Let there be light:
4 and there was light. And
God saw the light, that it
was good : and God divided
the light from the darkness,
5 And God called the light
Day, and the darkness he
called Night. And there
was evening and there was
morning, one day.
6 And God said, Let there
be a firmament in the midst
of the waters, and let it divide
the waters from the
7 waters. And God made
the firmament, and divided
the waters which were under
the firmament from the
waters which were above
the firmament : and it was
8 so. And God called the
firmament Heaven. And
there was evening and
there was morning, a second
day.
9 And God said, Let the
waters under the heaven
be gathered together unto
one place, and let the dry
land appear : and it was
10 so. And God called the
dry land Earth; and the
gathering together of the
waters called he Seas : and
God saw that it was good.

11. And God said, Let the earth bring forth grass, the herb yielding seed *and* the fruit-tree yielding fruit after his kind whose seed *is* in itself, upon the earth: and it was so.

12. And the earth brought forth grass, *and* herb yielding seed after his kind, and the tree yielding fruit, whose seed *was* in itself, after his kind; and God saw that *it was* good.

13. And the evening and the morning were the third day.

14. And God said, Let there be lights in the firmament of the heaven to divide the day from the night; and let them be for signs, and for seasons, and for days, and years.

15. And let them be for lights in the firmament of the heaven to give light upon the earth: and it was so.

16. And God made two great lights; the greater light to rule the day, and the lesser light to rule the night: *he made* the stars also.

17. And God set them in the firmament of the heaven to give light upon the earth.

18. And to rule over the day, and over the night, and to divide the light from the darkness: and God saw that *it was* good.

19. And the evening and the morning were the fourth day.

20. And God said, Let the waters bring forth abundantly the moving creature that hath life, and fowl *that* may fly above the earth, in the open firmament of heaven.

21. And God created great

11 And God said, Let the
earth put forth grass, herb
yielding seed, *and* fruit
tree bearing fruit after its
kind, wherein is the seed
thereof, upon the earth:
12 and it was so. And the
earth brought forth grass,
herb yielding seed after its
kind, and tree bearing
fruit, wherein is the seed
thereof, after its kind: and
God saw that it was good.
13 And there was evening
and there was morning, a
third day.
14 And God said, Let there
be lights in the firmament
of the heaven to divide the
day from the night; and
let them be for signs, and
for seasons, and for days,
15 and years: and let them be
for lights in the firmament
of the heaven to give light
upon the earth: and it was
16 so. And God made the
two great lights; the greater light to rule the day,
and the lesser light to rule
the night; *he made* the
17 stars also. And God set
them in the firmament of
the heaven to give light
18 upon the earth, and to rule
over the day and over the
night, and to divide the
light from the darkness:
and God saw that it was
19 good. And there was evening and there was morn-
ing, a fourth day.
20 And God said, Let the
waters bring forth abun-
dantly the moving creature
that hath life, and let fowl
fly above the earth in the

whales, and every living creature that moveth, which the waters brought forth abundantly after their kind: and every winged fowl after his kind: and God saw that *it was* good.

22. And God blessed them, saying, Be fruitful and multiply, and fill the waters in the seas, and let fowl multiply in the earth.

23. And the evening and the morning were the fifth day.

24. And God said, Let the earth bring forth the living creature after his kind, cattle and creeping thing and beast of the earth after his kind: and it was so.

25. And God made the beast of the earth after his kind, and cattle after their kind, and every thing that creepeth upon the earth after his kind: and God saw that *it was* good.

26. And God said, Let us make man in our image, after our likeness: and let them have dominion over the fish of the sea, and over the fowl of the air, and over the cattle, and over all the earth, and over every creeping thing that creepeth upon the earth.

27. So God created man in his *own* image, in the image of God created he him; male and female created he them.

28. And God blessed them, and God said unto them, Be fruitful and multiply, and replenish the earth, and subdue it: and have dominion over the fish of the sea, and over the fowl of the air, and over

open firmament of heaven.
21 And God created the great
sea-monsters and every
living creature that mov-
eth, which the waters
brought forth abundantly,
after their kinds, and every
winged fowl after its kind:
and God saw that it was
22 good. And God blessed
them, saying, Be fruitful,
and multiply, and fill the
waters in the seas, and let
fowl multiply in the earth.
23 And there was evening and
and there was morning, a
fifth day.
24 And God said, Let the
earth bring forth the living
creature after its kind, cattle, and creeping thing and
beast of the earth after its
kind: and it was so.
25 And God made the beast
of the earth after its kind,
and the cattle after their
kind, and every thing that
creepeth upon the ground
after its kind: and God
26 saw that it was good. And
God said, Let us make man
in our image, after our
likeness: and let them have
dominion over the fish of
the sea, and over the fowl
of the air, and over the
cattle, and over all the
earth, and over every
creeping thing that creep-
27 eth upon the earth. And
God created man in his
own image, in the image
of God created he him;
male and female created
28 he them. And God blessed
them: and God said unto
them, Be fruitful and mul-

every living thing that moveth upon the earth.

29. And God said, Behold, I have given you every herb bearing seed, which *is* upon the face of all the earth, and every tree, in the which *is* the fruit of a tree yielding seed; to you it shall be for meat.

30. And to every beast of the earth, and to every fowl of the air, and to every thing that creepeth upon the earth, wherein *there is* life, *I have given* every green herb for meat: and it was so.

31. And God saw every thing that he had made: and behold, *it was* very good. And the evening and the morning were the sixth day.

tiply, and replenish the
earth, and subdue it; and
have dominion over the
fish of the sea, and over
the fowl of the air, and
over every living thing
that moveth upon the
29 earth. And God said, Behold, I have given you
every herb yielding seed,
which is upon the face of
all the earth, and every
tree, in the which is the
fruit of a tree yielding
seed; to you it shall be for
30 meat. And to every beast
of the earth, and to every
fowl of the air, and to
every thing that creepeth
upon the earth, wherein
there is life, I have given
every green herb for meat:
31 and it was so. And God
saw every thing that he
had made, and, behold, it
was very good. And there
was evening and there was
morning, the sixth day.

THE TEN COMMANDMENTS.—EX. XX. 1-17.

AUTHORIZED VERSION.

And God spake all these words, saying,

2. I *am* the Lord thy God, which have brought thee out of the land of Egypt, out of the house of bondage.

3. Thou shalt have no other gods before me.

4. Thou shalt not make unto thee any graven image, or any likeness *of any thing* that *is* in heaven above, or that *is* in the earth beneath, or that *is* in the water under the earth:

5. Thou shalt not bow down

REVISED VERSION.

And God spake all these
words, saying,
2 I am the Lord thy God,
which brought thee out
of the land of Egypt, out
of the house of bondage.
3 Thou shalt have none other
4 gods before me. Thou
shalt not make unto thee
a graven image, nor the
likeness of any form that
is in the heaven above, or
that is in the earth beneath,
or that is in the water un-
5 der the earth. Thou shalt

thyself to them, nor serve them, for I the Lord thy God *am* a jealous God, visiting the iniquity of the fathers upon the children unto the third and fourth *generation* of them that hate me ;

6. And shewing mercy unto thousands of them that love me, and keep my commandments.

7. Thou shalt not take the name of the Lord thy God in vain : for the Lord will not hold him guiltless that taketh his name in vain.

8. Remember the Sabbath day to keep it holy.

9. Six days shalt thou labour, and do all thy work :

10. But the seventh day *is* the sabbath of the Lord thy God : *in it* thou shalt not do any work, thou, nor thy son, nor thy daughter, thy manservant, nor thy maidservant, nor thy cattle, nor thy stranger that *is* within thy gates :

11. For *in* six days the Lord made heaven and earth, the sea and all that in them *is*, and rested the seventh day : wherefore the Lord blessed the Sabbath day and hallowed it.

12. Honour thy father and thy mother ; that thy days may be long upon the land which the Lord thy God giveth thee.

13. Thou shalt not kill.

14. Thou shalt not commit adultery.

15. Thou shalt not steal.

16. Thou shalt not bear false witness against thy neighbour.

17. Thou shalt not covet thy neighbour's house, thou shalt

not bow down thyself unto
them, nor serve them : for
I the Lord thy God am a
jealous God, visiting the
iniquity of the fathers upon
the children, upon the third
and upon the fourth generation of them that hate me ;
6 And showing mercy unto
thousands of them that love
me and keep my command-
7 ments. Thou shalt not
take the name of the Lord
thy God in vain ; for the
Lord will not hold him
guiltless that taketh his
8 name in vain. Remember
the sabbath day, to keep it
9 holy. Six days shalt thou
labor and do all thy work ;
10 But the seventh day is a
sabbath unto the Lord thy
God : in it thou shalt not
do any work, thou nor thy
son, nor thy daughter, thy
manservant, nor thy maid-
servant, nor thy cattle, nor
thy stranger that is within
11 thy gates : For in six days
the Lord made heaven and
earth, the sea, and all that
in them is, and rested the
seventh day : wherefore the
Lord blessed the Sabbath
day, and hallowed it.
12 Honour thy father and
thy mother : that thy days
may be long upon the land
which the Lord thy God
13 giveth thee. Thou shalt
14 do no murder. Thou shalt
15 not commit adultery. Thou
16 shalt not steal. Thou
shalt not bear false wit-
ness against thy neighbor.
17 Thou shalt not covet thy
neighbor's house, thou

not covet thy neighbour's wife, nor his manservant, nor his maidservant, nor his ox, nor his ass, nor any thing that *is* thy neighbour's.

shalt not covet thy neighbor's wife, nor his manservant, nor his maidservant nor his ox, nor his ass, nor anything that is thy neighbor's.

THE BIRTH OF CHRIST.—MATT. ii. 1-12.

AUTHORIZED VERSION.

Now when Jesus was born in Bethlehem of Judea in the days of Herod the king behold, there came wise men from the east to Jerusalem, Saying, Where is he that is born King of the Jews? for we have seen his star in the east, and are come to worship him.

3. When Herod the king had heard these things, he was troubled, and all Jerusalem with him.

4. And when he had gathered all the chief priests and scribes of the people together, he demanded of them where Christ should be born.

5. And they said unto him, In Bethlehem of Judea; for thus it is written by the prophet.

6. And thou Bethlehem, in the land of Juda, art not the least among the princes of Juda, for out of thee shall come a Governor, that shall rule my people Israel.

7. Then Herod, when he had privily called the wise men, inquired of them diligently what time the star appeared.

8. And he sent them to Bethlehem, and said, Go and search diligently for the young

REVISED VERSION.

Now when Jesus was born
in Bethlehem of Judea in
the days of Herod the king,
behold—wise men from the
east came to Jerusalem,
2 saying, Where is he that is
born King of the Jews?
for we saw his star in the
east, and are come to
3 worship him. And when
Herod the king heard it,
he was troubled, and all
4 Jerusalem with him. And
gathering together all the
chief priests and scribes of
the people he inquired of
them where the Christ
5 should be born. And they
said unto him, In Bethlehem of Judea: for thus it
is written by the prophet,
6 And thou Bethlehem, land
of Judah, Art in no wise
least among the princes of
Judah: For out of thee
shall come forth a governor, which shall be shepherd of my people Israel.
7 Then Herod privily called
the wise men, and learned
of them carefully what time
8 the star appeared. And
he sent them to Bethlehem, and said, Go and
search out carefully concerning the young child;
and when ye have found

child; and when ye have found him, bring me word again, that I may come and worship him also.

9. When they had heard the king, they departed; and, lo, the star, which they saw in the east, went before them, till it came and stood over where the young child was.

10. When they saw the star, they rejoiced with exceeding great joy.

11. And when they were come into the house, they saw the young child with Mary his mother, and fell down, and worshipped him; and when they had opened their treasures, they presented unto him gifts; gold, and frankincense and myrrh.

12. And being warned of God in a dream that they should not return to Herod, they departed into their own country another way.

him, bring me word—that
I also may come and wor-
9 ship him. And they, having heard the king, went
their way; and lo, the
star, which they saw in
the east, went before them,
till it came and stood over
where the young child was.
10 And when they saw the
star, they rejoiced with ex-
11 ceeding great joy. And
they came into the house
and saw the young child
with Mary his mother; and
they fell down and wor-
shipped him; and opening
their treasures, they offered
unto him gifts, gold and
frankincense and myrrh.
12 And being warned of God
in a dream that they should
not return to Herod, they
departed into their own
country another way.

THE LORD'S PRAYER.—Matt. vi. 9-13.

AUTHORIZED VERSION.

9. After this manner therefore pray ye: Our Father which art in heaven, Hallowed be thy name.

10. Thy kingdom come. Thy will be done in earth as *it is* in heaven.

11. Give us this day our daily bread.

12. And forgive us our debts, as we forgive our debtors.

13. And lead us not into temptation, but deliver us from evil. For thine is the kingdom, and the power, and the glory, forever. Amen.

REVISED VERSION.

9 After this manner therefore pray ye: Our Father
which art in heaven, Hal-
10 lowed be thy name. Thy
kingdom come. Thy will be
done as in heaven, so on
11 earth. Give us this day our
12 daily bread. And forgive
us our debts, as we also
have forgiven our debtors.
13 And bring us not into
temptation, but deliver us
from the evil *one*.

NAMES AND TITLES

APPLIED TO OUR

LORD AND SAVIOUR JESUS CHRIST

IN THE HOLY SCRIPTURES.

Adam... ......1 Cor. xv. 45.
Advocate....... .1 John ii. 1.
Almighty...........Rev. i. 8.
Alpha and Omega ..Rev. i. 8.
Amen............Rev. iii. 14.
Angel of the Lord.
.........Gen. xvi. 7-11.
Anointed..........Psalm ii. 2.
Apostle............Heb. iii. 1.
Arm of the Lord..Isa. li. 9-10.
Author of Eternal Salvation.
..............Heb. v. 9.
Author of Faith...Heb. xii. 2.
Beginning and End,
..........Rev. xxii. 13.
Beginning of Creation of God,
............Rev. iii. 14.
Beloved.........Matt. xiii. 18.
Beloved Son......Matt. iii. 17,
............Luke iii. 22.
Blessed and only Potentate,
...........1 Tim. vi. 15.
Branch...........Zech. vi. 12.
Branch of Righteousness,
.........Jer. xxxiii. 15.
Bread............John vi. 41.
Bread from Heaven,
............John vi. 51.
Bread of God.....John vi. 33.
Bread of Life.....John vi. 35.
Bright and Morning Star,
..........Rev. xxii. 16.
Brightness of His Glory,
..............Heb. i. 3.
Captain of Salvation.
.............Heb. ii. 10.
Carpenter.........Mark vi. 3.
Carpenter's Son..Matt. xiii. 55.
Chief Corner-Stone.
............1 Peter ii. 6.
Chiefest among Ten Thousand,
............Song v. 10.
Child..............Isa. ix. 6.
Child Jesus....Luke ii. 27-43.
Chosen of God..1 Peter. ii. 4.
Christ....... ....John vi. 69.
Christ, a King..Luke xxiii. 2.
Christ Jesus.......Heb. iii. 1.
Christ Jesus our Lord,
............1 Tim. i. 12.
Christ of God.....Luke ix. 20.
Christ the Chosen of God,
.........Luke xxiii. 35.
Christ the Lord....Luke ii. 11.
Christ the Son of God,
............Acts ix. 20.
Christ, Son of the Blessed,
..........Mark xiv. 61.
Commander........Isa. lv. 4.
Consolation of Israel,
............Luke ii. 25.
Corner Stone..Isa. xxviii. 16,
............Eph. ii. 20.
Counsellor..........Isa. ix. 6.

Covenant..........Isa. xlii. 6.
David, their King.Jer. xxx. 9.
Day Spring........Luke i. 78.
Deliverer.........Rom. xi. 26.
Desire of All Nations.Hag. ii. 7.
Door..............John x. 9.
Door of the Sheep..John x. 7.
Elect.............Isa. xlii. 1.
Emmanuel....Matt. i. 23,
............Isa. vii. 14.
Ensign............Isa. xi. 10.
Everlasting Father..Isa. ix. 6.
Faithful and True.Rev. xix. 11.
Faithful Witness... Rev. i. 5.
Faithful and True Witness,
............Rev. iii. 14.
Finisher of Faith..Heb. xii. 2.
First and Last,
......Rev. xxii. 13, i. 17.
First Begotten ......Heb. i. 6.
First Begotten of the dead,
...............Rev. i. 5.
First-born among brethren,
..........Rom. viii. 29.
First-born from the
dead..........Col. i. 18.
First-born of every creature,
..............Col. i. 15.
First Fruits.....1 Cor. xv. 20.
Forerunner.......Heb. vi. 20.
Foundation......1 Cor. iii. xi.
Fountain opened.Zech. xiii. 1.
Friend of sinners..Matt. xi. 19.
Gift of God.......John iv. 10.
Glory of Israel....Luke ii. 32.
God blessed forever.Rom. ix. 5.
God manifest in the flesh
..........1 Tim. iii. 16.
God of Israel, the Saviour
............Isa. xlv. 15.
God of the whole earth,
..............Isa. liv. 5.
God our Saviour..1 Tim. ii. 3.
God's dear Son......Col. i. 13.
God with us.......Matt. i. 23.
Good Master....Matt. xix. 16.
Governor..........Matt. ii. 6.
Great Shepherd of the Sheep.
.... Heb. xiii. 20.
Great High Priest.Heb. iv. 14.
Good Shepherd....John x. 11.
Head of every man
............1 Cor. xi. 3.
Head of the Church.Col. i. 18.
Head of the Corner
................Matt. xxi. 42.
Heir of all things.. Heb. i. 1-2.
High Priest..Heb. iii. 1. v. 10.
High Priest of good things
to come.....Heb. ix. 11.
Holy Child Jesus..Acts iv. 30.
Holy One........Psa. xvi. 10.
Holy One of God...Mark i. 24.
Holy One of Israel.
Isa. xli. 14. liv. 5.......
Holy Thing........Luke i. 35.
Hope, Our.........1 Tim. i. 1.
Horn of Salvation..Luke i. 69.
I am..John viii. 58. Ex. 3. 14.
Image, express, of God's
person........Heb. i. 3.
Image of God.....2 Cor. iv. 4.
Immanuel..........Isa. vii. 14.
Jesus..............Matt. i. 21.
Jesus Christ........Matt. i. 1.
Jesus Christ, our Saviour

..............Tit. iii. 6.
Jesus of Nazareth..Mark i. 24.
Jesus of Nazareth, the King of the Jews..John xix. 19.
Jesus, the King of the Jews....Matt. xxvii. 37.
Jesus, the Son of God ....Heb iv. 14.
Jesus, the Son of Joseph ....John vi. 42.
Judge.............Acts x. 42.
Just..............Acts iii. 14.
Just Man......Matt. xxvii. 19.
Just One...Acts vii. 52, iii. 14.
Just Person...Matt. xxvii. 24.
Jehovah.........Isa. xxvi. 4.
King...........Luke xix. 38.
King of Glory.Psa. xxiv. 7-10.
King of Israel.....John i. 49.
King of kings...1 Tim. vi. 15. ....Rev. xvii. 14.
King of the Jews...Matt. ii. 2.
King of Zion.....Matt. xxi. 5.
King over all the earth ....Zech. xiv 9.
Lamb.............Rev. v. 6.
Lamb of God...John i. 29, 36.
Lawgiver......Isa. xxxiii. 22.
Life, Bread of.... John vi. 35.
Lamb that was slain ....Rev. v. 12.
Leader.............Isa. lv. 4.
Life..............John xiv. 6.
Life Our...........Col. iii. 4.
Light Everlasting..Isa. lx. 20.
Light of the world..John viii. 12. ix. 5.
Light to the Gentiles ....Isa. xlii. 6.
Light, True..John i. 9. xii. 35.
Lion of the tribe of Judah .. ..Rev. v. 5.
Living Bread.....John vi. 51.
Living Stone......1 Pet. ii. 4.
Lord.Matt. xxii. 43. Mark xi. 3.
Lord and Saviour Jesus Christ......2 Pet. i. 11.
Lord Christ........Col. iii. 24.
Lord from Heaven ....1 Cor. xv. 47.
Lord Jesus.......Acts vii. 59.
Lord Jesus Christ ....2 Thess. iii. 6.
Lord Jesus Christ our Saviour........Tit. i. 4.
Lord of all.........Acts x. 36.
Lord of Glory ...Jas. ii. 1. 1 Cor. ii. 8.
Lord of Hosts.....Isa. xliv. 6.
Lord of Lords....Rev. xix. 16. .... 1 Tim. vi. 15.
Lord, Mighty in Battle ....Psa. xxiv. 8.
Lord of the dead and living........Rom. xiv. 9.
Lord of the Sabbath ....Mark ii. 28.
Lord over All....Rom. x. xii.
Lord's Christ......Luke ii. 26.
Lord, Strong, and Mighty ....Psa. xxiv. 8.
Lord, The, our Righteousness.......Jer. xxiii. 6.
Lord, your Holy One ....Isa. xliii. 15.
Lord, your Redeemer

Shepherd and Bishop of Souls.......1 Pet. ii. 25.
Shepherd, Chief...1 Pet. v. 4.
Shepherd, Good...John x. 11.
Shepherd, Great. Heb. xiii. 20.
Shepherd of Israel ....Psa. lxxx. 1.
Shiloh..........Gen. xlix. 10.
Son Jesus Christ ....1 John iii. 23.
Son of David.....Matt. xxi. 9.
Son of God........Rev. ii. 18.
Son of Joseph....Luke iii. 23.
Son of man ......John iii. 13.
Son of Mary.......Mark vi. 3.
Son of the Blessed ....Mark xiv. 61.
Son of the Father. 2 John i. 3.
Son of the Highest. Luke i. 32.
Son of the Living God ....Matt. xvi. 16.
Son of the Most High God ....Mark v. 7.
Star and Sceptre. Num. 24. 17.
Stone...........Matt. xxi. 42.
Stone of Stumbling. 1 Pet. ii. 8.
Sun of Righteousness ....Mal. iv. 2.
Sure Foundation...Isa. 28. 16.
Surety of a better testament ....Heb. vii. 22.
Teacher...........John iii. 2.
The Beloved.........Eph. i. 6.
The Man.........John xix. 5.
The Only Wise God, our Saviour......Jude xxv.
Tried Stone....Isa. xxviii. 16.
True ....Rev. xix. 11.
True God........1 John v. 20.
True Vine........John xv. 1.
Truth............John xiv. 6.
Unspeakable Gift ....2 Cor. ix. 15.
Very Christ.......Acts ix. 22.
Vine....... .....John xv. 5.
Way.............John xiv. 6.
Which is, which was, which is to come.......Rev. i. 4.
Wisdom of God...1 Cor. i. 24.
Wisdom, Our.....1 Cor. i. 30.
Witness faithful and true ....Rev. iii. 14.
Witness to the People ....John xviii. 37.
Wonderful..........Isa. ix. 6.
Word............. .....John i. 1.
Word of God....Rev. xix. 13.
Word of Life......1 John i. 1.
Young Child....Matt. ii. 8-13.

SELECTED BIBLE READINGS.

[*Special Topics for Sundry Occasions.*]

A backslidden Church	Rev. iii. 14–22.
Fruitless Christians	Matt. xxi. 17–22.
God's judgments upon frivolity	Amos vi. 1–11.
God's cry to the backslider	Jer. iii. 12–25.
The backslider's return	Hos. vi. 1–7, and xiv. 1–9; Ps. 77.
Humiliation and confession before God	Ps. 51.
Guarding against backsliding	Heb. x. 19–31.
Churches worthy of imitation	Rev. iii. 1–13.
Building up the Church under difficulties	Neh. 4.
The mission of the Church	Isa. xlix. 8–23.
The victory of the Church of Christ	Micah iv. 1–7.
The Church's thanksgiving	Isa. xii.
The Church preparing for a revival	Isa. lx. 1–11.
The signs of a coming revival	Hab. iii. 1–19.
Prayer for revival answered	Hab. iii. 1–19.
A grand praise meeting	Ps. 98.
A personal experience	1 John i. 1–10.
A noble confession	Matt. xvi. 13–23.
A model testimony for Christ	Ps. xl. 1–11.
David tells how he was converted	Ps. 32.
Moses relates his experience	Ex. xviii. 1–12.
Christian experience in its lights and shadows	Ps. 13.
Preparing for battle	Eph. vi. 11–18.
Putting off the old man	Eph. iv. 17–32.
Meeting our obligations tc God	Mal. iii. 8–18.
Moral insanity	Eccl. ix. 3.
A complete consecration	Rom. xii. 1–8.
The blessings of obedience	Deut. xxviii. 1–12.
Christ's doctrine of prayer	Luke xi. 1–13.
The power of the word of God	Heb. iv. 9–16.
God's words a comfort in persecution	Ps. cxix. 81–96.
Christian forbearance	Rom. xv. 1–7.
Suffering unjustly	1 Peter iii. 12–22.
The keeping-power of God	1 Peter i. 1–21.

Preparing for victory..............................Josh. iii. 1–17.
A song of victory..............................Ex. xv. 1–22.
Reasons for loving God..............................Ps. 116.
The Lord's appeal to sinners..............................Isa. i. 2–20.
The condition of the godly and ungodly contrasted.. ......Ps. 1.
The death of Christ..............................Luke ix. 31.
The present and future state of the wicked........Job xxi. 7–30.
The responsibility of choice..............................Josh. xxiv. 15.
The safety of young men..............................Ps. cxix. 9.
The victories of salvation..............................Isa. xxv. 1–9.
The final triumph..............................Rev. 4.
The Church defined..............................1 Tim. iii. 15.
The providence of God.....Neh. ix. 6; Ps. xxxvi. 6; civ. 27, 28.
Comfort in sickness......................2 Cor. i. 3–7; Ps. xci. 15.
A national jubilee....... ....Esther viii. 15–17; ix. 20–32.
The teacher encouraged........ Ps. cxxvi. 5, 6; Mark iv. 26–29.
A memorial tribute......................Gen. xxxv. 20; l. 7–13.
What shall the harvest be........Gal. vi. 7, 8; Matt. xiii. 24–30.
Fasting and prayer............Ezra viii. 21–23; Matt. vi. 16–18.
Consolation in bereavement....John xiv. 1–6; 1 Thess. iv. 13–18.
The Christian's passport to the beyond..John xi. 6; Rev. vii. 9–17.
Assurance of faith......................Isa. xxxii. 17; Heb. vi. 11.
The boldness of faith............Isa. xxxv. 3, 4; 1 John iii. 21.
No cross no crown..........Matt. x. 38; James i. 12; Rev. ii. 10.
Preparation for death..2 Kings xxii. 19, 20; Ps. xc. 12; Amos iv. 12.
Support and victory in death..Rom. viii. 38, 39; 1 Cor. xv. 55–57.
Future punishment.......Ps. ix. 17; Rev. xxi. 8; 2 Thess. i. 6–9.
Perfection in holiness...2 Cor. vii. 1; 1 Peter i. 22; 1 John iv. 17.
Old age................Job v. 26; Ps. lxxi. 9, 18; Isa. xlvi. 4.
Victory over Satan promised........Rom. xvi. 10; 1 John v. 18.
Comfort in affliction. Jer. xxxi. 13; Rom. viii. 17, 18; Heb. xii. 5–11.
Witness of the spirit..Acts xv. 8, Rom. viii. 14–16; 1 John iii. 24.
Working out salvation........ 2 Pet. i. 5–10; Acts xxvii. 24–31.

PROPHECIES RELATING TO CHRIST.

Adoration by Magi, Ps. 72 : 10-15; Isa. 60 : 3-6.
Advent, Gen. 3 : 15; Deut. 18 : 15; Ps. 89 : 20; Isa. 2 : 2; 9 : 6; 28: 16; 32 : 1; 35 : 4; 42 : 6; 49 : 1; 55 : 4; Ezek. 34 : 24. Dan. 2 : 44; Mic. 4 : 1; Zech. 3 : 8. [2 : 7; Mal. 3 : 1;
Advent, time of, Gen. 49 : 10; Num. 24 : 17; Dan. 9 : 24; Hag.
Ascension and exaltation, Ps. 16: 11; 24: 7; 68: 18; 110: 1; 118: 19.
Betrayal by own friend, Ps. 41 : 9; 55 : 13.
" for thirty pieces, Zech. 11 : 12.
Betrayer's death, Ps. 55 : 15-23; 109 : 17.
Bone not to be broken, Ps. 34 : 20.
Burial with the rich, Isa. 53 : 9.
Casting lots for vesture, Ps. 22 : 18.
Conversion of Gentiles, Isa. 11 10; 42 : 1.
Crucifixion, Ps. 22 : 14-17.
Death in prime of life, Ps. 89 : 45; 102 : 24.
" with malefactors, Isa. 53 : 9-12. [14 : 4-6.
" attested by convulsions of nature, Amos. 5 : 20; 8 : 9; Zech.
Descent into Egypt, Hos. 11 : 1.
Desertion by disciples, Zech. 13 : 7.
Divinity, Ps. 2 : 11; 45 : 7; 72 : 8; 110 : 1; Isa. 9 : 6; 25 : 9; 40 : 10; Jer. 23 : 6; Mic. 5 : 2; Mal. 3 : 1.
Dominion universal and everlasting, Ps. 72 : 8; Isa. 9 : 7; Dan. 7 : 14.
False accusation, Ps. 27 : 12; 35 : 11; 109 : 2.
Forerunner of Christ, Isa. 40 : 3; Mal. 3 : 1; 4 : 5.
Galilee, ministry in, 9 : 1, 2.
Gall and vinegar, offer of, Ps. 69 : 21.
Generation, human, Gen. 12: 3; 18: 18; 21: 12; 22: 18; 26: 4; 28: 14; 49: 10; Ps. 18: 50; 89: 4; 29: 36; 132: 11; Isa. 11: 1; Jer. 23: 5; 33: 15.
Insult, buffeting, spitting, scourging, Ps. 35 : 15-21; Isa. 50 : 6.
Massacre of Innocents, Jer. 31 : 15.
Miraculous power, Isa. 35 : 5. [1; Isa. 59 : 20; Jer. 33 : 16.
Mission, Gen. 12 : 3; 69 : 10; Num. 24 : 19; Deut. 18 : 18; Ps. 21 :
Mocking, Ps. 22 : 16; 59 : 25.
Nativity, from virgin, Gen. 3 : 15; Isa. 7 : 14; Jer. 31 : 22.
" place of, Num. 24 : 17-19; Mic. 5 : 2.
Patience under suffering, Isa. 53 7-9.
Persecution, Ps. 22; 6; 35 : 7-12; 59 : 2; Isa. 49 : 7; 53 : 3.
Piercing, Ps. 22 : 16; Zech. 12 : 10; 13 : 6.
Prayer for enemies, Ps. 109 : 4.
Preacher, Ps. 2 : 7; Isa. 2 : 3; 61 : 1; Mic. 4 : 2.
Priest like Melchizedek, Ps. 110 : 4.
Prophet like Moses, Deut. 18 : 15.
Purchase of potter's field, Zech. 11 : 13.
Purification of temple, Ps. 69 : 9.
Rejection by Jews and Gentiles, Ps. 2 : 1; 22 : 12; 41 : 5.
Ressurection, Ps. 16 : 10; 30 : 3; 41 : 10; 118 : 17; Hos. 6 : 2.
Silence under accusation, Ps. 38 : 13; Isa. 53 : 7.
Spiritual graces, Ps. 45 : 7; Isa. 11 : 2; 42 : 1; 61 : 1.
Triumphal entry into Jerusalem, Ps. 8 : 2; Zech. 9; 9.
Vicarious suffering, Isa. 53 : 4 : 6-12; Dan. 9 : 26.

CHRONOLOGICAL INDEX
TO
THE BIBLE.

PERIOD I.

FROM THE CREATION TO DELUGE, 1,656 YEARS.

A.M.	B.C.		
1	4004	The creation of the world......................	Genesis i. 2.
	"	Fall of our first parents, Adam and Eve, from holiness and happiness, by disobeying God. Promise of a Saviour.........................	" iii.
2	4002	Cain born.....	" iv. 1.
3	4001	Abel born....................................	" iv. 2.
129	3875	Abel murdered by his brother Cain............	" iv. 8.
130	3874	Seth born, his father Adam, being 130 years old	" v. 3.
622	3382	Enoch born..................................	" v. 18, 19.
687	3317	Methuselah born.............................	" v. 21.
930	3074	Adam dies, age 930 years....................	" v. 5.
987	3017	Enoch translated, aged 365 years.............	" v. 24.
1042	2962	Seth dies, aged 912 years....................	" v. 8.
1056	2948	Noah born....................................	" v. 28, 29.
1536	2468	The deluge threatened, and Noah commissioned to preach repentance during 120 years..	" vi. 3-22. 1 Pet. iii. 20. 2 Pet. ii. 5.
1656	2348	Methuselah dies, aged 969 years................	Genesis v. 27.
		In the same year Noah enters into the ark, being 600 years old........................	" vii. 6, 7.

PERIOD II.

FROM THE DELUGE TO THE CALL OF ABRAHAM, 427 YEARS.

B.C.		
2347	Noah, with his family, leaves the ark after the deluge, and offering sacrifices, he receives the covenant of safety, of which the rainbow was the token..	Genesis viii. 18-20. " ix. 8-17.
2234	Babel built..	" xi.
2234	The confusion of languages, and dispersion of mankind..	" xi.
2233	Nimrod lays the first foundation of the Babylonian or Assyrian monarchy........................	" x. 8, 11.
2188	Mizraim lays the foundation of the Egyptian monarchy..	" x. 13.
1998	Noah dies, aged 950 years.........................	" ix. 29.
1996	Abram or Abraham born..........................	" xi. 26.

PERIOD III.

FROM ABRAHAM'S CALL TO THE EXODUS OF ISRAEL FROM EGYPT, 430 YEARS.

B. C.		
1936	Abram called from Chaldean idolatry, at 60 years of age	Genesis xi. 31.
1921	Abram's second call to Canaan	" xii. 1-4.
1913	Abram's victory over the kings, and rescue of Lot	" xiv. 1-24.
1910	Ishmael born, Abram being 86 years old	" xvi.
1997	God's covenant with Abram, changing his name to *Abraham*; circumcision instituted—Lot delivered, and Sodom, Gomorrah, Admah, and Zeboiim destroyed by fire	" 17-19.
1896	Isaac born, Abraham being 100 years old	" 21.
1871	Abraham offers Isaac as a burnt sacrifice to God	" 22. Heb. xi. 17-19. Jas. ii. 21.
1859	Sarah, Abraham's wife dies, aged 127 years	Genesis xxiii. 1.
1856	Isaac marries Rebecca	" xxiv.
1836	Jacob and Esau born, Isaac being 60 years old	" xxv. 26.
1821	Abraham dies, aged 175 years	" xxv. 7, 8.
1759	Jacob go to his uncle Laban in Syria, and marries his daughters, Leah and Rachel	" 28.
1746	Joseph born, Jacob being 90 years old	" xxx. 23, 24.
1739	Jacob returns to Canaan	" xxxi. 32.
1729	Joseph sold as a slave by his brethren	" 37.
1716	He explains Pharaoh's dreams, and is made governor of Egypt	" 41.
1706	Joseph's brethren settle in Egypt	" xliii. 44.
1689	Jacob foretells the advent of Messiah, and dies in Egypt, aged 147 years	" 49.
1636	Joseph dies, aged 110 years	" l. 26.
1574	Aaron born	Exod. vi. 20; vii. 7.
1571	Moses born	" ii. 1-10.
1531	Moses flees into Midian	" ii. 11-13.
1491	Moses commissioned by God to deliver Israel	" iii. 2.

PERIOD IV.

FROM THE EXODUS OF ISRAEL FROM EGYPT TO BUILDING SOLOMON'S TEMPLE, 487 YEARS.

B. C.		
1491	Miraculous passage of the Red sea by the Israelites	Exod. xiv. 15.
1490	The law delivered on Sinai	" xix. 40.
1452	Miriam, sister of Moses dies, aged 130 years	Num. xx. 1.
"	Aaron dies, aged 123 years	" xx. 28, 29.
1451	Moses dies, aged 120 years, Joshua his successor	Deut. 34.
"	The Israelites pass the river Jordan, the manna ceases, and Jericho taken	Josh. i. 6.
1443	Joshua dies, aged 110 years	" 24.
1296	Ruth's marriage to Boaz	Ruth iv. 10.
1156	Birth of Samson	Judges xiii. 24.
1155	Samuel born	1 Sam. i. 19.
1116	Eli, the high-priest, dies. Ark of God taken by the Philistines	" iv. 1.
1095	Saul anointed king of Israel	" x. 11, 12.

1085	David born	
1063	David anointed to be king, and slays Goliath	“ xvi. 13. “ xvii. 4-9.
1060	David's flight from Saul	“ 26.
1055	Saul is defeated in battle, and in despair kills himself. David acknowledged king by Judah	“ 31.
1048	Ishbosheth, king of Israel, assassinated, and the whole kingdom united under David	2 Sam. 1.
1047	Jerusalem taken from the Jebusites by David, and made the royal city	2 Sam. 5.
1035	David commits adultery with Bathsheba, and contrives the death of her husband Uriah	“ 11.
1034	David brought to repentance for his sin by Nathan the prophet, sent to him by the LORD	“ 12.
1033	Solomon is born	“ xii. 24.
1023	Absalom rebels against his father, and is slain by Joab	“ xv. 18.
1015	David causes Solomon to be proclaimed king defeating the rebellion of Adonijah	1 Kings 1.
1014	David dies, aged 70 years. Accession of Solomon.	“ 2.
1004	Solomon's temple finished, seven years building	“ vi. [illegible]
976	Death of Solomon. Revolt of ten tribes	

PERIOD V.

FROM THE BUILDING OF SOLOMON'S TEMPLE TO THE DESTRUCTION OF JERUSALEM AND CAPTIVITY OF THE JEWS IN BABYLON, 412 YEARS.

B.C.	KINGS OF JUDAH BEGAN TO REIGN.	KINGS OF ISRAEL BEGAN TO REIGN.	PROPHETS.
975	Rehoboam	Jereboam I.	Ahijah, Shemaiah.
958	Abijah, or Abijam	“	
955	Asa	Nadab (954)	Azariah.
953	“	Baasha	Hanani.
930	“	Elah	Jehu.
929	“	Zimai	
“	“	Omri	
918	“	Ahab	Elijah, 910-896.
914	Jehoshaphat	“	Micaiah.
897	“	Ahaziah	Elisha, 896-838.
896	“	Jehoram, or Joram	Jahaziel.
892	Jehoram	“	
885	Ahaziah	“	
884	Athaliah	Jehu	Jehoiada.
878	Joash, or Jehoahaz	“	
857	“	Jehoahaz	Jonah, 856-784.
839	Amaziah	Jehoash	
825	“	Jeroboam II.	
810	Uzziah or Azariah	“	Amos, 810-785.
784	“	Anarchy, 11 years	Hosea, 810-725.
773	“	Zechariah	Joel, 810-660.
772	“	Shallum; Menahem.	
761	“	Pekahiah	Isaiah, 810-698.
759	“	Pekah,	
758	Jotham	“	Micah, 758-699.
742	Ahaz	“	Oded.
730	“	Hoshea.	
726	Hezekiah	(Captivity, 721)	Nahum, 720-698.
698	Manasseh	“	
643	Amon	“	Zephaniah, 640-609.
641	Josiah	“	Jeremiah, 628-586.
610	Jehoahez, or Shallum.	“	Habakkuk, 612-598.
“	Jehoiakim	“	Daniel, 606-534.
599	Jehoiachin, or Coniah	“	
“	Zedekiah		
588	Babylonian captivity.		Obadiah, 588-583.

PERIOD VI.

FROM THE DESTRUCTION OF JERUSALEM BY NEBUCHADNEZZAR, TO THE BIRTH OF CHRIST, 588 YEARS.

B. C.	HISTORICAL EVENTS.	PROPHETS.
588	Destruction of Jerusalem by the Chaldeans, and captivity of the Jews.	
538	Babylon taken by Cyrus..........................	Ezekiel, 595-536.
536	Proclamation of Cyrus ; Zerubbabel and Joshua..	
534	Foundation of the temple.	
529	Artaxerxes (Cambyses) forbids the work.	
520	Favorable degree of Ahasuerus (Darius Hystaspes)	Haggai, 520-518.
518	Esther made queen..................................	Zechariah, 520-518.
515	The second temple finished.	
510	Haman's plot frustrated.	
484	Xerxes, king of Persia.	
464	Artaxerxes Longimanus.	
457	Ezra sent to govern Jerusalem.	
445	Nehemiah sent as governor.	
429	Completion of the wall of Jerusalem under Nehemiah..	Neh. vi. 15.
423	Darius Nothus......................................	Malachi, 436-420.
335	Alexander the Great invades Persia, and establishes the Macedonian or Grecian Empire.	
332	Jaddus high-priest.	
332	Alexander the Great, visits Jerusalem.	
323	Alexander dies.	
320	Ptolemæus Lagus surprises Jerusalem.	
312	Selencus obtains Syria.	
300	Simon the Just high-priest.	
277	Septuagint version made by order of Ptolemæus Philadelphus.	
203	Antiochus the Great obtains Palestine.	
170	Antiochus Epiphanes takes Jerusalem.	
167	His persecution.	
166	Judas Maccabæus governor.	
161	Jonathan governor.	
152	He becomes high-priest.	
143	Simon: treaty with the Romans and Lacedemonians.	
141	Sovereignity and priesthood conferred on Simon and his heirs.	
135	John Hyrcanus.	
107	Judas (Aristobulus) high-priest and king.	
88	Anna the prophetess born.	
63	Jerusalem taken by Pompey, and Judea made a Roman province.	
54	Crassus plunders the temple.	
40	Herod made kind.	
37	Herod the Great takes Jerusalem.	
28	Augustus Cæsar emperor of Rome.	
19	The poet Virgil dies.	
18	Herod begins to rebuild the temple.	
4	John the Baptist born.	
4	Christ born, 4 years before the era known as A. D.	

PERIOD VII.

FROM THE BIRTH OF JESUS CHRIST TO THE END OF THE FIRST CENTURY.

A.D.		
	Nativity of Jesus Christ, four years before A.D. 1.	Luke ii. 1-16.
8	Jesus visits Jerusalem........	" ii. 41-52.
22	Pilate sent from Rome as governor of Judea......	" iii. 1.
25	John Baptist begins his ministry........	Matt. iii. 1.
26	Jesus baptized by John........	" iii. 1.
29	Jesus Christ crucified, and rose from the dead....	" xxvii. 28.
36	Saul converted........	Acts ix. 13-9.
38	Conversion of the Gentiles........	" 10.
44	James beheaded by Herod; Peter liberated by an angel........	" xxii. 1-19.
63	Paul sent a prisoner to Rome........	" xxvi. 28.
65	The Jewish wars begins.	
66	Paul suffers martyrdom at Rome by order of Nero	2 Tim. iv. 6, 7.
67	The Roman general raises the seige of Jerusalem, by which an opportunity is afforded for the Christians to retire to Pella beyond Jordan, as admonished by Christ........	Matt. xxiv. 16-20.
70	Jerusalem beseiged and taken by Titus Vespasian, according to the predictions of Christ; when 1,100,000 Jews perished by famine, sword, fire. and cucifixion; besides 97,000 who were sold as slaves, and vast multitudes who perished in other parts of Judea........	Luke xix. 41-44.
71	Jerusalem and its temple razed to their foundations........	Matt. xxiv. 2.
95	John banished to the isle of Patmos, by Domitian.	Rev. i. 9.
96	John writes the Revelation.	
97	John liberated from exile. and writes his gospel	
100	John, the last surviving apostle, dies, about 100 years old.	

PROMINENT EVENTS IN ECCLESIASTICAL HISTORY.

FROM THE DEATH OF JOHN TO THE FALL OF THE WESTERN EMPIRE A.D. 101 TO 476.

101. Death of Clement Bishop of Rome.
106. Death of Ignatius Bishop of Antioch, by wild beasts.
107. Symeon, Bishop of Jerusalem crucified.
119. Fourth general Persecution under Adrian.
135. 580,000 Jews destroyed by Romans.
136. Adrian builds Ælia Capitalina on the right of Jerusalem.
147. Justin Martyr writes his first apology for Christianity.
152. The Council of Pergamos, the first on record.
167. Persecution of the Christians at Smyrna.
174. Polycarp and Pionices martyred.
177. Persecution at Lyons and Vienne. Bishop Pothinus martyred.
185. Death of Origen, the eminent Commentator.
189. The Saracens first appeared, defeated the Romans.
194. The Scriptures translated into Syriac.
195. The Scriptures translated unto Latin.
196. Tertullian writes his Apology for Christianity.
197. Fifth General Persecution under Severus.
202. Severus issues an Edict prohibiting Christians from disseminating their doctrines.
203. Death of Irenæus, Bishop of Lyons.
204. Origen, expounder of the Scriptures at Alexandria.
218. Death of Clement of Alexandria.
235. Sixth general persecution, under Maximinus.
242. Churches first used by Christians.
249. Seventh general persecution, under Decius.
259. Eighth general persecution under Valerian.
257. Martyrdom of Cyprian and Sixtus II. Bishop of Rome.
260. Temple of Diana at Ephesus burnt.
270. Birth of Eusebius, Bishop of Cæsarea.
272. The ninth general persecution, under Aurelian.
286. The North men attack the Roman Empire in the Wes and the Persians in the East.
302. The tenth persecution, under Diocletian.
306. Constantine Emperor in the West; Licinus in the East.
312. Constantine the Great embraces Christianity.
321. Constantine commands the Observance of Sunday on all his subjects.
325. Council of Nice condemns Arianism.
335. Death of Constantine the Great.
361. Julian the Apostate becomes Emperor.
385. Jerome translates the Hebrew Scripture in Latin.
397. Death of Ambrose, Archbishop of Milan.
407. Death of Chrysostom, Patriarch of Constantinople.
410. Rome sacked and burned by Alaric, King of the Visigoths.
415. Cyril becomes Bishop of Alexandria.
430. Death of Augustine,
461. Leo, the great Pope of Rome, claims to be vicar of Christ.
476. Extinction of the Western Empire by Goths.
476. The sacking of Rome by Odoacer was the great event which preceded the Middle or Dark ages.

SPECIAL PRAYERS IN THE OLD TESTAMENT.

Of whom recorded.	*Subjects.*	*Recorded in.*
Aaron and priests	The Aaronic blessing of Israel . .	Num. vi. 22-26
Abraham . . .	For a son	Gen. xv. 2
Abraham . . .	For Ishmael's acceptance	— xvii. 17-18.
Abraham . . .	For mercy on Sodom	— xviii. 23.
Abraham's servant	Success in his mission, to find a wife for Isaac	— xxiv. 12.
Agur	For moderation in his desires . .	Prov. xxx. 1.
Asa	When going to battle with Zerah the Ethiopian	2 Chron. xiv. 11.
Daniel	For the restoration of Jerusalem .	Dan. ix. 4.
David	Prayer for a blessing on his house	2 Sam. vii. 18.
David	After his sin with Beth-sheba . .	Ps. l. 1.
David	After numbering the people . . .	2 Sam. xxiv. 17.
David	Thanksgiving at close of life . . .	1 Chr. xxix. 10-19.
Elijah	For restoration of the widow's son	1 King xvii. 20.
Elijah	For Divine attestation of his mission	— xviii. 36.
Elijah	For death	— xix. 4.
Elisha	For his servant's eyes to be opened	2 Kings vi. 17.
Elisha	That the army sent to take him may be blinded	— vi. 18.
Ezekiel	Intercession for his people	Ezek. ix. 8.
Ezra	Confession of sin alliances with the heathen	Ezra ix. 6.
Habakkuk . . .	For revival of God's work	Hab. iii. 1-16.
Hannah	For the gift of a son	1 Sam. i. 1-11.
Hezekiah . . .	For protection against Sennacherib	2 Kin. xix. 15 ; Is. xxxvii. 16.
Hezekiah . . .	When dangerously ill	— xx. 3 ; Is. xxx. 3.
Hezekiah . . .	For the unprepared who had eaten of the passover	2 Chr. xxxvii. 18.
Israel	Expiation for undiscoved murder .	Deut. xxi. 6-8.
Israel	Confession on presenting firstfruits	— xxvi. 5-10.
Israel	The prayer of the tithing year . .	— xxvi. 13-15.
Jazeb	For the Divine blessing.	1 Chr. iv. 10.
Jacob	For deliverance from Esau . . .	Gen. xxxii. 9.
Jehoshaphat . .	For protection against the Moabites and Ammonites	2 Chr. xx. 6.
Jeremiah . . .	In a great famine	Jer. xiv. 7.
Jeremiah . . .	For comfort	— xv. 15-18.
Jonah	For deliverance from the great fish	Jonah ii. 2.
Joshua	After Achan's sin	Josh. vii. 7-9.
Levites	Confession of God's goodness and their sins	Neh. ix. 5.
Manoah	For Divine guidance in training his child	Judg. xiii. 8, 9.
Moses	Forgiveness for the people's idolatry	Ex. xxxii. 11; Deut. ix. 26.
Moses	For the Divine presence	— xxxiii. 12.
Moses	At the setting forth and stopping of the ark	Num. x. 35-36.
Moses	For Divine help to govern the Israelites	— xi. 11-15.
Moses	For Mariam, for cure from leprosy...	— xii. 13.
Moses	For the people disappointed at the spie's report	— xiv. 13-19.
Moses	For a successor	— xxvii. 15.
Moses	To enter Canaan	Deut. iii. 24.
Nehemiah . . .	For the remnant in captivity . .	Neh. i. 5.
Nehemiah . . .	For protection against Sanballat and Tobiah	— iv. 4.
Samson	To be avenged on his enemies . .	Judg. xvi. 28.
Solomon	For wisdom to govern Israel . . .	1 Kin. iii. 5-9.
Solomon	Dedication of the Temple	— viii. 23; 2 Chr. vi. 14.

MIRACLES RECORDED IN THE OLD TESTAMENT.

Aaron's rod turned into a serpent in Egypt	Exod. vii. 10-12
Plagues:—1. Water made blood "	—— 20-25
2. Frogs "	—— viii. 5-14
3. Lice "	—— 16-28
4. Flies "	—— 20-24
5. Murrian "	—— ix. 3-6
6. Boils and blains "	—— 8-11
7. Thunder and hail "	—— 22-26
8. Locusts "	—— x. 12-19
9. Darkness "	—— 21-23
10. Firstborn slain "	—— xii. 29, 30
Parting of the Red Sea "	—— xiv. 6, 21-31
The curing of the waters of Marah in the Wilderness	—— xv. 23-25
Feeding with manna "	—— xvi. 14-35
Water from the rock, at Rephidim "	—— xvii. 5-7
Death of Nadab and Abihu "	Lev. x. 1-2.
Burning of the congregation at Taberah "	Num. xi. 1-3
Death of Karoh, Dathan, and Abiram, &c. "	—— xvi. 31-35
Budding of Aaron's rod, at Kadesh "	—— xvii. 8
Water from the rock, at Meribah "	—— xx. 7-11
The brazen serpent "	—— xxi. 8-9
Balaam's ass speaking "	—— xxii. 21, 35
Stoppage of the Jordan stream "	Josh. iii. 14-17
Fall of Jericho, in Canaan.—Under Joshua	—— vi. 6-25
Staying of sun and moon " "	—— x. 12-14
Death of Uzzah, under the Kings	2 Sam. vi. 7
Jereboam's hand withered	1 Kings xiii. 4-6
By Elijah.—The staying of the cruse of oil and meal at Zarepath	—— xvii. 14-16
The raising of the widow's son at Zarepath	—— 17-24
The burning of the sacrifice on Mount Carmel	—— xviii. 30-38
Rain obtained	—— 41-45
Burning of the captains and their companies	2 Kings i. 10-12
Dividing of Jordan	—— ii. 7, 8
By Elisha.—Dividing of Jordan	—— ii. 14
Cure of waters of Jericho	—— 21, 22
Destruction of mocking children at Bethel	—— 24
Supply of water to the allied armies in Moab	—— iii. 16-20
Multiplication of widow's oil	—— iv. 2-7
Raising the Shunammite's son	—— 32-37
Feeding one hundred men with twenty loaves	—— 42-44
Healing the deadly pottage	—— 38-41
Cure of Naaman's leprosy, and its transfer to Gehazi	—— v. 10-14-27
Making an iron axe swim	—— vi. 5-7
Smiting the Syrian army	—— 18-20
Resurrection of dead man by touching Elisha's bones	—— xiii. 21.
Recorded by Isaiah.—Destruction of Sennacherib's army	—— xix. 35
Return of the sun by the dail of Ahaz	—— xx. 9-11
During Captivity.—Deliverance of the Three Children from the fiery furnance	Dan. iii. 19-27
Deliverance of Daniel from the lions	—— vi. 16-23
Miscellaneous.—Smiting of Philistines, and fall of Dagon	1 Sam. v. 3-12
Men of Beth-shemesh smitten	—— vi. 19
Thunder destroys Philistine	—— vii. 10-12
Thunder and Rain in harvest	—— xii. 18
Sound in the mulberry trees	2 Sam. v. 23-25
Smiting of Uzziah with leprosy	2 Chr. xxvi. 16-21
Deliverance of Jonah from the great fish	Jonah ii. 1-10

OUR LORD'S PARABLES.

PARABLES.	LOCALITY.	AUTHOR.	LESSONS.
The tares..............	Gennesaret	Matt. xiii.	Good and evil in life, and judgment
The hid treasures.....	"	" "	Value of the Gospel.
The goodly pearl.......	"	" "	Seeking salvation.
The draw-net...........	"	" "	Visible Church of Christ.
The unmerciful servant	Capernaum.....	" xviii.	Danger of ingratitude
The laborers in the vineyard............	Jerusalem......	" xx.	Call at various epochs.
The two sons...........	"	" xxi.	Insincerity and repentance.
The marriage of the king's son............	Mount of Olives	" xxii.	Need of righteousness.
The ten virgins........	" "	" xxv.	Watchful and careful profession.
The ten talents........	" "	" xxv.	Use of advantages.
The sheep and goats..	" "	" xxv.	Final separation of good and bad.
House on rock, and on the sand.........	Galilee..........	" vii.	Consistent and false profession.
The leaven.............	Gennesaret	" xiii.	Pervading influence of religion.
The lost sheep.........	Jerusalem......	" xviii.	Joy over penitent.
New cloth and old garment................	Capernaum.....	" ix.	New doctrine and old prejudices.
New wine in old bottles	"	" ix.	New spirit in unregenerate heart.
The sower..............	Gennesaret	" xiii.	Hearers divided into classes.
The mustard-seed	"	" xiii.	Spread of Gospel.
The wicked husbandmen.................	Jerusalem......	" xxi.	Rejection of Christ by the Jews.
The fig-tree and all the trees.................	Mount of Olives	" xxiv.	Indication of Second Advent.
The seed growing secretly................	Genessaret	Mark iv.	Growth of religion.
The householder........	"	" xiii.	Watchfulness.
The two debtors........	Galilee..........	Luke vii.	Gratitude for pardon.
The good Samaritan...	Jerusalem......	" x.	Compassion to suff'ring
The friend at midnight	"	" xi.	Perseverance in prayer
The rich fool...........	"	" xii.	Worldly-mindedness.
The wedding feast.....	"	" xii.	Vigilance towards Second Advent.
The wise steward......	"	" xii.	Conscientiousness in trust.
The barren fig-tree....	"	" xiii.	Unprofitableness under grace.
The great supper.......	"	" xiv.	Universality of the Divine call.
The piece of money....	"	" xv.	Joy over penitence.
The prodigal son	"	" xv.	Fatherly love.
The unjust steward....	"	" xvi.	Preparation of eternity
The rich man and Lazarus..................	"	" xvi.	Recompence of future life.
The unprofitable servants............	"	" xvii.	God's claim to all our services.
The unjust judge......	"	" xviii.	Advantage of persevering prayer.
The Pharisee and publican..................	"	" xviii.	Self-righteousness and humility.
The pounds............	"	" xix.	Diligence rewarded, sloth punished.

PARABLES IN THE OLD TESTAMENT.

Parables.	*By whom Spoken.*	*Recorded in.*
The ewe lamb	Nathan to David	2 Sam. xii. 1-4.
The two brethren striving	Widow of Tekoah . . .	—— xiv. 1-11.
Escaped captive	Man of the son of the prophet to Ahab	1 Kings xx. 35-40.
Vineyard and grapes . .	Isaiah to Judas and Jerusalem	Isaiah v. 1-7.
Eagles and vine	Ezekiel to Israel	Ezek. xvii. 3-10.
Lions whelps	" "	—— xix. 2-9.
The boiling pot	" "	—— xxiv. 3-5.
PARABOLIC FABLES.		
Trees choosing a king . .	Jotham to Shechemites .	Judg. ix. 7-15.
Strong bringing forth sweetness	Sampson	Judg. xiv. 14.
Micaiah's vision	. . . .	1 Kings xxii. 19-23.
Thistle and cedar . . .	Jehoash to Amaziah . .	2 Kings xiv. 9.

THE DISCOURSES OF JESUS.

ARRANGED IN CHRONOLOGICAL ORDER.

DISCOURSES.	PLACES.	RECORDED IN.
Conversation with Nicodemus	Jerusalem........	John iii. 1-21.
Conversation with woman of Samaria.	Sychar............	" iv. 1-42.
Discourse in the Synagogue of Nazareth..............................	Nazareth	Luke iv. 16-31.
Sermon upon the mount..............	"	Matt. v.; vii.
Instruction to the Apostles...........	Galilee...........	" x.
Denunciations against Chorazin, etc..	"	" xi. 20-24.
Discourses on occasion of healing the infirm man........................	Jerusalem	John v.
Discourse concerning the disciples plucking of corn on the Sabbath.....	Judea	Matt. xii. 1-8.
Reputation of his working miracles by the agency of Beelzebub............	Capernaum.... ..	" 22-37.
Discourse on the bread of life	"	John vii.
Discourse about internal purity.... ..	"	Matt. xv. 1-20.
Discourse against giving or taking offence, and concerning forgiveness of injuries..........................	"	" xviii.
Discourse at feast of tabernacles	Jerusalem	John vii.
Discourse on occasion of woman taken in adultery........................	"	" viii.; i. ii.
Discourse concerning the sheep.......	"	" x.
Denunciations against the Scribes and Pharisees..........................	Paræa.........	Luke xi. 29-36.
Discourse concerning humility and prudence............................	Galilee....	" xiv. 7-14.
Directions how to attain heaven......	Paræa.............	Matt. xix. 16-30
Discourse concerning his sufferings...	Jerusalem	" xx. 17-19.
Denunciations against the Pharisees..	"	" xxiii.
Prediction of the destruction of Jerusalem..............................	"	" xxiv.
The consolatory discourse	"	John xv.; xvii.
Discourse as he went to Gethsemane..	"	Matt. xxvi. 31-36.
Discourse to the disciples before his ascension..........................	"	" xxviii. 16-23.

THE MIRACLES OF CHIRST.

ARRANGED IN CHRONOLOGICAL ORDER.

MIRACLES.	PLACES.	RECORDED IN.
Turns water into wine..................	Cana..............	John ii. 1-11.
Cures the nobleman's son of Capernaum..........................	"	" iv. 46-64.
Causes a miraculous draught of fishes	Sea of Galilee.....	Luke v. 1-11.
Cures a demoniac....................	Capernaum.	Mark i. 22-38.
Heals Peter's wife mother of a fever..	"	" 30, 31.
Heals a leper.........................	"	" 40-45.
Heals the centurion's servant.........	"	Matt. viii. 5-13.
Raises the widow's son................	Nain..............	Luke vii. 11-17.
Calms the tempest.....................	Sea of Galilee.....	Matt. viii. 23-27.
Cures the demoniacs of Gadara.......	Gadara...........	" 28-34.
Cures a man of the palsy..............	Capernaum.	" ix. 1-8.
Restores to life the daughter of Jarius	"	" 18, 19, 28, 23.
Cures a woman diseased with a flux of blood................................	"	Luke viii. 43-46.
Restores to sight two blind men.......	"	Matt. ix. 27-31.
Heals one possessed with a dumb spirit	"	" 32, 33.
Cures an infirm man at Bethesda......	Jerusalem........	John v. 1-9.
Cures a man with a withered hand....	Judea.............	Matt. xii. 10-13.
Cures a demoniac.....................	Capernuam.......	" 22, 23.
Feeds miraculously five thousand.....	Decapolis	" xiv.; xv. 21.
Heals the woman of Canaan's daughter	Near Tyre........	" xv. 22-28.
Heals a man who was dumb and deaf..	Decapolis.........	Mark vii. 31-37-
Feeds miraculously four thousand....	"	Matt. xv. 32-39.
Gives sight to a blind man............	Bethsaida.........	Mark xiii. 22-26.
Cures a boy possessed of a devil.......	Tabor.............	Matt. xviii. 14-21.
Stater ($5.50) in the mouth of the fish.	Capernaum.......	Matt. xiii.
Restores to sight a man born blind....	Jerusalem.........	John ix.
When Christ passed unseen through the multitude......................	Nazareth..........	Luke iv.
The blind and dumb demoniac	Capernaum	" xi.
Heals a woman under an infirmity eighteen years......................	Galilee............	" xiii. 11-17.
Cures a dropsy........................	"	" xiv. 1-6.
Cleanses ten lepers....................	Samaria...........	" xvii. 11-19.
Raises Lazarus from the dead	Bethany..........	John xi.
Restores to sight two blind men	Jericho............	Matt. xx. 30-34.
Blasts the fig-tree.....................	Olivet............	" xxi. 18-21.
Heals the ear of Malchus.............	Gethsemane......	Luke xxii. 50, 51.
Legion of devils entering the swine...	Gadara...........	Matt. viii.; Mark vi.; Luke viii.
Causes the miraculous draught of fishes..............................	Sea of Galilee.....	John xxi. 1-14.

SPECIAL PRAYERS IN THE NEW TESTAMENT.

Of whom recorded.	*Subjects.*	*Recorded in.*
Lord's Prayer .	The model prayer	Matt. vi.
Jesus	Under suffering in Gethsemane .	" xxvi.
Jesus	Suspension of Divine consolation .	" xxvii.
Lord's prayer . .	St. Lukes account	Luke ii.
Pharisee " . .	Thanksgiving for his righteousness	" xviii. 11.
Publicans " . .	For Divine mercy	" xviii.
Jesus	See about (Matt. 26)	" xxii.
Dying Thief . .	To be remembered by Jesus . . .	" xxiii.
Jesus	For his murderers	" xxiii. 34.
Jesus	Imploring his Fathers aid	John xii.
Jesus	For himself, his apostle and all believers	" xvii.
Apostles	On choosing an apostles	Acts i. 24.
Primitive church	For support under persecution . .	" iv. 24.
Stephen	Commendation of his soul; forgiveness of his murderers	" vii. 59, 60.

THE MIRACLES RECORDED IN THE ACTS OF THE APOSTLES.

MIRACLES.	WHERE WROUGHT.	RECORDED IN.
Peter heals a lame man................	Jerusalem........	Acts ii. 1-11.
Ananias and Sapphira struck dead....	"	" v. 1-10.
Apostles performs many wonders.....	"	" v. 12-16.
Peter and John communicate the Holy Ghost..............................	Samaria.........	" viii. 14-17.
Peter healeth Eneas of a palsy........	Lydda............	" ix. 33-34.
——raiseth Tabitha, or Dorcas, to life	Joppa............	" ix. 37-41.
——delivered out of prison by an angel	Jerusalem........	" xii. 7-17.
God smites Herod, so that he dies.....	"	" xii. 21-23.
Elymas, the sorcerer, smitten with blindness...........................	Paphos...........	" xiii. 7-11.
Paul converted........................	Road to Damascus	" ix. 1-9.
——heals a cripple....................	Lystra...........	" xiv. 8-10.
——casts out a spirit of divination.....	Phillippi.........	" xvi. 17, 18.
——and Silas's prison doors opened by an earthquake.....................	"	" xvi. 25-27.
——communicates the Holy Ghost....	Corinth..........	" xix. 1-7.
——heals multitudes..................	"	" xix. 11, 12.
——restores Eutychus to life..........	Troas............	" xx. 9-12.
——shakes off the viper...............	Melita...........	" xxviii. 3-7.
——heals the father of Publius, and others..............................	"	" xxviii. 7-9.

TABLES OF WEIGHTS AND MEASURES.

JEWISH WEIGHTS.	Avoirdupois.				Troy.			
	lbs.	oz.	drs.		lbs.	oz.	dwt.	grs.
A gerah, ...	—	—	0·439	=	—	—	—	12
10 gerahs = 1 bekah .	—	—	4·39	=	—	—	5	0
2 bekaks = 1 shekel .	—	—	8·78	=	—	—	10	0
60 shekels = 1 maneh .	2	0	14·628	=	2	6	0	0
59 manehs = 1 talent .	102	13	11·428	=	125	0	0	0

LONG MEASURE.	ft.	in.
A digit or finger (Jer. lii. 21)	—	0·912
4 digits = 1 palm (Exod. xxxv. 25)	—	3·648
3 palms = 1 span (Exod. xxviii. 16) . . .	—	10·944
2 spans = 1 cubit (Gen. vi. 15)	1	9·888
4 cubits = 1 fathom (Acts xxvii. 28) . . .	7	3·552
1.5 fathoms = 1 reed (Ezek. xl. 3. 5)	10	11·328
13.3 reeds = 1 line (Ezek. xl. 3)	145	11·04

LAND MEASURE.	Eng. miles.	ft.
A cubit	—	1·824
400 cubits = 1 furlong (Luke xxiv. 13)	—	439 6
5 furlongs = 1 sabbath day's journey (John xi. 18 ; Acts i. 12)	—	2184·0
10 furlongs = 1 mile (Matt. v. 41)	1	1198·0
24 miles = 1 day's journey	33	232.0

LIQUID MEASURE.	gals.	pts.
A caph	—	0·625
1.3 caph = 1 log (Lev. xiv. 10)	—	0·833
4 logs = 1 cab		3·333
3 cabs = 1 hin (Exod. xxx. 24)	1	2
2 hins = 1 seah	2	4
3 seahs = 1 bath, or ephah (1 Kings vii. 26 ; John ii. 6)	7	4·5
10 ephahs = 1 kor, or homer (Isa. v. 10 ; Ezek. xiv. 14)	.75	5.25

DRY MEASURE.	pecks.	pts.
A gachal	—	0·1416
20 gachals = 1 cab (2 Kings vi. 25 ; Rev. vi. 6)	—	2·8333
1·8 cab = 1 omer (Exod. xvi. 36)	—	5·1
3.3 omers = 1 seah (Matt. xiii. 33)	1	1
3 seahs = 1 ephah (Ezek. xlv. 11)	3	3
5 ephahs = 1 letech (Hosea iii. 2)	16	0
2 letechs = 1 kor, or homer (Num. xi. 32 ; Hos. iii. 2)	32	0

N. B.—The above Tables will explain many texts in the Bible. Take Is. v. 10: "Yea, ten acres of vineyard shall yield one bath, and the seed of an homer shall yield an ephah." This curse upon the covetous man was, that 10 acres of vine should produce only 7 gallons of wine, i. e., one acre should yield less than 3 quarts ; and that 32 pecks of seed should only bring a crop of 3 pecks, or, in other words, that the harvest reaped should produce but one-tenth of the seed sown.

JEWISH MONEY.

In English and American ; the dollar being taken as 4s. 2d.

JEWISH.		ENGLISH. £	*s.*	*d.*		AMERICAN. *dols.*	*cents.*
A gerah (Exod. xxx. 13) . :	=	0	0	1·36	=	0	2·73
10 geraphs = 1 bekah (Exod. xxxviii. 26) .	=	0	1	1·68	=	0	27·37
2 bekahs = 1 shekel (Exod. xxx. 13; Is. vii. 23)	=	0	2	3.37	=	0	54·74
50 shekels = 1 maneh	=	5	14	0·75	=	27	37·50
60 manehs = 1 kikkar (talent)	=	342	3	9	=	1,642	50
A gold shekel	=	1	16	6	=	8	76
A talent of gold	=	5,475	0	0	=	26,280	0

N. B—A *shekel* would probably purchase nearly ten times as much as the same nominal amount will now. One *Roman* penny (8 1-2*d.*) was a good day's wages for a laborer.

ROMAN MONEY.

ROMAN.	ENGLISH *d.*		AMERICAN. *cents.*
A "farthing," *quadrans* (Matt. v. 23) = nearly	0·125	=	0.25
A "farthing," *as* = 4 *quadrantes* (Matt. x. 29) = nearly . .	0·5	=	1
A "penny," *denarius* 16 *asses* (Matt. xxii. 19) = nearly . .	8·50	=	17

N. B.—NAAMAN's offering to Elisha of 6,000 pieces (shekels) of gold amounted to more than £10,000 = 48,000 *dollars.*

The DEBTOR (Matt. xviii. 24) who had been forgiven 10,000 talents, i. e., £3,000,000 = 14,400,000 *dollars*, refused to forgive his fellowservant 100 pence, i. e., £3 10*s*. 10*d*. = 17 *dollars.*

JUDAS sold our Lord for 30 pieces of silver, i. e., £3 10*s*. 8*d*. = 16 *dollars*, 96 *cents*, the legal value of a slave, if he were killed by a beast.

JOSEPH was sold by his brethren for 20 pieces, i. e., £2 7*s*. = 11 *dollars*, 28 *cents.*

TIME.

The *Natural* Day was from sun-rise to sun-set.

The *Natural* Night was from sun-set to sun-rise.

The *Civil* Day was from sun-set one evening to sun-set the next ; for, "the Evening and the Morning were the first day."

NIGHT (*Ancient*).

First Watch (Lam. ii. 19) till midnight.
Middle Watch (Judg. vii. 19) till 3 a.m.
Morning Watch (Ex. xiv. 24) till 6 a.m.

NIGHT (*New Testament*).

1st. Watch, *evening*	=	6 to 9 p.m.
2d. Watch, *midnight*	=	9 to 12 p.m.
3d. Watch, *cock-crow*	=	12 to 3 a.m.
4th. Watch, *morning*	=	3 to 6 a.m.

DAY (*Ancient*).

Morning till about 10 a.m.
Heat of day till about 2 p.m.
Cool of day till about 6 p.m.

DAY (*New Testament*).

Third hour	=	6 to 9 a.m.
Sixth hour	=	9 to 12 midday.
Ninth hour	=	12 to 3 p.m.
Twelth hour	=	3 do 6 s.m.

THE JEWISH YEAR.

Month of Sacred Year.	Month of Civil Year.	Name.	Number of Days.	English Months.	Products.	Jewish Festivals.
I.	VII.	Abib, or Nisan (Exod.xii.2;xiii.4).	30	March, April.	Barley ripe. Fig in blossom.	Passover. Unleavened Bread.
II.	VIII.	Iyar, or Zif.	29	April, May.	Barley harvest.	
III.	IX.	Sivan.	30	May, June.	Wheat harvest.	Pentecost.
IV.	X.	Thammuz.	29	June, July.	Early vintage.	
V.	XI.	Ab (Ezra vii. 9).	30	July, August.	Ripe figs.	
VI.	XII.	Elul (Neh. vi. 15).	29	August, Sept.	General vintage.	
VII.	I.	Tisri (I Kings viii. 2).	30	Sept., Oct.	Ploughing and Sowing.	Feast of Trumpets. Atonement. Feast of Tabernacles.
VIII.	II.	Bul (I Kings vi. 38).	29	Oct., Nov.	Latter grapes.	
IX.	III.	Chisleu (Zech. vii. 1).	30	Nov., Dec.	Snow.	Dedication.
X.	IV.	Tebeth (Esth. ii. 16).	29	Dec., Jan.	Grass after rain.	
XI.	V.	Shebat (Zech. i. 7).	30	Jan., Feb	Winter fig.	
XII.	VI.	Adar (Ezra vi. 15).	29	Feb., March.	Almond blossom.	Purim.
XIII.		Ve-Adar, *Intercalary*.				

N.B.—The Sacred Year was reckoned from the moon after the vernal equinox.

The Civil Year began in September (the less productive period of the year).

The prophets speak of the *sacred* year; those engaged in secular pursuits, of the *civil* year. The year was divided into 12 *lunar* months, with a thirteenth, or *intercalary* month, every third year.

PAUL'S BENEDICTION.

The grace of the Lord Jesus Christ, and the love of God, and the communion of the Holy Ghost, be with you all. Amen.

II. Corinthians xiii. 14.